CONTENTS

CONTENTS

ILLUSTRATIONS

THE ESSENTIAL SAMUEL BUTLER

INTRODUCTION

SAMUEL BUTLER (1835-1902)

SAMUEL BUTLER was called in his lifetime *homo unius libri* — a man of one book. Nobody would so describe him now. The one book that, while he was alive, reached a wide public and in its particular *genre* became a classic was *Erewhon*, Butler's account of a strange people living in isolation 'over the range', who were at once so like and so unlike the author's Victorian contemporaries. Today, however, *Erewhon*, though it holds its place, is no longer Butler's best known or most admired work. *The Way of All Flesh*, written at intervals over a large part of his life and published soon after his death, is now by common consent his main claim to a secure place among the classics. *The Way* is altogether a bigger thing than *Erewhon*, full not merely of Butler's pungent humour but of *people* — which *Erewhon* emphatically is not. In *Erewhon* Butler was content to satirize ideas and manners without trying to embody them in real characters. The reader is not expected to regard Yram or Mr. Nosnibor or Arowhena or any other of the Erewhonians as more than pegs on which to hang the story and the satire. But in *The Way of All Flesh*, at any rate in all the first half of it, the satire is done through individuals whom the author has given us alive and kicking — mainly, as is so often the case, by drawing them from life, not just as they were, but so as to avoid reducing them to no more than embodied traits.

Erewhon, and also its sequel *Erewhon Revisited*, which is an exception to the general rule that sequels written long after fail to come off, are good books. *The Way of All Flesh* is, I am sure, a great one, even though its second half is a sad falling off from its first. It is also a long book — much too long to be reproduced in full in this volume — but it suffers less from drastic cutting than it would do if Butler had succeeded in keeping it up to the end. That, quite likely, he would have done if his friend, Miss Savage, had survived to cheer him on; for beyond doubt a good deal of the credit for the unblemished quality of all the first half is due to her. Readers who know Butler's correspondence with Miss Savage,[1] with its frequent references to the progress,

[1] *Letters between Samuel Butler and Miss Savage*, 1935.

or lack of progress, Butler was making with his novel, do not need to
be told this, or to be told that Miss Savage's letters (not Butler's) are
real masterpieces of their kind. So intimately was Miss Savage twined
into the composition of Butler's novel that, when she died while he
was in the middle of revising it, he locked it away as it was and never
had the heart to touch it again. That partly accounts for the falling off
— not only because the latter part went without the full benefit of Miss
Savage's comments, but also because it was never subjected to the
drastic pruning and re-writing which Butler gave to the first half.
Even if he had re-written the whole with uniform care, I doubt if he
could have sustained the standard of the opening chapters, and that for
an essentially simple reason. Throughout the earlier chapters of *The
Way of All Flesh* Butler was drawing on his own experiences, writing
about his own childhood and adolescence, moving in an atmosphere
that he knew at first hand, with an intimacy that comes out on every
page; whereas in the later chapters he was inventing not only the
episodes but the people too, and at such inventions he was no master.
I do not mean that in the first half of *The Way* he was putting his father
and mother and the rest of his relatives into the book just as they were:
he was not. He was exaggerating, as well as leaving out a great deal
that was not grist to his mill. But what he did put in was his interpretation of the actual — one-sided and often spiteful, no doubt, but
straight from nature as he saw it, heightened by art, selected by
memory, at many points deliberately caricatured, but never invented
out of nothing. To the end of time, critics will disagree about the
extent to which Butler was unfair to his father and mother and to the
rest of his victims. It does not really matter how unfair he was to them:
fair or unfair as portraits, the characters in the first half of *The Way*
are unmistakably alive, in the sense, not that any of them are whole
people, sculptured in the round so that one can walk round them and
look at them from all aspects, but that what they do they do in
character. They are portrayed, not at all as they supposed themselves
to be, but as they appeared to an acute, prejudiced observer, with a skin
too few and a long, unforgiving memory.

Erewhon is plain sailing: it is so because its satire is entirely impersonal,
and is simply a casting of opinions and criticisms of contemporary
institutions into the shape of a traveller's tale. It can be read without
the raising of any questions about its author, apart from his opinions
and judgments of value. *The Way of All Flesh*, on the other hand, is so

tangled up with Butler's own life and development as continually to provoke questions about what lies behind it. Did Butler's father really behave just like that to him; and, if so, was it because *his* father had behaved just like that to *him*? Or was Butler so 'difficult' a child as to be continually misconstruing his father's attitude? Did Butler's mother really day-dream as fantastically as Christina, or, if not so fantastically, fantastically enough to account for the portrait he gives of Mrs. Theobald Pontifex? Did something really happen about an 'Ellen' at Langar, and, if so, *what* really happened? Was either, or were both, of Butler's sisters really like Charlotte? How much did Butler really model Alethea Pontifex on Miss Savage? . . . and so on, endlessly, through a series of questions which the reader of *The Way* need not ask at all in order to enjoy the book, but is bound to begin asking as soon as he reads the correspondence with Miss Savage, or the *Note-Books*, or Henry Festing Jones's *Memoir*. For, if an author puts himself into his books, and makes no secret, as Butler made none, of putting in his relatives, his writings inevitably acquire a second interest that has nothing to do with their merits as literature, but provokes a curiosity that takes no denial. As a novel, *The Way of All Flesh* would be no better and no worse if it were all the sheer product of its author's imagination; but, knowing that it was not, the reader starts asking questions, and lively controversies develop between those who think that it was not at all 'nice' of Butler to make such bitter fun of his parents and those who become his eager partisans.

I do not propose, in this brief Introduction, to enter the lists of controversy. I have said elsewhere what I have to say on the matter;[1] and I have neither space nor inclination to repeat myself here. All that is relevant is that Butler, when he set about preparing for publication (after his death) his correspondence with Miss Savage, opened the door to the contention; for the letters are full of passages which link the story told in *The Way* to his own upbringing and especially to his relations with his father. Butler's views about Victorian family life were unequivocally expressed; and he made no secret of his views being rooted in his personal experience. He thought, and said again and again, that his father had come near to wrecking his life; and for this he cherished a resentment that he never got over. But he also held that what his father had done amiss was only what countless other fathers were doing and misguidedly counting to themselves for righteousness.

[1] In *Samuel Butler and The Way of All Flesh* (Home and van Thal, 1947).

Personal resentment barbed his arrows; but they were discharged at the institution — not merely at the individual who had exemplified it in Butler's personal case. Theobald Pontifex was not Canon Butler — and much less was old Mr. Pontifex Butler's authentic grandfather. They were both types, but he saved them from being merely types by using as much of the real people as fitted in with his generalized purpose.

So much for *The Way of All Flesh*, of which, unable for reasons of space to give anything like the whole, I have nevertheless given, I believe, *all* the best, and of the worse as little as I could without destroying the story. Of *Erewhon* I have given the greater part; for to give less would have taken the shape out of it. Regretfully, and solely for reasons of space, I have had to jettison one long section — 'The Book of the Machines' — which is highly characteristic, but can be left out without doing violence to the narrative. There are also some smaller omissions, made also simply in order to save space and, I hope, without much destructive effect. The sequel, *Erewhon Revisited*, I have left out altogether, despite a deep affection for it. There could have been room for but little, if justice was to be done to *The Way* and to *Erewhon* itself; and *Erewhon Revisited* is a book that needs to be read as a whole, and does not lend itself to selection. Much more than either of the others it has a connected plot; and much more than in *Erewhon* there are in it real people, and not merely pegs for opinion and satire. I hope this volume will induce more people to read it; for in comparison with *Erewhon* it has always been unduly neglected. The account of the 'Sun-Child' myth is admirably Butlerian; and the book contains a charming human portrait of George, the child of the original traveller who has become the Erewhonian god, and of Yram, the jailer's daughter, who has grown in the sequel into a much more real person than she was in *Erewhon* itself. I am sorry, too, to miss out Professors Hanky and Panky, and a good deal besides; but, good as *Erewhon Revisited* is, it is hardly part of the *essential* Butler in the same sense as *Erewhon* and *The Way of All Flesh*.

For the rest, I have given in full the *Memoir of the late John Pickard Owen* by his equally imaginary brother, from *The Fair Haven*; a selection, brief, but I hope appetizing, from the two volumes of the *Note-Books*; some verse, including of course the delectable *Psalm of Montreal*; and an essay, *The Deadlock in Darwinism*, as the best I could do towards recording in a short space the quintessence of Butler's views on evolution, which made him a pariah when he published them, but are treated a good deal more circumspectly by modern scientists who, knowing more of the matter in question, are more conscious of not knowing everything. It is, of course, impossible in this way to do justice to Butler's work in this field — work which, apart from occasional essays, fills four substantial volumes beginning with *Life and Habit* and ending with *Luck or Cunning*. What biologists now think of Butler's theories of evolution, based on Buffon and Lamarck and Erasmus Darwin, I am not quite sure: they are, I believe, inclined to be cagy on the subject. But that psychologists and sociologists have learnt a good deal from them there is no doubt at all; and *Unconscious Memory* is no longer the challenging title it was when Butler took it for the third of his evolutionary studies. What Butler's contemporaries failed to see — what he did not see at all clearly for himself — was that he was in truth constructing a theory of social, rather than of biological, evolution; for in the decades which followed the publication of *The Origin of Species* the biological aspect of the problem of evolution so dominated most men's minds as to blind them to the social factors unless they could squint at them through the spectacles of Biology. Butler was affected by this dominance, and cast his theory into the mould of an attack on Darwinism which was really no more than incidental to what he was trying to say. Non-scientists, such as Bernard Shaw, grasped what he was really driving at when most of the scientists were still dismissing him as a babbling amateur, and when most of the reading public, as he caustically observed, were much more ready to be shocked by his onslaughts on St. Darwin than by his habit of poking ungenial fun at the fundamentals of Christian theology. *The Fair Haven* and the Sun-Child myth shocked only the religious, who did not read Butler's books, and were shocked only at second hand; whereas his habit of blaspheming Science shocked the advanced people who might have read him, if their scientific mentors had not informed them *ex cathedra* that he was not worth the trouble.

Today, the reading public is no longer shockable so easily by either theological or scientific blasphemy. Nor can Butler's idol-smashing in the temples of Victorian domesticity either shock or excite as it once did. If there are still heavy fathers and devoted, day-dreaming wives and mothers, their children, in hitting back, are no longer behaving in an exceptionally rebellious way; and most parents have learnt to keep both their tempers and their unruly consciences under better control, as Butler wanted them to do. Parental tyranny has gone out of fashion; and Butler's exposure of it, appearing only in 1903, was already more than half a period piece before the world was given a chance of reading it. He was aware of this, and commented on the changing manners in his later *Note-Books*; but, in the matter of evolution, he did not live to see the mood alter so much. As a writer on human development, he remained a pariah to the day of his death.

Of the rest of Butler's uncommonly various series of books I can here give nothing, except a single sample from his translation of the *Odyssey*, designed to show the spirit in which he undertook the task of interpreting to the modern world the poem he most admired. Butler's idea of a good translation was that it should re-create for the new times and the new environment of language, and not mummify with what he called 'Wardour Street' English, the living force of the original. His translations were colloquial and aggressively modern at a time when such things were not done — though they have been done often since. In the case of the *Odyssey* there was also behind his version a theory — which got him into as bad odour with the classical scholars as his books on evolution had done with the scientists. Butler fully convinced himself that *The Authoress of the Odyssey* — to cite the title of his book on the matter — had been a young girl who had put herself into the poem as Nausicaa, the daughter of King Alcinous; and he adduced many ingenious arguments in support of his theory. He was equally certain that the entire geography of the poem was that of Sicily and of the seas and lands within easy reach of Sicily; and here again he was able, it must be agreed, to make out quite a plausible case. I have never been able to get up any excitement about either the authorship of the *Odyssey* or its provenance — any more than I have over the Baconian or other similar controversies; but I can quite see how Butler, having once hit on the notion from what he felt to be a feminine touch in the whole execution of the poem, was led to throw himself into the quest for evidence with the more zest because it gave him a chance of scoring off the classical pundits.

Having disposed of the *Odyssey*, Butler found a new world to conquer in an attempt to unravel the story lying behind Shakespeare's *Sonnets*. Here too his method was psychological: he tried to put himself into Shakespeare's mind and to trace out the vicissitudes of an amour which had given the Shakespearean scholars much trouble, not so much in searching out the truth as in evading it. In this case the quest had for him a deeper personal interest than the authorship of the *Odyssey*. It is impossible not to see him, in his study of the history of Shakespeare's affair, retracing in his mind the story of his own tangled relations with Pauli — whatever the actual character of those relations may have been. Butler's own sonnets, of which a few, out of not many, are given in this volume, were evidently influenced by Shakespeare's — indeed quite frankly so. In the sonnet to which he gave the curious title 'Academic Exercise', it is not easy to say how far he was re-telling Shakespeare's story, and how far his own.

From *Shakespeare's Sonnets reconsidered and in part Re-arranged* I have not attempted to make extracts. The book has to be read as a whole, or not at all. Nor has it seemed to me that I could fruitfully give isolated passages from Butler's Italian books, attractive as they are. *Alps and Sanctuaries* and *Ex Voto* are both charming and sensitive studies, full of Butler's deep love for Italy and — *Alps and Sanctuaries* above all — starred plentifully with characteristic Butlerisms that I could have extracted as companions to the passages selected from the *Note-Books*. I refrained only because I had too little space to do justice to everything and had some fear that a few passages, torn away from their context, might give a false impression — for it is in their Italian setting and as episodes in an Italian travel-book that they have their true place.

I hesitated again over *A First Year in Canterbury Settlement* — Butler's account, drawn from the letters he sent home, of his experience as a New Zealand up-country sheep-farmer in the early days of the colony. Of this book, which was put together and published by his father while he was still in New Zealand, Butler habitually spoke with dislike and even contempt. He resented the smoothings and excisions to which his father had subjected it; but, much more than this, he simply felt a dislike for anything with which his father had been concerned in relation to him. What Canon Butler left out or amended we have no means of knowing, for the original letters have not survived. But the book as we have it does not at all deserve the author's strictures: it is, on the contrary, graphic, well-written and never dull. It lacks, how-ever, the characteristic Butler touch: it might, thanks perhaps to Canon Butler's editorial labours, have been written by someone whose views were entirely orthodox and unprovocative, and who had never taken a pleasure in tormenting the virtuous. That Butler, even at this first stage of his career as a writer, already had the love for paradox and inversion of accepted sentiment that marks his later books we know from his contemporary contributions to the New Zealand *Press*. Perhaps he did not put this part of him into his letters home: if he did, his father certainly cut it out.

There remain, of Butler's major works — that is, apart from merely occasional writings — only his *Life and Letters of Dr. Samuel Butler* and his words for the post-Handelian oratorios which he composed in collaboration with Festing Jones. I know some who think highly of the *Life* of his grandfather; but for my part I find it disappointing. It was a curious labour of love. Dr. Butler was a head-master and a bishop — human classes for which his grandson felt no liking — and for most of his life he was content to dislike Dr. Butler by instinct, without troubling to find out anything about him. Bishop Butler, in addition to being a head-master and a dignitary of the Church, had been father to Canon Butler; and, to one with Butler's views on heredity, that seemed to be enough. Then, having come into possession of his grandfather's papers, he read them and discovered, much to his surprise, that the bishop had been a most likeable person, with none of the stuffiness, pomposity and hypocrisy he had been attributing to him, but, on the contrary, broad-minded, friendly, and with ideas about education well in advance of his time and offering a sharp contrast to those of Dr. Arnold, who was one of Butler's principal bugbears. The outcome was that Butler fell in love with the old gentleman, and wrote his life a good deal with the notion of making up for having treated him so unjustly in his thoughts. The great merit of the *Life and Letters* is that they let Dr. Butler speak for himself, with the least possible intrusion of his grandson's impishness: their fault is that, in doing this, Butler so held himself in check as to offer all too little by way of interpretation.

Of Butler's music I have no competence to speak. He regarded Handel not only as the world's greatest musician, but also as its greatest poet, putting him above Shakespeare. He believed that, after Handel, music had gone off on a false scent; and in his own music he held himself to be, not a mere imitator of Handel, but a revivalist who was attempting to take up the Handelian tradition and develop it in a nineteenth-century fashion. Handel, like Shakespeare, lived on in the popular mind: he was the people's musician as Shakespeare was the people's poet, and Butler believed in the soundness of the popular instinct. Handel was never long out of his mind: the statues in *Erewhon* made music out of Handel: Alethea's death in *The Way of All Flesh* had its Handelian requiem: in Italy, a scene would call up to Butler some bars of Handel's music, which he set down in *Alps and Sanctuaries* as companion illustrations to the drawings of places which adorned the book. Almost, for Butler, there was no other musician; and this was at a time when Handel was as much out of favour in the musical world, which was in transit from Beethoven to Wagner, as he was vigorously alive among lusty choirs at the Crystal Palace and in every industrial town. I have given two samples – both by Butler – one from *Narcissus* and one from *Ulysses*, as illustrations of Butler's attempt to reproduce the spirit of Handel's music in a form adapted to the conditions of his own time.

Butler's music – that is, his musical competition – came to him late in life. It was closely bound up with his friendship for Festing Jones, and it gave him great delight; but it was always secondary to his writing. His painting, on the other hand, was for many years his main preoccupation, in comparison with which writing books seemed to him a minor, and sometimes a dangerously distracting, pursuit. When he came back from New Zealand, and was able to follow his own bent, it was as a painter that he set out to win the only kind of immortality he valued or believed in. He had some, but only a little success: a few of his paintings have real quality – most of all, I think 'Family Prayers', which admirably captures the mood of the chapters about Battersby in *The Way of All Flesh*. I have had it reproduced, together with his Self-Portrait, as a frontispiece to this volume. But Butler found out, after years of trying, that he was not destined to be a good enough painter to win his immortality that way – and to make himself immortal was for him a deeply-rooted desire. Both *Erewhon* and the first draft of *The Way of All Flesh* were written while he still looked on himself mainly as a painter; and when in 1876 he renounced his hopes of painting well enough to satisfy his need, and made up his mind to be a writer first and foremost, the tasks he set himself first were the writing of *Life and Habit* and its sequels. Not till four years later, in 1880, did he start revising *The Way of All Flesh*, and before it was nearly done he was busy making himself into a composer of music. Then followed, in 1885, the death of Miss Savage and, the following year, his father's death and the affluence which came with it, enabling him to satisfy in full his taste for Italian journeyings and friendships, and to care much less – though he never ceased to care a good deal – about the failure of his books to sell.

From first to last there was a twist in Butler's nature. What he most resented in his upbringing was the attempt on his parents' part to force him into holy orders without giving him either a chance to think for himself or any inkling that there was another side to the case. He was well aware that this came of no conscious malice or deception on his father's part, though he sometimes spoke as if it did; but he felt strongly that the state of mind which made it possible for Canon Butler so completely to ignore both the case against Christian belief and the duty of presenting the case fairly to his son before he committed himself irrevocably was indefensible and inconsistent with wise or decent parenthood. It is strange that he contrived to pass through his years as an undergraduate at Cambridge without ever encountering 'infidelity' — for there was certainly plenty of it for him to meet with, had he been in a mood to look for it. But we must take his word for it that he did not make even a nodding acquaintance with unbelief until he had very nearly got committed to being a clergyman. This narrow escape rankled for the rest of his life, as it could not have done had the escape been less by the skin of his teeth. It accounts for a great deal of the violence of his feeling against his father and against the patriarchal notions which dominated Victorian family life. Yet, with all the extremity of his revulsion, he could never get away either from religion or from his family. His mind continued to occupy itself with religion, even when he had thrown over all belief in what is commonly called by that name. The *Note-Books* are full of irreverent remarks; but they are also full of a sense of an unseen, unknown reality, and as impatient of the atheist as of the believer. So with the family and family life: Butler never wearied of poking fun at them, or of saying nasty things about his own family, but he kept up with and visited his father and sisters and could never break away from them as he made Ernest break away from Theobald Pontifex. So too he had few good words for his old school — Shrewsbury; yet he became and remained one of its most faithful *alumni*; a regular attendant at 'old school' reunions, though every time he attended one he came away wondering why he had gone. There was a dualism in him in all these matters: he could not have hated so heartily had there not been in him also a part that hankered and even loved.

All this fits in with his manner of life. A *gamin* in his writing and in his intimate interchanges with Miss Savage — and indeed in some aspects of his own life — he had at the same time a desire to be 'respectable' in the ordinary, everyday Victorian sense of the word. He was not only afraid of being 'found out' — though of that he was afraid — he was also minded to observe the conventions because they were conventions and embodied the unconscious memory and the cunning of the social hive. A rebel in many things, he had a distaste for rebels; and especially he admired, quite without reserve, the 'gentleman'. He thought, like Burke, that the finest thing in human beings could be bred only over generations of affluence and leisure. He put down his picture of ideal humanity in the uninteresting Towneley of *The Way of All Flesh*. It was partly that he had a deep admiration for good looks, good health and *insouciance*; but it was more than that. There was an *alter ego* in him that scorned his literary and artistic pursuits and his will to achieve immortality by some other route than the obvious, usual one of marriage and procreation.

All his life Butler ran away, not from women, but from marriage, which had for him a terrifying quality of commitment akin to that of becoming a clergyman. He did not want to be tied: he wanted to be free to change his mind when he felt like changing it, without having to incur charges of failing in his duty. It was simpler to have no duties, except that of achieving something worth while — a duty which he entirely accepted. He depended much on friendship, and was very faithful to his friends. But being tied — as he long felt himself tied to Pauli — was a nightmare.

Butler wrote in all sixteen books, including his translations and his edition of Shakespeare's sonnets, but not the *Note-Books* or his various pamphlets and essays. Only three of these — *The Way of All Flesh* and the two *Erewhons* — are stories: four others set forth his theories on evolution and the mind of man: the rest make up a singularly miscellaneous and yet coherent collection. They are the record of a literary life spent in an unending series of paper-chases or games of hunt-the-slipper. Butler was always chasing something — the truth about the gospel story of the Resurrection, the truth about the manner of human heredity, the truth about the authorship and geography of the *Odyssey*, the truth about Shakespeare's love-affair, the truth about Tabachetti, the Italian sculptor whom he succeeded in proving to have been a Belgian, the truth about his own grandfather — but never, one feels, quite the truth about his father, and certainly never the whole truth about himself. He had, in all these quests, a rich enjoyment of the chase itself; and when he had settled a thing to his satisfaction, it was done with, as far as he was concerned. There were, however, as the *Note-Books* show, a good many things he never did settle, so as to have done with them. He kept on recurring to them, making new, overlapping entries about them, worrying at them even while he wondered why he worried. It was one of his frequent sayings that it was folly to learn anything until you became conscious of pain from not knowing it; but this is not so clear a precept as it sounds, because there is no telling what may afflict us with such pain, or why. Butler's *Note-Books* contain many warnings against the bad habit of going on asking oneself unanswerable questions, and in *The Way of All Flesh* he made Ernest Pontifex give it up. For himself, he never quite gave it up, despite his warnings.

How great a man Butler was, or what future generations will make of him, it is not very fruitful to ask. His contemporaries, save a few, left him severely alone, except for *Erewhon*, which they regarded simply as a whimsey. After his death, he had a most prompt renascence, due mainly to the publication of *The Way of All Flesh*, but also, not a little, to Bernard Shaw. Then he sank again, except for a limited, but devoted, flock of admirers, who got older without attracting an adequate inflow of young recruits. Today, he is again half in fashion, but only half, with *The Way* and the *Note-Books*, and the *Psalm of Montreal*, as his principal standard-bearers. *Life and Habit*, no longer a subversive work, is respected, but not much read; *The Fair Haven*, except the *Memoir*, is right out of the contemporary fashion; his translations of the *Iliad* and the *Odyssey* have never caught on; and I do not know if anyone plays his music. Within narrow limits, however, his immortality seems secure. I have been taken severely to task for calling *The Way of All Flesh* one of the greatest of English novels; but I still think it is, despite the falling off of its later chapters. It is at all events good enough to be secure of finding readers for as long as *Tom Jones*, *Vanity Fair*, or *The Pickwick Papers* – though not so many, I agree. Butler has won the immortality he wanted; and I hope this selection from some of his writings will send some of those who light upon it in search of the many good things I have not been able to include.

G. D. H. COLE

LIST OF SAMUEL BUTLER'S WORKS

1863   A First Year in Canterbury Settlement
1872   Erewhon, or Over the Range
1873   The Fair Haven
1877   Life and Habit
1879   Evolution Old and New
1880   Unconscious Memory
1881   Alps and Sanctuaries of Piedmont and the Canton Ticino
1885   Gavottes, Minuets, Fugues, and other short pieces for the Piano [with Henry Festing Jones]
1886   Luck or Cunning
1888   Ex Voto
1888   Narcissus: a Cantata in the Handelian Form [with H. Festing Jones]
1896   The Life and Letters of Dr. Samuel Butler
1897   The Authoress of the *Odyssey*
1898   The *Iliad* rendered into English Prose
1899   Shakespeare's Sonnets reconsidered and in part Re-arranged
1900   The *Odyssey* rendered into English Prose
1901   Erewhon Revisited
1903   The Way of All Flesh
1904   Seven Sonnets and A Psalm of Montreal (privately printed)
1904   Essays on Life, Art and Science
1904   Ulysses: an Oratorio [with H. Festing Jones]
1909   God the Known and God the Unknown [from *The Examiner* of 1879]
1912   The Note-Books of Samuel Butler
1913   The Humour of Homer and other Essays
1932   Butleriana (Nonesuch Press)
1934   Further Extracts from the Note-Books of Samuel Butler
1935   Letters between Samuel Butler and Miss Savage

TO CRITICS AND OTHERS

O Critics, cultured Critics!
Who will praise me after I am dead,
Who will see in me both more and less than I intended,
But who will swear that whatever it was it was all perfectly right:
You will think you are better than the people who, when I was alive,
swore that whatever I did was wrong
And damned my books for me as fast as I could write them;
But you will not be better, you will be just the same, neither better
nor worse,
And you will go for some future Butler as your fathers have gone
for me.
Oh! How I should have hated you!

But you, Nice People!
Who will be sick of me because the critics thrust me down your
throats,
But who would take me willingly enough if you were not bored
about me,
Or if you could have the cream of me — and surely this should
suffice:
Please remember that, if I were living, I should be upon your side
And should hate those who imposed me either on myself or others;
Therefore, I pray you, neglect me, burlesque me, boil me down, do
whatever you like with me,
But do not think that, if I were living, I should not aid and abet you.
There is nothing that even Shakespeare would enjoy more than a
good burlesque of *Hamlet*.

EREWHON

EDITOR'S PREFACE

BUTLER published *Erewhon* in 1872, with a Preface of three lines, as follows:

> The Author wishes it to be understood that Erewhon is pronounced as a word of three syllables, all short — thus, Ĕ-rĕ-whŏn.

A second edition, very slightly revised, with a new Preface, was published later in the year. Further editions were printed from the plates of the second edition until 1901, when Butler produced a revised and enlarged edition, with a further Preface, giving an account of the book's history. It had begun, he said, with an article on 'Darwin among the Machines', written and published in New Zealand (in the Christchurch *Press*) in 1863. A second article followed — also in the *Press*. After his return to England, he re-wrote 'Darwin among the Machines', and re-published it in G. J. Holyoake's *Reasoner* in 1865, with the title 'The Mechanical Creation'. Soon after this he wrote two more sections, 'The World of the Unborn' and 'The Musical Banks'. The book as a whole, incorporating these sections, was written during the winter of 1870-71. The sequel, *Erewhon Revisited*, was written in 1900-01.

From the revised version of *Erewhon* I have had to make, for reasons of space, the following omissions in the present volume:

CHAPTER X
> A short passage comparing Erewhonian ideas about disease with those of certain modern peoples.

CHAPTER XI
> The whole, which gives an account of 'Some Erewhonian Trials'.

CHAPTER XII
> The opening, containing comments on one of these trials, and a short passage nearer the end, amplifying the reference to Erewhonian prisons.

CHAPTER XVII
> A short passage comparing the 'high Ydgrunites' with 'the best class of Englishmen'.

27

CHAPTER XIX

The entire chapter, entitled 'The World of the Unborn' (and also, consequentially, the closing sentence of chapter XVIII, and the opening page or two of chapter XX).

CHAPTERS XXIII–XXV

Most regretfully, the entire chapters, being 'The Book of the Machines' (and also, consequentially, the opening sentences of chapter XXVI).

Apart from these omissions, the book is given entire, from the revised edition.

CHAPTER ONE

WASTE LANDS

I F the reader will excuse me, I will say nothing of my antecedents, nor
of the circumstances which led me to leave my native country; the
narrative would be tedious to him and painful to myself. Suffice it,
that when I left home it was with the intention of going to some new
colony, and either finding, or even perhaps purchasing, waste crown
land suitable for cattle or sheep farming, by which means I thought
that I could better my fortunes more rapidly than in England.

It will be seen that I did not succeed in my design, and that however
much I may have met with that was new and strange, I have been
unable to reap any pecuniary advantage.

It is true, I imagine myself to have made a discovery which, if I can
be the first to profit by it, will bring me a recompense beyond all
money computation, and secure me a position such as has not been
attained by more than some fifteen or sixteen persons since the creation
of the universe. But to this end I must possess myself of a considerable
sum of money: neither do I know how to get it, except by interesting
the public in my story, and inducing the charitable to come forward
and assist me. With this hope I now publish my adventures; but I do
so with great reluctance, for I fear that my story will be doubted unless
I tell the whole of it; and yet I dare not do so, lest others with more
means than mine should get the start of me. I prefer the risk of being
doubted to that of being anticipated, and have therefore concealed my
destination on leaving England, as also the point from which I began
my more serious and difficult journey.

My chief consolation lies in the fact that truth bears its own impress,
and that my story will carry conviction by reason of the internal
evidences for its accuracy. No one who is himself honest will doubt
my being so.

I reached my destination in one of the last months of 1868, but I dare
not mention the season, lest the reader should gather in which hemi-
sphere I was. The colony was one which had not been opened up even
to the most adventurous settlers for more than eight or nine years,
having been previously uninhabited, save by a few tribes of savages

29

who frequented the seaboard. The part known to Europeans consisted of a coast-line about eight hundred miles in length (affording three or four good harbours), and a tract of country extending inland for a space varying from two to three hundred miles, until it reached the offshoots of an exceedingly lofty range of mountains, which could be seen from far out upon the plains, and were covered with perpetual snow. The coast was perfectly well known both north and south of the tract to which I have alluded, but in neither direction was there a single harbour for five hundred miles, and the mountains, which descended almost into the sea, were covered with thick timber, so that none would think of settling.

With this bay of land, however, the case was different. The harbours were sufficient; the country was timbered, but not too heavily; it was admirably suited for agriculture; it also contained millions on millions of acres of the most beautifully grassed country in the world, and of the best suited for all manner of sheep and cattle. The climate was temperate, and very healthy; there were no wild animals, nor were the natives dangerous, being few in number and of an intelligent tractable disposition.

It may be readily understood that when once Europeans set foot upon this territory they were not slow to take advantage of its capabilities. Sheep and cattle were introduced, and bred with extreme rapidity; men took up their 50,000 or 100,000 acres of country, going inland one behind the other, till in a few years there was not an acre between the sea and the front ranges which was not taken up, and stations either for sheep or cattle were spotted about at intervals of some twenty or thirty miles over the whole country. The front ranges stopped the tide of squatters for some little time; it was thought that there was too much snow upon them for too many months in the year — that the sheep would get lost, the ground being too difficult for shepherding — that the expense of getting wool down to the ship's side would eat up the farmers' profits — and that the grass was too rough and sour for sheep to thrive upon; but one after another determined to try the experiment, and it was wonderful how successfully it turned out. Men pushed farther and farther into the mountains, and found a very considerable tract inside the front range, between it and another which was loftier still, though even this was not the highest, the great snowy one which could be seen from out upon the plains. This second range, however, seemed to mark the extreme limits of pastoral country; and it was here, at a small and newly founded station, that I was received as a cadet, and soon regularly employed. I was then just twenty-two years old.

I was delighted with the country and the manner of life. It was my daily business to go up to the top of a certain high mountain, and down one of its spurs on to the flat, in order to make sure that no sheep had crossed their boundaries. I was to see the sheep, not necessarily close at hand, nor to get them in a single mob, but to see enough of them here and there to feel easy that nothing had gone wrong; this was no difficult matter, for there were not above eight hundred of them; and, being all breeding ewes, they were pretty quiet.

There were a good many sheep which I knew, as two or three black ewes, and a black lamb or two, and several others which had some distinguishing mark whereby I could tell them. I would try and see all these, and if they were all there, and the mob looked large enough, I might rest assured that all was well. It is surprising how soon the eye becomes accustomed to missing twenty sheep out of two or three hundred. I had a telescope and a dog, and would take bread and meat and tobacco with me. Starting with early dawn, it would be night before I could complete my round; for the mountain over which I had to go was very high. In winter it was covered with snow, and the sheep needed no watching from above. If I were to see sheep-dung or tracks going down on to the other side of the mountain (where there was a valley with a stream — a mere *cul-de-sac*), I was to follow them, and look out for sheep; but I never saw any, the sheep always descending on to their own side, partly from habit, and partly because there was abundance of good sweet feed which had been burnt in the early spring, just before I came, and was now deliciously green and rich, while that on the other side had never been burnt, and was rank and coarse.

It was a monotonous life, but it was very healthy; and one does not much mind anything when one is well. The country was the grandest that can be imagined. How often have I sat on the mountain side and watched the waving downs, with the two white specks of huts in the distance, and the little square of garden behind them; the paddock with a patch of bright green oats above the huts, and the yards and wool-sheds down on the flat below; all seen as through the wrong end of a telescope, so clear and brilliant was the air, or as upon a colossal model or map spread out beneath me. Beyond the downs was a plain, going

31

down to a river of great size, on the farther side of which there were other high mountains, with the winter's snow still not quite melted; up the river, which ran winding in many streams over a bed some two miles broad, I looked upon the second great chain, and could see a narrow gorge where the river retired and was lost. I knew that there was a range still farther back; but except from one place near the very top of my own mountain, no part of it was visible: from this point, however, I saw, whenever there were no clouds, a single snow-clad peak, many miles away, and I should think about as high as any mountain in the world. Never shall I forget the utter loneliness of the prospect — only the little far-away homestead giving sign of human handiwork — the vastness of mountain and plain, of river and sky; the marvellous atmospheric effects — sometimes black mountains against a white sky, and then again, after cold weather, white mountains against a black sky — sometimes seen through breaks and swirls of cloud — and sometimes, which was best of all, I went up my mountain in a fog, and then got above the mist; going higher and higher, I would look down upon a sea of whiteness, through which would be thrust innumerable mountain tops that looked like islands.

I am there now, as I write; I fancy that I can see the downs, the huts, the plain, and the river-bed — that torrent pathway of desolation, with its distant roar of waters. Oh, wonderful! wonderful! so lonely and so solemn, with the sad grey clouds above, and no sound save a lost lamb bleating upon the mountain side, as though its little heart were breaking. Then there comes some lean and withered old ewe, with deep gruff voice and unlovely aspect, trotting back from the seductive pasture; now she examines this gully, and now that, and now she stands listening with uplifted head, that she may hear the distant wailing and obey it. Aha! they see, and rush towards each other. Alas! they are both mistaken; the ewe is not the lamb's ewe, they are neither kin nor kind to one another, and part in coldness. Each must cry louder, and wander farther yet; may luck be with them both that they may find their own at nightfall. But this is mere dreaming, and I must proceed.

I could not help speculating upon what might lie farther up the river and behind the second range. I had no money, but if I could only find workable country, I might stock it with borrowed capital, and consider myself a made man. True, the range looked so vast, that there seemed little chance of getting a sufficient road through it or over it;

but no one had yet explored it, and it is wonderful how one finds that one can make a path into all sorts of places (and even get a road for pack-horses) which from a distance appear inaccessible; the river was so great that it must drain an inner tract — at least I thought so; and though everyone said it would be madness to attempt taking sheep farther inland, I knew that only three years ago the same cry had been raised against the country which my master's flock was now over-running. I could not keep these thoughts out of my head as I would rest myself upon the mountain side; they haunted me as I went my daily rounds, and grew upon me from hour to hour, till I resolved that after shearing I would remain in doubt no longer, but saddle my horse, take as much provision with me as I could, and go and see for myself.

But over and above these thoughts came that of the great range itself. What was beyond it? Ah! who could say? There was no one in the whole world who had the smallest idea, save those who were them-selves on the other side of it — if, indeed, there was anyone at all. Could I hope to cross it? This would be the highest triumph that I could wish for; but it was too much to think of yet. I would try the nearer range, and see how far I could go. Even if I did not find country, might I not find gold, or diamonds, or copper, or silver? I would some-times lie flat down to drink out of a stream, and could see little yellow specks among the sand; were these gold? People said no; but then people always said there was no gold until it was found to be abundant: there was plenty of slate and granite, which I had always understood to accompany gold; and even though it was not found in paying quan-tities here, it might be abundant in the main ranges. These thoughts filled my head, and I could not banish them.

CHAPTER TWO

IN THE WOOL-SHED

AT last shearing came; and with the shearers there was an old native whom they had nicknamed Chowbok — though, I believe, his real name was Kahabuka. He was a sort of chief of the natives, could speak a little English, and was a great favourite with the mis-sionaries. He did not do any regular work with the shearers, but pretended to help in the yards, his real aim being to get the grog, which is always more freely circulated at shearing-time: he did not get much, for he was apt to be dangerous when drunk; and very little would make him so: still he did get it occasionally, and if one wanted to get anything out of him, it was the best bribe to offer him. I resolved to question him, and get as much information from him as I could. I did so. As long as I kept to questions about the nearer ranges, he was easy to get on with — he had never been there, but there were traditions among his tribe to the effect that there was no sheep-country; nothing, in fact, but stunted timber and a few river-bed flats. It was very difficult to reach; still there were passes: one of them up our own river, though not directly along the river-bed, the gorge of which was not practicable; he had never seen anyone who had been there: was there not enough on this side? But when I came to the main range, his manner changed at once. He became uneasy, and began to prevaricate and shuffle. In a very few minutes I could see that of this, too, there existed traditions in his tribe; but no efforts or coaxing could get a word from him about them. At last I hinted about grog, and presently he feigned consent: I gave it him; but as soon as he had drunk it he began shamming intoxication, and then went to sleep, or pretended to do so, letting me kick him pretty hard and never budging.

I was angry, for I had to go without my own grog and had got nothing out of him; so the next day I determined that he should tell me before I gave him any, or get none at all.

Accordingly, when night came and the shearers had knocked off work and had their supper, I got my share of rum in a tin pannikin and made a sign to Chowbok to follow me to the wool-shed, which he willingly did, slipping out after me, and no one taking any notice of either of us. When we got down to the wool-shed we lit a tallow candle, and having stuck it in an old bottle we sat down upon the wool bales and began to smoke. A wool-shed is a roomy place, built somewhat on the same plan as a cathedral, with aisles on either side full of pens for the sheep, a great nave, at the upper end of which the shearers work, and a further space for wool sorters and packers. It always refreshed me with a semblance of antiquity (precious in a new country), though I very well knew that the oldest wool-shed in the settlement was not more than seven years old, while this was only two. Chowbok pretended to expect his grog at once, though we both of us knew very well what the other was after, and that we were each playing against the other, the one for grog the other for information.

We had a hard fight: for more than two hours he had tried to put me off with lies, but had carried no conviction; during the whole time we had been morally wrestling with one another and had neither of us apparently gained the least advantage. At length, however, I had become sure that he would give in ultimately, and that with a little further patience I should get his story out of him. As upon a cold day in winter, when one has churned (as I had often had to do), and churned in vain, and the butter makes no sign of coming, at last one tells by the sound that the cream has gone to sleep, and then upon a sudden the butter comes, so I had churned at Chowbok until I perceived that he had arrived, as it were, at the sleepy stage, and that with a continuance of steady quiet pressure the day was mine. On a sudden, without a word of warning, he rolled two bales of wool (his strength was very great) into the middle of the floor, and on the top of these he placed another crosswise; he snatched up an empty wool-pack, threw it like a mantle over his shoulders, jumped upon the uppermost bale, and sat upon it. In a moment his whole form was changed. His high shoulders dropped; he set his feet close together, heel to heel and toe to toe; he laid his arms and hands close alongside of his body, the palms following his thighs; he held his head high but quite straight, and his eyes stared right in front of him; but he frowned horribly, and assumed an expression of face that was positively fiendish. At the best of times Chowbok was very ugly, but he now exceeded all conceivable limits of the hideous. His mouth extended almost from ear to ear, grinning horribly and showing all his teeth; his eyes glared, though they remained quite fixed, and his forehead was contracted with a most malevolent scowl.

I am afraid my description will have conveyed only the ridiculous side of his appearance; but the ridiculous and the sublime are near, and the grotesque fiendishness of Chowbok's face approached this last, if it did not reach it. I tried to be amused, but I felt a sort of creeping at the roots of my hair and over my whole body, as I looked and wondered what he could possibly be intending to signify. He continued thus for about a minute, sitting bolt upright, as stiff as a stone, and making this fearful face. Then there came from his lips a low moaning like the wind, rising and falling by infinitely small gradations till it became almost a shriek, from which it descended and died away; after that, he jumped down from the bale and held up the extended fingers of both his hands, as one who should say 'Ten', though I did not then understand him.

EREWHON

For myself, I was open-mouthed with astonishment. Chowbok rolled the bales rapidly into their place, and stood before me shuddering as in great fear; horror was written upon his face — this time quite involuntarily — as though the natural panic of one who had committed an awful crime against unknown and superhuman agencies. He nodded his head and gibbered, and pointed repeatedly to the mountains. He would not touch the grog, but after a few seconds he made a run through the wool-shed door into the moonlight; nor did he reappear till next day at dinner-time, when he turned up, looking very sheepish and abject in his civility towards myself.

Of his meaning I had no conception. How could I? All I could feel sure of was, that he had a meaning which was true and awful to himself. It was enough for me that I believed him to have given me the best he had and all he had. This kindled my imagination more than if he had told me intelligible stories by the hour together. I knew not what the great snowy ranges might conceal, but I could no longer doubt that it would be something well worth discovering.

I kept aloof from Chowbok for the next few days, and showed no desire to question him further; when I spoke to him I called him Kahabuka, which gratified him greatly: he seemed to have become afraid of me, and acted as one who was in my power. Having therefore made up my mind that I would begin exploring as soon as shearing was over, I thought it would be a good thing to take Chowbok with me; so I told him that I meant going to the nearer ranges for a few days' prospecting, and that he was to come too. I made him promises of nightly grog, and held out the chances of finding gold. I said nothing about the main range, for I knew it would frighten him. I would get him as far up our own river as I could, and trace it if possible to its source. I would then either go on by myself, if I felt my courage equal to the attempt, or return with Chowbok. So, as soon as ever shearing was over and the wool sent off, I asked leave of absence, and obtained it. Also, I bought an old pack-horse and pack-saddle, so that I might take plenty of provisions, and blankets, and a small tent. I was to ride and find fords over the river; Chowbok was to follow and lead the pack-horse, which would also carry him over the fords. My master let me have tea and sugar, ship's biscuits, tobacco, and salt mutton, with two or three bottles of good brandy; for, as the wool was now sent down, abundance of provisions would come up with the empty drays.

36

Everything being now ready, all the hands on the station turned out to see us off, and we started on our journey, not very long after the summer solstice of 1870.

CHAPTER THREE

UP THE RIVER

THE first day we had an easy time, following up the great flats by the river-side, which had already been twice burned, so that there was no dense undergrowth to check us, though the ground was often rough, and we had to go a good deal upon the river-bed. Towards nightfall we had made a matter of some five-and-twenty miles, and camped at the point where the river entered upon the gorge.

The weather was delightfully warm, considering that the valley in which we were encamped must have been at least two thousand feet above the level of the sea. The river-bed was here about a mile and a half broad and entirely covered with shingle over which the river ran in many winding channels, looking, when seen from above, like a tangled skein of ribbon, and glistening in the sun. We knew that it was liable to very sudden and heavy freshets; but even had we not known it, we could have seen it by the snags of trees, which must have been carried long distances, and by the mass of vegetable and mineral *débris* which was banked against their lower side, showing that at times the whole river-bed must be covered with a roaring torrent many feet in depth and of ungovernable fury. At present the river was low, there being but five or six streams, too deep and rapid for even a strong man to ford on foot, but to be crossed safely on horseback. On either side of it there were still a few acres of flat, which grew wider and wider down the river, till they became the large plains on which we looked from my master's hut. Behind us rose the lowest spurs of the second range, leading abruptly to the range itself; and at a distance of half a mile began the gorge, where the river narrowed and became boisterous and terrible. The beauty of the scene cannot be conveyed in language. The one side of the valley was blue with evening shadow, through which loomed forest and precipice, hillside and mountain top; and the other was still brilliant with the sunset gold. The wide and wasteful river with its ceaseless rushing — the beautiful water-birds, too, which abounded upon the islets and were so tame that we could come close up to them — the ineffable purity of the air — the solemn peacefulness of the untrodden region — could there be a more delightful and exhilarating combination?

We set about making our camp, close to some large bush which came down from the mountains on to the flat, and tethered out our horses upon ground as free as we could find it from anything round which they might wind the rope and get themselves tied up. We dared not let them run loose, lest they might stray down the river home again. We then gathered wood and lit the fire. We filled a tin pannikin with water and set it against the hot ashes to boil. When the water boiled we threw in two or three large pinches of tea and let them brew.

We had caught half a dozen young ducks in the course of the day — an easy matter, for the old birds made such a fuss in attempting to decoy us away from them — pretending to be badly hurt, as they say the plover does — that we could always find them by going about in the opposite direction to the old bird till we heard the young ones crying: then we ran them down, for they could not fly though they were nearly full grown. Chowbok plucked them a little and singed them a good deal. Then we cut them up and boiled them in another pannikin, and this completed our preparations.

When we had done supper it was quite dark. The silence and freshness of the night, the occasional sharp cry of the wood-hen, the ruddy glow of the fire, the subdued rushing of the river, the sombre forest, and the immediate foreground of our saddles, packs and blankets, made a picture worthy of a Salvator Rosa or a Nicolas Poussin. I call it to mind and delight in it now, but I did not notice it at the time. We next to never know when we are well off: but this cuts two ways — for if we did, we should perhaps know better when we are ill off also; and I have sometimes thought that there are as many ignorant of the one as of the other. He who wrote, 'O fortunatos nimium sua si bona nôrint agricolas,' might have written quite as truly, 'O infortunatos nimium sua si mala norint'; and there are few of us who are not protected from the keenest pain by our inability to see what it is that we have done, what we are suffering, and what we truly are. Let us be grateful to the mirror for revealing to us our appearance only.

We found as soft a piece of ground as we could — though it was all stony — and having collected grass and so disposed of ourselves that we had a little hollow for our hip-bones, we strapped our blankets around us and went to sleep. Waking in the night, I saw the stars overhead and the moonlight bright upon the mountains. The river was ever rushing; I heard one of our horses neigh to its companion, and was assured that they were still at hand; I had no care of mind or body, save that I had doubtless many difficulties to overcome; there came upon me a delicious sense of peace, a fullness of contentment which I do not believe can be felt by any but those who have spent days consecutively on horseback, or at any rate in the open air.

Next morning we found our last night's tea-leaves frozen at the bottom of the pannikins, though it was not nearly the beginning of autumn; we breakfasted as we had supped, and were on our way by six o'clock. In half an hour we had entered the gorge, and turning round a corner we bade farewell to the last sight of my master's country.

The gorge was narrow and precipitous; the river was now only a few yards wide, and roared and thundered against rocks of many tons in weight; the sound was deafening, for there was a great volume of water. We were two hours in making less than a mile, and that with danger, sometimes in the river and sometimes on the rock. There was that damp black smell of rocks covered with slimy vegetation, as near some huge waterfall where spray is ever rising. The air was clammy and cold. I cannot conceive how our horses managed to keep their footing, especially the one with the pack, and I dreaded the having to return almost as much as going forward. I suppose this lasted three miles, but it was well midday when the gorge got a little wider, and a small stream came into it from a tributary valley. Further progress up the main river was impossible, for the cliffs descended like walls; so we went up the side stream, Chowbok seeming to think that here must be the pass of which reports existed among his people. We now incurred less of actual danger but more fatigue, and it was only after infinite trouble, owing to the rocks and tangled vegetation, that we got ourselves and our horses upon the saddle from which this small stream descended; by that time clouds had descended upon us, and it was raining heavily. Moreover, it was six o'clock and we were tired out, having made perhaps six miles in twelve hours.

On the saddle there was some coarse grass which was in full seed, and therefore very nourishing for the horses; also abundance of anise and sow-thistle, of which they are extravagantly fond, so we turned them loose and prepared to camp. Everything was soaking wet and we were half-perished with cold; indeed, we were very uncomfortable. There was brushwood about, but we could get no fire till we had shaved off the wet outside of some dead branches and filled our pockets with the dry inside chips. Having done this we managed to start a fire, nor did we allow it to go out when we had once started it; we pitched the tent, and by nine o'clock were comparatively warm and dry. Next morning it was fine; we broke camp, and after advancing a short distance we found that, by descending over ground less difficult than yesterday's, we should come again upon the river-bed, which had opened out above the gorge; but it was plain at a glance that there was no available sheep country, nothing but a few flats covered with scrub on either side the river, and mountains which were perfectly worthless. But we could see the main range. There was no mistake about this. The glaciers were tumbling down the mountain sides like cataracts, and seemed actually to descend upon the river-bed; there could be no serious difficulty in reaching them by following up the river, which was wide and open; but it seemed rather an objectless thing to do, for the main range looked hopeless, and my curiosity about the nature of the country above the gorge was now quite satisfied; there was no money in it whatever, unless there should be minerals, of which I saw no more signs than lower down.

However, I resolved that I would follow the river up, and not return until I was compelled to do so. I would go up every branch as far as I could, and wash well for gold. Chowbok liked seeing me do this, but it never came to anything, for we did not even find the colour. His dislike of the main range appeared to have worn off, and he made no objections to approaching it. I think he thought there was no danger of my trying to cross it, and he was not afraid of anything on this side; besides, we might find gold. But the fact was that he had made up his mind what to do if he saw me getting too near it.

We passed three weeks in exploring, and never did I find time go more quickly. The weather was fine, though the nights got very cold. We followed every stream but one, and always found it led us to a glacier which was plainly impassable, at any rate without a larger party and ropes. One stream remained, which I should have followed up already, had not Chowbok said that he had risen early one morning while I was yet asleep, and after going up it for three or four miles, had seen that it was impossible to go farther. I had long ago discovered that he was a great liar, so I was bent on going up myself; in brief, I did

40

so; so far from being impossible, it was quite easy travelling; and after five or six miles I saw a saddle at the end of it, which, though covered deep in snow, was not glaciered, and which did verily appear to be part of the main range itself. No words can express the intensity of my delight. My blood was all on fire with hope and elation; but on looking round for Chowbok, who was behind me, I saw to my surprise and anger that he had turned back, and was going down the valley as hard as he could. He had left me.

THE SADDLE

I COOEYED to him, but he would not hear. I ran after him, but he had got too good a start. Then I sat down on a stone and thought the matter carefully over. It was plain that Chowbok had designedly attempted to keep me from going up this valley, yet he had shown no unwillingness to follow me anywhere else. What could this mean, unless that I was now upon the route by which alone the mysteries of the great ranges could be revealed? What then should I do? Go back at the very moment when it had become plain that I was on the right scent? Hardly; yet to proceed alone would be both difficult and dangerous. It would be bad enough to return to my master's run, and pass through the rocky gorges, with no chance of help from another should I get into a difficulty; but to advance for any considerable distance without a companion would be next door to madness. Accidents which are slight when there is another at hand (as the spraining of an ankle, or the falling into some place whence escape would be easy by means of an outstretched hand and a bit of rope) may be fatal to one who is alone. The more I pondered the less I liked it; and yet, the less could I make up my mind to return when I looked at the saddle at the head of the valley, and noted the comparative ease with which its smooth sweep of snow might be surmounted; I seemed to see my way almost from my present position to the very top. After much thought, I resolved to go forward until I should come to some place which was really dangerous, but then to return. I should thus, I hoped, at any rate reach the top of the saddle, and satisfy myself as to what might be on the other side.

I had no time to lose, for it was now between ten and eleven in the morning. Fortunately I was well equipped, for on leaving the camp and the horses at the lower end of the valley I had provided myself (according to my custom) with everything that I was likely to want for four or five days. Chowbok had carried half, but had dropped his whole swag — I suppose, at the moment of his taking flight — for I came upon it when I ran after him. I had, therefore, his provisions as well as my own. Accordingly, I took as many biscuits as I thought I could carry, and also some tobacco, tea, and a few matches. I rolled all these things (together with a flask nearly full of brandy, which I had kept in my pocket for fear lest Chowbok should get hold of it) inside my blankets, and strapped them very tightly, making the whole into a long roll of some seven feet in length and six inches in diameter. Then I tied the two ends together, and put the whole round my neck and over one shoulder. This is the easiest way of carrying a heavy swag, for one can rest one's self by shifting the burden from one shoulder to the other. I strapped my pannikin and a small axe about my waist, and thus equipped began to ascend the valley, angry at having been misled by Chowbok, but determined not to return till I was compelled to do so.

I crossed and recrossed the stream several times without difficulty, for there were many good fords. At one o'clock I was at the foot of the saddle; for four hours I mounted, the last two on the snow, where the going was easier; by five, I was within ten minutes of the top, in a state of excitement greater, I think, than I had ever known before. Ten minutes more, and the cold air from the other side came rushing upon me.

A glance. I was *not* on the main range.

Another glance. There was an awful river, muddy and horribly angry, roaring over an immense river-bed, thousands of feet below me.

It went round to the westward, and I could see no farther up the valley, save that there were enormous glaciers which must extend round the source of the river, and from which it must spring.

Another glance, and then I remained motionless.

There was an easy pass in the mountains directly opposite to me, through which I caught a glimpse of an immeasurable extent of blue and distant plains.

Easy? Yes, perfectly easy; grassed nearly to the summit, which was, as it were, an open path between two glaciers, from which an inconsiderable stream came tumbling down over rough but very possible hillsides, till it got down to the level of the great river, and formed a flat where there was grass and a small bush of stunted timber.

Almost before I could believe my eyes, a cloud had come up from the valley on the other side, and the plains were hidden. What wonderful luck was mine! Had I arrived five minutes later, the cloud would have been over the pass, and I should not have known of its existence. Now that the cloud was there, I began to doubt my memory, and to be uncertain whether it had been more than a blue line of distant vapour that had filled up the opening. I could only be certain of this much, namely, that the river in the valley below must be the one next to the northward of that which flowed past my master's station; of this there could be no doubt. Could I, however, imagine that my luck should have led me up a wrong river in search of a pass, and yet brought me to the spot where I could detect the one weak place in the fortifications of a more northern basin? This was too improbable. But even as I doubted there came a rent in the cloud opposite, and a second time I saw blue lines of heaving downs, growing gradually fainter, and retiring into a far space of plain. It was substantial; there had been no mistake whatsoever. I had hardly made myself perfectly sure of this, ere the rent in the clouds joined up again and I could see nothing more.

What, then, should I do? The night would be upon me shortly, and I was already chilled with standing still after the exertion of climbing. To stay where I was would be impossible; I must either go backwards or forwards. I found a rock which gave me shelter from the evening wind, and took a good pull at the brandy flask, which immediately warmed and encouraged me.

I asked myself, Could I descend upon the river-bed beneath me? It was impossible to say what precipices might prevent my doing so. If I were on the river-bed, dare I cross the river? I am an excellent swimmer, yet, once in that frightful rush of waters, I should be hurled whithersoever it willed, absolutely powerless. Moreover, there was my swag; I should perish of cold and hunger if I left it, but I should certainly be drowned if I attempted to carry it across the river. These were serious considerations, but the hope of finding an immense tract of available sheep country (which I was determined that I would monopolize as far as I possibly could) sufficed to outweigh them; and, in a few minutes, I felt resolved that, having made so important a discovery as a pass into a country which was probably as valuable as that on our own side of the ranges, I would follow it up and ascertain its value, even though I should pay the penalty of failure with life itself. The more I thought, the more determined I became either to win fame and perhaps fortune, by entering upon this unknown world, or give up life in the attempt. In fact, I felt that life would be no longer valuable if I were to have seen so great a prize and refused to grasp at the possible profits therefrom.

I had still an hour of good daylight during which I might begin my descent on to some suitable camping-ground, but there was not a moment to be lost. At first I got along rapidly, for I was on the snow, and sank into it enough to save me from falling, though I went forward straight down the mountain side as fast as I could; but there was less snow on this side than on the other, and I had soon done with it, getting on to a coomb of dangerous and very stony ground, where a slip might have given me a disastrous fall. But I was careful with all my speed, and got safely to the bottom, where there were patches of course grass, and an attempt here and there at brushwood; what was below this I could not see. I advanced a few hundred yards farther, and found that I was on the brink of a frightful precipice, which no one in his senses would attempt descending. I bethought me, however, to try the creek which drained the coomb, and see whether it might not have made itself a smoother way. In a few minutes I found myself at the upper end of a chasm in the rocks, something like Twll Dhu, only on a greatly larger scale; the creek had found its way into it, and had worn a deep channel through a material which appeared softer than that upon the other side of the mountain. I believe it must have been a different geological formation, though I regret to say that I cannot tell what it was.

I looked at this rift in great doubt; then I went a little way on either side of it, and found myself looking over the edge of horrible precipices on to the river, which roared some four or five thousand feet below me. I dared not think of getting down at all, unless I committed myself to the rift, of which I was hopeful when I reflected that the rock was soft, and that the water might have worn its channel tolerably evenly through the whole extent. The darkness was increasing with every minute, but I should have twilight for another half-hour, so I went into the chasm (though by no means without fear), and resolved to return and camp, and try some other path next day, should I come to any serious difficulty. In about five minutes I had completely lost my head; the side of the rift became hundreds of feet in height, and overhung so that I could not see the sky. It was full of rocks, and I had many falls and bruises. I was wet through from falling into the water, of which there was no great volume, but it had such force that I could do nothing against it; once I had to leap down a not inconsiderable waterfall into a deep pool below, and my swag was so heavy that I was very nearly drowned. I had indeed a hairbreadth escape; but, as luck would have it, Providence was on my side. Shortly afterwards I began to fancy that the rift was getting wider, and that there was more brushwood. Presently I found myself on an open grassy slope, and feeling my way a little farther along the stream, I came upon a flat place with wood, where I could camp comfortably; which was well, for it was now quite dark.

My first care was for my matches; were they dry? The outside of my swag had got completely wet; but, on undoing the blankets, I found things warm and dry within. How thankful I was! I lit a fire, and was grateful for its warmth and company. I made myself some tea and ate two of my biscuits: my brandy I did not touch, for I had little left, and might want it when my courage failed me. All that I did, I did almost mechanically, for I could not realize my situation to myself, beyond knowing that I was alone, and that return through the chasm which I had just descended would be impossible. It is a dreadful feeling that of being cut off from all one's kind. I was still full of hope, and built golden castles for myself as soon as I was warmed with food and fire; but I do not believe that any man could long retain his reason in such solitude, unless he had the companionship of animals. One begins doubting one's own identity.

I remember deriving comfort even from the sight of my blankets, and the sound of my watch ticking — things which seemed to link me to other people; but the screaming of the wood-hens frightened me, as also a chattering bird which I had never heard before, and which seemed to laugh at me; though I soon got used to it, and before long could fancy that it was many years since I had first heard it.

I took off my clothes, and wrapped my inside blanket about me, till my things were dry. The night was very still, and I made a roaring fire; so I soon got warm, and at last could put my clothes on again. Then I strapped my blanket round me, and went to sleep as near the fire as I could.

I dreamed that there was an organ placed in my master's wool-shed; the wool-shed faded away, and the organ seemed to grow and grow amid a blaze of brilliant light, till it became like a golden city upon the side of a mountain, with rows upon rows of pipes set in cliffs and precipices, one above the other, and in mysterious caverns, like that of Fingal, within whose depths I could see the burnished pillars gleaming. In the front there was a flight of lofty terraces, at the top of which I could see a man with his head buried forward towards a keyboard, and his body swaying from side to side amid the storm of huge arpeggioed harmonies that came crashing overhead and round. Then there was one who touched me on the shoulder, and said, 'Do you not see? it is Handel' — but I had hardly apprehended, and was trying to scale the terraces, and get near him, when I awoke, dazzled with the vividness and distinctness of the dream.

A piece of wood had burned through, and the ends had fallen into the ashes with a blaze; this, I supposed, had both given me my dream and robbed me of it. I was bitterly disappointed, and sitting up on my elbow, came back to reality and my strange surroundings as best I could.

I was thoroughly aroused — moreover, I felt a foreshadowing as though my attention were arrested by something more than the dream, although no sense in particular was as yet appealed to. I held my breath and waited, and then I heard — was it fancy? Nay; I listened again and again, and I *did* hear a faint and extremely distant sound of music, like that of an Aeolian harp, borne upon the wind which was blowing fresh and chill from the opposite mountains.

The roots of my hair thrilled. I listened, but the wind had died; and, fancying that it must have been the wind itself — no; on a sudden I remembered the noise which Chowbok had made in the wool-shed. Yes; it was that.

Thank Heaven, whatever it was, it was over now. I reasoned with myself, and recovered my firmness. I became convinced that I had only been dreaming more vividly than usual. Soon I began even to laugh, and think what a fool I was to be frightened at nothing, reminding myself that even if I were to come to a bad end it would be no such dreadful matter after all. I said my prayers, a duty which I had too often neglected, and in a little time fell into a really refreshing sleep, which lasted till broad daylight, and restored me. I rose, and searching among the embers of my fire, I found a few live coals and soon had a blaze again. I got breakfast, and was delighted to have the company of several small birds, which hopped about me and perched on my boots and hands. I felt comparatively happy, but I can assure the reader that I had had a far worse time of it than I have told him; and I strongly recommend him to remain in Europe if he can; or, at any rate, in some country which has been explored and settled, rather than go into places where others have not been before him. Exploring is delightful to look forward to and back upon, but it is not comfortable at the time, unless it be of such an easy nature as not to deserve the name.

CHAPTER FIVE

THE RIVER AND THE RANGE

MY next business was to descend upon the river. I had lost sight of the pass which I had seen from the saddle, but had made such notes of it that I could not fail to find it. I was bruised and stiff, and my boots had begun to give, for I had been going on rough ground for more than three weeks; but, as the day wore on, and I found myself descending without serious difficulty, I became easier. In a couple of hours I got among pine forests where there was little under-growth, and descended quickly till I reached the edge of another precipice, which gave me a great deal of trouble, though I eventually managed to avoid it. By about three or four o'clock I found myself on the river-bed.

From calculations which I made as to the height of the valley on the other side the saddle over which I had come, I concluded that the saddle itself could not be less than nine thousand feet high; and I should think that the river-bed, on to which I now descended, was three thousand feet above the sea-level. The water had a terrific current, with a fall of not less than forty to fifty feet per mile. It was certainly the river next to the northward of that which flowed past my master's run, and would have to go through an impassable gorge (as is commonly the case with the rivers of that country) before it came upon known parts. It was reckoned to be nearly two thousand feet above the sea-level where it came out of the gorge on to the plains.

As soon as I got to the river-side I liked it even less than I thought I should. It was muddy, being near its parent glaciers. The stream was wide, rapid and rough, and I could hear the smaller stones knocking against each other under the rage of the waters, as upon a seashore.

Fording was out of the question. I could not swim and carry my swag, and I dared not leave my swag behind me. My only chance was to make a small raft; and that would be difficult to make, and not at all safe when it was made — not for one man in such a current.

As it was too late to do much that afternoon, I spent the rest of it in going up and down the river-side, and seeing where I should find the most favourable crossing. Then I camped early, and had a quiet comfortable night with no more music, for which I was thankful, as it had haunted me all day, although I perfectly well knew that it had been nothing but my own fancy, brought on by the reminiscence of what I had heard from Chowbok and by the over-excitement of the preceding evening.

Next day I began gathering the dry bloom stalks of a kind of flag or iris-looking plant, which was abundant, and whose leaves, when torn into strips, were as strong as the strongest string. I brought them to the waterside, and fell to making myself a kind of rough platform, which should suffice for myself and my swag if I could only stick to it. The stalks were ten or twelve feet long, and very strong, but light and hollow. I made my raft entirely of them, binding bundles of them at right angles to each other, neatly and strongly, with strips from the leaves of the same plant, and tying other rods across. It took me all day till nearly four o'clock to finish the raft, but I had still enough daylight for crossing, and resolved on doing so at once.

I had selected a place where the river was broad and comparatively still, some seventy or eighty yards above a furious rapid. At this spot I had built my raft. I now launched it, made my swag fast to the middle, and got on to it myself, keeping in my hand one of the longest blossom stalks, so that I might punt myself across as long as the water was shallow enough to let me do so. I got on pretty well for twenty or thirty yards from the shore, but even in this short space I nearly upset my raft by shifting too rapidly from one side to the other. The water then became much deeper, and I leaned over so far in order to get the bloom rod to the bottom that I had to stay still, leaning on the rod for a few seconds. Then, when I lifted up the rod from the ground, the current was too much for me and I found myself being carried down the rapid. Everything in a second flew past me, and I had no more control over the raft; neither can I remember anything except hurry, and noise, and waters which in the end upset me. But it all came right, and I found myself near the shore, not more than up to my knees in water and pulling my raft to land, fortunately upon the left bank of the river, which was the one I wanted. When I had landed I found that I was about a mile, or perhaps a little less, below the point from which I started. My swag was wet upon the outside, and I was myself dripping; but I had gained my point, and knew that my difficulties were for a time over. I then lit my fire and dried myself; having done so I caught some of the young ducks and sea-gulls, which were abundant on and near the river-bed, so that I had not only a good meal, of which I was in great want, having had an insufficient diet from the time that Chowbok left me, but was also well provided for the morrow.

I thought of Chowbok, and felt how useful he had been to me, and in how many ways I was the loser by his absence, having now to do all sorts of things for myself which he had hitherto done for me, and could do infinitely better than I could. Moreover, I had set my heart upon making him a real convert to the Christian religion, which he had already embraced outwardly, though I cannot think that it had taken deep root in his impenetrably stupid nature. I used to catechize him by our camp fire, and explain to him the mysteries of the Trinity and of original sin, with which I was myself familiar, having been the grandson of an archdeacon by my mother's side, to say nothing of the fact that my father was a clergyman of the English Church. I was therefore sufficiently qualified for the task, and was the more inclined to it, over and above my real desire to save the unhappy creature from an eternity of torture, by recollecting the promise of St. James, that if anyone converted a sinner (which Chowbok surely was) he should hide a multitude of sins. I reflected, therefore, that the conversion of Chowbok might in some degree compensate for irregularities and shortcomings in my own previous life, the remembrance of which had been more than once unpleasant to me during my recent experiences.

Indeed, on one occasion I had even gone so far as to baptize him, as well as I could, having ascertained that he had certainly not been both christened and baptized, and gathering (from his telling me that he had received the name William from the missionary) that it was probably the first-mentioned rite to which he had been subjected. I thought it great carelessness on the part of the missionary to have omitted the second, and certainly more important, ceremony which I have always understood precedes christening both in the case of infants and of adult converts; and when I thought of the risks we were both incurring I determined that there should be no further delay. Fortunately it was

not yet twelve o'clock, so I baptized him at once from one of the pannikins (the only vessels I had) reverently, and, I trust, efficiently. I then
set myself to work to instruct him in the deeper mysteries of our belief,
and to make him, not only in name, but in heart a Christian.

It is true that I might not have succeeded, for Chowbok was very
hard to teach. Indeed, on the evening of the same day that I baptized
him he tried for the twentieth time to steal the brandy, which made me
rather unhappy as to whether I could have baptized him rightly. He
had a prayer-book — more than twenty years old — which had been
given him by the missionaries, but the only thing in it which had taken
any living hold upon him was the title of Adelaide, the Queen
Dowager, which he would repeat whenever strongly moved or
touched, and which did really seem to have some deep spiritual
significance to him, though he could never completely separate her
individuality from that of Mary Magdalene, whose name had also
fascinated him, though in a less degree.

He was indeed stony ground, but by digging about him I might have
at any rate deprived him of all faith in the religion of his tribe, which
would have been half way towards making him a sincere Christian;
and now all this was cut off from me, and I could neither be of further
spiritual assistance to him nor he of bodily profit to myself; besides, any
company was better than being quite alone.

I got very melancholy as these reflections crossed me, but when I had
boiled the ducks and eaten them I was much better. I had a little tea
left and about a pound of tobacco, which should last me for another
fortnight with moderate smoking. I had also eight ship's biscuits, and,
most precious of all, about six ounces of brandy, which I presently
reduced to four, for the night was cold.

I rose with early dawn, and in an hour I was on my way, feeling
strange, not to say weak, from the burden of solitude, but full of hope
when I considered how many dangers I had overcome, and that this
day should see me at the summit of the dividing range.

After a slow but steady climb of between three and four hours,
during which I met with no serious hindrance, I found myself upon a
tableland, and close to a glacier which I recognized as marking the
summit of the pass. Above it towered a succession of rugged precipices
and snowy mountain sides. The solitude was greater than I could bear;
the mountain upon my master's sheep-run was a crowded thorough-
fare in comparison with this sombre sullen place. The air, moreover,

was dark and heavy, which made the loneliness even more oppressive. There was an inky gloom over all that was not covered with snow and ice. Grass there was none.

Each moment I felt increasing upon me that dreadful doubt as to my own identity — as to the continuity of my past and present existence — which is the first sign of that distraction which comes on those who have lost themselves in the bush. I had fought against this feeling hitherto, and had conquered it; but the intense silence and gloom of this rocky wilderness were too much for me, and I felt that my power of collecting myself was beginning to be impaired.

I rested for a little while, and then advanced over very rough ground, until I reached the lower end of the glacier. Then I saw another glacier, descending from the eastern side into a small lake. I passed along the western side of the lake, where the ground was easier, and when I had got about half way I expected that I should see the plains which I had already seen from the opposite mountains; but it was not to be so, for the clouds rolled up to the very summit of the pass, though they did not overlip it on to the side from which I had come. I therefore soon found myself enshrouded by a cold thin vapour, which prevented my seeing more than a very few yards in front of me. Then I came upon a large patch of old snow, in which I could distinctly trace the half-melted tracks of goats — and in one place, as it seemed to me, there had been a dog following them. Had I lighted upon a land of shepherds? The ground, where not covered with snow, was so poor and stony, and there was so little herbage, that I could see no sign of a path or regular sheep-track. But I could not help feeling rather uneasy as I wondered what sort of a reception I might meet with if I were to come suddenly upon inhabitants. I was thinking of this, and proceeding cautiously through the mist, when I began to fancy that I saw some objects darker than the cloud looming in front of me. A few steps brought me nearer, and a shudder of unutterable horror ran through me when I saw a circle of gigantic forms, many times higher than myself, upstanding grim and grey through the veil of cloud before me.

I suppose I must have fainted, for I found myself some time afterwards sitting upon the ground, sick and deadly cold. There were the figures, quite still and silent, seen vaguely through the thick gloom, but in human shape indisputably.

A sudden thought occurred to me, which would have doubtless struck me at once had I not been prepossessed with forebodings at the time that I first saw the figures, and had not the cloud concealed them from me — I mean that they were not living beings, but statues. I determined that I would count fifty slowly, and be sure that the objects were not alive if during that time I could detect no sign of motion.

How thankful was I when I came to the end of my fifty and there had been no movement!

I counted a second time — but again all was still.

I then advanced timidly forward, and in another moment I saw that my surmise was correct. I had come upon a sort of Stonehenge of rude and barbaric figures seated as Chowbok had sat when I questioned him in the wool-shed, and with the same superhumanly malevolent expression upon their faces. They had been all seated, but two had fallen. They were barbarous — neither Egyptian, nor Assyrian, nor Japanese — different from any of these, and yet akin to all. They were six or seven times larger than life, of great antiquity, worn and lichen grown. They were ten in number. There was snow upon their heads and wherever snow could lodge. Each statue had been built of four or five enormous blocks, but how these had been raised and put together is known to those alone who raised them. Each was terrible after a different kind. One was raging furiously, as in pain and great despair; another was lean and cadaverous with famine; another cruel and idiotic, but with the silliest simper that can be conceived — this one had fallen, and looked exquisitely ludicrous in his fall — the mouths of all were more or less open, and as I looked at them from behind, I saw that their heads had been hollowed.

I was sick and shivering with cold. Solitude had unmanned me already, and I was utterly unfit to have come upon such an assembly of fiends in such a dreadful wilderness and without preparation. I would have given everything I had in the world to have been back at my master's station; but that was not to be thought of; my head was failing, and I felt sure that I could never get back alive.

Then came a gust of howling wind, accompanied with a moan from one of the statues above me. I clasped my hands in fear. I felt like a rat caught in a trap, as though I would have turned and bitten at whatever thing was nearest me. The wildness of the wind increased, the moans grew shriller, coming from several statues, and swelling into a chorus. I almost immediately knew what it was, but the sound was so unearthly that this was but little consolation. The inhuman beings into whose hearts the Evil One had put it to conceive these statues, had made their heads into a sort of organ-pipe, so that their mouths should catch the wind and sound with its blowing. It was horrible. However brave a man might be, he could never stand such a concert, from such lips, and in such a place. I heaped every invective upon them that my tongue could utter as I rushed away from them into the mist, and even after I had lost sight of them, and turning my head round could see nothing but the storm-wraiths driving behind me, I heard their ghostly chanting, and felt as though one of them would rush after me and grip me in his hand and throttle me.

I may say here that, since my return to England, I heard a friend playing some chords upon the organ which put me very forcibly in mind of the Erewhonian statues (for Erewhon is the name of the country upon which I was now entering). They rose most vividly to my recollection the moment my friend began. They are as follows, and are by the greatest of all musicians:[1]

Prelude : arpeggio.

[1] See Handel's compositions for the harpischord, published by Litolf, p. 78.

CHAPTER SIX

INTO EREWHON

AND now I found myself on a narrow path which followed a small watercourse. I was too glad to have an easy track for my flight, to lay hold of the full significance of its existence. The thought, however, soon presented itself to me that I must be in an inhabited country, but one which was yet unknown. What, then, was to be my fate at the hands of its inhabitants? Should I be taken and offered up as a burnt-offering to those hideous guardians of the pass? It might be so. I shuddered at the thought, yet the horrors of solitude had now fairly possessed me; and so dazed was I, and chilled, and woebegone, that I could lay hold of no idea firmly amid the crowd of fancies that kept wandering in upon my brain.

I hurried onward — down, down, down. More streams came in; then there was a bridge, a few pine logs thrown over the water; but they gave me comfort, for savages do not make bridges. Then I had a treat such as I can never convey on paper — a moment, perhaps, the most striking and unexpected in my whole life — the one I think that, with some three or four exceptions, I would most gladly have again, were I able to recall it. I got below the level of the clouds, into a burst of brilliant evening sunshine. I was facing the north-west, and the sun was full upon me. Oh, how its light cheered me! But what I saw! It was such an expanse as was revealed to Moses when he stood upon the summit of Mount Sinai, and beheld that promised land which it was not to be his to enter. The beautiful sunset sky was crimson and gold; blue, silver and purple; exquisite and tranquillizing; fading away therein were plains, on which I could see many a town and city, with buildings that had lofty steeples and rounded domes. Nearer beneath me lay ridge behind ridge, outline behind outline, sunlight behind shadow, and shadow behind sunlight, gully and serrated ravine. I saw large pine forests, and the glitter of a noble river winding its way upon the plains; also many villages and hamlets, some of them quite near at hand; and it was on these that I pondered most. I sank upon the ground at the foot of a large tree and thought what I had best do; but I could not collect myself. I was quite tired out; and presently, feeling warmed by the sun, and quieted, I fell off into a profound sleep.

I was awoke by the sound of tinkling bells, and looking up, I saw four or five goats feeding near me. As soon as I moved, the creatures turned their heads towards me with an expression of infinite wonder. They did not run away, but stood stock-still, and looked at me from every side, as I at them. Then came the sound of chattering and laughter, and there approached two lovely girls, of about seventeen or eighteen years old, dressed each in a sort of linen gaberdine, with a girdle round the waist. They saw me. I sat quite still and looked at them, dazzled with their extreme beauty. For a moment they looked at me and at each other in great amazement; then they gave a little frightened cry and ran off as hard as they could.

'So that's that,' said I to myself, as I watched them scampering. I knew that I had better stay where I was and meet my fate, whatever it was to be, and even if there were a better course, I had no strength left to take it. I must come into contact with the inhabitants sooner or later, and it might as well be sooner. Better not to seem afraid of them, as I should do by running away and being caught with a hue and cry tomorrow or next day. So I remained quite still and waited. In about an hour I heard distant voices talking excitedly, and in a few minutes I saw the two girls bringing up a party of six or seven men well armed with bows and arrows and pikes. There was nothing for it, so I remained sitting quite still, even after they had seen me, until they came close up. Then we all had a good look at one another.

Both the girls and the men were very dark in colour, but not more so than the South Italians or Spaniards. The men wore no trousers, but were dressed nearly the same as the Arabs whom I have seen in Algeria. They were of the most magnificent presence, being no less strong and handsome than the women were beautiful; and not only this, but their

expression was courteous and benign. I think they would have killed
me at once if I had made the slightest show of violence; but they gave
me no impression of their being likely to hurt me so long as I was quiet.
I am not much given to liking anybody at first sight, but these people
impressed me much more favourably than I should have thought
possible, so that I could not fear them as I scanned their faces one after
another. They were all powerful men. I might have been a match for
any one of them singly, for I have been told that I have more to glory
in the flesh than in any other respect, being over six feet and proportionately strong; but any two could have soon mastered me, even were
I not so bereft of energy by my recent adventures. My colour seemed
to surprise them most, for I have light hair, blue eyes and a fresh complexion. They could not understand how these things could be; my
clothes also seemed quite beyond them. Their eyes kept wandering all
over me, and the more they looked the less they seemed able to make
me out.

At last I raised myself upon my feet, and leaning upon my stick, I
spoke whatever came into my head to the man who seemed foremost
among them. I spoke in English, though I was very sure that he would
not understand. I said that I had no idea what country I was in; that I
had stumbled upon it almost by accident, after a series of hairbreadth
escapes; and that I trusted they would not allow any evil to overtake
me now that I was completely at their mercy. All this I said quietly
and firmly, with hardly any change of expression. They could not
understand me, but they looked approvingly to one another, and
seemed pleased (so I thought) that I showed no fear nor acknowledgment of inferiority – the fact being that I was exhausted beyond the
sense of fear. Then one of them pointed to the mountain, in the direction of the statues, and made a grimace in imitation of one of them. I
laughed and shuddered expressively, whereon they all burst out
laughing too, and chattered hard to one another. I could make out
nothing of what they said, but I think they thought it rather a good
joke that I had come past the statues. Then one among them came
forward and motioned me to follow, which I did without hesitation,
for I dared not thwart them; moreover, I liked them well enough, and
felt tolerably sure that they had no intention of hurting me.

In about a quarter of an hour we got to a small hamlet built on the
side of a hill, with a narrow street and houses huddled up together.
The roofs were large and overhanging. Some few windows were

glazed, but not many. Altogether the village was exceedingly like one of those that one comes upon in descending the less known passes over the Alps on to Lombardy. I will pass over the excitement which my arrival caused. Suffice it, that though there was abundance of curiosity, there was no rudeness. I was taken to the principal house, which seemed to belong to the people who had captured me. There I was hospitably entertained, and a supper of milk and goat's flesh with a kind of oatcake was set before me, of which I ate heartily. But all the time I was eating I could not help turning my eyes upon the two beautiful girls whom I had first seen and who seemed to consider me as their lawful prize — which indeed I was, for I would have gone through fire and water for either of them.

Then came the inevitable surprise at seeing me smoke, which I will spare the reader; but I noticed that when they saw me strike a match, there was a hubbub of excitement which, it struck me, was not altogether unmixed with disapproval; why, I could not guess. Then the women retired, and I was left alone with the men, who tried to talk to me in every conceivable way; but we could come to no understanding, except that I was quite alone, and had come from a long way over the mountains. In the course of time they grew tired, and I very sleepy. I made signs as though I would sleep on the floor in my blankets, but they gave me one of their bunks with plenty of dried fern and grass, on to which I had no sooner laid myself than I fell fast asleep; nor did I awake till well into the following day, when I found myself in the hut with two men keeping guard over me and an old woman cooking. When I woke the men seemed pleased, and spoke to me as though bidding me good morning in a pleasant tone.

I went out of doors to wash in a creek which ran a few yards from the house. My hosts were as engrossed with me as ever; they never took their eyes off me, following every action that I did, no matter how trifling, and each looking towards the other for his opinion at every touch and turn. They took great interest in my ablutions, for they seemed to have doubted whether I was in all respects human like themselves. They even laid hold of my arms and overhauled them, and expressed approval when they saw that they were strong and muscular. They now examined my legs, and especially my feet. When they desisted they nodded approvingly to each other; and when I had combed and brushed my hair, and generally made myself as neat and well arranged as circumstances would allow, I could see that their respect for me increased greatly, and that they were by no means sure that they had treated me with sufficient deference — a matter on which I am not competent to decide. All I know is that they were very good to me, for which I thanked them heartily, as it might well have been otherwise.

For my own part, I liked them and admired them, for their quiet self-possession and dignified ease impressed me pleasurably at once. Neither did their manner make me feel as though I were personally distasteful to them — only that I was a thing utterly new and unlooked for, which they could not comprehend. Their type was more that of the most robust Italians than any other; their manners also were eminently Italian, in their entire unconsciousness of self. Having travelled a good deal in Italy, I was struck with little gestures of the hand and shoulders, which constantly reminded me of that country. My feeling was that my wisest plan would be to go on as I had begun, and be simply myself for better or worse, such as I was, and take my chance accordingly.

I thought of these things while they were waiting for me to have done washing, and on my way back. Then they gave me breakfast — hot bread and milk, and fried flesh of something between mutton and venison. Their ways of cooking and eating were European, though they had only a skewer for a fork, and a sort of butcher's knife to cut with. The more I looked at everything in the house, the more I was struck with its quasi-European character; and had the walls only been pasted over with extracts from the *Illustrated London News* and *Punch*, I could have almost fancied myself in a shepherd's hut upon my master's sheep-run. And yet everything was slightly different. It was much the same with the birds and flowers on the other side, as compared with the English ones. On my arrival I had been pleased at noticing that nearly all the plants and birds were very like common English ones; thus, there was a robin, and a lark, and a wren, and daisies, and dandelions; not quite the same as the English, but still very like them — quite like enough to be called by the same name; so now, here, the ways of these two men, and the things they had in the house, were all very nearly the same as in Europe. It was not at all like going to China or Japan, where everything that one sees is strange. I was, indeed, at once struck with the primitive character of their appliances, for they seemed to be some five or six hundred years behind Europe in their inventions; but this is the case in many an Italian village.

INTO EREWHON

All the time that I was eating my breakfast I kept speculating as to
what family of mankind they could belong to; and shortly there came
an idea into my head, which brought the blood into my cheeks with
excitement as I thought of it. Was it possible that they might be the
lost ten tribes of Israel, of whom I had heard both my grandfather and
my father make mention as existing in an unknown country, and
awaiting a final return to Palestine? Was it possible that *I* might have
been designed by Providence as the instrument of their conversion? Oh,
what a thought was this! I laid down my skewer and gave them a hasty
survey. There was nothing of a Jewish type about them; their noses
were distinctly Grecian, and their lips, though full, were not Jewish.

How could I settle this question? I knew neither Greek nor Hebrew,
and even if I should get to understand the language here spoken, I
should be unable to detect the roots of either of these tongues. I had
not been long enough among them to ascertain their habits, but they
did not give me the impression of being a religious people. This too
was natural: the ten tribes had been always lamentably irreligious. But
could I not make them change? To restore the lost ten tribes of Israel to
a knowledge of the only truth; here would be indeed an immortal
crown of glory! My heart beat fast and furious as I entertained the
thought. What a position would it not ensure me in the next world;
or perhaps even in this! What folly it would be to throw such a chance
away! I should rank next to the Apostles, if not as high as they — certainly above the minor prophets, and possibly above any Old Testament writer except Moses and Isaiah. For such a future as this I would
sacrifice all that I have without a moment's hesitation, could I be
reasonably assured of it. I had always cordially approved of missionary
efforts, and had at times contributed my mite towards their support
and extension; but I had never hitherto felt drawn towards becoming
a missionary myself; and indeed had always admired, and envied, and
respected them, more than I had exactly liked them. But if these people
were the lost ten tribes of Israel, the case would be widely different; the
opening was too excellent to be lost, and I resolved that should I see
indications which appeared to confirm my impression that I had indeed
come upon the missing tribes, I would certainly convert them.

I may here mention that this discovery is the one to which I alluded
in the opening pages of my story. Time strengthened the impression
made upon me at first; and, though I remained in doubt for several
months, I feel now no longer uncertain.

59

When I had done eating, my hosts approached, and pointed down
the valley leading to their own country, as though wanting to show
that I must go with them; at the same time they laid hold of my arms,
and made as though they would take me, but used no violence. I
laughed, and motioned my hand across my throat, pointing down the
valley as though I was afraid lest I should be killed when I got there.
But they divined me at once, and shook their heads with much
decision, to show that I was in no danger. Their manner quite reassured
me; and in half an hour or so I had packed up my swag, and was eager
for the forward journey, feeling wonderfully strengthened and
refreshed by good food and sleep, while my hope and curiosity were
aroused to the very utmost by the extraordinary position in which I
found myself.

But already my excitement had begun to cool; and I reflected that
these people might not be the ten tribes after all; in which case I could
not but regret that my hopes of making money, which had led me into
so much trouble and danger, were almost annihilated by the fact that
the country was full to overflowing, with a people who had probably
already developed its more available resources. Moreover, how was I
to get back? For there was something about my hosts which told me
that they had got me, and meant to keep me, in spite of all their
goodness.

CHAPTER SEVEN

FIRST IMPRESSIONS

WE followed an Alpine path for some four miles, now hundreds
of feet above a brawling stream which descended from the
glaciers, and now nearly alongside it. The morning was cold
and somewhat foggy, for the autumn had made great strides latterly.
Sometimes we went through forests of pine, or rather yew trees,
though they looked like pine; and I remember that now and again we
passed a little wayside shrine, wherein there would be a statue of great
beauty, representing some figure, male or female, in the very heyday
of youth, strength and beauty, or of the most dignified maturity and
old age. My hosts always bowed their heads as they passed one of these

shrines, and it shocked me to see statues that had no apparent object, beyond the chronicling of some unusual individual excellence or beauty, receive so serious a homage. However, I showed no sign of wonder or disapproval; for I remembered that to be all things to all men was one of the injunctions of the Gentile Apostle, which for the present I should do well to heed. Shortly after passing one of these chapels we came suddenly upon a village which started up out of the mist; and I was alarmed lest I should be made an object of curiosity or dislike. But it was not so. My guides spoke to many in passing, and those spoken to showed much amazement. My guides, however, were well known, and the natural politeness of the people prevented them from putting me to any inconvenience; but they could not help eyeing me, nor I them. I may as well say at once what my after-experience taught me — namely, that with all their faults and extraordinary obliquity of mental vision upon many subjects, they are the very best-bred people that I ever fell in with.

The village was just like the one we had left, only rather larger. The streets were narrow and unpaved, but very fairly clean. The vine grew outside many of the houses; and there were some with signboards, on which was painted a bottle and a glass, that made me feel much at home. Even on this ledge of human society there was a stunted growth of shoplets, which had taken root and vegetated somehow, though as in an air mercantile of the bleakest. It was here as hitherto: all things were generically the same as in Europe, the differences being of species only; and I was amused at seeing in a window some bottles with barley-sugar and sweetmeats for children, as at home; but the barley-sugar was in plates, not in twisted sticks, and was coloured blue. Glass was plentiful in the better houses.

Lastly, I should say that the people were of a physical beauty which was simply amazing. I never saw anything in the least comparable to them. The women were vigorous, and had a most majestic gait, their heads being set upon their shoulders with a grace beyond all power of expression. Each feature was finished, eyelids, eyelashes and ears being almost invariably perfect. Their colour was equal to that of the finest Italian paintings; being of the clearest olive, and yet ruddy with a glow of perfect health. Their expression was divine; and as they glanced at me timidly but with parted lips in great bewilderment, I forgot all thoughts of their conversion in feelings that were far more earthly. I was dazzled as I saw one after the other, of whom I could only feel that each was the loveliest I had ever seen. Even in middle age they were still comely, and the old grey-haired women at their cottage doors had a dignity, not to say majesty, of their own.

The men were as handsome as the women beautiful. I have always delighted in and reverenced beauty; but I felt simply abashed in the presence of such a splendid type — a compound of all that is best in Egyptian, Greek and Italian. The children were infinite in number, and exceedingly merry; I need hardly say that they came in for their full share of the prevailing beauty. I expressed by signs my admiration and pleasure to my guides, and they were greatly pleased. I should add that all seemed to take a pride in their personal appearance, and that even the poorest (and none seemed rich) were well-kempt and tidy. I could fill many pages with a description of their dress and the ornaments which they wore, and a hundred details which struck me with all the force of novelty; but I must not stay to do so.

When we had got past the village the fog rose, and revealed magnificent views of the snowy mountains and their nearer abutments, while in front I could now and again catch glimpses of the great plains which I had surveyed on the preceding evening. The country was highly cultivated, every ledge being planted with chestnuts, walnuts and apple trees from which the apples were now gathering. Goats were abundant; also a kind of small black cattle, in the marshes near the river, which was now fast widening, and running between larger flats from which the hills receded more and more. I saw a few sheep with rounded noses and enormous tails. Dogs were there in plenty, and very English; but I saw no cats, nor indeed are these creatures known, their place being supplied by a sort of small terrier.

In about four hours of walking from the time we started, and after passing two or three more villages, we came upon a considerable town, and my guides made many attempts to make me understand something, but I gathered no inkling of their meaning, except that I need be under no apprehension of danger. I will spare the reader any description of the town, and would only bid him think of Domodossola or Faido. Suffice it that I found myself taken before the chief magistrate, and by his orders was placed in an apartment with two other people, who were the first I had seen looking anything but well and handsome. In fact, one of them was plainly very much out of health, and coughed violently from time to time in spite of manifest efforts to suppress it. The other looked pale and ill but he was marvellously self-contained, and it was impossible to say what was the matter with him. Both of them appeared astonished at seeing one who was evidently a stranger, but they were too ill to come up to me, and form conclusions concerning me. These two were first called out; and in about a quarter of an hour I was made to follow them, which I did in some fear, and with much curiosity.

The chief magistrate was a venerable-looking man, with white hair and beard and a face of great sagacity. He looked me all over for about five minutes, letting his eyes wander from the crown of my head to the soles of my feet, up and down, and down and up; neither did his mind seem in the least clearer when he had done looking than when he began. He at length asked me a single short question, which I supposed meant 'Who are you?' I answered in English quite composedly as though he would understand me, and endeavoured to be my very most natural self as well as I could. He appeared more and more puzzled, and then retired, returning with two others much like himself. Then they took me into an inner room, and the two fresh arrivals stripped me, while the chief looked on. They felt my pulse, they looked at my tongue, they listened at my chest, they felt all my muscles; and at the end of each operation they looked at the chief and nodded, and said something in a tone quite pleasant, as though I were all right. They even pulled down my eyelids, and looked, I suppose, to see if they were bloodshot; but it was not so. At length they gave up; and I think that all were satisfied of my being in the most perfect health, and very robust to boot. At last the old magistrate made me a speech of about five minutes long, which the other two appeared to think greatly to the point, but from which I gathered nothing. As soon as it was ended, they proceeded to overhaul my swag and the contents of my pockets. This gave me little uneasiness, for I had no money with me, nor anything which they were at all likely to want, or which I cared about losing. At least I fancied so, but I soon found my mistake.

They got on comfortably at first, though they were much puzzled with my tobacco-pipe and insisted on seeing me use it. When I had shown them what I did with it, they were astonished but not displeased, and seemed to like the smell. But by and by they came to my watch, which I had hidden away in the inmost pocket that I had, and had forgotten when they began their search. They seemed concerned and uneasy as soon as they got hold of it. They then made me open it and show the works; and when I had done so they gave signs of very grave displeasure, which disturbed me all the more because I could not conceive wherein it could have offended them.

I remember that when they first found it I had thought of Paley, and how he tells us that a savage on seeing a watch would at once conclude that it was designed. True, these people were not savages, but I none the less felt sure that this was the conclusion they would arrive at; and I was thinking what a wonderfully wise man Archdeacon Paley must have been, when I was aroused by a look of horror and dismay upon the face of the magistrate, a look which conveyed to me the impression that he regarded my watch not as having been designed, but rather as the designer of himself and of the universe; or as at any rate one of the great first causes of all things.

Then it struck me that this view was quite as likely to be taken as the other by a people who had no experience of European civilization, and I was a little piqued with Paley for having led me so much astray; but I soon discovered that I had misinterpreted the expression on the magistrate's face, and that it was one not of fear, but hatred. He spoke to me solemnly and sternly for two or three minutes. Then, reflecting that this was of no use, he caused me to be conducted through several passages into a large room, which I afterwards found was the museum of the town, and wherein I beheld a sight which astonished me more than anything that I had yet seen.

It was filled with cases containing all manner of curiosities — such as skeletons, stuffed birds and animals, carvings in stone (whereof I saw several that were like those on the saddle, only smaller), but the greater part of the room was occupied by broken machinery of all descriptions. The larger specimens had a case to themselves, and tickets with writing on them in a character which I could not understand. There were fragments of steam engines, all broken and rusted; among them I saw a cylinder and piston, a broken fly-wheel and part of a crank, which was laid on the ground by their side. Again, there was a very old carriage whose wheels in spite of rust and decay, I could see, had been designed originally for iron rails. Indeed, there were fragments of a great many of our own most advanced inventions; but they seemed all to be several hundred years old, and to be placed where they were, not for instruction, but curiosity. As I said before, all were marred and broken.

We passed many cases, and at last came to one in which there were several clocks and two or three old watches. Here the magistrate stopped, and opening the case began comparing my watch with the others. The design was different, but the thing was clearly the same. On this he turned to me and made me a speech in a severe and injured tone of voice, pointing repeatedly to the watches in the case, and to my own; neither did he seem in the least appeased until I made signs to him that he had better take my watch and put it with the others. This had some effect in calming him. I said in English (trusting to tone and manner to convey my meaning) that I was exceedingly sorry if I had been found to have anything contraband in my possession; that I had had no intention of evading the ordinary tolls, and that I would gladly forfeit the watch if my doing so would atone for an unintentional violation of the law. He began presently to relent, and spoke to me in a kinder manner. I think he saw that I had offended without knowledge; but I believe the chief thing that brought him round was my not seeming to be afraid of him, although I was quite respectful; this, and my having light hair and complexion, on which he had remarked previously by signs, as every one else had done.

I afterwards found that it was reckoned a very great merit to have fair hair, this being a thing of the rarest possible occurrence, and greatly admired and envied in all who were possessed of it. However that might be, my watch was taken from me; but our peace was made, and I was conducted back to the room where I had been examined. The magistrate then made me another speech, whereon I was taken to a building hard by, which I soon discovered to be the common prison of the town, but in which an apartment was assigned me separate from the other prisoners. The room contained a bed, table and chairs, also a fireplace and a washing-stand. There was another door, which opened on to a balcony, with a flight of steps descending into a walled garden of some size. The man who conducted me into this room made signs to me that I might go down and walk in the garden whenever I pleased, and intimated that I should shortly have something brought me to eat. I was allowed to retain my blankets, and the few things which I had wrapped inside them, but it was plain that I was to consider myself a prisoner — for how long a period I could not by any means determine. He then left me alone.

CHAPTER EIGHT

IN PRISON

A ND now for the first time my courage completely failed me. It
is enough to say that I was penniless, and a prisoner in a foreign
country, where I had no friend, nor any knowledge of the
customs or language of the people. I was at the mercy of men with
whom I had little in common. And yet, engrossed as I was with my
extremely difficult and doubtful position, I could not help feeling
deeply interested in the people among whom I had fallen. What was
the meaning of that room full of old machinery which I had just seen,
and of the displeasure with which the magistrate had regarded my
watch? The people had very little machinery now. I had been struck
with this over and over again, though I had not been more than four-
and-twenty hours in the country. They were about as far advanced as
Europeans of the twelfth or thirteenth century; certainly not more so.
And yet they must have had at one time the fullest knowledge of our
own most recent inventions. How could it have happened that having
been once so far in advance they were now as much behind us? It was
evident that it was not from ignorance. They knew my watch as a
watch when they saw it; and the care with which the broken machines
were preserved and ticketed, proved that they had not lost the recollection of their former civilization. The more I thought, the less I could
understand it; but at last I concluded that they must have worked out
their mines of coal and iron, till either none were left, or so few, that
the use of these metals was restricted to the very highest nobility. This
was the only solution I could think of; and, though I afterwards found
how entirely mistaken it was, I felt quite sure then that it must be the
right one.

I had hardly arrived at this opinion for above four or five minutes,
when the door opened, and a young woman made her appearance with
a tray, and a very appetizing smell of dinner. I gazed upon her with
admiration as she laid a cloth and set a savoury-looking dish upon the
table. As I beheld her I felt as though my position was already much
ameliorated, for the very sight of her carried great comfort. She was
not more than twenty, rather above the middle height, active and
strong, but yet most delicately featured; her lips were full and sweet;
her eyes were of a deep hazel, and fringed with long and springing
eyelashes; her hair was neatly braided from off her forehead; her com-

66

plexion was simply exquisite; her figure as robust as was consistent with the most perfect female beauty, yet not more so; her hands and feet might have served as models to a sculptor. Having set the stew upon the table, she retired with a glance of pity, whereon (remembering pity's kinsman) I decided that she should pity me a little more. She returned with a bottle and a glass, and found me sitting on the bed with my hands over my face, looking the very picture of abject misery, and, like all pictures, rather untruthful. As I watched her, through my fingers, out of the room again, I felt sure that she was exceedingly sorry for me. Her back being turned, I set to work and ate my dinner, which was excellent.

She returned in about an hour to take away; and there came with her a man who had a great bunch of keys at his waist, and whose manner convinced me that he was the jailer. I afterwards found that he was father to the beautiful creature who had brought me my dinner. I am not a much greater hypocrite than other people, and do what I would, I could not look so very miserable. I had already recovered from my dejection, and felt in a most genial humour both with my jailer and his daughter. I thanked them for their attention towards me; and, though they could not understand, they looked at one another and laughed and chattered till the old man said something or other which I suppose was a joke; for the girl laughed merrily and ran away, leaving her father to take away the dinner things. Then I had another visitor, who was not so prepossessing, and who seemed to have a great idea of himself and a small one of me. He brought a book with him, and pens and paper — all very English; and yet, neither paper, nor printing, nor binding, nor pen, nor ink, were quite the same as ours.

He gave me to understand that he was to teach me the language and that we were to begin at once. This delighted me, both because I should be more comfortable when I could understand and make myself understood, and because I supposed that the authorities would hardly teach me the language if they intended any cruel usage towards me afterwards. We began at once, and I learnt the names of everything in the room, and also the numerals and personal pronouns. I found to my sorrow that the resemblance to European things, which I had so frequently observed hitherto, did not hold good in the matter of language; for I could detect no analogy whatever between this and any tongue of which I have the slightest knowledge — a thing which made me think it possible that I might be learning Hebrew.

I must detail no longer; from this time my days were spent with a monotony which would have been tedious but for the society of Yram, the jailer's daughter, who had taken a great fancy for me and treated me with the utmost kindness. The man came every day to teach me the language, but my real dictionary and grammar were Yram; and I consulted them to such purpose that I made the most extraordinary progress, being able at the end of a month to understand a great deal of the conversation which I overheard between Yram and her father. My teacher professed himself well satisfied, and said he should make a favourable report of me to the authorities. I then questioned him as to what would probably be done with me. He told me that my arrival had caused great excitement throughout the country, and that I was to be detained a close prisoner until the receipt of advices from the Government. My having had a watch, he said, was the only damaging feature in the case. And then, in answer to my asking why this should be so, he gave me a long story of which with my imperfect knowledge of the language I could make nothing whatever, except that it was a very heinous offence, almost as bad (at least, so I thought I understood him) as having typhus fever. But he said he thought my light hair would save me.

I was allowed to walk in the garden; there was a high wall so that I managed to play a sort of hand fives, which prevented my feeling the bad effects of my confinement, though it was stupid work playing alone. In the course of time people from the town and neighbourhood began to pester the jailer to be allowed to see me, and on receiving handsome fees he let them do so. The people were good to me; almost too good, for they were inclined to make a lion of me, which I hated — at least the women were; only they had to beware of Yram, who was a young lady of a jealous temperament, and kept a sharp eye both on me and on my lady visitors. However, I felt so kindly towards her, and was so entirely dependent upon her for almost all that made my life a blessing and a comfort to me, that I took good care not to vex her, and we remained excellent friends. The men were far less inquisitive, and would not, I believe, have come near me of their own accord; but the women made them come as escorts. I was delighted with their handsome mien, and pleasant genial manners.

My food was plain, but always varied and wholesome, and the good red wine was admirable. I had found a sort of wort in the garden, which I sweated in heaps and then dried, obtaining thus a substitute for tobacco; so that what with Yram, the language, visitors, fives in the garden, smoking and bed, my time slipped by more rapidly and pleasantly than might have been expected. I also made myself a small flute; and being a tolerable player, amused myself at times with playing snatches from operas, and airs such as 'Oh where and oh where', and 'Home, sweet home'. This was of great advantage to me, for the people of the country were ignorant of the diatonic scale and could hardly believe their ears on hearing some of our most common melodies. Often, too, they would make me sing; and I could at any time make Yram's eyes swim with tears by singing 'Villikins and his Dinah', 'Billy Taylor', 'The Ratcatcher's Daughter', or as much of them as I could remember.

I had one or two discussions with them because I never would sing on Sunday (of which I kept count in my pocket-book), except chants and hymn tunes; of these I regret to say that I had forgotten the words, so that I could only sing the tune. They appeared to have little or no religious feeling, and to have never so much as heard of the divine institution of the Sabbath, so they ascribed my observance of it to a fit of sulkiness, which they remarked as coming over me upon every seventh day. But they were very tolerant, and one of them said to me quite kindly that she knew how impossible it was to help being sulky at times, only she thought I ought to see some one if it became more serious — a piece of advice which I then failed to understand, though I pretended to take it quite as a matter of course.

Once only did Yram treat me in a way that was unkind and unreasonable — at least so I thought it at the time. It happened thus. I had been playing fives in the garden and got much heated. Although the day was cold, for autumn was now advancing, and Cold Harbour (as the name of the town in which my prison was should be translated) stood fully 3000 feet above the sea, I had played without my coat and waistcoat, and took a sharp chill on resting myself too long in the open air without protection. The next day I had a severe cold and felt really poorly. Being little used even to the lightest ailments, and thinking that it would be rather nice to be petted and cossetted by Yram, I certainly did not make myself out to be any better than I was; in fact, I remember that I made the worst of things, and took it into my head to consider myself upon the sick list. When Yram brought me my breakfast I complained somewhat dolefully of my indisposition, expecting the sympathy and humouring which I should have received from my mother and sisters at home. Not a bit of it. She fired up in an instant, and asked me what I meant by it, and how I dared to presume to mention such a thing, especially when I considered in what place I was. She had the best mind to tell her father, only that she was afraid the consequences would be so very serious for me. Her manner was so injured and decided, and her anger so evidently unfeigned, that I forgot my cold upon the spot, begging her by all means to tell her father if she wished to do so, and telling her that I had no idea of being shielded by her from anything whatever; presently mollifying, after having said as many biting things as I could, I asked her what it was that I had done amiss, and promised amendment as soon as ever I became aware of it. She saw that I was really ignorant, and had had no intention of being rude to her; whereon it came out that illness of any sort was considered in Erewhon to be highly criminal and immoral; and that I was liable, even for catching cold, to be had up before the magistrates and imprisoned for a considerable period — an announcement which struck me dumb with astonishment.

I followed up the conversation as well as my imperfect knowledge of the language would allow, and caught a glimmering of her position with regard to ill-health; but I did not even then fully comprehend it, nor had I as yet any idea of the other extraordinary perversions of thought which existed among the Erewhonians, but with which I was soon to become familiar. I propose, therefore, to make no mention of what passed between us on this occasion, save that we were reconciled, and that she brought me surreptitiously a glass of hot spirits and water before I went to bed, as also a pile of extra blankets, and that next morning I was quite well. I never remember to have lost a cold so rapidly.

This little affair explained much which had hitherto puzzled me. It seemed that the two men who were examined before the magistrates on the day of my arrival in the country, had been given in charge on account of ill health, and were both condemned to a long term of imprisonment with hard labour; they were now expiating their offence in this very prison, and their exercise ground was a yard separated by my fives wall from the garden in which I walked. This accounted for the sounds of coughing and groaning which I had often noticed as coming from the other side of the wall; it was high, and I had not dared to climb it for fear the jailer should see me and think that I was trying to escape; but I had often wondered what sort of people they could be on the other side, and had resolved on asking the jailer; but I seldom saw him, and Yram and I generally found other things to talk about.

Another month flew by, during which I made such progress in the language that I could understand all that was said to me, and express myself with tolerable fluency. My instructor professed to be astonished with the progress I had made; I was careful to attribute it to the pains he had taken with me and to his admirable method of explaining my difficulties, so we became excellent friends.

My visitors became more and more frequent. Among them there were some, both men and women, who delighted me entirely by their simplicity, unconsciousness of self, kindly genial manners, and last, but not least, by their exquisite beauty; there came others less well-bred, but still comely and agreeable people, while some were snobs pure and simple.

At the end of the third month the jailer and my instructor came together to visit me and told me that communications had been received from the Government to the effect that if I had behaved well and seemed generally reasonable, and if there could be no suspicion at all about my bodily health and vigour, and if my hair was really light, and my eyes blue and complexion fresh, I was to be sent up at once to the metropolis in order that the King and Queen might see me and converse with me; but that when I arrived there I should be set at liberty, and a suitable allowance would be made me. My teacher also told me that one of the leading merchants had sent me an invitation to repair to his house and to consider myself his guest for as long a time as I chose. 'He is a delightful man,' continued the interpreter, 'but has suffered terribly from' (here there came a long word which I could not quite catch, only it was much longer than kleptomania), 'and has but lately recovered from embezzling a large sum of money under singularly distressing circumstances; but he has quite got over it, and the straighteners say that he has made a really wonderful recovery; you are sure to like him.'

CHAPTER NINE

TO THE METROPOLIS

WITH the above words the good man left the room before I had time to express my astonishment at hearing such extraordinary language from the lips of one who seemed to be a reputable member of society. 'Embezzle a large sum of money under singularly distressing circumstances!' I exclaimed to myself, 'and ask *me* to go and stay with him! I shall do nothing of the sort — compromise myself at the very outset in the eyes of all decent people, and give the death-blow to my chances of either converting them if they are the lost tribes of Israel, or making money out of them if they are not! No. I will do anything rather than that.' And when I next saw my teacher I told him that I did not at all like the sound of what had been proposed for me, and that I would have nothing to do with it. For by my education and the example of my own parents, and I trust also in some degree from inborn instinct, I have a very genuine dislike for all unhandsome dealings in money matters, though none can have a greater regard for money than I have, if it be got fairly.

The interpreter was much surprised by my answer, and said that I should be very foolish if I persisted in my refusal.

'Mr. Nosnibor,' he continued, 'is a man of at least 500,000 horse-power' (for their way of reckoning and classifying men is by the number of foot pounds which they have money enough to raise, or more roughly by their horse-power), 'and keeps a capital table; besides, his two daughters are among the most beautiful women in Erewhon.'

When I heard all this, I confess that I was much shaken, and inquired whether he was favourably considered in the best society.

'Certainly,' was the answer, 'no man in the country stands higher.'

He then went on to say that one would have thought from my manner that my proposed host had had jaundice or pleurisy or been generally unfortunate, and that I was in fear of infection.

'I am not much afraid of infection,' said I, impatiently, 'but I have some regard for my character; and if I know a man to be an embezzler of other people's money, be sure of it, I will give him as wide a berth as I can. If he were ill or poor —'

'Ill or poor!' interrupted the interpreter, with a face of great alarm. 'So that's your notion of propriety! You would consort with the basest criminals, and yet deem simple embezzlement a bar to friendly inter-course. I cannot understand you.'

'But I am poor myself,' cried I.

'You were,' said he; 'and you were liable to be severely punished for it — indeed, at the council which was held concerning you, this fact was very nearly consigning you to what I should myself consider a well-deserved chastisement' (for he was getting angry, and so was I); 'but the Queen was so inquisitive, and wanted so much to see you, that she petitioned the King and made him give you his pardon, and assign you a pension in consideration of your meritorious complexion. It is lucky for you that he has not heard what you have been saying now, or he would be sure to cancel it.'

As I heard these words my heart sank within me. I felt the extreme difficulty of my position, and how wicked I should be in running counter to established usage. I remained silent for several minutes, and then said that I should be happy to accept the embezzler's invitation — on which my instructor brightened and said I was a sensible fellow. But I felt very uncomfortable. When he had left the room, I mused over the conversation which had just taken place between us, but I could make nothing out of it, except that it argued an even greater perversity of mental vision than I had been yet prepared for. And this made me wretched; for I cannot bear having much to do with people who think differently from myself. All sorts of wandering thoughts kept coming into my head. I thought of my master's hut, and my seat upon the mountain side, where I had first conceived the insane idea of exploring. What years and years seemed to have passed since I had begun my journey!

I thought of my adventures in the gorge, and on the journey hither, and of Chowbok. I wondered what Chowbok told them about me when he got back — he had done well in going back, Chowbok had. He was not handsome — nay, he was hideous; and it would have gone hardly with him. Twilight drew on, and rain pattered against the windows. Never yet had I felt so unhappy, except during three days of sea-sickness at the beginning of my voyage from England. I sat musing and in great melancholy, until Yram made her appearance with light and supper. She too, poor girl, was miserable; for she had heard that I was to leave them. She had made up her mind that I was to remain always in the town, even after my imprisonment was over; and I fancy had resolved to marry me though I had never so much as hinted at her doing so. So what with the distressingly strange conversation with my teacher, my own friendless condition, and Yram's melancholy, I felt more unhappy than I can describe, and remained so till I got to bed, and sleep sealed my eyelids.

On awakening next morning I was much better. It was settled that I was to make my start in a conveyance which was to be waiting for me at about eleven o'clock, and the anticipation of change put me in good spirits, which even the tearful face of Yram could hardly altogether derange. I kissed her again and again, assured her that we should meet hereafter, and that in the meanwhile I should be ever mindful of her kindness. I gave her two of the buttons off my coat and a lock of my hair as a keepsake, taking a goodly curl from her own beautiful head in return; and so, having said goodbye a hundred times, till I was fairly overcome with her great sweetness and her sorrow, I tore myself away from her and got downstairs to the *calèche* which was in waiting. How thankful I was when it was all over, and I was driven away and out of sight. Would that I could have felt that it was out of mind also! Pray heaven that it is so now, and that she is married happily among her own people, and has forgotten me!

And now began a long and tedious journey with which I should hardly trouble the reader if I could. He is safe, however, for the simple reason that I was blindfolded during the greater part of the time. A bandage was put upon my eyes every morning, and was only removed at night when I reached the inn at which we were to pass the night. We travelled slowly, although the roads were good. We drove but one horse, which took us our day's journey from morning till evening, about six hours, exclusive of two hours' rest in the middle of the day. I do not suppose we made above thirty or thirty-five miles on an average. Each day we had a fresh horse. As I have said already, I could see nothing of the country. I only know that it was level, and that several times we had to cross large rivers in ferryboats. The inns were clean and comfortable. In one or two of the larger towns they were quite sumptuous, and the food was good and well cooked. The same wonderful health and grace and beauty prevailed everywhere.

I found myself an object of great interest; so much so, that the driver told me he had to keep our route secret, and at times to go to places that were not directly on our road, in order to avoid the press that would otherwise have awaited us. Every evening I had a reception, and grew heartily tired of having to say the same things over and over again in answer to the same questions, but it was impossible to be angry with people whose manners were so delightful. They never once asked after my health, or even whether I was fatigued with my journey; but their first question was almost invariably an inquiry after my temper, the naivety of which astonished me till I became used to it. One day, being tired and cold, and weary of saying the same thing over and over again, I turned a little brusquely on my questioner and said that I was exceedingly cross, and that I could hardly feel in a worse humour with myself and every one else than at that moment. To my surprise, I was met with the kindest expressions of condolence, and heard it buzzed about the room that I was in an ill temper; whereon people began to give me nice things to smell and to eat, which really did seem to have some temper-mending quality about them, for I soon felt pleased and was at once congratulated upon being better. The next morning two or three people sent their servants to the hotel with sweetmeats, and inquiries whether I had quite recovered from my ill humour. On receiving the good things I felt in half a mind to be ill-tempered every evening; but I disliked the condolences and the inquiries, and found it most comfortable to keep my natural temper, which is smooth enough generally.

Among those who came to visit me were some who had received a liberal education at the Colleges of Unreason, and taken the highest degrees in hypothetics, which are their principal study. These gentlemen had now settled down to various employments in the country, as straighteners, managers and cashiers of the Musical Banks, priests of religion, or what not, and carrying their education with them they diffused a leaven of culture throughout the country. I naturally questioned them about many of the things which had puzzled me since my arrival. I inquired what was the object and meaning of the statues which I had seen upon the plateau of the pass. I was told that they dated from a very remote period, and that there were several other such groups in the country, but none so remarkable as the one which I had seen. They had a religious origin, having been designed to propitiate the gods of deformity and disease. In former times it had been the custom to make expeditions over the ranges, and capture the ugliest of Chowbok's ancestors whom they could find, in order to sacrifice them in the presence of these deities, and thus avert ugliness and disease from the Erewhonians themselves. It had been whispered (but my informant assured me untruly) that centuries ago they had even offered up some of their own people who were ugly or out of health, in order to make examples of them; these detestable customs, however, had been long discontinued; neither was there any present observance of the statues.

I had the curiosity to inquire what would be done to any of Chowbok's tribe if they crossed over into Erewhon. I was told that nobody knew, inasmuch as such a thing had not happened for ages. They would be too ugly to be allowed to go at large, but not so much so as to be criminally liable. Their offence in having come would be a moral one; but they would be beyond the straightener's art. Possibly they would be consigned to the Hospital for Incurable Bores, and made to work at being bored for so many hours a day by the Erewhonian inhabitants of the hospital, who are extremely impatient of one another's boredom, but would soon die if they had no one whom they might bore — in fact, that they would be kept as professional borees. When I heard this, it occurred to me that some rumours of its substance might perhaps have become current among Chowbok's people; for the agony of his fear had been too great to have been inspired by the mere dread of being burnt alive before the statues.

I also questioned them about the museum of old machines, and the cause of the apparent retrogression in all arts, sciences and inventions. I learnt that about four hundred years previously, the state of mechanical knowledge was far beyond our own, and was advancing with prodigious rapidity, until one of the most learned professors of hypothetics wrote an extraordinary book (from which I propose to give extracts later on), proving that the machines were ultimately destined to supplant the race of man, and to become instinct with a vitality as different from, and superior to, that of animals, as animal to vegetable life. So convincing was his reasoning, or unreasoning, to this effect, that he carried the country with him; and they made a clean sweep of all machinery that had not been in use for more than two hundred and seventy-one years (which period was arrived at after a series of compromises), and strictly forbade all further improvements and inventions under pain of being considered in the eye of the law to be labouring under typhus fever, which they regard as one of the worst of all crimes.

This is the only case in which they have confounded mental and physical diseases, and they do it even here as by an avowed legal fiction. I became uneasy when I remembered about my watch; but they comforted me with the assurance that transgression in this matter was now so unheard of, that the law could afford to be lenient towards an utter stranger, especially towards one who had such a good character (they meant physique), and such beautiful light hair. Moreover, the watch was a real curiosity, and would be a welcome addition to the metropolitan collection; so they did not think I need let it trouble me seriously.

I will write, however, more fully upon this subject when I deal with the Colleges of Unreason, and the Book of the Machines.

In about a month from the time of our starting I was told that our journey was nearly over. The bandage was now dispensed with, for it seemed impossible that I should ever be able to find my way back without being captured. Then we rolled merrily along through the streets of a handsome town, and got on to a long, broad and level road, with poplar trees on either side. The road was raised slightly above the surrounding country, and had formerly been a railway; the fields on either side were in the highest conceivable cultivation, but the harvest and also the vintage had been already gathered. The weather had got cooler more rapidly than could be quite accounted for by the progress of the season; so I rather thought that we must have been making away from the sun, and were some degrees farther from the equator than when we started. Even here the vegetation showed that the climate was a hot one, yet there was no lack of vigour among the people; on the contrary, they were a very hardy race, and capable of great endurance. For the hundredth time I thought that, take them all round, I had never seen their equals in respect of physique, and they looked as good-natured as they were robust. The flowers were for the most part over, but their absence was in some measure compensated for by a profusion of delicious fruit, closely resembling the figs, peaches and pears of Italy and France. I saw no wild animals, but birds were plentiful and much as in Europe, but not tame as they had been on the other side the ranges. They were shot at with the cross-bow and with arrows, gunpowder being unknown, or at any rate not in use.

We were now nearing the metropolis and I could see great towers and fortifications, and lofty buildings that looked like palaces. I began to be nervous as to my reception; but I had got on very well so far, and resolved to continue upon the same plan as hitherto — namely, to behave just as though I were in England until I saw that I was making a blunder, and then to say nothing till I could gather how the land lay.

We drew nearer and nearer. The news of my approach had got abroad, and there was a great crowd collected on either side the road, who greeted me with marks of most respectful curiosity, keeping me bowing constantly in acknowledgment from side to side.

When we were about a mile off, we were met by the Mayor and several Councillors, among whom was a venerable old man, who was introduced to me by the Mayor (for so I suppose I should call him) as the gentleman who had invited me to his house. I bowed deeply and told him how grateful I felt to him, and how gladly I would accept his hospitality. He forbade me to say more, and pointing to his carriage, which was close at hand, he motioned me to a seat therein. I again bowed profoundly to the Mayor and Councillors, and drove off with my entertainer, whose name was Senoj Nosnibor. After about half a mile the carriage turned off the main road, and we drove under the walls of the town till we reached a *palazzo* on a slight eminence, and just on the outskirts of the city. This was Senoj Nosnibor's house, and nothing can be imagined finer. It was situated near the magnificent and venerable ruins of the old railway station, which formed an imposing feature from the gardens of the house. The grounds, some ten or a dozen acres in extent, were laid out in terraced gardens, one above the other, with flights of broad steps ascending and descending the declivity of the garden. On these steps there were statues of most exquisite workmanship. Besides the statues there were vases filled with various shrubs that were new to me; and on either side the flights of steps there were rows of old cypresses and cedars, with grassy alleys between them. Then came choice vineyards and orchards of fruit trees in full bearing.

The house itself was approached by a court-yard, and round it was a corridor on to which rooms opened, as at Pompeii. In the middle of the court there was a bath and a fountain. Having passed the court we came to the main body of the house, which was two storeys in height. The rooms were large and lofty; perhaps at first they looked rather bare of furniture, but in hot climates people generally keep their rooms more bare than they do in colder ones. I missed also the sight of a grand piano or some similar instrument, there being no means of producing music in any of the rooms save the larger drawing-room, where there were half a dozen large bronze gongs, which the ladies used occasionally to beat about at random. It was not pleasant to hear them, but I have heard quite as unpleasant music both before and since.

Mr. Nosnibor took me through several spacious rooms till we reached a boudoir where were his wife and daughters, of whom I had heard from the interpreter. Mrs. Nosnibor was about forty years old, and still handsome, but she had grown very stout; her daughters were in the prime of youth and exquisitely beautiful. I gave the preference almost at once to the younger, whose name was Arowhena; for the elder sister was haughty, while the younger had a very winning manner. Mrs. Nosnibor received me with the perfection of courtesy, so that I must have indeed been shy and nervous if I had not at once felt welcome. Scarcely was the ceremony of my introduction well completed before a servant announced that dinner was ready in the next room. I was exceedingly hungry, and the dinner was beyond all praise. Can the reader wonder that I began to consider myself in excellent quarters? 'That man embezzle money?' thought I to myself; 'impossible.'

But I noticed that my host was uneasy during the whole meal, and that he ate nothing but a little bread and milk; towards the end of dinner there came a tall lean man with a black beard, to whom Mr. Nosnibor and the whole family paid great attention; he was the family straightener. With this gentleman Mr. Nosnibor retired into another room, from which there presently proceeded a sound of weeping and wailing. I could hardly believe my ears, but in a few minutes I got to know for a certainty that they came from Mr. Nosnibor himself.

'Poor papa,' said Arowhena, as she helped herself composedly to the salt, 'how terribly he has suffered.'

'Yes,' answered her mother, 'but I think he is quite out of danger now.'

Then they went on to explain to me the circumstances of the case, and the treatment which the straightener had prescribed, and how successful he had been — all which I will reserve for another chapter, and put rather in the form of a general summary of the opinions current upon these subjects than in the exact words in which the facts were delivered to me; the reader, however, is earnestly requested to believe that both in this next chapter and in those that follow it I have endeavoured to adhere most conscientiously to the strictest accuracy, and that I have never willingly misrepresented, though I may have sometimes failed to understand all the bearings of an opinion or custom.

CHAPTER TEN

CURRENT OPINIONS

THIS is what I gathered. That in that country if a man falls into ill health, or catches any disorder, or fails bodily in any way before he is seventy years old, he is tried before a jury of his countrymen, and if convicted is held up to public scorn and sentenced more or less severely as the case may be. There are subdivisions of illnesses into crimes and misdemeanours as with offences amongst ourselves — a man being punished very heavily for serious illness, while failure of eyes or hearing in one over sixty-five, who has had good health hitherto, is dealt with by fine only, or imprisonment in default of payment. But if a man forges a cheque, or sets his house on fire, or robs with violence from the person, or does any other such things as are criminal in our own country, he is either taken to a hospital and most carefully tended at the public expense, or if he is in good circumstances, he lets it be known to all his friends that he is suffering from a severe fit of immorality, just as we do when we are ill, and they come and visit him with great solicitude, and inquire with interest how it all came about, what symptoms first showed themselves, and so forth — questions which he will answer with perfect unreserve; for bad conduct, though considered no less deplorable than illness with ourselves, and as unquestionably indicating something seriously wrong with the individual who misbehaves, is nevertheless held to be the result of either pre-natal or post-natal misfortune.

The strange part of the story, however, is that though they ascribe moral defects to the effect of misfortune either in character or surroundings, they will not listen to the plea of misfortune in cases that in England meet with sympathy and commiseration only. Ill luck of any kind, or even ill treatment at the hands of others, is considered an offence against society, inasmuch as it makes people uncomfortable to hear of it. Loss of fortune, therefore, or loss of some dear friend on whom another was much dependent, is punished hardly less severely than physical delinquency.

In the following chapter I will give a few examples of the way in which what we should call misfortune, hardship or disease are dealt with by the Erewhonians, but for the moment will return to their treatment of cases that with us are criminal. As I have already said, these, though not judicially punishable, are recognized as requiring correction. Accordingly, there exists a class of men trained in soul-craft, whom they call straighteners, as nearly as I can translate a word which literally means 'one who bends back the crooked'. These men practise much as medical men in England, and receive a quasi-sur-reptitious fee on every visit. They are treated with the same unreserve, and obeyed as readily, as our own doctors — that is to say, on the whole sufficiently — because people know that it is to their interest to get well as soon as they can, and that they will not be scouted as they would be if their bodies were out of order, even though they may have to undergo a very painful course of treatment.

When I say that they will not be scouted, I do not mean that an Erewhonian will suffer no social inconvenience in consequence, we will say, of having committed fraud. Friends will fall away from him because of his being less pleasant company, just as we ourselves are disinclined to make companions of those who are either poor or poorly. No one with any sense of self-respect will place himself on an equality in the matter of affection with those who are less lucky than himself in birth, health, money, good looks, capacity or anything else. Indeed, that dislike and even disgust should be felt by the fortunate for the unfortunate, or at any rate for those who have been discovered to have met with any of the more serious and less familiar misfortunes, is not only natural, but desirable for any society, whether of man or brute.

The fact, therefore, that the Erewhonians attach none of that guilt to crime which they do to physical ailments, does not prevent the more selfish among them from neglecting a friend who has robbed a bank, for instance, till he has fully recovered; but it does prevent them from even thinking of treating criminals with that contemptuous tone which would seem to say, 'I, if I were you, should be a better man than you are,' a tone which is held quite reasonable in regard to physical ailment. Hence, though they conceal ill health by every cunning and hypocrisy and artifice which they can devise, they are quite open about the most flagrant mental diseases, should they happen to exist, which to do the people justice is not often. Indeed, there are some who are, so to speak, spiritual valetudinarians, and who make themselves exceedingly ridiculous by their nervous supposition that they are wicked, while they are very tolerable people all the time. This however is exceptional; and on the whole they use much the same reserve or unreserve about the state of their moral welfare as we do about our health.

Hence all the ordinary greetings among ourselves, such as, How do you do? and the like, are considered signs of gross ill-breeding; nor do the politer classes tolerate even such a common complimentary remark as telling a man that he is looking well. They salute each other with, 'I hope you are good this morning', or 'I hope you have recovered from the snappishness from which you were suffering when I last saw you'; and if the person saluted has not been good, or is still snappish, he says so at once and is condoled with accordingly. Indeed, the straighteners have gone so far as to give names from the hypothetical language (as taught at the Colleges of Unreason) to all known forms of mental indisposition, and to classify them according to a system of their own, which, though I could not understand it, seemed to work well in practice; for they are always able to tell a man what is the matter with him as soon as they have heard his story, and their familiarity with the long names assures him that they thoroughly understand his case.

The reader will have no difficulty in believing that the laws regarding ill health were frequently evaded by the help of recognized fictions, which every one understood, but which it would be considered gross ill-breeding to even seem to understand. Thus, a day or two after my arrival at the Nosnibor's, one of the many ladies who called on me made excuses for her husband's only sending his card, on the ground that when going through the public market-place that morning he had stolen a pair of socks. I had already been warned that I should never show surprise, so I merely expressed my sympathy, and said that though I had only been in the capital so short a time, I had already had a very narrow escape from stealing a clothes brush, and that though I had resisted temptation so far, I was sadly afraid that if I saw any object of special interest that was neither too hot nor too heavy, I should have to put myself in the straightener's hands.

Mrs. Nosnibor, who had been keeping an ear on all that I had been saying, praised me when the lady had gone. Nothing, she said, could have been more polite according to Erewhonian etiquette. She then explained that to have stolen a pair of socks, or 'to have the socks' (in more colloquial language), was a recognized way of saying that the person in question was slightly indisposed.

In spite of all this they have a keen sense of the enjoyment consequent upon what they call being 'well'. They admire mental health and love it in other people, and take all the pains they can (consistently with their other duties) to secure it for themselves. They have an extreme dislike to marrying into what they consider unhealthy families. They send for the straightener at once whenever they have been guilty of anything seriously flagitious — often even if they think that they are on the point of committing it; and though his remedies are sometimes exceedingly painful, involving close confinement for weeks, and in some cases the most cruel physical tortures, I never heard of a reasonable Erewhonian refusing to do what his straightener told him, any more than of a reasonable Englishman refusing to undergo even the most frightful operation, if his doctors told him it was necessary.

We in England never shrink from telling our doctor what is the matter with us merely through the fear that he will hurt us. We let him do his worst upon us, and stand it without a murmur, because we are not scouted for being ill, and because we know that the doctor is doing his best to cure us, and that he can judge of our case better than we can; but we should conceal all illness if we were treated as the Erewhonians are when they have anything the matter with them; we should do the same as with moral and intellectual diseases — we should feign health with the most consummate art, till we were found out, and should hate a single flogging given in the way of mere punishment more than the amputation of a limb, if it were kindly and courteously performed from a wish to help us out of our difficulty, and with the full consciousness on the part of the doctor that it was only by an accident of constitution that he was not in the like plight himself. So the Erewhonians take a flogging once a week, and a diet of bread and water for two or three months together, whenever their straightener recommends it.

I do not suppose that even my host, on having swindled a confiding widow out of the whole of her property, was put to more actual suffering than a man will readily undergo at the hands of an English doctor. And yet he must have had a very bad time of it. The sounds I heard were sufficient to show that his pain was exquisite, but he never shrank from undergoing it. He was quite sure that it did him good; and I think he was right. I cannot believe that that man will ever embezzle money again. He may — but it will be a long time before he does so.

During my confinement in prison, and on my journey, I had already discovered a great deal of the above; but it still seemed surpassingly strange, and I was in constant fear of committing some piece of rudeness, through my inability to look at things from the same standpoint as my neighbours; but after a few weeks' stay with the Nosnibors, I got to understand things better, especially on having heard all about my host's illness, of which he told me fully and repeatedly.

It seemed that he had been on the Stock Exchange of the city for many years and had amassed enormous wealth, without exceeding the limits of what was generally considered justifiable, or at any rate, permissible dealing; but at length on several occasions he had become aware of a desire to make money by fraudulent representations, and had actually dealt with two or three sums in a way which had made him rather uncomfortable. He had unfortunately made light of it and pooh-poohed the ailment, until circumstances eventually presented themselves which enabled him to cheat upon a very considerable scale: — he told me what they were, and they were about as bad as anything could be, but I need not detail them — he seized the opportunity, and became aware, when it was too late, that he must be seriously out of order. He had neglected himself too long.

He drove home at once, broke the news to his wife and daughters as gently as he could, and sent off for one of the most celebrated straighteners of the kingdom to a consultation with the family practitioner, for the case was plainly serious. On the arrival of the straightener he told his story, and expressed his fear that his morals must be permanently impaired.

The eminent man reassured him with a few cheering words, and then proceeded to make a more careful diagnosis of the case. He inquired concerning Mr. Nosnibor's parents — had their moral health been good? He was answered that there had not been anything seriously amiss with them, but that his maternal grandfather, whom he was supposed to resemble somewhat in person, had been a consummate scoundrel and had ended his days in a hospital — while a brother of his father's, after having led a most flagitious life for many years, had been at last cured by a philosopher of a new school, which as far as I could understand it bore much the same relation to the old as homoeopathy to allopathy. The straightener shook his head at this, and laughingly replied that the cure must have been due to nature. After a few more questions he wrote a prescription and departed.

I saw the prescription. It ordered a fine to the State of double the money embezzled, no food but bread and milk for six months, and a severe flogging once a month for twelve. I was surprised to see that no part of the fine was to be paid to the poor woman whose money had been embezzled, but on inquiry I learned that she would have been prosecuted in the Misplaced Confidence Court, if she had not escaped its clutches by dying shortly after she had discovered her loss.

As for Mr. Nosnibor, he had received his eleventh flogging on the day of my arrival. I saw him later on the same afternoon, and he was still twinged; but there had been no escape from following out the straightener's prescription, for the so-called sanitary laws of Erewhon are very rigorous, and unless the straightener was satisfied that his orders had been obeyed, the patient would have been taken to a hospital (as the poor are), and would have been much worse off. Such at least is the law, but it is never necessary to enforce it.

On a subsequent occasion I was present at an interview between Mr. Nosnibor and the family straightener, who was considered competent to watch the completion of the cure. I was struck with the delicacy with which he avoided even the remotest semblance of inquiry after the physical well-being of his patient, though there was a certain yellowness about my host's eyes which argued a bilious habit of body. To have taken notice of this would have been a gross breach of professional etiquette. I was told, however, that a straightener sometimes thinks it right to glance at the possibility of some slight physical disorder if he finds it important in order to assist him in his diagnosis; but the answers which he gets are generally untrue or evasive, and he forms his own conclusions upon the matter as well as he can. Sensible men have been known to say that the straightener should in strict confidence be told of every physical ailment that is likely to bear upon the case; but people are naturally shy of doing this, for they do not like lowering themselves in the opinion of the straightener, and his ignorance of medical science is supreme. I heard of one lady, indeed, who had the hardihood to confess that a furious outbreak of ill-humour and extravagant fancies for which she was seeking advice was possibly the result of indisposition. 'You should resist that,' said the straightener, in a kind, but grave voice, 'we can do nothing for the bodies of our patients; such matters are beyond our province, and I desire that I may hear no further particulars.' The lady burst into tears, and promised faithfully that she would never be unwell again.

But to return to Mr. Nosnibor. As the afternoon wore on many carriages drove up with callers to inquire how he had stood his flogging. It had been very severe, but the kind inquiries upon every side gave him great pleasure, and he assured me that he felt almost tempted to do wrong again by the solicitude with which his friends had treated him during his recovery; in this I need hardly say that he was not serious.

During the remainder of my stay in the country Mr. Nosnibor was constantly attentive to his business, and largely increased his already great possessions; but I never heard a whisper to the effect of his having been indisposed a second time, or made money by other than the most strictly honourable means. I did hear afterwards in confidence that there had been reason to believe that his health had been not a little affected by the straightener's treatment, but his friends did not choose to be over-curious upon the subject, and on his return to his affairs it was by common consent passed over as hardly criminal in one who was otherwise so much afflicted. For they regard bodily ailments as the more venial in proportion as they have been produced by causes independent of the constitution. Thus if a person ruin his health by excessive indulgence at the table or by drinking, they count it to be almost a part of the mental disease which brought it about, and so it goes for little, but they have no mercy on such illnesses as fevers or catarrhs or lung diseases, which to us appear to be beyond the control of the individual. They are only more lenient towards the diseases of the young — such as measles, which they think to be like sowing one's wild oats — and look over them as pardonable indiscretions if they have not been too serious, and if they are atoned for by complete subsequent recovery.

It is hardly necessary to say that the office of straightener is one which requires long and special training. It stands to reason that he who would cure a moral ailment must be practically acquainted with it in all its bearings. The student for the profession of straightener is required to set apart certain seasons for the practice of each vice in turn, as a religious duty. These seasons are called 'fasts', and are continued by the student until he finds that he really can subdue all the more usual vices in his own person, and hence can advise his patients from the results of his own experience.

Those who intend to be specialists, rather than general practitioners, devote themselves more particularly to the branch in which their practice will mainly lie. Some students have been obliged to continue their exercises during their whole lives, and some devoted men have actually died as martyrs to the drink, or gluttony, or whatever branch of vice they may have chosen for their especial study. The greater number, however, take no harm by the excursions into the various departments of vice which it is incumbent upon them to study.

For the Erewhonians hold that unalloyed virtue is not a thing to be immoderately indulged in. I was shown more than one case in which the real or supposed virtues of parents were visited upon the children to the third and fourth generation. The straighteners say that the most that can be truly said for virtue is that there is a considerable balance in its favour, and that it is on the whole a good deal better to be on its side than against it; but they urge that there is much pseudo-virtue going about, which is apt to let people in very badly before they find it out. Those men, they say, are best who are not remarkable either for vice or virtue. I told them about Hogarth's idle and industrious apprentices, but they did not seem to think that the industrious apprentice was a very nice person.

CHAPTER TWELVE

MALCONTENTS

I MAY here mention that only a few years before my arrival in the country, the treatment of all convicted invalids had been much more barbarous than now, for no physical remedy was provided, and prisoners were put to the severest labour in all sorts of weather, so that most of them soon succumbed to the extreme hardships which they suffered; this was supposed to be beneficial in some ways, inasmuch as it put the country to less expense for the maintenance of its criminal class; but the growth of luxury had induced a relaxation of the old severity, and a sensitive age would no longer tolerate what appeared to be an excess of rigour, even towards the most guilty; moreover, it was found that juries were less willing to convict, and justice was often cheated because there was no alternative between virtually condemning a man to death and letting him go free; it was also held that the country paid in recommittals for its over-severity; for those who had been imprisoned even for trifling ailments were often permanently disabled by their imprisonment; and when a man had been once convicted, it was probable that he would seldom afterwards be off the hands of the country.

These evils had long been apparent and recognized; yet people were too indolent, and too indifferent to suffering not their own, to bestir themselves about putting an end to them, until at last a benevolent reformer devoted his whole life to effecting the necessary changes. He divided all illnesses into three classes — those affecting the head, the trunk, and the lower limbs — and obtained an enactment that all diseases of the head, whether internal or external, should be treated with laudanum, those of the body with castor-oil, and those of the lower limbs with an embrocation of strong sulphuric acid and water.

It may be said that the classification was not sufficiently careful, and that the remedies were ill chosen; but it is a hard thing to initiate any reform, and it was necessary to familiarize the public mind with the principle, by inserting the thin end of the wedge first; it is not, therefore, to be wondered at that among so practical a people there should still be some room for improvement. The mass of the nation are well pleased with existing arrangements, and believe that their treatment of criminals leaves little or nothing to be desired; but there is an energetic minority who hold what are considered to be extreme opinions, and who are not at all disposed to rest contented until the principle lately admitted has been carried further.

I was at some pains to discover the opinions of these men, and their reasons for entertaining them. They are held in great odium by the generality of the public, and are considered as subverters of all morality whatever. The malcontents, on the other hand, assert that illness is the inevitable result of certain antecedent causes, which, in the great majority of cases, were beyond the control of the individual, and that therefore a man is only guilty for being in a consumption in the same way as rotten fruit is guilty for having gone rotten. True, the fruit must be thrown on one side as unfit for man's use, and the man in a consumption must be put in prison for the protection of his fellow-citizens; but these radicals would not punish him further than by loss of liberty and a strict surveillance. So long as he was prevented from injuring society, they would allow him to make himself useful by supplying whatever of society's wants he could supply. If he succeeded in thus earning money, they would have him made as comfortable in prison as possible, and would in no way interfere with his liberty more than was necessary to prevent him from escaping, or from becoming more severely indisposed within the prison walls; but they would deduct from his earnings the expenses of his board, lodging, surveillance, and half those of his conviction. If he was too ill to do anything for his support in prison, they would allow him nothing but bread and water, and very little of that.

These people say further, that the greater part of the illness which exists in their country is brought about by the insane manner in which it is treated.

They believe that illness is in many cases just as curable as the moral diseases which they see daily cured around them, but that a great reform is impossible till men learn to take a juster view of what physical obliquity proceeds from. Men will hide their illnesses as long as they are scouted on its becoming known that they are ill; it is the scouting, not the physic, which produces the concealment; and if a man felt that the news of his being in ill health would be received by his neighbour as a deplorable fact, but one as much the result of necessary antecedent causes as though he had broken into a jeweller's shop and stolen a valuable diamond necklace — as a fact which might just as easily have happened to themselves, only that they had the luck to be better born or reared; and if they also felt that they would not be made more uncomfortable in the prison than the protection of society against infection and the proper treatment of their own disease actually demanded, men would give themselves up to the police as readily on perceiving that they had taken smallpox, as they go now to the straightener when they feel that they are on the point of forging a will, or running away with somebody else's wife.

But the main argument on which they rely is that of economy; for they know that they will sooner gain their end by appealing to men's pockets, in which they have generally something of their own, than to their heads, which contain for the most part little but borrowed or stolen property; and also, they believe it to be the readiest test and the one which has most to show for itself. If a course of conduct can be shown to cost a country less, and this by no dishonourable saving and with no indirectly increased expenditure in other ways, they hold that it requires a good deal to upset the arguments in favour of its being adopted, and whether rightly or wrongly I cannot pretend to say, they think that the more medicinal and humane treatment of the diseased of which they are the advocates would in the long run be much cheaper to the country; but I did not gather that these reformers were opposed to meeting some of the more violent forms of illness with the cat-of-nine-tails, or with death; for they saw no so effectual way of checking

89

them; they would therefore both flog and hang, but they would do so pitifully.

I have perhaps dwelt too long upon opinions which can have no possible bearing upon our own, but I have not said the tenth part of what these would-be reformers urged upon me. I feel, however, that I have sufficiently trespassed upon the attention of the reader.

CHAPTER THIRTEEN

THE VIEWS OF THE EREWHONIANS CONCERNING DEATH

THE Erewhonians regard death with less abhorrence than disease. If it is an offence at all, it is one beyond the reach of the law, which is therefore silent on the subject; but they insist that the greater number of those who are commonly said to die, have never yet been born — not, at least, into that unseen world which is alone worthy of consideration. As regards this unseen world I understand them to say that some miscarry in respect to it before they have even reached the seen, and some after, while few are ever truly born into it at all — the greater part of all the men and women over the whole country miscarrying before they reach it. And they say that this does not matter so much as we think it does.

As for what we call death, they argue that too much has been made of it. The mere knowledge that we shall one day die does not make us very unhappy; no one thinks that he or she will escape, so that none are disappointed. We do not care greatly even though we know that we have not long to live; the only thing that would seriously affect us would be the knowing — or rather thinking that we know — the precise moment at which the blow will fall. Happily no one can ever certainly know this, though many try to make themselves miserable by endeavouring to find it out. It seems as though there were some power somewhere which mercifully stays us from putting that sting into the tail of death, which we would put there if we could, and which ensures that though death must always be a bugbear, it shall never under any conceivable circumstances be more than a bugbear.

For even though a man is condemned to die in a week's time and is shut up in a prison from which it is certain that he cannot escape, he will always hope that a reprieve may come before the week is over. Besides, the prison may catch fire, and he may be suffocated not with a rope, but with common ordinary smoke; or he may be struck dead by lightning while exercising in the prison yards. When the morning is come on which the poor wretch is to be hanged, he may choke at his breakfast, or die from failure of the heart's action before the drop has fallen; and even though it has fallen, he cannot be quite certain that he is going to die, for he cannot know this till his death has actually taken place, and it will be too late then for him to discover that he was going to die at the appointed hour after all. The Erewhonians, therefore, hold that death, like life, is an affair of being more frightened than hurt.

They burn their dead, and the ashes are presently scattered over any piece of ground which the deceased may himself have chosen. No one is permitted to refuse this hospitality to the dead; people, therefore, generally choose some garden or orchard which they may have known and been fond of when they were young. The superstitious hold that those whose ashes are scattered over any land become its jealous guardians from that time forward; and the living like to think that they shall become identified with this or that locality where they have once been happy.

They do not put up monuments, nor write epitaphs, for their dead, though in former ages their practice was much as ours, but they have a custom which comes to much the same thing, for the instinct of preserving the name alive after the death of the body seems to be common to all mankind. They have statues of themselves made while they are still alive (those, that is, who can afford it), and write inscriptions under them, which are often quite as untruthful as are our own epitaphs — only in another way. For they do not hesitate to describe themselves as victims to ill temper, jealousy, covetousness and the like, but almost always lay claim to personal beauty, whether they have it or not, and, often, to the possession of a large sum in the funded debt of the country. If a person is ugly he does not sit as a model for his own statue, although it bears his name. He gets the handsomest of his friends to sit for him, and one of the ways of paying a compliment to another is to ask him to sit for such a statue. Women generally sit for their own statues, from a natural disinclination to admit the superior beauty of a friend, but they expect to be idealized. I understood that the multitude of these statues was beginning to be felt as an encumbrance in almost every family, and that the custom would probably before long fall into desuetude.

Indeed, this has already come about to the satisfaction of every one, as regards the statues of public men — not more than three of which can be found in the whole capital. I expressed my surprise at this, and was told that some five hundred years before my visit, the city had been so overrun with these pests, that there was no getting about, and people were worried beyond endurance by having their attention called at every touch and turn to something, which, when they had attended to it, they found not to concern them. Most of these statues were mere attempts to do for some man or woman what an animal-stuffer does more successfully for a dog, or bird, or pike. They were generally foisted on the public by some coterie that was trying to exalt itself in exalting someone else, and not unfrequently they had no other inception than desire on the part of some member of the coterie to find a job for a young sculptor to whom his daughter was engaged. Statues so begotten could never be anything but deformities, and this is the way in which they are sure to be begotten, as soon as the art of making them at all has become widely practised.

I know not why, but all the noblest arts hold in perfection but for a very little moment. They soon reach a height from which they begin to decline, and when they have begun to decline it is a pity that they cannot be knocked on the head; for an art is like a living organism — better dead than dying. There is no way of making an aged art young again; it must be born anew and grow up from infancy as a new thing, working out its own salvation from effort to effort in all fear and trembling.

The Erewhonians five hundred years ago understood nothing of all this — I doubt whether they even do so now. They wanted to get the nearest thing they could to a stuffed man whose stuffing should not grow mouldy. They should have had some such an establishment as our Madame Tussaud's, where the figures wear real clothes, and are painted up to nature. Such an institution might have been made self-supporting, for people might have been made to pay before going in. As it was, they had let their poor, cold, grimy, colourless heroes and heroines loaf about in squares and in corners of streets in all weathers, without any attempt at artistic sanitation — for there was no provision for burying their dead works of art out of their sight — no drainage, so to speak, whereby statues that had been sufficiently assimilated, so as to form part of the residuary impression of the country, might be carried away out of the system. Hence they put them up with a light heart on the cackling of their coteries, and they and their children had to live, often enough, with some wordy windbag whose cowardice had cost the country untold loss in blood and money.

At last the evil reached such a pitch that the people rose, and with indiscriminate fury destroyed good and bad alike. Most of what was destroyed was bad, but some few works were good, and the sculptors of today wring their hands over some of the fragments that have been preserved in museums up and down the country. For a couple of hundred years or so, not a statue was made from one end of the kingdom to the other, but the instinct for having stuffed men and women was so strong, that people at length again began to try to make them. Not knowing how to make them, and having no academies to mislead them, the earliest sculptors of this period thought things out for themselves, and again produced works that were full of interest, so that in three or four generations they reached a perfection hardly if at all inferior to that of several hundred years earlier.

On this the same evils recurred. Sculptors obtained high prices — the art became a trade — schools arose which professed to sell the holy spirit of art for money; pupils flocked from far and near to buy it, in the hopes of selling it later on, and were struck purblind as a punishment for the sin of those who sent them. Before long a second iconoclastic fury would infallibly have followed, but for the prescience of a statesman who succeeded in passing an Act to the effect that no statue of any public man or woman should be allowed to remain unbroken for more than fifty years, unless at the end of that time a jury of twenty-four men taken at random from the street pronounced in favour of its being allowed a second fifty years of life. Every fifty years this reconsideration was to be repeated, and unless there was a majority of eighteen in favour of the retention of the statue, it was to be destroyed.

Perhaps a simpler plan would have been to forbid the erection of a statue to any public man or woman till he or she had been dead at least one hundred years, and even then to insist on reconsideration of the claims of the deceased and the merit of the statue every fifty years — but the working of the Act brought about results that on the whole were satisfactory. For in the first place, many public statues that would have been voted under the old system, were not ordered, when it was known that they would be almost certainly broken up after fifty years, and in the second, public sculptors knowing their work to be so ephemeral, scamped it to an extent that made it offensive even to the most uncultured eye. Hence before long subscribers took to paying the sculptor for the statue of their dead statesmen, on condition that he did not make it. The tribute of respect was thus paid to the deceased, the public sculptors were not mulcted, and the rest of the public suffered no inconvenience.

I was told, however, that an abuse of this custom is growing up, inasmuch as the competition for the commission not to make a statue is so keen, that sculptors have been known to return a considerable part of the purchase money to the subscribers, by an arrangement made with them beforehand. Such transactions, however, are always clandestine. A small inscription is let into the pavement, where the public statue would have stood, which informs the reader that such a statue has been ordered for the person, whoever he or she may be, but that as yet the sculptor has not been able to complete it. There has been no Act to repress statues that are intended for private consumption, but as I have said, the custom is falling into desuetude.

Returning to Erewhonian customs in connection with death, there is one which I can hardly pass over. When anyone dies, the friends of the family write no letters of condolence, neither do they attend the scattering, nor wear mourning, but they send little boxes filled with artificial tears, and with the name of the sender painted neatly upon the outside of the lid. The tears vary in number from two to fifteen or sixteen, according to degree of intimacy or relationship; and people sometimes find it a nice point of etiquette to know the exact number which they ought to send. Strange as it may appear, this attention is highly valued, and its omission by those from whom it might be expected is keenly felt. These tears were formerly stuck with adhesive plaster to the cheeks of the bereaved, and were worn in public for a few months after the death of a relative; they were then banished to the hat or bonnet, and are now no longer worn.

The birth of a child is looked upon as a painful subject on which it is kinder not to touch; the illness of the mother is carefully concealed until the necessity for signing the birth-formula (of which hereafter) renders further secrecy impossible, and for some months before the event the family live in retirement, seeing very little company. When the offence is over and done with, it is condoned by the common want of logic; for this merciful provision of nature, this buffer against collisions, this friction which upsets our calculations but without which existence would be intolerable, this crowning glory of human invention whereby we can be blind and see at one and the same moment, this blessed inconsistency, exists here as elsewhere; and though the strictest writers on morality have maintained that it is wicked for a woman to have children at all, inasmuch as it is wrong to be out of health that good may come, yet the necessity of the case has caused a general feeling in favour of passing over such events in silence, and of assuming their non-existence except in such flagrant cases as force themselves on the public notice. Against these the condemnation of society is inexorable, and if it is believed that the illness has been dangerous and protracted, it is almost impossible for a woman to recover her former position in society.

The above conventions struck me as arbitrary and cruel, but they put a stop to many fancied ailments; for the situation, so far from being considered interesting, is looked upon as savouring more or less distinctly of a very reprehensible condition of things, and the ladies take care to conceal it as long as they can even from their own husbands, in anticipation of a severe scolding as soon as the misdemeanour is discovered. Also the baby is kept out of sight, except on the day of signing the birth-formula, until it can walk and talk. Should the child unhappily die, a coroner's inquest is inevitable, but in order to avoid disgracing a family which may have been hitherto respected, it is almost invariably found that the child was over seventy-five years old, and died from the decay of nature.

MAHAINA

I CONTINUED my sojourn with the Nosnibors. In a few days Mr. Nosnibor had recovered from his flogging, and was looking forward with glee to the fact that the next would be the last. I did not think that there seemed any occasion even for this; but he said it was better to be on the safe side, and he would make up the dozen. He now went to his business as usual; and I understood that he was never more prosperous, in spite of his heavy fine. He was unable to give me much of his time during the day; for he was one of those valuable men who are paid, not by the year, month, week, or day, but by the minute. His wife and daughters, however, made much of me, and introduced me to their friends, who came in shoals to call upon me.

One of these persons was a lady called Mahaina. Zulora (the elder of my host's daughters) ran up to her and embraced her as soon as she entered the room, at the same time inquiring tenderly after her 'poor dipsomania'. Mahaina answered that it was just as bad as ever; she was a perfect martyr to it, and her excellent health was the only thing which consoled her under her affliction.

Then the other ladies joined in with condolences and the never-failing suggestions which they had ready for every mental malady. They recommended their own straightener and disparaged Mahaina's. Mrs. Nosnibor had a favourite nostrum, but I could catch little of its nature. I heard the words 'full confidence that the desire to drink will cease when the formula has been repeated . . . this confidence is *everything* . . . far from undervaluing a thorough determination never to touch spirits again . . . fail too often . . . formula a *certain cure* [with great emphasis] . . . prescribed form . . . full conviction.' The conversation then became more audible, and was carried on at considerable length. I should perplex myself and the reader by endeavouring to follow the ingenious perversity of all they said; enough, that in the course of time the visit came to an end, and Mahaina took her leave receiving affectionate embraces from all the ladies. I had remained in the background after the first ceremony of introduction, for I did not like the looks of Mahaina, and the conversation displeased me. When she left the room I had some consolation in the remarks called forth by her departure.

At first they fell to praising her very demurely. She was all this, that and the other, till I disliked her more and more at every word, and inquired how it was that the straighteners had not been able to cure her as they had cured Mr. Nosnibor.

There was a shade of significance on Mrs. Nosnibor's face as I said this, which seemed to imply that she did not consider Mahaina's case to be quite one for a straightener. It flashed across me that perhaps the poor woman did not drink at all. I knew that I ought not to have inquired, but I could not help it, and asked point blank whether she did or not.

'We can none of us judge of the condition of other people,' said Mrs.

Nosnibor in a gravely charitable tone and with a look towards Zulora.

'Oh, mamma,' answered Zulora, pretending to be half angry but rejoiced at being able to say out what she was already longing to insinuate, 'I don't believe a word of it. It's all indigestion. I remember staying in the house with her for a whole month last summer, and I am sure she never once touched a drop of wine or spirits. The fact is, Mahaina is a very weakly girl, and she pretends to get tipsy in order to win a forbearance from her friends to which she is not entitled. She is not strong enough for her calisthenic exercises, and she knows she would be made to do them unless her inability was referred to moral causes.'

Here the younger sister, who was ever sweet and kind, remarked that she thought Mahaina did tipple occasionally. 'I also think,' she added, 'that she sometimes takes poppy juice.'

'Well, then, perhaps she does drink sometimes,' said Zulora; 'but she would make us all think that she does it much oftener in order to hide her weakness.'

And so they went on for half an hour and more, bandying about the question as to how far their late visitor's intemperance was real or no. Every now and then they would join in some charitable commonplace, and would pretend to be all of one mind that Mahaina was a person whose bodily health would be excellent if it were not for her unfortunate inability to refrain from excessive drinking; but as soon as this appeared to be fairly settled they began to be uncomfortable until they had undone their work and left some serious imputation upon her constitution. At last, seeing that the debate had assumed the character of a cyclone or circular storm, going round and round and round and round till one could never say where it began nor where it ended, I made some apology for an abrupt departure and retired to my own room.

Here at least I was alone, but I was very unhappy. I had fallen upon a set of people who, in spite of their high civilization and many excellences, had been so warped by the mistaken views presented to them during childhood from generation to generation, that it was impossible to see how they could ever clear themselves. Was there nothing which I could say to make them feel that the constitution of a person's body was a thing over which he or she had had at any rate no initial control whatever, while the mind was a perfectly different thing, and capable of being created anew and directed according to the pleasure of its possessor? Could I never bring them to see that while habits of mind and character were entirely independent of initial mental force and early education, the body was so much a creature of parentage and circumstances, that no punishment for ill health should be ever tolerated save as a protection from contagion, and that even where punishment was inevitable it should be attended with compassion? Surely, if the unfortunate Mahaina were to feel that she could avow her bodily weakness without fear of being despised for her infirmities, and if there were medical men to whom she could fairly state her case, she should not hesitate about doing so through the fear of taking nasty medicine. It was possible that her malady was incurable (for I had heard enough to convince me that her dipsomania was only a pretence and that she was temperate in all her habits); in that case she might perhaps be justly subject to annoyances or even to restraint; but who could say whether she was curable or not, until she was able to make a clean breast of her symptoms instead of concealing them? In their eagerness to stamp out disease, these people overshot their mark; for people had become so clever at dissembling — they painted their faces with such consummate skill — they repaired the decay of time and the effects of mischance with such profound dissimulation — that it was really impossible to say whether anyone was well or ill till after an intimate acquaintance of months or years. Even then the shrewdest were constantly mistaken in their judgments, and marriages were often contracted with most deplorable results, owing to the art with which infirmity had been concealed.

It appeared to me that the first step towards the cure of disease should be the announcement of the fact to a person's near relations and friends. If anyone had a headache, he ought to be permitted within reasonable limits to say so at once, and to retire to his own bedroom and take a pill, without everyone's looking grave and tears being shed and all the rest of it. As it was, even upon hearing it whispered that somebody else was subject to headaches, a whole company must look as though they had never had a headache in their lives. It is true they were not very prevalent, for the people were the healthiest and most comely imaginable, owing to the severity with which ill health was treated; still, even the best were liable to be out of sorts sometimes, and there were few families that had not a medicine-chest in a cupboard somewhere.

CHAPTER FIFTEEN

THE MUSICAL BANKS

ON my return to the drawing-room, I found that the Mahaina current had expended itself. The ladies were just putting away their work and preparing to go out. I asked them where they were going. They answered with a certain air of reserve that they were going to the bank to get some money.

Now I had already collected that the mercantile affairs of the Erewhonians were conducted on a totally different system from our own; I had, however, gathered little hitherto, except that they had two distinct commercial systems, of which the one appealed more strongly to the imagination than anything to which we are accustomed in Europe, inasmuch as the banks that were conducted upon this system were decorated in the most profuse fashion, and all mercantile transactions were accompanied with music, so that they were called Musical Banks, though the music was hideous to a European ear.

As for the system itself I never understood it, neither can I do so now; they have a code in connection with it, which I have not the slightest doubt that they understand, but no foreigner can hope to do so. One rule runs into, and against, another as in a most complicated grammar, or as in Chinese pronunciation, wherein I am told that the slightest change in accentuation or tone of voice alters the meaning of a whole sentence. Whatever is incoherent in my description must be referred to the fact of my never having attained to a full comprehension of the subject.

So far, however, as I could collect anything certain, I gathered that they have two distinct currencies, each under the control of its own banks and mercantile codes. One of these (the one with the Musical Banks) was supposed to be *the* system, and to give out the currency in which all monetary transactions should be carried on; and as far as I could see, all who wished to be considered respectable, kept a larger or smaller balance at these banks. On the other hand, if there is one thing of which I am more sure than another, it is that the amount so kept had no direct commercial value in the outside world; I am sure that the managers and cashiers of the Musical Banks were not paid in their own currency. Mr. Nosnibor used to go to these banks, or rather to the great mother bank of the city, sometimes but not very often.

He was a pillar of one of the other kind of banks, though he appeared to hold some minor office also in the musical ones. The ladies generally went alone, as indeed was the case in most families, except on state occasions.

I had long wanted to know more of this strange system, and had the greatest desire to accompany my hostess and her daughters. I had seen them go out almost every morning since my arrival and had noticed that they carried their purses in their hands, not exactly ostentatiously, yet just so as that those who met them should see whither they were going. I had never, however, yet been asked to go with them myself.

It is not easy to convey a person's manner by words, and I can hardly give any idea of the peculiar feeling that came upon me when I saw the ladies on the point of starting for the bank. There was a something of regret, a something as though they would wish to take me with them, but did not like to ask me, and yet as though I were hardly to ask to be taken. I was determined, however, to bring matters to an issue with my hostess about my going with them, and after a little parleying, and many inquiries as to whether I was perfectly sure that I myself wished to go, it was decided that I might do so.

We passed through several streets of more or less considerable houses, and at last turning round a corner we came upon a large piazza, at the end of which was a magnificent building, of a strange but noble architecture and of great antiquity. It did not open directly on to the piazza, there being a screen, through which was an archway, between the piazza and the actual precincts of the bank. On passing under the archway we entered upon a green sward, round which there ran an arcade or cloister, while in front of us uprose the majestic towers of the bank and its venerable front, which was divided into three deep recesses and adorned with all sorts of marbles and many sculptures. On either side there were beautiful old trees wherein the birds were busy by the hundred, and a number of quaint but substantial houses of singularly comfortable appearance; they were situated in the midst of orchards and gardens, and gave me an impression of great peace and plenty.

Indeed it had been no error to say that this building was one that appealed to the imagination; it did more — it carried both imagination and judgment by storm. It was an epic in stone and marble, and so powerful was the effect it produced on me, that as I beheld it I was charmed and melted. I felt more conscious of the existence of a remote past. One knows of this always, but the knowledge is never so living as in the actual presence of some witness to the life of bygone ages. I felt how short a space of human life was the period of our own existence. I was more impressed with my own littleness, and much more inclinable to believe that the people whose sense of the fitness of things was equal to the upraising of so serene a handiwork, were hardly likely to be wrong in the conclusions they might come to upon any subject. My feeling certainly was that the currency of this bank must be the right one.

We crossed the sward and entered the building. If the outside had been impressive the inside was even more so. It was very lofty and divided into several parts by walls which rested upon massive pillars; the windows were filled with stained glass descriptive of the principal commercial incidents of the bank for many ages. In a remote part of the building there were men and boys singing; this was the only disturbing feature, for as the gamut was still unknown, there was no music in the country which could be agreeable to a European ear. The singers seemed to have derived their inspirations from the songs of birds and the wailing of the wind, which last they tried to imitate in melancholy cadences that at times degenerated into a howl. To my thinking the noise was hideous, but it produced a great effect upon my companions, who professed themselves much moved. As soon as the singing was over, the ladies requested me to stay where I was while they went inside the place from which it had seemed to come.

During their absence certain reflections forced themselves upon me.

In the first place, it struck me as strange that the building should be so nearly empty; I was almost alone, and the few besides myself had been led by curiosity, and had no intention of doing business with the bank. But there might be more inside. I stole up to the curtain, and ventured to draw the extreme edge of it on one side. No, there was hardly anyone there. I saw a large number of cashiers, all at their desks ready to pay cheques, and one or two who seemed to be the managing partners. I also saw my hostess and her daughters and two or three other ladies; also three or four old women and the boys from one of the neighbouring Colleges of Unreason; but there was no one else. This did not look as though the bank was doing a very large business; and yet I had always been told that every one in the city dealt with this establishment.

I cannot describe all that took place in these inner precincts, for a sinister-looking person in a black gown came and made unpleasant gestures at me for peeping. I happened to have in my pocket one of the Musical Bank pieces, which had been given me by Mrs. Nosnibor, so I tried to tip him with it; but having seen what it was, he became so angry that I had to give him a piece of the other kind of money to pacify him. When I had done this he became civil directly. As soon as he was gone I ventured to take a second look, and saw Zulora in the very act of giving a piece of paper which looked like a cheque to one of the cashiers. He did not examine it, but putting his hand into an antique coffer hard by, he pulled out a quantity of metal pieces apparently at random, and handed them over without counting them; neither did Zulora count them, but put them into her purse and went back to her seat after dropping a few pieces of the other coinage into an alms box that stood by the cashier's side. Mrs. Nosnibor and Arowhena then did likewise, but a little later they gave all (so far as I could see) that they had received from the cashier back to a verger, who I have no doubt put it back into the coffer from which it had been taken. They then began making towards the curtain; whereon I let it drop and retreated to a reasonable distance.

They soon joined me. For some few minutes we all kept silence, but at last I ventured to remark that the bank was not so busy today as it probably often was. On this Mrs. Nosnibor said that it was indeed melancholy to see what little heed people paid to the most precious of all institutions. I could say nothing in reply, but I have ever been of opinion that the greater part of mankind do approximately know where they get that which does them good.

Mrs. Nosnibor went on to say that I must not think there was any want of confidence in the bank because I had seen so few people there; the heart of the country was thoroughly devoted to these establishments, and any sign of their being in danger would bring in support from the most unexpected quarters. It was only because people knew them to be so very safe, that in some cases (as she lamented to say in Mr. Nosnibor's) they felt that their support was unnecessary. Moreover, these institutions never departed from the safest and most approved banking principles. Thus they never allowed interest on deposit, a thing now frequently done by certain bubble companies, which by doing an illegitimate trade had drawn many customers away; and even the shareholders were fewer than formerly, owing to the innovations of these unscrupulous persons, for the Musical Banks paid little or no dividend, but divided their profits by way of bonus on the original shares once in every thirty thousand years; and as it was now only two thousand years since there had been one of these distributions, people felt that they could not hope for another in their own time and preferred investments whereby they got some more tangible return; all which, she said, was very melancholy to think of.

Having made these last admissions, she returned to her original statement, namely, that every one in the country really supported these banks. As to the fewness of the people, and the absence of the able-bodied, she pointed out to me with some justice that this was exactly what we ought to expect. The men who were most conversant about the stability of human institutions, such as the lawyers, men of science, doctors, statesmen, painters and the like, were just those who were most likely to be misled by their own fancied accomplishments, and to be made unduly suspicious by their licentious desire for greater present return, which was at the root of nine-tenths of the opposition; by their vanity, which would prompt them to affect superiority to the prejudices of the vulgar; and by the stings of their own conscience, which was constantly upbraiding them in the most cruel manner on account of their bodies, which were generally diseased.

Let a person's intellect (she continued) be never so sound, unless his body is in absolute health, he can form no judgment worth having on matters of this kind. The body is everything; it need not perhaps be such a strong body (she said this because she saw that I was thinking of the old and infirm-looking folks whom I had seen in the bank,) but it must be in perfect health; in this case, the less active strength it had the more free would be the working of the intellect, and therefore the sounder the conclusion. The people, then, whom I had seen at the bank were in reality the very ones whose opinions were most worth having; they declared its advantages to be incalculable, and even professed to consider the immediate return to be far larger than they were entitled to; and so she ran on, nor did she leave off till we had got back to the house.

She might say what she pleased, but her manner carried no conviction, and later on I saw signs of general indifference to these banks that were not to be mistaken. Their supporters often denied it, but the denial was generally so couched as to add another proof of its existence. In commercial panics, and in times of general distress, the people as a mass did not so much as even think of turning to these banks. A few might do so, some from habit and early training, some from the instinct that prompts us to catch at any straw when we think ourselves drowning, but few from a genuine belief that the Musical Banks could save them from financial ruin, if they were unable to meet their engagements in the other kind of currency.

In conversation with one of the Musical Bank managers I ventured to hint this as plainly as politeness would allow. He said that it had been more or less true till lately; but that now they had put fresh stained-glass windows into all the banks in the country, and repaired the buildings, and enlarged the organs; the presidents, moreover, had taken to riding in omnibuses and talking nicely to people in the streets, and to remembering the ages of their children, and giving them things when they were naughty, so that all would henceforth go smoothly.

'But haven't you done anything to the money itself?' said I, timidly.

'It is not necessary,' he rejoined, 'not in the least necessary, I assure you.'

And yet anyone could see that the money given out at these banks was not that with which people bought their bread, meat and clothing. It was like it at a first glance, and was stamped with designs that were often of great beauty; it was not, again, a spurious coinage, made with the intention that it should be mistaken for the money in actual use; it was more like a toy money, or the counters used for certain games at cards; for, notwithstanding the beauty of the designs, the material on which they were stamped was as nearly valueless as possible. Some were covered with tinfoil, but the greater part were frankly of a cheap base metal the exact nature of which I was not able to determine. Indeed they were made of a great variety of metals, or, perhaps more accurately, alloys, some of which were hard, while others would bend easily and assume almost any form which their possessor might desire at the moment.

Of course everyone knew that their commercial value was *nil*, but all those who wished to be considered respectable thought it incumbent upon them to retain a few coins in their possession, and to let them be seen from time to time in their hands and purses. Not only this, but they would stick to it that the current coin of the realm was dross in comparison with the Musical Bank coinage. Perhaps, however, the strangest thing of all was that these very people would at times make fun in small ways of the whole system; indeed, there was hardly any insinuation against it which they would not tolerate and even applaud in their daily newspapers if written anonymously, while if the same thing were said without ambiguity to their faces — nominative case, verb and accusative being all in their right places, and doubt impossible — they would consider themselves very seriously and justly outraged, and accuse the speaker of being unwell.

I never could understand (neither can I quite do so now, though I begin to see better what they mean) why a single currency should not suffice them; it would seem to me as though all their dealings would have been thus greatly simplified; but I was met with a look of horror if ever I dared to hint at it. Even those who to my certain knowledge kept only just enough money at the Musical Banks to swear by, would call the other banks (where their securities really lay) cold, deadening, paralysing and the like.

I noticed another thing, moreover, which struck me greatly. I was taken to the opening of one of these banks in a neighbouring town, and saw a large assemblage of cashiers and managers. I sat opposite them and scanned their faces attentively. They did not please me; they lacked, with few exceptions, the true Erewhonian frankness; and an equal number from any other class would have looked happier and better men. When I met them in the streets they did not seem like other people, but had, as a general rule, a cramped expression upon their faces which pained and depressed me.

Those who came from the country were better; they seemed to have lived less as a separate class, and to be freer and healthier; but in spite of my seeing not a few whose looks were benign and noble, I could not help asking myself concerning the greater number of those whom I met, whether Erewhon would be a better country if their expression were to be transferred to the people in general. I answered myself emphatically, no. The expression on the faces of the high Ydgrunites was that which one would wish to diffuse, and not that of the cashiers.

A man's expression is his sacrament; it is the outward and visible sign of his inward and spiritual grace, or want of grace; and as I looked at the majority of these men, I could not help feeling that there must be a something in their lives which had stunted their natural development, and that they would have been more healthily minded in any other profession. I was always sorry for them, for in nine cases out of ten they were well-meaning persons; they were in the main very poorly paid; their constitutions were as a rule above suspicion; and there were recorded numberless instances of their self-sacrifice and generosity; but they had had the misfortune to have been betrayed into a false position at an age for the most part when their judgment was not matured, and after having been kept in studied ignorance of the real difficulties of the system. But this did not make their position the less a false one, and its bad effects upon themselves were unmistakable.

Few people would speak quite openly and freely before them, which struck me as a very bad sign. When they were in the room every one would talk as though all currency save that of the Musical Banks should be abolished; and yet they knew perfectly well that even the cashiers themselves hardly used the Musical Bank money more than other people. It was expected of them that they should appear to do so, but this was all. The less thoughtful of them did not seem particularly unhappy, but many were plainly sick at heart, though perhaps they hardly knew it, and would not have owned to being so. Some few were opponents of the whole system; but these were liable to be dismissed from their employment at any moment, and this rendered them very careful, for a man who had once been cashier at a Musical Bank was out of the field for other employment, and was generally unfitted for it by reason of that course of treatment which was commonly called his education. In fact it was a career from which retreat was virtually impossible, and into which young men were generally induced to enter before they could be reasonably expected, considering their training, to have formed any opinions of their own. Not unfrequently, indeed, they were induced, by what we in England should call undue influence, concealment and fraud. Few indeed were those who had the courage to insist on seeing both sides of the question before they committed themselves to what was practically a leap in the dark. One would have thought that caution in this respect was an elementary principle — one of the first things that an honourable man would teach his boy to understand; but in practice it was not so.

I even saw cases in which parents bought the right of presenting to the office of cashier at one of these banks, with the fixed determination that some one of their sons (perhaps a mere child) should fill it. There was the lad himself — growing up with every promise of becoming a good and honourable man — but utterly without warning concerning the iron shoe which his natural protector was providing for him. Who could say that the whole thing would not end in a lifelong lie, and vain chafing to escape? I confess that there were few things in Erewhon which shocked me more than this.

Yet we do something not so very different from this even in England,

and as regards the dual commercial system, all countries have, and have had, a law of the land, and also another law, which, though professedly more sacred, has far less effect on their daily life and actions. It seems as though the need for some law over and above, and sometimes even conflicting with, the law of the land, must spring from something that lies deep down in man's nature; indeed, it is hard to think that man could ever have become man at all, but for the gradual evolution of a perception that though this world looms so large when we are in it, it may seem a little thing when we have got away from it.

When man had grown to the perception that in the everlasting Is-and-Is-Not of nature, the world and all that it contains, including man, is at the same time both seen and unseen, he felt the need of two rules of life, one for the seen, and the other for the unseen side of things. For the laws affecting the seen world he claimed the sanction of seen powers; for the unseen (of which he knows nothing save that it exists and is powerful) he appealed to the unseen power (of which, again, he knows nothing save that it exists and is powerful) to which he gives the name of God.

Some Erewhonian opinions concerning the intelligence of the unborn embryo, that I regret my space will not permit me to lay before the reader, have led me to conclude that the Erewhonian Musical Banks, and perhaps the religious systems of all countries, are now more or less of an attempt to uphold the unfathomable and unconscious instinctive wisdom of millions of past generations, against the comparatively shallow, consciously reasoning and ephemeral conclusions drawn from that of the last thirty or forty.

The saving feature of the Erewhonian Musical Bank system (as distinct from the quasi-idolatrous views which coexist with it, and on which I will touch later) was that while it bore witness to the existence of a kingdom that is not of this world, it made no attempt to pierce the veil that hides it from human eyes. It is here that almost all religions go wrong. Their priests try to make us believe that they know more about the unseen world than those whose eyes are still blinded by the seen, can ever know — forgetting that while to deny the existence of an unseen kingdom is bad, to pretend that we know more about it than its bare existence is no better.

This chapter is already longer than I intended, but I should like to say that in spite of the saving feature of which I have just spoken, I cannot help thinking that the Erewhonians are on the eve of some great change in their religious opinions, or at any rate in that part of them which finds expression through their Musical Banks. So far as I could see, fully ninety per cent of the population of the metropolis looked upon these banks with something not far removed from contempt. If this is so, any such startling event as is sure to arise sooner or later, may serve as nucleus to a new order of things that will be more in harmony with both the heads and hearts of the people.

CHAPTER SIXTEEN

AROWHENA

THE reader will perhaps have learned by this time a thing which I had myself suspected before I had been twenty-four hours in Mr. Nosnibor's house — I mean, that though the Nosnibors showed me every attention, I could not cordially like them, with the exception of Arowhena who was quite different from the rest. They were not fair samples of Erewhonians. I saw many families with whom they were on visiting terms, whose manners charmed me more than I know how to say, but I never could get over my original prejudice against Mr. Nosnibor for having embezzled the money. Mrs. Nosnibor, too, was a very worldly woman, yet to hear her talk one would have thought that she was singularly the reverse; neither could I endure Zulora; Arowhena however was perfection.

She it was who ran all the little errands for her mother and Mr. Nosnibor and Zulora, and gave those thousand proofs of sweetness and unselfishness which some one member of a family is generally required to give. All day long it was Arowhena this and Arowhena that; but she never seemed to know that she was being put upon, and was always bright and willing from morning till evening. Zulora certainly was very handsome, but Arowhena was infinitely the more graceful of the two and was the very *ne plus ultra* of youth and beauty. I will not attempt to describe her, for anything that I could say would fall so far short of the reality as only to mislead the reader. Let him think of the very loveliest that he can imagine, and he will still be below the truth. Having said this much, I need hardly say that I had fallen in love with her.

She must have seen what I felt for her, but I tried my hardest not to let it appear even by the slightest sign. I had many reasons for this. I had no idea what Mr. and Mrs. Nosnibor would say to it; and I knew that Arowhena would not look at me (at any rate not yet) if her father and mother disapproved, which they probably would, considering that I had nothing except the pension of about a pound a day of our money which the King had granted me. I did not yet know of a more serious obstacle.

In the meantime, I may say that I had been presented at court, and was told that my reception had been considered as singularly gracious; indeed, I had several interviews both with the King and Queen, at which from time to time the Queen got everything from me that I had in the world, clothes and all, except the two buttons I had given to Yram, the loss of which seemed to annoy her a good deal. I was presented with a court suit, and her Majesty had my old clothes put upon a wooden dummy, on which they probably remain, unless they have been removed in consequence of my subsequent downfall. His Majesty's manners were those of a cultivated English gentleman. He was much pleased at hearing that our government was monarchical, and that the mass of the people were resolute that it should not be changed; indeed, I was so much encouraged by the evident pleasure with which he heard me, that I ventured to quote to him those beautiful lines of Shakespeare's:

> There's a divinity doth hedge a king,
> Rough hew him how we may;

but I was sorry I had done so afterwards, for I do not think his Majesty admired the lines as much as I could have wished.

There is no occasion for me to dwell further upon my experience of the court, but I ought perhaps to allude to one of my conversations with the King, inasmuch as it was pregnant with the most important consequences.

He had been asking me about my watch, and inquiring whether such dangerous inventions were tolerated in the country from which I came. I owned with some confusion that watches were not uncommon; but observing the gravity which came over his Majesty's face I presumed to say that they were fast dying out, and that we had few if any other mechanical contrivances of which he was likely to disapprove. Upon his asking me to name some of our most advanced machines, I did not

dare to tell him of our steam-engines and railroads and electric tele-
graphs, and was puzzling my brains to think what I could say, when,
of all things in the world, balloons suggested themselves, and I gave
him an account of a very remarkable ascent which was made some
years ago. The King was too polite to contradict, but I felt sure that he
did not believe me, and from that day forward though he always
showed me the attention which was due to my genius (for in this light
was my complexion regarded), he never questioned me about the
manners and customs of my country.

To return, however, to Arowhena. I soon gathered that neither Mr.
nor Mrs. Nosnibor would have any objection to my marrying into the
family; a physical excellence is considered in Erewhon as a set-off
against almost any other disqualification, and my light hair was
sufficient to make me an eligible match. But along with this welcome
fact I gathered another which filled me with dismay; I was expected to
marry Zulora, for whom I had already conceived a great aversion.

At first I hardly noticed the little hints and the artifices which were
resorted to in order to bring us together, but after a time they became
too plain. Zulora, whether she was in love with me or not, was bent on
marrying me, and I gathered in talking with a young gentleman of my
acquaintance who frequently visited the house and whom I greatly
disliked, that it was considered a sacred and inviolable rule that whoever
married into a family must marry the eldest daughter at that time unmarried. The young gentleman urged this upon me so frequently that
I at last saw he was in love with Arowhena himself, and wanted me to
get Zulora out of the way; but others told me the same story as to the
custom of the country, and I saw there was a serious difficulty. My
only comfort was that Arowhena snubbed my rival and would not
look at him. Neither would she look at me; nevertheless there was a
difference in the manner of her disregard; this was all I could get
from her.

Not that she avoided me; on the contrary I had many a *tête-à-tête*
with her, for her mother and sister were anxious for me to deposit some
part of my pension in the Musical Banks, this being in accordance with
the dictates of their goddess Ydgrun, of whom both Mrs. Nosnibor and
Zulora were great devotees. I was not sure whether I had kept
my secret from being perceived by Arowhena herself, but none of
the others suspected me, so she was set upon me to get me to open an
account, at any rate *pro forma* with the Musical Banks; and I need

hardly say that she succeeded. But I did not yield at once, I enjoyed the process of being argued with too keenly to lose it by a prompt concession; besides, a little hesitation rendered the concession itself more valuable. It was in the course of conversations on this subject that I learned the more defined religious opinions of the Erewhonians, that coexist with the Musical Bank system, but are not recognized by those curious institutions. I will describe them as briefly as possible in the following chapters before I return to the personal adventures of Arowhena and myself.

They were idolaters, though of a comparatively enlightened kind; but here, as in other things, there was a discrepancy between their professed and actual belief, for they had a genuine and potent faith which existed without recognition alongside of their idol worship.

The gods whom they worship openly are personifications of human qualities, as justice, strength, hope, fear, love, etc. etc. The people think that prototypes of these have a real objective existence in a region far beyond the clouds, holding, as did the ancients, that they are like men and women both in body and passion, except that they are even comelier and more powerful, and also that they can render themselves invisible to human eyesight. They are capable of being propitiated by mankind and of coming to the assistance of those who ask their aid. Their interest in human affairs is keen, and on the whole beneficent; but they become very angry if neglected, and punish rather the first they come upon, than the actual person who has offended them; their fury being blind when it is raised, though never raised without reason. They will not punish with any less severity when people sin against them from ignorance, and without the chance of having had knowledge; they will take no excuses of this kind, but are even as the English law, which assumes itself to be known to everyone.

Thus they have a law that two pieces of matter may not occupy the same space at the same moment, which law is presided over and administered by the gods of time and space jointly, so that if a flying stone and a man's head attempt to outrage these gods, by 'arrogating a right which they do not possess' (for so it is written in one of their books), and to occupy the same space simultaneously, a severe punishment, sometimes even death itself, is sure to follow, without any regard to whether the stone knew that the man's head was there, or the head the stone; this at least is their view of the common accidents of life. Moreover, they hold their deities to be quite regardless of motives. With them it is the thing done which is everything, and the motive goes for nothing.

Thus they hold it strictly forbidden for a man to go without common air in his lungs for more than a very few minutes; and if by any chance he gets into the water, the air-god is very angry, and will not suffer it; no matter whether the man got into the water by accident or on purpose, whether through the attempt to save a child or through presumptuous contempt of the air-god, the air-god will kill him, unless he keeps his head high enough out of the water, and thus gives the air-god his due.

This with regard to the deities who manage physical affairs. Over and above these they personify hope, fear, love and so forth, giving them temples and priests, and carving likenesses of them in stone, which they verily believe to be faithful representations of living beings who are only not human in being more than human. If anyone denies the objective existence of these divinities, and says that there is really no such being as a beautiful woman called Justice, with her eyes blinded and a pair of scales, positively living and moving in a remote and ethereal region, but that justice is only the personified expression of certain modes of human thought and action — they say that he denies the existence of justice in denying her personality, and that he is a wanton disturber of men's religious convictions. They detest nothing so much as any attempt to lead them to higher spiritual conceptions of the deities whom they profess to worship. Arowhena and I had a pitched battle on this point, and should have had many more but for my prudence in allowing her to get the better of me.

I am sure that in her heart she was suspicious of her own position for she returned more than once to the subject. 'Can you not see,' I had exclaimed, 'that the fact of justice being admirable will not be affected by the absence of a belief in her being also a living agent? Can you really think that men will be one whit less hopeful because they no longer believe that hope is an actual person?' She shook her head, and said that with men's belief in the personality all incentive to the reverence of the thing itself, as justice or hope, would cease; men from that hour would never be either just or hopeful again.

I could not move her, nor, indeed, did I seriously wish to do so. She deferred to me in most things, but she never shrank from maintaining her opinions if they were put in question; nor does she to this day abate one jot of her belief in the religion of her childhood, though in com-

pliance with my repeated entreaties she has allowed herself to be baptized into the English Church. She has, however, made a gloss upon
her original faith to the effect that her baby and I are the only human
beings exempt from the vengeance of the deities for not believing in
their personality. She is quite clear that we are exempted. She should
never have so strong a conviction of it otherwise. How it has come
about she does not know, neither does she wish to know; there are
things which it is better not to know and this is one of them; but when
I tell her that I believe in her deities as much as she does — and that it
is a difference about words, not things, she becomes silent with a slight
emphasis.

I own that she very nearly conquered me once; for she asked me
what I should think if she were to tell me that my God, whose nature
and attributes I had been explaining to her, was but the expression for
man's highest conception of goodness, wisdom and power; that in
order to generate a more vivid conception of so great and glorious a
thought, man had personified it and called it by a name; that it was an
unworthy conception of the Deity to hold Him personal, inasmuch as
escape from human contingencies became thus impossible; that the real
thing men should worship was the Divine, whereinsoever they could
find it; that 'God' was but man's way of expressing his sense of the
Divine; that as justice, hope, wisdom, etc., were all parts of goodness,
so God was the expression which embraced all goodness and all good
power; that people would no more cease to love God on ceasing to
believe in His objective personality, than they had ceased to love justice
on discovering that she was not really personal; nay, that they would
never truly love Him till they saw Him thus.

She said all this in her artless way, and with none of the coherence
with which I have here written it; her face kindled, and she felt sure
that she had convinced me that I was wrong, and that justice was a
living person. Indeed I did wince a little; but I recovered myself
immediately, and pointed out to her that we had books whose genuine-
ness was beyond all possibility of doubt, as they were certainly none of
them less than 1800 years old; that in these there were the most authentic accounts of men who had been spoken to by the Deity Himself,
and of one prophet who had been allowed to see the back parts of God
through the hand that was laid over his face.

This was conclusive; and I spoke with such solemnity that she was a
little frightened, and only answered that they too had their books, in

which their ancestors had seen the gods; on which I saw that further argument was not at all likely to convince her; and fearing that she might tell her mother what I had been saying, and that I might lose the hold upon her affections which I was beginning to feel pretty sure that I was obtaining, I began to let her have her own way, and to convince me; neither till after we were safely married did I show the cloven hoof again.

Nevertheless, her remarks have haunted me, and I have since met with many very godly people who have had a great knowledge of divinity, but no sense of the divine; and again, I have seen a radiance upon the face of those who were worshipping the divine either in art or nature — in picture or statue — in field or cloud or sea — in man, woman or child — which I have never seen kindled by any talking about the nature and attributes of God. Mention but the word divinity, and our sense of the divine is clouded.

CHAPTER SEVENTEEN

YDGRUN AND THE YDGRUNITES

I N spite of all the to-do they make about their idols, and the temples they build, and the priests and priestesses whom they support, I could never think that their professed religion was more than skin-deep; but they had another which they carried with them into all their actions; and although no one from the outside of things would suspect it to have any existence at all, it was in reality their great guide, the mariner's compass of their lives; so that there were very few things which they ever either did, or refrained from doing, without reference to its precepts.

Now I suspected that their professed faith had no great hold upon them — firstly, because I often heard the priests complain of the prevailing indifference, and they would hardly have done so without reason; secondly, because of the show which was made, for there was none of this about the worship of the goddess Ydgrun, in whom they really did believe; thirdly, because though the priests were constantly abusing Ydgrun as being the great enemy of the gods, it was well known that she had no more devoted worshippers in the whole country than these very persons, who were often priests of Ydgrun rather than of their own deities. Neither am I by any means sure that these were not the best of the priests.

Ydgrun certainly occupied a very anomalous position; she was held to be both omnipresent and omnipotent, but she was not an elevated conception, and was sometimes both cruel and absurd. Even her most devoted worshippers were a little ashamed of her, and served her more with heart and in deed than with their tongues. Theirs was no lip service; on the contrary, even when worshipping her most devoutly, they would often deny her. Take her all in all, however, she was a beneficent and useful deity, who did not care how much she was denied so long as she was obeyed and feared, and who kept hundreds of thousands in those paths which make life tolerably happy, who would never have been kept there otherwise, and over whom a higher and more spiritual ideal would have had no power.

I greatly doubt whether the Erewhonians are yet prepared for any better religion, and though (considering my gradually strengthened conviction that they were the representatives of the lost tribes of Israel) I would have set about converting them at all hazards had I seen the remotest prospect of success, I could hardly contemplate the displacement of Ydgrun as the great central object of their regard without admitting that it would be attended with frightful consequences; in fact were I a mere philosopher, I should say that the gradual raising of the popular conception of Ydgrun would be the greatest spiritual boon which could be conferred upon them, and that nothing could effect this except example. I generally found that those who complained most loudly that Ydgrun was not high enough for them had hardly as yet come up to the Ydgrun standard, and I often met with a class of men whom I called to myself 'high Ydgrunites' (the rest being Ydgrunites, and low Ydgrunites), who, in the matter of human conduct and the affairs of life, appeared to me to have got about as far as it is in the right nature of man to go.

They were gentlemen in the full sense of the word; and what has one not said in saying this? They seldom spoke of Ydgrun, or even alluded to her, but would never run counter to her dictates without ample reason for doing so; in such cases they would override her with due self-reliance, and the goddess seldom punished them; for they are brave, and Ydgrun is not. They had most of them a smattering of the hypothetical language, and some few more than this, but only a few. I do not think that this language has had much hand in making them what they are; but rather that the fact of their being generally possessed of its rudiments was one great reason for the reverence paid to the hypothetical language itself.

Being inured from youth to exercises and athletics of all sorts, and living fearlessly under the eye of their peers, among whom there exists a high standard of courage, generosity, honour and every good and manly quality — what wonder that they should have become, so to speak, a law unto themselves; and, while taking an elevated view of the goddess Ydgrun, they should have gradually lost all faith in the recognized deities of the country? These they do not openly disregard, for conformity until absolutely intolerable is a law of Ydgrun, yet they have no real belief in the objective existence of beings which so readily explain themselves as abstractions, and whose personality demands a quasi-materialism which it baffles the imagination to realize. They keep their opinions, however, greatly to themselves, inasmuch as most of their countrymen feel strongly about the gods, and they hold it wrong to give pain, unless for some greater good than seems likely to arise from their plain speaking.

I always liked and admired these men, and although I could not help deeply regretting their certain ultimate perdition (for they had no sense of a hereafter, and their only religion was that of self-respect and consideration for other people), I never dared to take so great a liberty with them as to attempt to put them in possession of my own religious convictions, in spite of my knowing that they were the only ones which could make them really good and happy, either here or hereafter. I did try sometimes, being impelled to do so by a strong sense of duty, and by my deep regret that so much that was admirable should be doomed to ages if not eternity of torture; but the words stuck in my throat as soon as I began.

Whether a professional missionary might have a better chance I know not; such persons must doubtless know more about the science of conversion; for myself, I could only be thankful that I was in the right path, and was obliged to let others take their chance as yet. If the plan fails by which I propose to convert them myself, I would gladly contribute my mite towards the sending two or three trained missionaries, who have been known as successful converters of Jews and Mohammedans; but such have seldom much to glory in the flesh, and when I think of the high Ydgrunites, and of the figure which a missionary would probably cut among them, I cannot feel sanguine that much good would be arrived at. Still the attempt is worth making, and the worst danger to the missionaries themselves would be that of being sent to the hospital where Chowbok would have been sent had he come with me into Erewhon.

Taking then their religious opinions as a whole, I must own that the Erewhonians are superstitious, on account of the views which they hold of their professed gods, and their entirely anomalous and inexplicable worship of Ydgrun, a worship at once the most powerful, yet most devoid of formalism, that I ever met with; but in practice things worked better than might have been expected, and the conflicting claims of Ydgrun and the gods were arranged by unwritten compromises (for the most part in Ydgrun's favour), which in ninety-nine cases out of a hundred were very well understood.

I could not conceive why they should not openly acknowledge high Ydgrunism, and discard the objective personality of hope, justice, etc.; but whenever I so much as hinted at this, I found that I was on dangerous ground. They would never have it; returning constantly to the assertion that ages ago the divinities were frequently seen, and that the moment their personality was disbelieved in, men would leave off practising even those ordinary virtues which the common experience of mankind has agreed on as being the greatest secret of happiness. 'Who ever heard,' they asked, indignantly, 'of such things as kindly training, a good example and an enlightened regard to one's own welfare, being able to keep men straight?' In my hurry, forgetting things which I ought to have remembered, I answered that if a person could not be kept straight by these things, there was nothing that could straighten him, and that if he were not ruled by the love and fear of men whom he had seen, neither would he be so by that of the gods whom he had not seen.

At one time indeed I came upon a small but growing sect who believed, after a fashion, in the immortality of the soul and the resurrection from the dead; they taught that those who had been born with feeble and diseased bodies and had passed their lives in ailing, would be tortured eternally hereafter; but that those who had been born strong and healthy and handsome would be rewarded for ever and ever. Of moral qualities or conduct they made no mention.

Bad as this was, it was a step in advance, inasmuch as they did hold out a future state of some sort, and I was shocked to find that for the most part they met with opposition, on the score that their doctrine was based upon no sort of foundation, also that it was immoral in its tendency, and not to be desired by any reasonable beings.

When I asked how it could be immoral, I was answered that, if firmly held, it would lead people to cheapen this present life, making it appear to be an affair of only secondary importance; that it would thus distract men's minds from the perfecting of this world's economy, and was an impatient cutting, so to speak, of the Gordian knot of life's problems, whereby some people might gain present satisfaction to themselves at the cost of infinite damage to others; that the doctrine tended to encourage the poor in their improvidence, and in a debasing acquiescence in ills which they might well remedy; that the rewards were illusory and the result, after all, of luck, whose empire should be bounded by the grave; that its terrors were enervating and unjust; and that even the most blessed rising would be but the disturbing of a still more blessed slumber.

To all which I could only say that the thing had been actually known to happen, and that there were several well-authenticated instances of people having died and come to life again — instances which no man in his senses could doubt.

'If this be so,' said my opponent, 'we must bear it as best we may.'

I then translated for him, as well as I could, the noble speech of Hamlet in which he says that it is the fear lest worse evils may befall us after death which alone prevents us from rushing into death's arms.

'Nonsense,' he answered, 'no man was ever yet stopped from cutting his throat by any such fears as your poet ascribes to him — and your poet probably knew this perfectly well. If a man cuts his throat he is at bay, and thinks of nothing but escape, no matter whither, provided he can shuffle off his present. No. Men are kept at their posts, not by the fear that if they quit them they may quit a frying-pan for a fire, but by the hope that if they hold on, the fire may burn less fiercely. "The respect," to quote your poet, "that makes calamity of so long a life," is the consideration that though calamity may live long, the sufferer may live longer still.'

On this, seeing that there was little probability of our coming to an agreement, I let the argument drop, and my opponent presently left me with as much disapprobation as he could show without being overtly rude.

CHAPTER EIGHTEEN

BIRTH FORMULAE

I HEARD what follows not from Arowhena, but from Mr. Nosnibor and some of the gentlemen who occasionally dined at the house; they told me that the Erewhonians believe in pre-existence; and not only this (of which I will write more fully in the next chapter), but they believe that it is of their own free act and deed in a previous state that they come to be born into this world at all. They hold that the unborn are perpetually plaguing and tormenting the married of both sexes, fluttering about them incessantly, and giving them no peace either of mind or body until they have consented to take them under their protection. If this were not so (this at least is what they urge), it would be a monstrous freedom for one man to take with another, to say that he should undergo the chances and changes of this mortal life without any option in the matter. No man would have any right to get married at all, inasmuch as he can never tell what frightful misery his doing so may entail forcibly upon a being who cannot be unhappy as long as he does not exist. They feel this so strongly that they are resolved to shift the blame on to other shoulders; and have fashioned a long mythology as to the world in which the unborn people live, and what they do, and the arts and machinations to which they have recourse in order to get themselves into our own world. But of this more anon; what I would relate here is their manner of dealing with those who do come.

It is a distinguishing peculiarity of the Erewhonians that when they profess themselves to be quite certain about any matter, and avow it as a base on which they are to build a system of practice, they seldom quite believe in it. If they smell a rat about the precincts of a cherished institution, they will always stop their noses to it if they can.

This is what most of them did in this matter of the unborn, for I cannot (and never could) think that they seriously believed in their mythology concerning pre-existence; they did and they did not; they did not know themselves what they believed; all they did know was that it was a disease not to believe as they did. The only thing of which they were quite sure was that it was the pestering of the unborn which caused them to be brought into this world, and that they would not have been here if they would have only let peaceable people alone.

It would be hard to disprove this position, and they might have a good case if they would only leave it as it stands. But this they will not do; they must have assurance doubly sure; they must have the written word of the child itself as soon as it is born, giving the parents indemnity from all responsibility on the score of its birth, and asserting its own pre-existence. They have therefore devised something which they call a birth formula — a document which varies in words according to the caution of parents, but is much the same practically in all cases; for it has been the business of the Erewhonian lawyers during many ages to exercise their skill in perfecting it and providing for every contingency.

These formulae are printed on common paper at a moderate cost for the poor; but the rich have them written on parchment and handsomely bound, so that the getting up of a person's birth formula is a test of his social position. They commence by setting forth, That whereas A. B. was a member of the kingdom of the unborn, where he was well provided for in every way, and had no cause of discontent, etc. etc., he did of his own wanton depravity and restlessness conceive a desire to enter into this present world; that thereon having taken the necessary steps as set forth in laws of the unborn kingdom, he did with malice aforethought set himself to plague and pester two unfortunate people who had never wronged him, and who were quite contented and happy until he conceived this base design against their peace; for which wrong he now humbly entreats their pardon.

He acknowledges that he is responsible for all physical blemishes and deficiencies which may render him answerable to the laws of his country; that his parents have nothing whatever to do with any of these things; and that they have a right to kill him at once if they be so minded, though he entreats them to show their marvellous goodness and clemency by sparing his life. If they will do this, he promises to be their most obedient and abject creature during his earlier years, and indeed all his life, unless they should see fit in their abundant generosity to remit some portion of his service hereafter. And so the formula continues, going sometimes into very minute details, according to the fancies of family lawyers, who will not make it any shorter than they can help.

The deed being thus prepared, on the third or fourth day after the birth of the child, or as they call it, the 'final importunity', the friends gather together, and there is a feast held, where they are all very melancholy — as a general rule, I believe, quite truly so — and make presents to the father and mother of the child in order to console them for the injury which has just been done them by the unborn.

By-and-by the child himself is brought down by his nurse, and the company begin to rail upon him, upbraiding him for his impertinence, and asking him what amends he proposes to make for the wrong that he has committed, and how he can look for care and nourishment from those who have perhaps already been injured by the unborn on some ten or twelve occasions; for they say of people with large families, that they have suffered terrible injuries from the unborn; till at last, when this has been carried far enough, someone suggests the formula, which is brought out and solemnly read to the child by the family straightener. This gentleman is always invited on these occasions, for the very fact of intrusion into a peaceful family shows a depravity on the part of the child which requires his professional services.

On being teased by the reading and tweaked by the nurse, the child will commonly begin to cry, which is reckoned a good sign, as showing a consciousness of guilt. He is thereon asked, Does he assent to the formula? on which, as he still continues crying and can obviously make no answer, some one of the friends comes forward and undertakes to sign the document on his behalf, feeling sure (so he says) that the child would do it if he only knew how, and that he will release the present signer from his engagement on arriving at maturity. The friend then inscribes the signature of the child at the foot of the parchment, which is held to bind the child as much as though he had signed it himself.

Even this, however, does not fully content them, for they feel a little uneasy until they have got the child's own signature after all. So when he is about fourteen, these good people partly bribe him by promises of greater liberty and good things, and partly intimidate him through their great power of making themselves actively unpleasant to him, so that though there is a show of freedom made, there is really none; they also use the offices of the teachers in the Colleges of Unreason, till at last, in one way or another, they take very good care that he shall sign the paper by which he professes to have been a free agent in coming into the world, and to take all the responsibility of having done so on to his own shoulders. And yet, though this document is obviously the most important which anyone can sign in his whole life, they will have him do so at an age when neither they nor the law will for many a year allow anyone else to bind him to the smallest obligation, no matter how righteously he may owe it, because they hold him too young to know what he is about, and do not consider it fair that he should commit himself to anything that may prejudice him in after years.

I own that all this seemed rather hard, and not of a piece with the many admirable institutions existing among them. I once ventured to say a part of what I thought about it to one of the Professors of Unreason. I did it very tenderly, but his justification of the system was quite out of my comprehension. I remember asking him whether he did not think it would do harm to a lad's principles, by weakening his sense of the sanctity of his word and of truth generally, that he should be led into entering upon a solemn declaration as to the truth of things about which all that he can certainly know is that he knows nothing — whether, in fact, the teachers who so led him, or who taught anything as a certainty of which they were themselves uncertain, were not earning their living by impairing the truth-sense of their pupils (a delicate organization mostly,) and by vitiating one of their most sacred instincts.

The Professor, who was a delightful person, seemed greatly surprised at the view which I took, but it had no influence with him whatsoever. No one, he answered, expected that the boy either would or could know all that he said he knew; but the world was full of compromises; and there was hardly any affirmation which would bear being interpreted literally. Human language was too gross a vehicle of thought — thought being incapable of absolute translation. He added, that as there can be no translation from one language into another which shall not scant the meaning somewhat, or enlarge upon it, so there is no language which can render thought without a jarring and a harshness somewhere — and so forth; all of which seemed to come to this in the end, that it was the custom of the country, and that the Erewhonians were a conservative people; that the boy would have to begin compromising sooner or later, and this was part of his education in the art. It was perhaps to be regretted that compromise should be as necessary as it was; still it was necessary, and the sooner the boy got to understand it the better for himself. But they never tell this to the boy.

CHAPTER TWENTY

WHAT THEY MEAN BY IT

IN spite of not a few modifications in practice of a theory which is itself revolting, the relations between children and parents in that country are less happy than in Europe. It was rarely that I saw cases of real hearty and intense affection between the old people and the young ones. Here and there I did so, and was quite sure that the children, even at the age of twenty, were fonder of their parents than they were of anyone else; and that of their own inclination, being free to choose what company they would, they would often choose that of their father and mother. The straightener's carriage was rarely seen at the door of those houses. I saw two or three such cases during the time that I remained in the country, and cannot express the pleasure which I derived from a sight suggestive of so much goodness and wisdom and forbearance, so richly rewarded, yet I firmly believe that the same thing would happen in nine families out of ten if the parents were merely to remember how they felt when they were young, and actually to behave towards their children as they would have had their own parents behave towards themselves. But this, which would appear to be so simple and obvious, seems also to be a thing which not one in a hundred thousand is able to put in practice. It is only the very great and good who have any living faith in the simplest axioms; and there are few who are so holy as to feel that 19 and 13 make 32 as certainly as 2 and 2 make 4.

I am quite sure that if this narrative should ever fall into Erewhonian hands, it will be said that what I have written about the relations between parents and children being seldom satisfactory is an infamous perversion of facts, and that in truth there are few young people who do not feel happier in the society of their nearest relations[1] than in any other. Mr. Nosnibor would be sure to say this. Yet I cannot refrain from expressing an opinion that he would be a good deal embarrassed if his deceased parents were to reappear and propose to pay him a six months' visit. I doubt whether there are many things which he would regard as a greater infliction. They had died at a ripe old age some twenty years before I came to know him, so the case is an extreme one; but surely if they had treated him with what in his youth he had felt to

---

[1] What a *safe* word 'relation' is; how little it predicates! yet it has overgrown 'kinsman'.

be true unselfishness, his face would brighten when he thought of them to the end of his life.

In the one or two cases of true family affection which I met with, I am sure that the young people who were so genuinely fond of their fathers and mothers at eighteen, would at sixty be perfectly delighted were they to get the chance of welcoming them as their guests. There is nothing which could please them better, except perhaps to watch the happiness of their own children and grandchildren.

This is how things should be. It is not an impossible ideal; it is one which actually does exist in some few cases, and might exist in almost all, with a little more patience and forbearance upon the parents' part; but it is rare at present — so rare that they have a proverb which I can only translate in a very roundabout way, but which says that the great happiness of some people in a future state will consist in watching the distress of their parents on returning to eternal companionship with their grandfathers and grandmothers; whilst 'compulsory affection' is the idea which lies at the root of their word for the deepest anguish.

There is no talisman in the word 'parent' which can generate miracles of affection, and I can well believe that my own child might find it less of a calamity to lose both Arowhena and myself when he is six years old, than to find us again when he is sixty — a sentence which I would not pen did I not feel that by doing so I was giving him something like a hostage, or at any rate putting a weapon into his hands against me, should my selfishness exceed reasonable limits.

Money is at the bottom of all this to a great extent. If the parents would put their children in the way of earning a competence earlier than they do, the children would soon become self-supporting and independent. As it is, under the present system, the young ones get old enough to have all manner of legitimate wants (that is, if they have any 'go' about them) before they have learnt the means of earning money to pay for them; hence they must either do without them, or take more money than the parents can be expected to spare. This is due chiefly to the schools of Unreason, where a boy is taught upon hypothetical principles, as I will explain hereafter; spending years in being incapacitated for doing this, that, or the other (he hardly knows what), during all which time he ought to have been actually doing the thing itself, beginning at the lowest grades, picking it up through actual practice, and rising according to the energy which is in him.

These schools of Unreason surprised me much. It would be easy to fall into pseudo-utilitarianism, and I would fain believe that the system may be good for the children of very rich parents, or for those who show a natural instinct to acquire hypothetical lore; but the misery was that their Ydgrun-worship required all people with any pretence to respectability to send their children to some one or other of these schools, mulcting them of years of money. It astonished me to see what sacrifices the parents would make in order to render their children as nearly useless as possible; and it was hard to say whether the old suffered most from the expense which they were thus put to, or the young from being deliberately swindled in some of the most important branches of human inquiry, and directed into false channels or left to drift in the great majority of cases.

I cannot think I am mistaken in believing that the growing tendency to limit families by infanticide — an evil which was causing general alarm throughout the country — was almost entirely due to the way in which education had become a fetish from one end of Erewhon to the other. Granted that provisions should be made whereby every child should be taught reading, writing and arithmetic, but here compulsory state-aided education should end, and the child should begin (with all due precautions to ensure that he is not overworked) to acquire the rudiments of that art whereby he is to earn his living.

He cannot acquire these in what we in England call schools of technical education; such schools are cloister life as against the rough and tumble of the world; they unfit, rather than fit for work in the open. An art can only be learned in the workshop of those who are winning their bread by it.

Boys, as a rule, hate the artificial, and delight in the actual; give them the chance of earning, and they will soon earn. When parents find that their children, instead of being made artificially burdensome, will early begin to contribute to the well-being of the family, they will soon leave off killing them, and will seek to have that plenitude of offspring which they now avoid. As things are, the state lays greater burdens on parents than flesh and blood can bear, and then wrings its hands over an evil for which it is itself mainly responsible.

With the less well-dressed classes the harm was not so great; for among these, at about ten years old, the child has to begin doing something; if he is capable he makes his way up; if he is not, he is at any rate not made more incapable by what his friends are pleased to call his education. People find their level as a rule; and though they unfortunately sometimes miss it, it is in the main true that those who have valuable qualities are perceived to have them and can sell them. I think that the Erewhonians are beginning to become aware of these things, for there was much talk about putting a tax upon all parents whose children were not earning a competence according to their degrees by the time they were twenty years old. I am sure that if they will have the courage to carry it through they will never regret it; for the parents will take care that the children shall begin earning money (which means 'doing good' to society) at an early age; then the children will be independent early, and they will not press on the parents, nor the parents on them, and they will like each other better than they do now.

This is the true philanthropy. He who makes a colossal fortune in the hosiery trade, and by his energy has succeeded in reducing the price of woollen goods by the thousandth part of a penny in the pound — this man is worth ten professional philanthropists. So strongly are the Erewhonians impressed with this, that if a man has made a fortune of over £20,000 a year they exempt him from all taxation, considering him as a work of art, and too precious to be meddled with; they say, 'How very much he must have done for society before society could have been prevailed upon to give him so much money'; so magnificent an organization overawes them; they regard it as a thing dropped from heaven.

'Money,' they say, 'is the symbol of duty, it is the sacrament of having done for mankind that which mankind wanted. Mankind may not be a very good judge, but there is no better.' This used to shock me at first, when I remembered that it had been said on high authority that they who have riches shall enter hardly into the kingdom of heaven; but the influence of Erewhon had made me begin to see things in a new light, and I could not help thinking that they who have not riches shall enter more hardly still.

People oppose money to culture, and imply that if a man has spent his time in making money he will not be cultivated — fallacy of fallacies! As though there could be a greater aid to culture than the having earned an honourable independence, and as though any amount of culture will do much for the man who is penniless, except make him feel his position more deeply. The young man who was told to sell all his goods and give to the poor, must have been an entirely exceptional person if the advice was given wisely, either for him or for the poor; how much more often does it happen that we perceive a man to have all sorts of good qualities except money, and feel that his real duty lies in getting every halfpenny that he can persuade others to pay him for his services, and becoming rich. It has been said that the love of money is the root of all evil. The want of money is so quite as truly.

The above may sound irreverent, but it is conceived in a spirit of the most utter reverence for those things which do alone deserve it — that is, for the things which are, which mould us and fashion us, be they what they may; for the things that have power to punish us, and which will punish us if we do not heed them; for our masters therefore. But I am drifting away from my story.

They have another plan about which they are making a great noise and fuss, much as some are doing with women's rights in England. A party of extreme radicals have professed themselves unable to decide upon the superiority of age or youth. At present all goes on the supposition that it is desirable to make the young old as soon as possible. Some would have it that this is wrong, and that the object of education should be to keep the old young as long as possible. They say that each age should take it turn and turn about, week by week, one week the old to be top-sawyers, and the other the young, drawing the line at thirty-five years of age; but they insist that the young should be allowed to inflict corporal chastisement on the old, without which the old would be quite incorrigible. In any European country this would be out of the question; but it is not so there, for the straighteners are constantly ordering people to be flogged, so that they are familiar with the notion. I do not suppose that the idea will be ever acted upon; but its having been even mooted is enough to show the utter perversion of the Erewhonian mind.

CHAPTER TWENTY-ONE

THE COLLEGES OF UNREASON

I HAD now been a visitor with the Nosnibors for some five or six months, and though I had frequently proposed to leave them and take apartments of my own, they would not hear of my doing so. I suppose they thought I should be more likely to fall in love with Zulora if I remained, but it was my affection for Arowhena that kept me.

During all this time both Arowhena and myself had been dreaming, and drifting towards an avowed attachment, but had not dared to face the real difficulties of the position. Gradually, however, matters came to a crisis in spite of ourselves, and we got to see the true state of the case, all too clearly.

One evening we were sitting in the garden, and I had been trying in every stupid roundabout way to get her to say that she should be at any rate sorry for a man, if he really loved a woman who would not marry him. I had been stammering and blushing, and been as silly as anyone could be, and I suppose had pained her by fishing for pity for myself in such a transparent way, and saying nothing about her own need of it; at any rate, she turned upon me with a sweet sad smile and said, 'Sorry? I am sorry for myself; I am sorry for you; and I am sorry for everyone.' The words had no sooner crossed her lips than she bowed her head, gave me a look as though I were to make no answer, and left me.

The words were few and simple, but the manner with which they were uttered was ineffable; the scales fell from my eyes, and I felt that I had no right to try and induce her to infringe one of the most inviolable customs of her country, as she needs must do if she were to marry me. I sat for a long while thinking, and when I remembered the sin and shame and misery which an unrighteous marriage — for as such it would be held in Erewhon — would entail, I became thoroughly ashamed of myself for having been so long self-blinded. I write coldly now, but I suffered keenly at the time, and should probably retain a much more vivid recollection of what I felt, had not all ended so happily.

As for giving up the idea of marrying Arowhena, it never so much as entered my head to do so; the solution must be found in some other direction than this. The idea of waiting till somebody married Zulora was to be no less summarily dismissed. To marry Arowhena at once in Erewhon — this had already been abandoned; there remained therefore but one alternative, and that was to run away with her, and get her with me to Europe, where there would be no bar to our union save my own impecuniosity, a matter which gave me no uneasiness.

To this obvious and simple plan I could see but two objections that deserved the name — the first, that perhaps Arowhena would not come; the second, that it was almost impossible for me to escape even alone, for the King had himself told me that I was to consider myself a prisoner on parole, and that the first sign of my endeavouring to escape would cause me to be sent to one of the hospitals for incurables. Besides, I did not know the geography of the country, and even were I to try and find my way back, I should be discovered long before I had reached the pass over which I had come. How then could I hope to be able to take Arowhena with me? For days and days I turned these difficulties over in my mind, and at last hit upon as wild a plan as was ever suggested by extremity. This was to meet the second difficulty; the first gave me less uneasiness, for when Arowhena and I next met after our interview in the garden I could see that she had suffered not less acutely than myself.

I resolved that I would have another interview with her — the last for the present — that I would then leave her, and set to work upon maturing my plan as fast as possible. We got a chance of being alone together, and then I gave myself the loose rein, and told her how passionately and devotedly I loved her. She said little in return, but her tears (which I could not refrain from answering with my own) and the little she did say were quite enough to show me that I should meet with no obstacle from her. Then I asked her whether she would run a terrible risk which we should share in common, if, in case of success, I could take her to my own people, to the home of my mother and sisters, who would welcome her very gladly. At the same time I pointed out that the chances of failure were far greater than those of success, and that the probability was that even though I could get so far as to carry my design into execution, it would end in death to us both.

I was not mistaken in her; she said that she believed I loved her as much as she loved me, and that she would brave anything if I could only assure her that what I proposed would not be thought dishonourable in England; she could not live without me, and would rather die with me than alone; that death was perhaps the best for us both; that I must plan, and that when the hour came I was to send for her, and trust her not to fail me; and so after many tears and embraces, we tore ourselves away.

I then left the Nosnibors, took a lodging in the town, and became melancholy to my heart's content. Arowhena and I used to see each other sometimes, for I had taken to going regularly to the Musical Banks, but Mrs. Nosnibor and Zulora both treated me with considerable coldness. I felt sure that they suspected me. Arowhena looked miserable, and I saw that her purse was now always as full as she could fill it with the Musical Bank money — much fuller than of old. Then the horrible thought occurred to me that her health might break down, and that she might be subjected to a criminal prosecution. Oh! how I hated Erewhon at that time.

I was still received at court, but my good looks were beginning to fail me, and I was not such an adept at concealing the effects of pain as the Erewhonians are. I could see that my friends began to look concerned about me, and was obliged to take a leaf out of Mahaina's book, and pretend to have developed a taste for drinking. I even consulted a straightener as though this were so, and submitted to much discomfort. This made matters better for a time, but I could see that my friends thought less highly of my constitution as my flesh began to fall away.

I was told that the poor made an outcry about my pension, and I saw a stinging article in an anti-ministerial paper, in which the writer went so far as to say that my having light hair reflected little credit upon me, inasmuch as I had been reported to have said that it was a common thing in the country from which I came. I have reason to believe that Mr. Nosnibor himself inspired this article. Presently it came round to me that the King had begun to dwell upon my having been possessed of a watch, and to say that I ought to be treated medicinally for having told him a lie about the balloons. I saw misfortune gathering around me in every direction, and felt that I should have need of all my wits and a good many more, if I was to steer myself and Arowhena to a good conclusion.

There were some who continued to show me kindness, and strange to say, I received the most from the very persons from whom I should have least expected it — I mean from the cashiers of the Musical Banks. I had made the acquaintance of several of these persons, and now that I frequented their bank, they were inclined to make a good deal of me. One of them, seeing that I was thoroughly out of health, though of course he pretended not to notice it, suggested that I should take a little change of air and go down with him to one of the principal towns, which was some two or three days' journey from the metropolis, and the chief seat of the Colleges of Unreason; he assured me that I should be delighted with what I saw, and that I should receive a most hospitable welcome. I determined therefore to accept the invitation.

We started two or three days later, and after a night on the road, we arrived at our destination towards evening. It was now full spring, and as nearly as might be ten months since I had started with Chowbok on my expedition, but it seemed more like ten years. The trees were in their freshest beauty, and the air had become warm without being oppressively hot. After having lived so many months in the metropolis, the sight of the country, and the country villages through which we passed refreshed me greatly, but I could not forget my troubles. The last five miles or so were the most beautiful part of the journey, for the country became more undulating, and the woods were more extensive; but the first sight of the city of the colleges itself was the most delightful of all. I cannot imagine that there can be any fairer in the whole world, and I expressed my pleasure to my companion, and thanked him for having brought me.

We drove to an inn in the middle of the town, and then, while it was still light, my friend the cashier, whose name was Thims, took me for a stroll in the streets and in the court-yards of the principal colleges. Their beauty and interest were extreme; it was impossible to see them without being attracted towards them; and I thought to myself that he must be indeed an ill-grained and ungrateful person who can have been a member of one of these colleges without retaining an affectionate feeling towards it for the rest of his life. All my misgivings gave way at once when I saw the beauty and venerable appearance of this delightful city. For half an hour I forgot both myself and Arowhena.

After supper Mr. Thims told me a good deal about the system of education which is here practised. I already knew a part of what I heard, but much was new to me, and I obtained a better idea of the Erewhonian position than I had done hitherto; nevertheless there were parts of the scheme of which I could not comprehend the fitness, although I fully admit that this inability was probably the result of my having been trained so very differently and to my being then much out of sorts.

The main feature in their system is the prominence which they give to a study which I can only translate by the word 'hypothetics'. They argue thus – that to teach a boy merely the nature of the things which exist in the world around him, and about which he will have to be conversant during his whole life, would be giving him but a narrow and shallow conception of the universe, which it is urged might contain all manner of things which are not now to be found therein. To open his eyes to these possibilities, and so to prepare him for all sorts of emergencies, is the object of this system of hypothetics. To imagine a set of utterly strange and impossible contingencies, and require the youths to give intelligent answers to the questions that arise therefrom, is reckoned the fittest conceivable way of preparing them for the actual conduct of their affairs in after life.

Thus they are taught what is called the hypothetical language for many of their best years — a language which was originally composed at a time when the country was in a very different state of civilization to what it is at present, a state which has long since disappeared and been superseded. Many valuable maxims and noble thoughts which were at one time concealed in it have become current in their modern literature, and have been translated over and over again into the language now spoken. Surely then it would seem enough that the study of the original language should be confined to the few whose instincts led them naturally to pursue it.

But the Erewhonians think differently; the store they set by this hypothetical language can hardly be believed; they will even give anyone a maintenance for life if he attains a considerable proficiency in the study of it; nay, they will spend years in learning to translate some of their own good poetry into the hypothetical language — to do so with fluency being reckoned a distinguishing mark of a scholar and a gentleman. Heaven forbid that I should be flippant, but it appeared to me to be a wanton waste of good human energy that men should spend years and years in the perfection of so barren an exercise, when their own civilization presented problems by the hundred which cried aloud for solution and would have paid the solver handsomely; but people know their own affairs best. If the youths chose it for themselves I should have wondered less; but they do not choose it; they have it thrust upon them, and for the most part are disinclined towards it. I can only say that all I heard in defence of the system was insufficient to make me think very highly of its advantages.

The arguments in favour of the deliberate development of the unreasoning faculties were much more cogent. But here they depart from the principles on which they justify their study of hypothetics; for they base the importance which they assign to hypothetics upon the fact of their being a preparation for the extraordinary, while their study of Unreason rests upon its developing those faculties which are required for the daily conduct of affairs. Hence their professorships of Inconsistency and Evasion, in both of which studies the youths are examined before being allowed to proceed to their degree in hypothetics. The more earnest and conscientious students attain to a proficiency in these subjects which is quite surprising; there is hardly any inconsistency so glaring but they soon learn to defend it, or injunction so clear that they cannot find some pretext for disregarding it.

Life, they urge, would be intolerable if men were to be guided in all they did by reason and reason only. Reason betrays men into the drawing of hard and fast lines, and to the defining by language — language being like the sun, which rears and then scorches. Extremes are alone logical, but they are always absurd; the mean is illogical, but an illogical mean is better than the sheer absurdity of an extreme. There are no follies and no unreasonablenesses so great as those which can apparently be irrefragably defended by reason itself, and there is hardly an error into which men may not easily be led if they base their conduct upon reason only.

Reason might very possibly abolish the double currency; it might even attack the personality of Hope and Justice. Besides, people have such a strong natural bias towards it that they will seek it for themselves and act upon it quite as much as or more than is good for them; there is no need of encouraging reason. With unreason the case is different. She is the natural complement of reason, without whose existence reason itself were non-existent.

If, then, reason would be non-existent were there no such thing as unreason, surely it follows that the more unreason there is, the more reason there must be also? Hence the necessity for the development of unreason, even in the interests of reason herself. The Professors of Unreason deny that they undervalue reason; none can be more convinced than they are, that if the double currency cannot be rigorously deduced as a necessary consequence of human reason, the double currency should cease forthwith; but they say that it must be deduced from no narrow and exclusive view of reason which should deprive that admirable faculty of the one-half of its own existence. Unreason is a part of reason; it must therefore be allowed its full share in stating the initial conditions.

CHAPTER TWENTY-TWO

THE COLLEGES OF UNREASON — *continued*

OF genius they make no account, for they say that everyone is a genius, more or less. No one is so physically sound that no part of him will be even a little unsound, and no one is so diseased but that some part of him will be healthy — so no man is so mentally and morally sound, but that he will be in part both mad and wicked; and no man is so mad and wicked but he will be sensible and honourable in part. In like manner there is no genius who is not also a fool, and no fool who is not also a genius.

When I talked about originality and genius to some gentlemen whom I met at a supper party given by Mr. Thims in my honour, and said that original thought ought to be encouraged, I had to eat my words at once. Their view evidently was that genius was like offences — needs must that it come, but woe unto that man through whom it comes. A man's business, they hold, is to think as his neighbours do, for Heaven help him if he thinks good what they count bad. And really it is hard to see how the Erewhonian theory differs from our own, for the word 'idiot' only means a person who forms his opinions for himself.

The venerable Professor of Worldly Wisdom, a man verging on eighty but still hale, spoke to me very seriously on this subject in consequence of the few words that I had imprudently let fall in defence of genius. He was one of those who carried most weight in the university, and had the reputation of having done more perhaps than any other living man to suppress any kind of originality.

'It is not our business,' he said, 'to help students to think for themselves. Surely this is the very last thing which one who wishes them well should encourage them to do. Our duty is to ensure that they shall think as we do, or at any rate, as we hold it expedient to say we do.' In some respects, however, he was thought to hold somewhat radical opinions, for he was President of the Society for the Suppression of Useless Knowledge, and for the Completer Obliteration of the Past.

As regards the tests that a youth must pass before he can get a degree, I found that they have no class lists, and discourage anything like competition among the students; this, indeed, they regard as self-seeking and unneighbourly. The examinations are conducted by way of papers written by the candidate on set subjects, some of which are known to him beforehand, while others are devised with a view of testing his general capacity and *savoir faire*.

My friend the Professor of Worldly Wisdom was the terror of the greater number of students; and, so far as I could judge, he very well might be, for he had taken his Professorship more seriously than any of the other Professors had done. I heard of his having plucked one poor fellow for want of sufficient vagueness in his saving clauses paper. Another was sent down for having written an article on a scientific subject without having made free enough use of the words 'carefully', 'patiently' and 'earnestly'. One man was refused a degree for being too often and too seriously in the right, while a few days before I came a whole batch had been plucked for insufficient distrust of printed matter.

About this there was just then rather a ferment, for it seems that the Professor had written an article in the leading university magazine, which was well known to be by him, and which abounded in all sorts of plausible blunders. He then set a paper which afforded the examinees an opportunity of repeating these blunders — which, believing the article to be by their own examiner, they of course did. The Professor plucked every single one of them, but his action was considered to have been not quite handsome.

I told them of Homer's noble line to the effect that a man should strive ever to be foremost and in all things to outvie his peers; but they said that no wonder the countries in which such a detestable maxim was held in admiration were always flying at one another's throats.

'Why,' asked one Professor, 'should a man want to be better than his neighbours? Let him be thankful if he is no worse.'

I ventured feebly to say that I did not see how progress could be made in any art or science, or indeed in anything at all, without more or less self-seeking, and hence unamiability.

'Of course it cannot,' said the Professor, 'and therefore we object to progress.'

After which there was no more to be said. Later on, however, a young Professor took me aside and said he did not think I quite understood their views about progress.

'We like progress,' he said, 'but it must commend itself to the common sense of the people. If a man gets to know more than his neighbours he should keep his knowledge to himself till he has sounded them, and seen whether they agree, or are likely to agree with him.' He said it was as immoral to be too far in front of one's own age, as to lag too far behind it. 'If a man can carry his neighbours with him, he may say what he likes; but if not, what insult can be more gratuitous than the telling them what they do not want to know? A man should remember that intellectual over-indulgence is one of the most insidious and disgraceful forms that excess can take. Granted that everyone should exceed more or less, inasmuch as absolutely perfect sanity would drive any man mad the moment he reached it, but . . .'

He was now warming to his subject and I was beginning to wonder how I should get rid of him, when the party broke up, and though I promised to call on him before I left, I was unfortunately prevented from doing so.

I have now said enough to give English readers some idea of the strange views which the Erewhonians hold concerning unreason, hypothetics and education generally. In many respects they were sensible enough, but I could not get over the hypothetics, especially the turning their own good poetry into the hypothetical language. In the course of my stay I met one youth who told me that for fourteen years the hypothetical language had been almost the only thing that he had been taught, although he had never (to his credit, as it seemed to me) shown the slightest proclivity towards it, while he had been endowed with not inconsiderable ability for several other branches of human learning. He assured me that he would never open another hypothetical book after he had taken his degree, but would follow out the bent of his own inclinations. This was well enough, but who could give him his fourteen years back again?

I sometimes wondered how it was that the mischief done was not more clearly perceptible, and that the young men and women grew up as sensible and goodly as they did, in spite of the attempts almost deliberately made to warp and stunt their growth. Some doubtless received damage, from which they suffered to their life's end; but many seemed little or none the worse, and some, almost the better. The reason would seem to be that the natural instinct of the lads in most cases so absolutely rebelled against their training, that do what the teachers might they could never get them to pay serious heed to it. The consequence was that the boys only lost their time, and not so much of this as might have been expected, for in their hours of leisure they were actively engaged in exercises and sports which developed their physical nature, and made them at any rate strong and healthy.

Moreover, those who had any special tastes could not be restrained from developing them; they would learn what they wanted to learn and liked, in spite of obstacles which seemed rather to urge them on than to discourage them, while for those who had no special capacity, the loss of time was of comparatively little moment; but in spite of these alleviations of the mischief, I am sure that much harm was done to the children of the sub-wealthy classes, by the system which passes current among the Erewhonians as education. The poorest children suffered least — if destruction and death have heard the sound of wisdom, to a certain extent poverty has done so also.

And yet perhaps, after all, it is better for a country that its seats of learning should do more to suppress mental growth than to encourage it. Were it not for a certain priggishness which these places infuse into so great a number of their *alumni*, genuine work would become dangerously common. It is essential that by far the greater part of what is said or done in the world should be so ephemeral as to take itself away quickly; it should keep good for twenty-four hours, or even twice as long, but it should not be good enough a week hence to prevent people from going on to something else. No doubt the marvellous development of journalism in England, as also the fact that our seats of learning aim rather at fostering mediocrity than anything higher, is due to our subconscious recognition of the fact that it is even more necessary to check exuberance of mental development than to encourage it. There can be no doubt that this is what our academic bodies do, and they do it the more effectually because they do it only subconsciously. They think they are advancing healthy mental assimilation and digestion, whereas in reality they are little better than cancer in the stomach.

Let me return, however, to the Erewhonians. Nothing surprised me more than to see the occasional flashes of common sense with which one branch of study or another was lit up, while not a single ray fell upon so many others. I was particularly struck with this on strolling into the Art School of the University. Here I found that the course of study was divided into two branches — the practical and the commercial — no student being permitted to continue his studies in the actual practice of the art he had taken up, unless he made equal progress in its commercial history.

Thus those who were studying painting were examined at frequent intervals in the prices which all the leading pictures of the last fifty or a hundred years had realized, and in the fluctuations in their values when (as often happened) they had been sold and resold three of four times. The artist, they contend, is a dealer in pictures, and it is as important for him to learn how to adapt his wares to the market, and to know approximately what kind of a picture will fetch how much, as it is for him to be able to paint the picture. This, I suppose, is what the French mean by laying so much stress upon 'values'.

As regards the city itself, the more I saw the more enchanted I became. I dare not trust myself with any description of the exquisite beauty of the different colleges, and their walks and gardens. Truly in these things alone there must be a hallowing and refining influence which is in itself half an education, and which no amount of error can wholly spoil. I was introduced to many of the Professors, who showed me every hospitality and kindness; nevertheless I could hardly avoid a sort of suspicion that some of those whom I was taken to see had been so long engrossed in their own study of hypothetics that they had become the exact antitheses of the Athenians in the days of St. Paul; for whereas the Athenians spent their lives in nothing save to see and to hear some new thing, there were some here who seemed to devote themselves to the avoidance of every opinion with which they were not perfectly familiar, and regarded their own brains as a sort of sanctuary, to which if an opinion had once resorted, none other was to attack it.

I should warn the reader, however, that I was rarely sure what the men whom I met while staying with Mr. Thims really meant; for there was no getting anything out of them if they scented even a suspicion that they might be what they call 'giving themselves away'. As there is hardly any subject on which this suspicion cannot arise, I found it difficult to get definite opinions from any of them, except on such subjects as the weather, eating and drinking, holiday excursions or games of skill.

If they cannot wriggle out of expressing an opinion of some sort, they will commonly retail those of someone who has already written upon the subject, and conclude by saying that though they quite admit that there is an element of truth in what the writer has said, there are many points on which they are unable to agree with him. Which these points were, I invariably found myself unable to determine; indeed, it seemed to be counted the perfection of scholarship and good breeding among them not to have — much less to express — an opinion on any subject on which it might prove later that they had been mistaken. The art of sitting gracefully on a fence has never, I should think, been brought to greater perfection than at the Erewhonian Colleges of Unreason.

Even when, wriggle as they may, they find themselves pinned down to some expression of definite opinion, as often as not they will argue in support of what they perfectly well know to be untrue. I repeatedly met with reviews and articles even in their best journals, between the lines of which I had little difficulty in detecting a sense exactly contrary to the one ostensibly put forward. So well is this understood, that a man must be a mere tyro in the arts of Erewhonian polite society unless he instinctively suspects a hidden 'yea' in every 'nay' that meets him. Granted that it comes to much the same in the end, for it does not matter whether 'yea' is called 'yea' or 'nay', so long as it is understood which it is to be; but our own more direct way of calling a spade a spade, rather than a rake, with the intention that everyone should understand it as a spade, seems more satisfactory. On the other hand, the Erewhonian system lends itself better to the suppression of that downrightness which it seems the express aim of Erewhonian philosophy to discountenance.

However this may be, the fear-of-giving-themselves-away disease was fatal to the intelligence of those infected by it, and almost everyone at the Colleges of Unreason had caught it to a greater or less degree. After a few years atrophy of the opinions invariably supervened, and the sufferer became stone dead to everything except the more superficial aspects of those material objects with which he came most in contact. The expression on the faces of these people was repellent; they did not, however, seem particularly unhappy, for they none of them had the faintest idea that they were in reality more dead than alive. No cure for this disgusting fear-of-giving-themselves-away disease has yet been discovered.

It was during my stay in the city of the Colleges of Unreason — a city whose Erewhonian name is so cacophonous that I refrain from giving it—that I learned the particulars of the revolution which had ended in the destruction of so many of the mechanical inventions which were formerly in common use.

Mr. Thims took me to the rooms of a gentleman who had a great reputation for learning, but who was also, so Mr. Thims told me, rather a dangerous person, inasmuch as he had attempted to introduce an adverb into the hypothetical language. He had heard of my watch and been exceedingly anxious to see me, for he was accounted the most learned antiquary in Erewhon on the subject of mechanical lore. We fell to talking upon the subject, and when I left he gave me a reprinted copy of the work with brought the revolution about.

It had taken place some five hundred years before my arrival; people had long become thoroughly used to the change, although at the time that it was made the country was plunged into the deepest misery, and a reaction which followed had very nearly proved successful. Civil war raged for many years, and is said to have reduced the number of the inhabitants by one half. The parties were styled the machinists and the anti-machinists, and in the end, as I have said already, the latter got the victory, treating their opponents with such unparalleled severity that they extirpated every trace of opposition.

The wonder was that they allowed any mechanical appliances to remain in the kingdom, neither do I believe that they would have done so had not the Professors of Inconsistency and Evasion made a stand against the carrying of the new principles to their legitimate conclusions. These Professors, moreover, insisted that during the struggle the anti-machinists should use every known improvement in the art of war, and several new weapons, offensive and defensive, were invented while it was in progress. I was surprised at there remaining so many mechanical specimens as are seen in the museums, and at students having rediscovered their past uses so completely; for at the time of the revolution the victors wrecked all the more complicated machines, and burned all treatises on mechanics, and all engineers' workshops — thus, so they thought, cutting the mischief out root and branch, at an incalculable cost of blood and treasure.

Certainly they had not spared their labour, but work of this description can never be perfectly achieved; and when, some two hundred years before my arrival, all passion upon the subject had cooled down, and no one save a lunatic would have dreamed of reintroducing forbidden inventions, the subject came to be regarded as a curious antiquarian study, like that of some long-forgotten religious practices among ourselves. Then came the careful search for whatever fragments could be found, and for any machines that might have been hidden away, and also numberless treatises were written showing what the functions of each rediscovered machine had been; all being done with no idea of using such machinery again, but with the feelings of an

English antiquarian concerning Druidical monuments or flint arrow–
heads.

On my return to the metropolis, during the remaining weeks, or
rather days, of my sojourn in Erewhon I made a résumé in English of
the work which brought about the already mentioned revolution. My
ignorance of technical terms has led me doubtless into many errors,
and I have occasionally, where I found translation impossible, sub–
stituted purely English names and ideas for the original Erewhonian
ones, but the reader may rely on my general accuracy.[1]

THE VIEWS OF AN EREWHONIAN
PROPHET CONCERNING THE RIGHTS
OF ANIMALS

THE series of revolutions on which I shall now briefly touch shows
this even more plainly than the way (already dealt with) in which
at a later date they cut their throats in the matter of machinery;
for if the second of the two reformers of whom I am about to speak
had had his way — or rather the way that he professed to have — the
whole race would have died of starvation within a twelvemonth.
Happily common sense, though she is by nature the gentlest
creature living, when she feels the knife at her throat, is apt to develop
unexpected powers of resistance, and to send doctrinaires flying, even
when they have bound her down and think they have her at their
mercy. What happened, so far as I could collect it from the best
authorities, was as follows:

Some two thousand five hundred years ago the Erewhonians were
still uncivilized, and lived by hunting, fishing, a rude system of agricul–
ture and plundering such few other nations as they had not yet com–
pletely conquered. They had no schools or systems of philosophy, but
by a kind of dog-knowledge did that which was right in their own
eyes and in those of their neighbours; the common sense, therefore, of
the public being as yet unvitiated, crime and disease were looked upon
much as they are in other countries.

But with the gradual advance of civilization and increase in material

[1] The Book of the Machines has been omitted for reasons of space. See Introduction.

prosperity, people began to ask questions about things that they had hitherto taken as matters of course, and one old gentleman, who had great influence over them by reason of the sanctity of his life, and his supposed inspiration by an unseen power, whose existence was now beginning to be felt, took it into his head to disquiet himself about the rights of animals — a question that so far had disturbed nobody.

All prophets are more or less fussy, and this old gentleman seems to have been one of the more fussy ones. Being maintained at the public expense, he had ample leisure, and not content with limiting his attention to the rights of animals, he wanted to reduce right and wrong to rules, to consider the foundations of duty and of good and evil, and otherwise to put all sorts of matters on a logical basis, which people whose time is money are content to accept on no basis at all.

As a matter of course, the basis on which he decided that duty could alone rest was one that afforded no standing-room for many of the old-established habits of the people. These, he assured them, were all wrong, and whenever anyone ventured to differ from him, he referred the matter to the unseen power with which he alone was in direct communication, and the unseen power invariably assured him that he was right. As regards the rights of animals he taught as follows:

'You know,' he said, 'how wicked it is of you to kill one another. Once upon a time your forefathers made no scruple about not only killing, but also eating their relations. No one would now go back to such detestable practices, for it is notorious that we have lived much more happily since they were abandoned. From this increased prosperity we may confidently deduce the maxim that we should not kill and eat our fellow-creatures. I have consulted the higher power by whom you know that I am inspired, and he has assured me that this conclusion is irrefragable.

'Now it cannot be denied that sheep, cattle, deer, birds and fishes are our fellow-creatures. They differ from us in some respects, but those in which they differ are few and secondary, while those that they have in common with us are many and essential. My friends, if it was wrong of you to kill and eat your fellow-men, it is wrong also to kill and eat fish, flesh and fowl. Birds, beasts and fishes have as full a right to live as long as they can unmolested by man, as man has to live un-molested by his neighbours. These words, let me again assure you, are not mine, but those of the higher power which inspires me.

'I grant,' he continued, 'that animals molest one another, and that some of them go so far as to molest man, but I have yet to learn that we should model our conduct on that of the lower animals. We should endeavour, rather, to instruct them, and bring them to a better mind. To kill a tiger, for example, who has lived on the flesh of men and women whom he has killed, is to reduce ourselves to the level of the tiger, and is unworthy of people who seek to be guided by the highest principles in all, both their thoughts and actions.

'The unseen power who has revealed himself to me alone among you, has told me to tell you that you ought by this time to have out-grown the barbarous habits of your ancestors. If, as you believe, you know better than they, you should do better. He commands you, therefore, to refrain from killing any living being for the sake of eating it. The only animal food that you may eat, is the flesh of any birds, beasts or fishes that you may come upon as having died a natural death, or any that may have been born prematurely, or so deformed that it is a mercy to put them out of their pain; you may also eat all such animals as have committed suicide. As regards vegetables you may eat all those that will let you eat them with impunity.'

So wisely and so well did the old prophet argue, and so terrible were the threats he hurled at those who should disobey him, that in the end he carried the more highly educated part of the people with him, and presently the poorer classes followed suit, or professed to do so. Having seen the triumph of his principles, he was gathered to his fathers, and no doubt entered at once into full communion with that unseen power whose favour he had already so pre-eminently enjoyed.

He had not, however, been dead very long, before some of his more ardent disciples took it upon them to better the instruction of their master. The old prophet had allowed the use of eggs and milk, but his disciples decided that to eat a fresh egg was to destroy a potential chicken, and that this came to much the same as murdering a live one. Stale eggs, if it was quite certain that they were too far gone to be able to be hatched, were grudgingly permitted, but all eggs offered for sale had to be submitted to an inspector, who, on being satisfied that they were addled, would label them 'Laid not less than three months' from the date, whatever it might happen to be. These eggs, I need hardly say, were only used in puddings, and as a medicine in certain cases where an emetic was urgently required. Milk was forbidden inasmuch as it could not be obtained without robbing some calf of its natural sustenance, and thus endangering its life.

It will be easily believed that at first there were many who gave the new rules outward observance, but embraced every opportunity of indulging secretly in those flesh-pots to which they had been accustomed. It was found that animals were continually dying natural deaths under more or less suspicious circumstances. Suicidal mania, again, which had hitherto been confined exclusively to donkeys, became alarmingly prevalent even among such for the most part self-respecting creatures as sheep and cattle. It was astonishing how some of these unfortunate animals would scent out a butcher's knife if there was one within a mile of them, and run right up against it if the butcher did not get it out of their way in time.

Dogs, again, that had been quite law-abiding as regards domestic poultry, tame rabbits, sucking pigs or sheep and lambs, suddenly took to breaking beyond the control of their masters, and killing anything that they were told not to touch. It was held that any animal killed by a dog had died a natural death, for it was the dog's nature to kill things, and he had only refrained from molesting farm-yard creatures hitherto because his nature had been tampered with. Unfortunately the more these unruly tendencies became developed, the more the common people seemed to delight in breeding the very animals that would put temptation in the dog's way. There is little doubt, in fact, that they were deliberately evading the law; but whether this was so or no they sold or ate everything their dogs had killed.

Evasion was more difficult in the case of the larger animals, for the magistrates could not wink at all the pretended suicides of pigs, sheep and cattle that were brought before them. Sometimes they had to convict, and a few convictions had a very terrorizing effect — whereas in the case of animals killed by a dog, the marks of the dog's teeth could be seen, and it was practically impossible to prove malice on the part of the owner of the dog.

Another fertile source of disobedience to the law was furnished by a decision of one of the judges that raised a great outcry among the more fervent disciples of the old prophet. The judge held that it was lawful to kill any animal in self-defence, and that such conduct was so natural on the part of a man who found himself attacked, that the attacking creature should be held to have died a natural death. The High Vegetarians had indeed good reason to be alarmed, for hardly had this decision become generally known before a number of animals, hitherto harmless, took to attacking their owners with such ferocity, that it became necessary to put them to a natural death. Again, it was quite common at that time to see the carcase of a calf, lamb or kid exposed for sale with a label from the inspector certifying that it had been killed in self-defence. Sometimes even the carcase of a lamb or calf was exposed as 'warranted still-born', when it presented every appearance of having enjoyed at least a month of life.

As for the flesh of animals that had *bona fide* died a natural death, the permission to eat it was nugatory, for it was generally eaten by some other animal before man got hold of it; or failing this it was often poisonous, so that practically people were forced to evade the law by some of the means above spoken of, or to become vegetarians. This last alternative was so little to the taste of the Erewhonians, that the laws against killing animals were falling into desuetude, and would very likely have been repealed, but for the breaking out of a pestilence, which was ascribed by the priests and prophets of the day to the lawlessness of the people in the matter of eating forbidden flesh. On this, there was a reaction; stringent laws were passed, forbidding the use of meat in any form or shape, and permitting no food but grain, fruits and vegetables to be sold in shops and markets. These laws were enacted about two hundred years after the death of the old prophet who had first unsettled people's minds about the rights of animals; but they had hardly been passed before people again began to break them.

I was told that the most painful consequence of all this folly did not lie in the fact that law-abiding people had to go without animal food — many nations do this and seem none the worse, and even in flesh-eating countries such as Italy, Spain and Greece, the poor seldom see meat from year's end to year's end. The mischief lay in the jar which undue prohibition gave to the consciences of all but those who were strong enough to know that though conscience as a rule boons, it can also bane. The awakened conscience of an individual will often lead him to do things in haste that he had better have left undone, but the conscience of a nation awakened by a respectable old gentleman who has an unseen power up his sleeve will pave hell with a vengeance.

Young people were told that it was a sin to do what their fathers had done unhurt for centuries; those, moreover, who preached to them about the enormity of eating meat, were an unattractive academic folk, and though they overawed all but the bolder youths, there were few who did not in their hearts dislike them. However much the young person might be shielded, he soon got to know that men and women of the world — often far nicer people than the prophets who preached abstention — continually spoke sneeringly of the new doctrinaire laws, and were believed to set them aside in secret, though they dared not do so openly. Small wonder, then, that the more human among the student classes were provoked by the touch-not, taste-not, handle-not precepts of their rulers, into questioning much that they would otherwise have unhesitatingly accepted.

One sad story is on record about a young man of promising amiable disposition, but cursed with more conscience than brains, who had been told by his doctor (for as I have above said disease was not yet held to be criminal) that he ought to eat meat, law or no law. He was much shocked and for some time refused to comply with what he deemed the unrighteous advice given him by his doctor; at last, however, finding that he grew weaker and weaker, he stole secretly on a dark night into one of those dens in which meat was surreptitiously sold, and bought a pound of prime steak. He took it home, cooked it in his bedroom when everyone in the house had gone to rest, ate it, and though he could hardly sleep for remorse and shame, felt so much better next morning that he hardly knew himself.

Three or four days later, he again found himself irresistibly drawn to this same den. Again he bought a pound of steak, again he cooked and ate it, and again, in spite of much mental torture, on the following morning felt himself a different man. To cut the story short, though he never went beyond the bounds of moderation, it preyed upon his mind that he should be drifting, as he certainly was, into the ranks of the habitual law-breakers.

All the time his health kept on improving, and though he felt sure that he owed this to the beefsteaks, the better he became in body, the more his conscience gave him no rest; two voices were for ever ringing in his ears — the one saying, 'I am Common Sense and Nature; heed me, and I will reward you as I rewarded your fathers before you.' But the other voice said: 'Let not that plausible spirit lure you to your ruin. I am Duty; heed me, and I will reward you as I rewarded your fathers before you.'

Sometimes he even seemed to see the faces of the speakers. Common Sense looked so easy, genial and serene, so frank and fearless, that do what he might he could not mistrust her; but as he was on the point of following her, he would be checked by the austere face of Duty, so grave, but yet so kindly; and it cut him to the heart that from time to time he should see her turn pitying away from him as he followed after her rival.

The poor boy continually thought of the better class of his fellow-students, and tried to model his conduct on what he thought was theirs. 'They,' he said to himself, 'eat a beefsteak? Never.' But they most of them ate one now and again, unless it was a mutton chop that tempted them. And they used him for a model much as he did them. 'He,' they would say to themselves, 'eat a mutton chop? Never.' One night, however, he was followed by one of the authorities, who was always prowling about in search of law-breakers, and was caught coming out of the den with half a shoulder of mutton concealed about his person. On this, even though he had not been put in prison, he would have been sent away with his prospects in life irretrievably ruined; he therefore hanged himself as soon as he got home.

CHAPTER TWENTY-SEVEN

THE VIEWS OF AN EREWHONIAN PHILOSOPHER CONCERNING THE RIGHTS OF VEGETABLES

LET me leave this unhappy story, and return to the course of events among the Erewhonians at large. No matter how many laws they passed increasing the severity of the punishments inflicted on those who ate meat in secret, the people found means of setting them aside as fast as they were made. At times, indeed, they would become almost obsolete, but when they were on the point of being repealed, some national disaster or the preaching of some fanatic would reawaken the conscience of the nation, and people were imprisoned by the thousand for illicitly selling and buying animal food.

About six or seven hundred years, however, after the death of the old prophet, a philosopher appeared, who, though he did not claim to have any communication with an unseen power, laid down the law with as much confidence as if such a power had inspired him. Many think that this philosopher did not believe his own teaching, and, being in secret a great meat-eater, had no other end in view than reducing the prohibition against eating animal food to an absurdity, greater even than an Erewhonian Puritan would be able to stand.

Those who take this view hold that he knew how impossible it would be to get the nation to accept legislation that it held to be sinful; he knew also how hopeless it would be to convince people that it was not wicked to kill a sheep and eat it, unless he could show them that they must either sin to a certain extent, or die. He, therefore, it is believed, made the monstrous proposals of which I will now speak.

He began by paying a tribute of profound respect to the old prophet, whose advocacy of the rights of animals, he admitted, had done much to soften the national character, and enlarge its views about the sanctity of life in general. But he urged that times had now changed; the lesson of which the country had stood in need had been sufficiently learnt, while as regards vegetables much had become known that was not even suspected formerly, and which, if the nation was to persevere in that strict adherence to the highest moral principles which had been the secret of its prosperity hitherto, must necessitate a radical change in its attitude towards them.

It was indeed true that much was now known that had not been suspected formerly, for the people had had no foreign enemies, and, being both quick-witted and inquisitive into the mysteries of nature, had made extraordinary progress in all the many branches of art and science. In the chief Erewhonian museum I was shown a microscope of considerable power, that was ascribed by the authorities to a date much about that of the philosopher of whom I am now speaking, and was even supposed by some to have been the instrument with which he had actually worked.

This philosopher was Professor of Botany in the chief seat of learning then in Erewhon, and whether with the help of the microscope still preserved, or with another, had arrived at a conclusion now universally accepted among ourselves — I mean, that all, both animals and plants, have had a common ancestry, and that hence the second should be deemed as much alive as the first. He contended, therefore, that animals and plants were cousins, and would have been seen to be so, all along, if people had not made an arbitrary and unreasonable division between what they chose to call the animal and vegetable kingdoms.

He declared, and demonstrated to the satisfaction of all those who were able to form an opinion upon the subject, that there is no difference appreciable either by the eye, or by any other test, between a germ that will develop into an oak, a vine, a rose, and one that (given

148

its accustomed surroundings) will become a mouse, an elephant or a man.

He contended that the course of any germ's development was dictated by the habits of the germs from which it was descended, and of whose identity it had once formed part. If a germ found itself placed as the germs in the line of its ancestry were placed, it would do as its ancestors had done, and grow up into the same kind of organism as theirs. If it found the circumstances only a little different, it would make shift (successfully or unsuccessfully) to modify its development accordingly; if the circumstances were widely different, it would die, probably without an effort at self-adaptation. This, he argued, applied equally to the germs of plants and of animals.

He therefore connected all, both animal and vegetable development, with intelligence, either spent and now unconscious, or still unspent and conscious; and in support of his view as regards vegetable life, he pointed to the way in which all plants have adapted themselves to their habitual environment. Granting that vegetable intelligence at first sight appears to differ materially from animal, yet, he urged, it is like it in the one essential fact that though it has evidently busied itself about matters that are vital to the well-being of the organism that possesses it, it has never shown the slightest tendency to occupy itself with any-thing else. This, he insisted, is as great a proof of intelligence as any living being can give.

'Plants,' said he, 'show no sign of interesting themselves in human affairs. We shall never get a rose to understand that five times seven are thirty-five, and there is no use in talking to an oak about fluctuations in the price of stocks. Hence we say that the oak and the rose are unintelligent, and on finding that they do not understand our business conclude that they do not understand their own. But what can a creature who talks in this way know about intelligence? Which shows greater signs of intelligence? He, or the rose and oak?

'And when we call plants stupid for not understanding our business, how capable do we show ourselves of understanding theirs? Can we form even the faintest conception of the way in which a seed from a rose tree turns earth, air, warmth and water into a rose full-blown? Where does it get its colour from? From the earth, air, etc.? Yes — but how? Those petals of such ineffable texture — that hue that outvies the cheek of a child — that scent, again? Look at earth, air and water — these are all the raw material that the rose has got to work with; does it show any sign of want of intelligence in the alchemy with which it turns mud into rose leaves? What chemist can do anything comparable? Why does no one try? Simply because everyone knows that no human intelligence is equal to the task. We give it up. It is the rose's department; let the rose attend to it — and be dubbed unintelligent because it baffles us by the miracles it works, and the unconcerned business-like way in which it works them.

'See what pains, again, plants take to protect themselves against their enemies. They scratch, cut, sting, make bad smells, secrete the most dreadful poisons (which Heaven only knows how they contrive to make), cover their precious seeds with spines like those of a hedgehog, frighten insects with delicate nervous systems by assuming portentous shapes, hide themselves, grow in inaccessible places, and tell lies so plausibly as to deceive even their subtlest foes.

'They lay traps smeared with bird-lime, to catch insects, and persuade them to drown themselves in pitchers which they have made of their leaves, and fill with water; others make themselves, as it were, into living rat-traps, which close with a spring on any insect that settles upon them; others make their flowers into the shape of a certain fly that is a great pillager of honey, so that when the real fly comes it thinks that the flowers are bespoke, and goes on elsewhere. Some are so clever as even to overreach themselves, like the horse-radish, which gets pulled up and eaten for the sake of that pungency with which it protects itself against underground enemies. If, on the other hand, they think that any insect can be of service to them, see how pretty they make themselves.

'What is to be intelligent if to know how to do what one wants to do, and to do it repeatedly, is not to be intelligent? Some say that the rose seed does not want to grow into a rose bush. Why, then, in the name of all that is reasonable, does it grow? Likely enough it is unaware of the want that is spurring it on to action. We have no reason to suppose that a human embryo knows that it wants to grow into a baby, or a baby into a man. Nothing ever shows signs of knowing what it is either wanting or doing, when its conviction both as to what it wants, and how to get it, have been settled beyond further power of question. The less signs living creatures give of knowing what they do, provided they do it, and do it repeatedly and well, the greater proof they give that in reality they know how to do it, and have done it already on an infinite number of past occasions.

'Someone may say,' he continued: ' "What do you mean by talking about an infinite number of past occasions? When did a rose seed make itself into a rose bush on any past occasion?"

'I answer this question with another. "Did the rose seed ever form part of the identity of the rose bush on which it grew?" Who can say that it did not? Again I ask: "Was this rose bush ever linked by all those links that we commonly consider as constituting personal identity, with the seed from which it in its turn grew?" Who can say that it was not?

'Then, if rose seed number two is a continuation of the personality of its parent rose bush, and if that rose bush is a continuation of the personality of the rose seed from which it sprang, rose seed number two must also be a continuation of the personality of the earlier rose seed. And this rose seed must be a continuation of the personality of the preceding rose seed — and so back and back *ad infinitum*. Hence it is impossible to deny continued personality between any existing rose seed and the earliest seed that can be called a rose seed at all.

'The answer, then, to our objector is not far to seek. The rose seed did what it now does in the persons of its ancestors — to whom it has been so linked as to be able to remember what those ancestors did when they were placed as the rose seed now is. Each stage of development brings back the recollection of the course taken in the preceding stage, and the development has been so often repeated, that all doubt — and with all doubt, all consciousness of action — is suspended.

'But an objector may still say: "Granted that the linking between all successive generations has been so close and unbroken, that each one of them may be conceived as able to remember what it did in the persons of its ancestors — how do you show that it actually did remember?"

'The answer is: "By the action which each generation takes — an action which repeats all the phenomena that we commonly associate with memory — which is explicable on the supposition that it has been guided by memory — and which has neither been explained, nor seems ever likely to be explained on any other theory than the supposition that there is an abiding memory between successive generations."

'Will anyone bring an example of any living creature, whose action we can understand, performing an ineffably difficult and intricate action, time after time, with invariable success, and yet not knowing how to do it, and never having done it before? Show me the example and I will say no more, but until it is shown me, I shall credit action where I cannot watch it, with being controlled by the same laws as when it is within our ken. It will become unconscious as soon as the skill that directs it has become perfected. Neither rose seed, therefore, nor embryo should be expected to show signs of knowing that they know what they know — if they showed such signs, the fact of their knowing what they want, and how to get it, might more reasonably be doubted.'

Some of the passages already given in chapter xxiii were obviously inspired by the one just quoted. As I read it, in a reprint shown me by a Professor who had edited much of the early literature on the subject, I could not but remember the one in which our Lord tells His disciples to consider the lilies of the field, who neither toil nor spin, but whose raiment surpasses even that of Solomon in all his glory.

'They toil not, neither do they spin'? Is that so? 'Toil not'? Perhaps not, now that the method of procedure is so well known as to admit of no further question — but it is not likely that lilies came to make themselves so beautifully without having ever taken any pains about the matter. 'Neither do they spin'? Not with a spinning-wheel; but is there no textile fabric in a leaf?

What would the lilies of the field say if they heard one of us declaring that they neither toil nor spin? They would say, I take it, much what we should if we were to hear of their preaching humility on the text of Solomons, and saying, 'Consider the Solomons in all their glory, they toil not neither do they spin.' We should say that the lilies were talking about things that they did not understand, and that though the Solomons do not toil nor spin, yet there had been no lack of either toiling or spinning before they came to be arrayed so gorgeously.

Let me now return to the Professor. I have said enough to show the general drift of the arguments on which he relied in order to show that vegetables are only animals under another name, but have not stated his case in anything like the fullness with which he laid it before the public. The conclusion he drew, or pretended to draw, was that if it was sinful to kill and eat animals, it was not less sinful to do the like by vegetables, or their seeds. None such, he said, should be eaten, save what had died a natural death, such as fruit that was lying on the ground and about to rot, or cabbage-leaves that had turned yellow in late autumn. These and other like garbage he declared to be the only food that might be eaten with a clear conscience. Even so the eater must plant the pips of any apples or pears that he may have eaten, or any plum-stones, cherry-stones, and the like, or he would come near to incurring the guilt of infanticide. The grain of cereals, according to him, was out of the question, for every such grain had a living soul as much as man had, and had as good a right as man to possess that soul in peace.

Having thus driven his fellow-countrymen into a corner at the point of a logical bayonet, from which they felt that there was no escape, he proposed that the question what was to be done should be referred to an oracle in which the whole country had the greatest confidence, and to which recourse was always had in times of special perplexity. It was whispered that a near relation of the philosopher's was lady's-maid to the priestess who delivered the oracle, and the Puritan party declared that the strangely unequivocal answer of the oracle was obtained by backstairs influence; but whether this was so or no, the response as nearly as I can translate it was as follows:

> He who sins aught
> Sins more than he ought;
> But he who sins nought
> Has much to be taught.
> Beat or be beaten,
> Eat or be eaten,
> Be killed or kill;
> Choose which you will.

It was clear that this response sanctioned, at any rate, the destruction of vegetable life when wanted as food by man; and so forcibly had the philosopher shown that what was sauce for vegetables was so also for animals, that, though the Puritan party made a furious outcry, the acts forbidding the use of meat were repealed by a considerable majority. Thus, after several hundred years of wandering in the wilderness of philosophy, the country reached the conclusions that common sense had long since arrived at. Even the Puritans, after a vain attempt to subsist on a kind of jam made of apples and yellow cabbage-leaves, succumbed to the inevitable, and resigned themselves to a diet of roast beef and mutton, with all the usual adjuncts of a modern dinner-table.

One would have thought that the dance they had been led by the old prophet, and that still madder dance which the Professor of Botany had gravely, but as I believe insidiously, proposed to lead them, would have made the Erewhonians for a long time suspicious of prophets whether they professed to have communications with an unseen power or no; but so engrained in the human heart is the desire to believe that some people really do know what they say they know, and can thus save them from the trouble of thinking for themselves, that in a short time would-be philosophers and faddists became more powerful than ever, and gradually led their countrymen to accept all those absurd views of life, some account of which I have given in my earlier chapters. Indeed, I can see no hope for the Erewhonians till they have got to understand that reason, uncorrected by instinct, is as bad as instinct uncorrected by reason.

CHAPTER TWENTY-EIGHT

ESCAPE

THOUGH busily engaged in translating the extracts given in the last five chapters, I was also laying matters in train for my escape with Arowhena. And indeed it was high time, for I received an intimation from one of the cashiers of the Musical Banks, that I was to be prosecuted in a criminal court ostensibly for measles, but really for having owned a watch, and attempted the reintroduction of machinery.

I asked, why measles? and was told that there was a fear lest extenuating circumstances should prevent a jury from convicting me, if I were indicted for typhus or smallpox, but that a verdict would probably be obtained for measles, a disease which could be sufficiently punished in a person of my age. I was given to understand that unless some unexpected change should come over the mind of his Majesty, I might expect the blow to be struck within a very few days.

My plan was this — that Arowhena and I should escape in a balloon together. I fear that the reader will disbelieve this part of my story, yet in no other have I endeavoured to adhere more conscientiously to facts, and can only throw myself upon his charity.

I had already gained the ear of the Queen, and had so worked upon her curiosity that she promised to get leave for me to have a balloon made and inflated; I pointed out to her that no complicated machinery would be wanted — nothing, in fact, but a large quantity of oiled silk, a car, a few ropes, etc. etc., and some light kind of gas, such as the antiquarians who were acquainted with the means employed by the ancients for the production of the lighter gases could easily instruct her workmen how to provide. Her eagerness to see so strange a sight as the ascent of a human being into the sky overcame any scruples of conscience that she might have otherwise felt, and she set the antiquarians about showing her workmen how to make the gas, and sent her maids to buy, and oil, a very large quantity of silk (for I was determined that the balloon should be a big one), even before she began to try and gain the King's permission; this, however, she now set herself to do, for I had sent her word that my prosecution was imminent.

As for myself, I need hardly say that I knew nothing about balloons; nor did I see my way to smuggling Arowhena into the car; nevertheless, knowing that we had no other chance of getting away from Erewhon, I drew inspiration from the extremity in which we were placed, and made a pattern from which the Queen's workmen were able to work successfully. Meanwhile the Queen's carriage-builders set about making the car, and it was with the attachments of this to the balloon that I had the greatest difficulty; I doubt, indeed, whether I should have succeeded here, but for the great intelligence of a foreman, who threw himself heart and soul into the matter, and often both foresaw requirements, the necessity for which had escaped me, and suggested the means of providing for them.

It happened that there had been a long drought, during the latter part of which prayers had been vainly offered up in all the temples of the air god. When I first told her Majesty that I wanted a balloon, I said my intention was to go up into the sky and prevail upon the air god by means of a personal interview. I own that this proposition bordered on the idolatrous, but I have long since repented of it, and am little likely ever to repeat the offence. Moreover, the deceit, serious though it was, will probably lead to the conversion of the whole country.

When the Queen told his Majesty of my proposal, he at first not only ridiculed it, but was inclined to veto it. Being, however, a very uxorious husband, he at length consented — as he eventually always did to everything on which the Queen had set her heart. He yielded all the more readily now, because he did not believe in the possibility of my ascent: he was convinced that even though the balloon should mount afew feet into the air, it would collapse immediately, whereon I should fall and break my neck, and he should be rid of me. He demonstrated this to her so convincingly, that she was alarmed, and tried to talk me into giving up the idea, but on finding that I persisted in my wish to have the balloon made, she produced an order from the King to the effect that all facilities I might require should be afforded me.

At the same time her Majesty told me that my attempted ascent would be made an article of impeachment against me in case I did not succeed in prevailing on the air god to stop the drought. Neither King nor Queen had any idea that I meant going right away if I could get the wind to take me, nor had they any conception of the existence of a certain steady upper current of air which was always setting in one direction, as could be seen by the shape of the higher clouds, which pointed invariably from south-east to north-west. I had myself long noticed this peculiarity in the climate, and attributed it, I believe justly, to a trade wind which was constant at a few thousand feet above the earth, but was disturbed by local influences at lower elevations.

My next business was to break the plan to Arowhena, and to devise the means for getting her into the car. I felt sure that she would come with me, but had made up my mind that if her courage failed her, the whole thing should come to nothing. Arowhena and I had been in constant communication through her maid, but I had thought it best not to tell her the details of my scheme till everything was settled. The time had now arrived, and I arranged with the maid that I should be admitted by a private door into Mr. Nosnibor's garden at about dusk on the following evening.

I came at the appointed time; the girl let me into the garden and bade me wait in a secluded alley until Arowhena should come. It was now early summer, and the leaves were so thick upon the trees that even though someone else had entered the garden I could have easily hidden myself. The night was one of extreme beauty; the sun had long set, but there was still a rosy gleam in the sky over the ruins of the railway station; below me was the city already twinkling with lights, while beyond it stretched the plains for many a league until they blended with the sky. I just noted these things, but I could not heed them. I could heed nothing, till, as I peered into the darkness of the alley, I perceived a white figure gliding swiftly towards me. I bounded towards it, and ere thought could either prompt or check, I had caught Arowhena to my heart and covered her unresisting cheek with kisses.

So overjoyed were we that we knew not how to speak; indeed, I do not know when we should have found words and come to our senses, if the maid had not gone off into a fit of hysterics, and awakened us to the necessity of self-control; then, briefly and plainly, I unfolded what I proposed; I showed her the darkest side, for I felt sure that the darker the prospect the more likely she was to come. I told her that my plan would probably end in death for both of us, and that I dared not press it — that at a word from her it should be abandoned; still that there was just a possibility of our escaping together to some part of the world where there would be no bar to our getting married, and that I could see no other hope.

She made no resistance, not a sign or hint of doubt or hesitation. She would do all I told her, and come whenever I was ready; so I bade her send her maid to meet me nightly — told her that she must put a good face on, look as bright and happy as she could, so as to make her father and mother and Zulora think that she was forgetting me — and be ready at a moment's notice to come to the Queen's workshops, and be concealed among the ballast and under rugs in the car of the balloon; and so we parted.

I hurried my preparations forward, for I feared rain, and also that the King might change his mind; but the weather continued dry, and in another week the Queen's workmen had finished the balloon and car, while the gas was ready to be turned on into the balloon at any moment. All being now prepared I was to ascend on the following morning. I had stipulated for being allowed to take abundance of rugs and wrappings as protection from the cold of the upper atmosphere, and also ten or a dozen good-sized bags of ballast.

I had nearly a quarter's pension in hand, and with this I fee'd Arowhena's maid, and bribed the Queen's foreman — who would, I believe, have given me assistance even without a bribe. He helped me to secrete food and wine in the bags of ballast, and on the morning of my ascent he kept the other workmen out of the way while I got Arowhena into the car. She came with early dawn, muffled up, and in her maid's dress. She was supposed to be gone to an early performance at one of the Musical Banks, and told me that she should not be missed till breakfast, but that her absence must then be discovered. I arranged the ballast about her so that it should conceal her as she lay at the bottom of the car, and covered her with wrappings. Although it still wanted some hours of the time fixed for my ascent, I could not trust myself one moment from the car, so I got into it at once, and watched the gradual inflation of the balloon. Luggage I had none, save the provisions hidden in the ballast bags, the books of mythology, and the treatises on the machines, with my own manuscript diaries and translations.

I sat quietly, and awaited the hour fixed for my departure — quiet outwardly, but inwardly I was in an agony of suspense lest Arowhena's absence should be discovered before the arrival of the King and Queen, who were to witness my ascent. They were not due yet for another two hours, and during this time a hundred things might happen, any one of which would undo me.

At last the balloon was full; the pipe which had filled it was removed, the escape of the gas having been first carefully precluded. Nothing remained to hinder the balloon from ascending but the hands and weight of those who were holding on to it with ropes. I strained my eyes for the coming of the King and Queen, but could see no sign of their approach. I looked in the direction of Mr. Nosnibor's house — there was nothing to indicate disturbance, but it was not yet breakfast time. The crowd began to gather; they were aware that I was under the displeasure of the court, but I could detect no signs of my being unpopular. On the contrary, I received many kindly expressions of regard and encouragement, with good wishes as to the result of my journey.

I was speaking to one gentleman of my acquaintance, and telling him the substance of what I intended to do when I had got into the presence of the air god (what he thought of me I cannot guess, for I am sure that he did not believe in the objective existence of the air god, nor that I myself believed in it), when I became aware of a small crowd of people running as fast as they could from Mr. Nosnibor's house towards the Queen's workshops. For the moment my pulse ceased beating, and then, knowing that the time had come when I must either do or die, I called vehemently to those who were holding the ropes (some thirty men) to let go at once, and made gestures signifying danger, and that there would be mischief if they held on longer. Many obeyed; the rest were too weak to hold on to the ropes, and were forced to let them go. On this the balloon bounded suddenly upwards, but my own feeling was that the earth had dropped off from me, and was sinking fast into the open space beneath.

This happened at the very moment that the attention of the crowd was divided, the one half paying heed to the eager gestures of those coming from Mr. Nosnibor's house, and the other to the exclamations

from myself. A minute more and Arowhena would doubtless have
been discovered, but before that minute was over, I was at such a height
above the city that nothing could harm me, and every second both the
town and the crowd became smaller and more confused. In an
incredibly short time, I could see little but a vast wall of blue plains
rising up against me, towards whichever side I looked.

At first, the balloon mounted vertically upwards, but after about five
minutes, when we had already attained a very great elevation, I fancied
that the objects on the plain beneath began to move from under me. I
did not feel so much as a breath of wind, and could not suppose that the
balloon itself was travelling. I was, therefore, wondering what this
strange movement of fixed objects could mean, when it struck me that
people in a balloon do not feel the wind inasmuch as they travel with
it and offer it no resistance. Then I was happy in thinking that I must
now have reached the invariable trade wind of the upper air, and that
I should be very possibly wafted for hundreds or even thousands of
miles, far from Erewhon and the Erewhonians.

Already I had removed the wrappings and freed Arowhena; but I
soon covered her up with them again, for it was already very cold, and
she was half stupefied with the strangeness of her position.

And now began a time, dream-like and delirious, of which I do not
suppose that I shall ever recover a distinct recollection. Some things I
can recall — as that we were ere long enveloped in vapour which froze
upon my moustache and whiskers; then comes a memory of sitting for
hours and hours in a thick fog, hearing no sound but my own breathing
and Arowhena's (for we hardly spoke) and seeing no sight but the car
beneath us and beside us, and the dark balloon above.

Perhaps the most painful feeling when the earth was hidden was that
the balloon was motionless, though our only hope lay in our going
forward with an extreme of speed. From time to time through a rift
in the clouds I caught a glimpse of earth, and was thankful to perceive
that we must be flying forward faster than in an express train; but no
sooner was the rift closed than the old conviction of our being
stationary returned in full force, and was not to be reasoned with; there
was another feeling also which was nearly as bad; for as a child that
fears it has gone blind in a long tunnel if there is no light, so ere the
earth had been many minutes hidden, I became half frightened lest we
might not have broken away from it clean and for ever. Now and
again, I ate and gave food to Arowhena, but by guess-work as regards

time. Then came darkness, a dreadful dreary time, without even the moon to cheer us.

With dawn the scene was changed; the clouds were gone and morning stars were shining; the rising of the splendid sun remains still impressed upon me as the most glorious that I have ever seen; beneath us there was an embossed chain of mountains with snow fresh fallen upon them; but we were far above them; we both of us felt our breathing seriously affected, but I would not allow the balloon to descend a single inch, not knowing for how long we might not need all the buoyancy which we could command; indeed I was thankful to find that, after nearly four-and-twenty hours, we were still at so great a height above the earth.

In a couple of hours we had passed the ranges, which must have been some hundred and fifty miles across, and again I saw a tract of level plain extending far away to the horizon. I knew not where we were, and dared not descend, lest I should waste the power of the balloon, but I was half hopeful that we might be above the country from which I had originally started. I looked anxiously for any sign by which I could recognize it, but could see nothing, and feared that we might be above some distant part of Erewhon, or a country inhabited by savages. While I was still in doubt, the balloon was again wrapped in clouds, and we were left to blank space and to conjectures.

The weary time dragged on. How I longed for my unhappy watch! I felt as though not even time was moving, so dumb and spellbound were our surroundings. Sometimes I would feel my pulse, and count its beats for half an hour together; anything to mark the time — to prove that it was there, and to assure myself that we were within the blessed range of its influence, and not gone adrift into the timelessness of eternity.

I had been doing this for the twentieth or thirtieth time, and had fallen into a light sleep; I dreamed wildly of a journey in an express train, and of arriving at a railway station where the air was full of the sound of locomotive engines blowing off steam with a horrible and tremendous hissing; I woke frightened and uneasy, but the hissing and crashing noises pursued me now that I was awake, and forced me to own that they were real. What they were I knew not, but they grew gradually fainter and fainter, and after a time were lost. In a few hours the clouds broke, and I saw beneath me that which made the chilled blood run colder in my viens. I saw the sea, and nothing but the sea;

in the main black, but flecked with white heads of storm-tossed, angry waves.

Arowhena was sleeping quietly at the bottom of the car, and as I looked at her sweet and saintly beauty, I groaned, and cursed myself for the misery into which I had brought her; but there was nothing for it now.

I sat and waited for the worst, and presently I saw signs as though that worst were soon to be at hand, for the balloon had begun to sink. On first seeing the sea I had been impressed with the idea that we must have been falling but now there could be no mistake, we were sinking, and that fast. I threw out a bag of ballast, and for a time we rose again, but in the course of a few hours the sinking recommenced, and I threw out another bag.

Then the battle commenced in earnest. It lasted all that afternoon and through the night until the following evening. I had seen never a sail nor a sign of a sail, though I had half blinded myself with straining my eyes incessantly in every direction; we had parted with everything but the clothes which we had upon our backs; food and water were gone, all thrown out to the wheeling albatrosses, in order to save us a few hours or even minutes from the sea. I did not throw away the books till we were within a few feet of the water, and clung to my manuscripts to the very last. Hope there seemed none whatever — yet, strangely enough we were neither of us utterly hopeless, and even when the evil that we dreaded was upon us, and that which we greatly feared had come, we sat in the car of the balloon with the waters up to our middle, and still smiled with a ghastly hopefulness to one another.

He who has crossed the St. Gothard will remember that below Andermatt there is one of those Alpine gorges which reach the very utmost limits of the sublime and terrible. The feelings of the traveller have become more and more highly wrought at every step, until at last the naked and overhanging precipices seem to close above his head, as he crosses a bridge hung in mid-air over a roaring waterfall, and enters on the darkness of a tunnel, hewn out of the rock.

What can be in store for him on emerging? Surely something even wilder and more desolate than that which he has seen already; yet his imagination is paralysed, and can suggest no fancy or vision of anything to surpass the reality which he has just witnessed. Awed and breathless he advances; when lo! the light of the afternoon sun welcomes him as he leaves the tunnel, and behold a smiling valley — a babbling brook, a village with tall belfries, and meadows of brilliant green — these are the things which greet him, and he smiles to himself as the terror passes away and in another moment is forgotten.

So fared it now with ourselves. We had been in the water some two or three hours, and the night had come upon us. We had said farewell for the hundredth time, and had resigned ourselves to meet the end; indeed I was myself battling with a drowsiness from which it was only too probable that I should never wake, when suddenly Arowhena touched me on the shoulder, and pointed to a light and to a dark mass which was bearing right upon us. A cry for help — loud and clear and shrill — broke forth from both of us at once, and in another five minutes we were carried by kind and tender hands on to the deck of an Italian vessel.

CHAPTER TWENTY-NINE

CONCLUSION

T H E ship was the *Principe Umberto*, bound from Callao to Genoa; she carried a number of emigrants to Rio, had gone thence to Callao, where she had taken in a cargo of guano, and was now on her way home. The captain was a certain Giovanni Gianni, a native of Sestri; he has kindly allowed me to refer to him in case the truth of my story should be disputed; but I grieve to say that I suffered him to mislead himself in some important particulars. I should add that when we were picked up we were a thousand miles from land.

As soon as we were on board, the captain began questioning us about the siege of Paris, from which city he had assumed that we must have come, notwithstanding our immense distance from Europe. As may be supposed, I had not heard a syllable about the war between France and Germany, and was too ill to do more than assent to all that he chose to put into my mouth. My knowledge of Italian is very imperfect, and I gathered little from anything that he said; but I was glad to conceal the true point of our departure, and resolved to take any cue that he chose to give me.

The line that thus suggested itself was that there had been ten or twelve others in the balloon, that I was an English Milord, and Arowhena a Russian Countess; that all the others had been drowned,

162

and that the dispatches which we had carried were lost. I came afterwards to learn that this story would not have been credible, had not the captain been for some weeks at sea, for I found that when we were picked up, the Germans had already long been masters of Paris. As it was, the captain settled the whole story for me, and I was well content.

In a few days we sighted an English vessel bound from Melbourne to London with wool. At my earnest request in spite of stormy weather which rendered it dangerous for a boat to take us from one ship to the other, the captain consented to signal the English vessel, and we were received on board, but we were transferred with such difficulty that no communication took place as to the manner of our being found. I did indeed hear the Italian mate who was in charge of the boat shout out something in French to the effect that we had been picked up from a balloon, but the noise of the wind was so great, and the captain understood so little French that he caught nothing of the truth, and it was assumed that we were two persons who had been saved from shipwreck. When the captain asked me in what ship I had been wrecked, I said that a party of us had been carried out to sea in a pleasure-boat by a strong current, and that Arowhena (whom I described as a Peruvian lady) and I were alone saved.

There were several passengers, whose goodness towards us we can never repay. I grieve to think that they cannot fail to discover that we did not take them fully into our confidence; but had we told them all, they would not have believed us, and I was determined that no one should hear of Erewhon, or have the chance of getting there before me, as long as I could prevent it. Indeed, the recollection of the many falsehoods which I was then obliged to tell, would render my life miserable were I not sustained by the consolations of my religion. Among the passengers there was a most estimable clergyman, by whom Arowhena and I were married within a very few days of our coming on board.

After a prosperous voyage of about two months, we sighted the Land's End, and in another week we were landed at London. A liberal subscription was made for us on board the ship, so that we found ourselves in no immediate difficulty about money. I accordingly took Arowhena down into Somersetshire, where my mother and sisters had resided when I last heard of them. To my great sorrow I found that my mother was dead, and that her death had been accelerated by the report of my having been killed, which had been brought to my employer's station by Chowbok. It appeared that he must have waited for a few days to see whether I returned, that he then considered it safe to assume that I should never do so, and had accordingly made up a story about my having fallen into a whirlpool of seething waters while coming down the gorge homeward. Search was made for my body, but the rascal had chosen to drown me in a place where there would be no chance of its ever being recovered.

My sisters were both married, but neither of their husbands was rich. No one seemed overjoyed on my return; and I soon discovered that when a man's relations have once mourned for him as dead, they seldom like the prospect of having to mourn for him a second time.

Accordingly I returned to London with my wife, and through the assistance of an old friend supported myself by writing good little stories for the magazines, and for a tract society. I was well paid; and I trust that I may not be considered presumptuous in saying that some of the most popular of the brochures which are distributed in the streets, and which are to be found in the waiting-rooms of the railway stations, have proceeded from my pen. During the time that I could spare, I arranged my notes and diary till they assumed their present shape. There remains nothing for me to add, save to unfold the scheme which I propose for the conversion of Erewhon.

That scheme has only been quite recently decided upon as the one which seems most likely to be successful.

It will be seen at once that it would be madness for me to go with ten or a dozen subordinate missionaries by the same way as that which led me to discover Erewhon. I should be imprisoned for typhus, besides being handed over to the straighteners for having run away with Arowhena; an even darker fate, to which I dare hardly again allude, would be reserved for my devoted fellow-labourers. It is plain, therefore, that some other way must be found for getting at the Erewhonians, and I am thankful to say that such another way is not wanting. One of the rivers which descends from the Snowy Mountains, and passes through Erewhon, is known to be navigable for several hundred miles from its mouth. Its upper waters have never yet been explored, but I feel little doubt that it will be found possible to take a light gunboat (for we must protect ourselves) to the outskirts of the Erewhonian country.

I propose, therefore, that one of those associations should be formed in which the risk of each of the members is confined to the amount of his stake in the concern. The first step would be to draw up a prospectus. In this I would advise that no mention should be made of the fact that the Erewhonians are the lost tribes. The discovery is one of absorbing interest to myself, but it is of a sentimental rather than commercial value, and business is business. The capital to be raised should not be less than fifty thousand pounds, and might be either in five or ten pound shares as hereafter determined. This should be amply sufficient for the expenses of an experimental voyage.

When the money had been subscribed, it would be our duty to charter a steamer of some twelve or fourteen hundred tons burden, and with accommodation for a cargo of steerage passengers. She should carry two or three guns in case of her being attacked by savages at the mouth of the river. Boats of considerable size should be also provided, and I think it would be desirable that these also should carry two or three six-pounders. The ship should be taken up the river as far as was considered safe, and a picked party should then ascend in the boats. The presence both of Arowhena and myself would be necessary at this stage, inasmuch as our knowledge of the language would disarm suspicion, and facilitate negotiations.

We should begin by representing the advantages afforded to labour in the colony of Queensland, and point out to the Erewhonians that by emigrating thither, they would be able to amass, each and all of them, enormous fortunes — a fact which would be easily provable by a reference to statistics. I have no doubt that a very great number might be thus induced to come back with us in the larger boats, and that we could fill our vessel with emigrants in three or four journeys.

Should we be attacked, our course would be even simpler, for the Erewhonians have no gunpowder, and would be so surprised with its effects that we should be able to capture as many as we chose; in this case we should feel able to engage them on more advantageous terms, for they would be prisoners of war. But even though we were to meet with no violence, I doubt not that a cargo of seven or eight hundred Erewhonians could be induced, when they were once on board the vessel, to sign an agreement which should be mutually advantageous both to us and them.

We should then proceed to Queensland, and dispose of our engagement with the Erewhonians to the sugar-growers of that settlement, who are in great want of labour; it is believed that the money thus realized would enable us to declare a handsome dividend, and leave a considerable balance, which might be spent in repeating our operations, and bringing over other cargoes of Erewhonians, with fresh consequent profits. In fact we could go backwards and forwards as long as there was a demand for labour in Queensland, or indeed in any other Christian colony, for the supply of Erewhonians would be unlimited, and they could be packed closely and fed at a very reasonable cost.

It would be my duty and Arowhena's to see that our emigrants should be boarded and lodged in the households of religious sugar-growers; these persons would give them the benefit of that instruction whereof they stand so greatly in need. Each day, as soon as they could be spared from their work in the plantations, they would be assembled for praise, and be thoroughly grounded in the Church Catechism, while the whole of every Sabbath should be devoted to singing psalms and church-going.

This must be insisted upon, both in order to put a stop to any uneasy feeling which might show itself either in Queensland or in the mother country as to the means whereby the Erewhonians had been obtained, and also because it would give our own shareholders the comfort of reflecting that they were saving souls and filling their own pockets at one and the same moment. By the time the emigrants had got too old for work they would have become thoroughly instructed in religion; they could then be shipped back to Erewhon and carry the good seed with them.

I can see no hitch nor difficulty about the matter, and trust that this book will sufficiently advertise the scheme to insure the subscription of the necessary capital; as soon as this is forthcoming I will guarantee that I convert the Erewhonians not only into good Christians but into a source of considerable profit to the shareholders.

I should add that I cannot claim the credit for having originated the above scheme. I had been for months at my wit's end, forming plan after plan for the evangelization of Erewhon, when by one of those special interpositions which should be a sufficient answer to the sceptic, and make even the most confirmed rationalist irrational, my eye was directed to the following paragraph in *The Times* newspaper, of one of the first days in January 1872:

POLYNESIANS IN QUEENSLAND. — The Marquis of Normanby, the new Governor of Queensland, has completed his inspection of the northern districts of the colony. It is stated that at Mackay, one of the best sugar-growing districts, his Excellency saw a good deal of the Polynesians. In the course of a speech to those who entertained him there, the Marquis said: 'I have been told that the means by which Polynesians were obtained were not legitimate, but I have failed to perceive this, in so far at least as Queensland is concerned; and, if one can judge by the countenances and manners of the Polynesians, they experience no regret at their position.' But his Excellency pointed out the advantage of giving them religious instruction. It would tend to set at rest an uneasy feeling which at present existed in the country to know that they were inclined to retain the Polynesians, and teach them religion.

I feel that comment is unnecessary, and will therefore conclude with one word of thanks to the reader who may have had the patience to follow me through my adventures without losing his temper; but with two, for any who may write at once to the Secretary of the Erewhon Evangelization Company, Limited (at the address which shall hereafter be advertised), and request to have his name put down as a shareholder.

P.S. — I had just received and corrected the last proof of the foregoing volume, and was walking down the Strand from Temple Bar to Charing Cross, when on passing Exeter Hall I saw a number of devout-looking people crowding into the building with faces full of interested and complacent anticipation. I stopped, and saw an announcement that a missionary meeting was to be held forthwith, and that the native missionary, the Rev. William Habakkuk, from —— (the colony from which I had started on my adventures), would be introduced, and make a short address. After some little difficulty I obtained admission, and heard two or three speeches, which were prefatory to the introduction of Mr. Habakkuk. One of these struck me as perhaps the most presumptuous that I had ever heard. The speaker said that the races of whom Mr. Habakkuk was a specimen, were in all probability the lost ten tribes of Israel. I dared not contradict him then, but I felt angry and injured at hearing the speaker jump to so preposterous a conclusion upon such insufficient grounds. The discovery of the ten tribes was mine, and mine only. I was still in the very height of indignation, when there was a murmur of expectation in the hall, and Mr. Habakkuk was brought forward. The reader may judge of my surprise at finding that he was none other than my old friend Chowbok!

My jaw dropped, and my eyes almost started out of my head with astonishment. The poor fellow was dreadfully frightened, and the storm of applause which greeted his introduction seemed only to add to his confusion. I dare not trust myself to report his speech — indeed I could hardly listen to it, for I was nearly choked with trying to suppress my feelings. I am sure that I caught the words 'Adelaide, the Queen Dowager', and I thought that I heard 'Mary Magdalene' shortly afterwards, but I had then to leave the hall for fear of being turned out. While on the staircase, I heard another burst of prolonged and rapturous applause, so I suppose the audience were satisfied.

The feelings that came uppermost in my mind were hardly of a very solemn character, but I thought of my first acquaintance with Chowbok, of the scene in the wool-shed, of the innumerable lies he had told me, of his repeated attempts upon the brandy, and of many an incident which I have not thought it worth while to dwell upon; and I could not but derive some satisfaction from the hope that my own efforts might have contributed to the change which had been doubtless wrought upon him, and that the rite which I had performed, however unprofessionally, on that wild upland river-bed, had not been wholly without effect. I trust that what I have written about him in the earlier part of my book may not be libellous, and that it may do him no harm with his employers. He was then unregenerate. I must certainly find him out and have a talk with him; but before I shall have time to do so these pages will be in the hands of the public.

At the last moment I see a probability of a complication which causes me much uneasiness. Please subscribe quickly. Address to the Mansion House, care of the Lord Mayor, whom I will instruct to receive names and subscriptions for me until I can organize a committee.

THE WAY OF ALL FLESH

EDITOR'S PREFACE

*T*HE *Way of All Flesh,* written between 1872 and 1885, was not published until 1903, the year after Butler's death. A second edition appeared in 1908, and it has been often reprinted since. For a further account of its composition refer to the Introduction to this volume. It is a long book, and only a fairly small part of it, taken mainly from the first half, can be reprinted here. The first half, which was heavily revised and in part rewritten, is much better than the later chapters, though these too contain many characteristic passages. As the extracts given here necessarily fail to tell the whole story, I give a bare outline of the plot, which was constructed to some extent in accordance with Butler's theories of heredity.

The book opens with an old man called Pontifex, by trade a carpenter and also parish clerk, and his strong-minded wife. Old Pontifex, who rose to become a small master builder, was also an amateur artist and an enthusiastic musician. He is presented as a man of the most amiable and upright character. His only son, George Pontifex, born fifteen years after his parents' marriage, was taken up by an uncle, his mother's brother, by name Fairlie, who was a publisher of religious books, and, showing 'a good healthy sense of *meum,* and as little of *tuum* as he could help', in due course fell heir to and greatly improved the business. George Pontifex had five children, of whom three — the two sons and the youngest of the three daughters — come into the story. John, the elder son, succeeded to the business; Theobald, the younger, became a clergyman, after his 'doubts' had been summarily disposed of, in the manner shown in these extracts, by parental discipline. The daughter, Alethea, remained unmarried, to befriend Theobald's son, Ernest, who is the central figure of the story.

The older generations of the Pontifex family serve only as background for the central theme, which is a study of the relations between Ernest Pontifex and his parents. The imaginary narrator is one Edward Overton, a friend of the family, who is represented as a writer of burlesques for the stage, and serves as the mouthpiece of Butler's own opinions. Overton is a close friend of Alethea Pontifex, whose character is said to have been drawn largely from Butler's friend, Miss Savage. Alethea Pontifex, dying in middle life after endeavouring to help Ernest to find his own feet in his struggle against his parents' domination, leaves her fortune to Overton, in secret trust for Ernest, to be handed over to him at Overton's discretion when he has reached manhood and had time to find his way about in the world. But before this point is reached, there is a great deal about Theobald himself and about his relations with his father, George Pontifex the publisher. An account is given of Theobald's years at Cambridge, followed by his ineffectual struggle against his father's insistence on ordination, and by his own half-hearted wooing of Christina, one of the numerous daughters of a country clergyman near Cambridge, for whom Theobald acts as part-time curate. Then come years of 'engagement' before Theobald at last gets a living, and becomes able to marry. The episode in the coach, after the marriage ceremony, establishing Theobald's mastery over Christina, is included among these extracts. Then we get in the book a carefully-drawn picture of the life at Battersby, Theobald's cure of souls, of Christina's day-dreaming, and of the upbringing of their children, especially Ernest Pontifex. Ernest is sent in due course to Roughborough School, under its celebrated head master, Dr. Skinner — one of Butler's best creations, based only in part on his own experiences at Shrewsbury. Aunt Alethea settles in Roughborough, in order to be near Ernest, and encourages his taste for music by enabling him to build an organ for himself. Then her death throws Ernest back upon his parents. He in turn is sent to Cambridge, and is coerced by Theobald into taking orders — a fate which Butler had narrowly escaped at the hands of his own father. Theobald goes to work in a slum parish, and there falls in with a fellow-curate named Pryer, of extreme high church views and no morals, who robs him of his money by leading him into wild speculations and then disappears. At this point Ernest, who has got into no end of a mental and moral muddle under Pryer's influence, mistakes an honest girl for a prostitute, and is sent to prison for attempting to rape her. Overton appears on the scene, but is unable to save his ward and makes up his mind to do nothing about Alethea's money till Ernest comes out of jail, and he can see what the effect of his experiences is likely to be. In due course Ernest is released, and finds himself badly at a loose end until he has a chance meeting in the street with a girl called Ellen, who had been a housemaid at his father's rectory. She had come into the story earlier when she had been dismissed on being found to be with child. Ernest, still a schoolboy, had espoused her cause without understanding what was the matter, and had got into sore disgrace for giving her his watch, which she was subsequently accused of stealing when she had pawned it. By the time Ernest, after his release from prison, again met Ellen, she had become a prostitute and had taken to drink; but he did not realize either of these things at all fully, and insisted on marrying her, despite Overton's protests. Overton, still holding back most of Alethea's money, and not telling Ernest of it for fear of what might happen, helped Ernest and Ellen to set up a second-hand clothes shop. Ellen became for a time a reformed character, and they managed well and happily till she went back to drinking. They had children; but their life together presently became intolerable. He was almost at the end of his endurance when a second chance meeting brought deliverance. He met John, his father's old coachman, who told him he had married Ellen and separated from her long before Ernest met her after his release from jail. Finding his marriage to be no marriage, Ernest allowed Overton to arrange for a separation, and decided to farm out his children to a decent, happy couple at Gravesend, who had a large family of their own and undertook to bring them up. These people were bargemen, and Ernest, still ignorant of his expectations, wanted his children to be brought up to earn a simple, honest living. When this was all arranged, Overton, deeming Ernest's probation to be over, at last told him about, and handed over, Alethea's money, which did not change his decision about the children, though it enabled him later to set them up in life with a barge of their own apiece for his son and for the 'foster-brother' whom his daughter married. Ernest himself settled down, *à la Butler*, in rooms in the Temple, and took to writing books about philosophy and the art of living which few wanted to read. With this *dénouement* the book quietly peters out into a *finale* which is, in effect, an account of Butler's own later life. What I have to say of *The Way of All Flesh* as a whole has been said in the Introduction, and need not be repeated here. The reader can judge for himself whether, having read these samples, he wants to go on and read the whole. If he has not, I hope he will; for I do not like having to anthologize it, even though I am fairly confident of having chosen most of the best.

CHAPTER ONE

WHEN I was a small boy at the beginning of the century I remember an old man who wore knee-breeches and worsted stockings, and who used to hobble about the street of our village with the help of a stick. He must have been getting on for eighty in the year 1807, earlier than which date I suppose I can hardly remember him, for I was born in 1802. A few white locks hung about his ears, his shoulders were bent and his knees feeble, but he was still hale, and was much respected in our little world of Paleham. His name was Pontifex.

His wife was said to be his master; I have been told she brought him a little money, but it cannot have been much. She was a tall, square-shouldered person (I have heard my father call her a Gothic woman) who had insisted on being married to Mr. Pontifex when he was young and too good-natured to say nay to any woman who wooed him. The pair had lived not unhappily together, for Mr. Pontifex's temper was easy and he soon learned to bow before his wife's more stormy moods.

Mr. Pontifex was a carpenter by trade; he was also at one time parish clerk; when I remember him, however, he had so far risen in life as to be no longer compelled to work with his own hands. In his earlier days he had taught himself to draw. I do not say he drew well, but it was surprising he should draw as well as he did. My father, who took the living of Paleham about the year 1797, became possessed of a good many of old Mr. Pontifex's drawings, which were always of local subjects, and so unaffectedly painstaking that they might have passed for the work of some good early master. I remember them as hanging up framed and glazed in the study at the Rectory, and tinted, as all else in the room was tinted, with the green reflected from the fringe of ivy leaves that grew around the windows. I wonder how they will actually cease and come to an end as drawings, and into what new phases of being they will then enter.

Not content with being an artist, Mr. Pontifex must needs also be a musician. He built the organ in the church with his own hands, and made a smaller one which he kept in his own house. He could play as much as he could draw, not very well according to professional standards, but much better than could have been expected. I myself showed a taste for music at an early age, and old Mr. Pontifex on

175

finding it out, as he soon did, became partial to me in consequence.

It may be thought that with so many irons in the fire he could hardly be a very thriving man, but this was not the case. His father had been a day labourer, and he had himself begun life with no other capital than his good sense and good constitution; now, however, there was a goodly show of timber about his yard, and a look of solid comfort over his whole establishment. Towards the close of the eighteenth century and not long before my father came to Paleham, he had taken a farm of about ninety acres, thus making a considerable rise in life. Along with the farm there went an old-fashioned but comfortable house with a charming garden and an orchard. The carpenter's business was now carried on in one of the outhouses that had once been part of some conventual buildings, the remains of which could be seen in what was called the Abbey Close. The house itself, embosomed in honeysuckles and creeping roses, was an ornament to the whole village, nor were its internal arrangements less exemplary than its outside was ornamental. Report said that Mrs. Pontifex starched the sheets for her best bed, and I can well believe it.

How well do I remember her parlour half filled with the organ which her husband had built, and scented with a withered apple or two from the *pyrus japonica* that grew outside the house; the picture of the prize ox over the chimney-piece, which Mr. Pontifex himself had painted; the transparency of the man coming to show light to a coach upon a snowy night, also by Mr. Pontifex; the little old man and little old woman who told the weather; the china shepherd and shepherdess; the jars of feathery flowering grasses with a peacock's feather or two among them to set them off, and the china bowls full of dead rose leaves dried with bay salt. All has long since vanished and become a memory, faded but still fragrant to myself.

Nay, but her kitchen — and the glimpses into a cavernous cellar beyond it, wherefrom came gleams from the pale surfaces of milk cans, or it may be of the arms and face of a milkmaid skimming the cream; or again her storeroom, where among other treasures she kept the famous lipsalve which was one of her especial glories, and of which she would present a shape yearly to those whom she delighted to honour. She wrote out the recipe for this and gave it to my mother a year or two before she died, but we could never make it as she did. When we were children she used sometimes to send her respects to my mother, and ask leave for us to come and take tea with her. Right well she used to ply us. As for her temper, we never met such a delightful old lady in our lives; whatever Mr. Pontifex may have had to put up with, we had no cause for complaint, and then Mr. Pontifex would play to us upon the organ, and we would stand round him open-mouthed and think him the most wonderfully clever man that ever was born, except of course our papa.

Mrs. Pontifex had no sense of humour, at least I can call to mind no signs of this, but her husband had plenty of fun in him, though few would have guessed it from his appearance. I remember my father once sent me down to his workshop to get some glue, and I happened to come when old Pontifex was in the act of scolding his boy. He had got the lad — a pudding-headed fellow — by the ear and was saying, 'What? Lost again — smothered o' wit.' (I believe it was the boy who was himself supposed to be a wandering soul, and who was thus addressed as lost.) 'Now, look here, my lad,' he continued, 'some boys are born stupid, and thou art one of them; some achieve stupidity — that's thee again, Jim — thou wast both born stupid and has greatly increased thy birthright — and some' (and here came a climax during which the boy's head and ear were swayed from side to side) 'have stupidity thrust upon them, which, if it please the Lord, shall not be thy case, my lad, for I will thrust stupidity from thee, though I have to box thine ears in doing so,' but I did not see that the old man really did box Jim's ears, or do more than pretend to frighten him, for the two understood one another perfectly well. Another time I remember hearing him call the village rat-catcher by saying, 'Come hither, thou three-days-and-three-nights, thou,' alluding, as I afterwards learned, to the rat-catcher's periods of intoxication; but I will tell no more of such trifles. My father's face would always brighten when old Pontifex's name was mentioned. 'I tell you, Edward,' he would say to me, 'old Pontifex was not only an able man, but he was one of the very ablest men that ever I knew.'

This was more than I as a young man was prepared to stand. 'My dear father,' I answered, 'what did he do? He could draw a little, but could he to save his life have got a picture into the Royal Academy exhibition? He built two organs and could play the Minuet in *Samson* on one and the March in *Scipio* on the other; he was a good carpenter and a bit of a wag; he was a good old fellow enough, but why make him out so much abler than he was?'

'My boy,' returned my father, 'you must not judge by the work, but by the work in connection with the surroundings. Could Giotto or Filippo Lippi, think you, have got a picture into the Exhibition? Would a single one of those frescoes we went to see when we were at Padua have the remotest chance of being hung, if it were sent in for exhibition now? Why, the Academy people would be so outraged that they would not even write to poor Giotto to tell him to come and take his fresco away. Phew!' continued he, waxing warm, 'if old Pontifex had had Cromwell's chances he would have done all that Cromwell did, and have done it better; if he had had Giotto's chances he would have done all that Giotto did, and done it no worse; as it was, he was a village carpenter, and I will undertake to say he never scamped a job in the whole course of his life.'

'But,' said I, 'we cannot judge people with so many "ifs". If old Pontifex had lived in Giotto's time he might have been another Giotto, but he did not live in Giotto's time.'

'I tell you, Edward,' said my father with some severity, 'we must judge men not so much by what they do, as by what they make us feel that they have it in them to do. If a man has done enough either in painting, music or the affairs of life, to make me feel that I might trust him in an emergency he has done enough. It is not by what a man has actually put upon his canvas, nor yet by the acts which he has set down, so to speak, upon the canvas of his life that I will judge him, but by what he makes me feel that he felt and aimed at. If he has made me feel that he felt those things to be lovable which I hold lovable myself I ask no more; his grammar may have been imperfect, but still I have understood him; he and I are *en rapport*; and I say again, Edward, that old Pontifex was not only an able man, but one of the very ablest men I ever knew.'

Against this there was no more to be said, and my sisters eyed me to silence. Somehow or other my sisters always did eye me to silence when I differed from my father.

'Talk of his successful son,' snorted my father, whom I had fairly roused. 'He is not fit to black his father's boots. He has his thousands of pounds a year, while his father had perhaps three thousand shillings a year towards the end of his life. He *is* a successful man; but his father, hobbling about Paleham Street in his grey worsted stockings, broad-brimmed hat and brown swallow-tailed coat, was worth a hundred of George Pontifexes, for all his carriages and horses and the airs he gives himself.'

'But yet,' he added, 'George Pontifex is no fool either.' And this brings us to the second generation of the Pontifex family with whom we need concern ourselves.

CHAPTER TWO

OLD Mr. Pontifex had married in the year 1750, but for fifteen years his wife bore no children. At the end of that time Mrs. Pontifex astonished the whole village by showing unmistakable signs of a disposition to present her husband with an heir or heiress. Hers had long ago been considered a hopeless case, and when on consulting the doctor concerning the meaning of certain symptoms she was informed of their significance, she became very angry and abused the doctor roundly for talking nonsense. She refused to put so much as a piece of thread into a needle in anticipation of her confinement and would have been absolutely unprepared, if her neighbours had not been better judges of her condition than she was, and got things ready without telling her anything about it. Perhaps she feared Nemesis, though assuredly she knew not who or what Nemesis was; perhaps she feared the doctor had made a mistake and she should be laughed at; from whatever cause, however, her refusal to recognize the obvious arose, she certainly refused to recognize it, until one snowy night in January the doctor was sent for with all urgent speed across the rough country roads. When he arrived he found two patients, not one, in need of his assistance, for a boy had been born who was in due time christened George, in honour of his then reigning majesty.

To the best of my belief George Pontifex got the greater part of his nature from this obstinate old lady, his mother — a mother who though she loved no one else in the world except her husband (and him only after a fashion) was most tenderly attached to the unexpected child of her old age; nevertheless she showed it little.

The boy grew up into a sturdy, bright-eyed, little fellow, with plenty of intelligence, and perhaps a trifle too great readiness of book learning. Being kindly treated at home, he was as fond of his father and mother as it was in his nature to be of anyone, but he was fond of no one else. He had a good healthy sense of *meum*, and as little of *tuum* as he could help. Brought up much in the open air in one of the best situated and healthiest villages in England, his little limbs had fair play, and in those days children's brains were not overtasked as they now are; perhaps it was for this very reason that the boy showed an avidity to learn. At seven or eight years old he could read, write and sum better than any other boy of his age in the village. My father was not yet rector of Paleham, and did not remember George Pontifex's childhood, but I have heard neighbours tell him that the boy was looked upon as unusually quick and forward. His father and mother were naturally proud of their offspring, and his mother was determined that he should one day become one of the kings and counsellors of the earth.

It is one thing, however, to resolve that one's son shall win some of life's larger prizes, and another to square matters with fortune in this respect. George Pontifex might have been brought up as a carpenter and succeeded in no other way than as succeeding his father as one of the minor magnates of Paleham, and yet have been a more truly successful man than he actually was — for I take it there is not much more solid success in this world than what fell to the lot of old Mr. and Mrs. Pontifex; it happened, however, that about the year 1780, when George was a boy of fifteen, a sister of Mrs. Pontifex's, who had married a Mr. Fairlie, came to pay a few days' visit at Paleham. Mr. Fairlie was a publisher, chiefly of religious works, and had an establishment in Paternoster Row; he had risen in life, and his wife had risen with him. No very close relations had been maintained between the sisters for some years, and I forget exactly how it came about that Mr. and Mrs. Fairlie were guests in the quiet but exceedingly comfortable house of their sister and brother-in-law; but for some reason or other the visit was paid, and little George soon succeeded in making his way into his uncle and aunt's good graces. A quick, intelligent boy with a good address, a sound constitution and coming of respectable parents, has a potential value which a practised business man who has need of many subordinates is little likely to overlook. Before his visit was over Mr. Fairlie proposed to the lad's father and mother that he should put him into his own business, at the same time promising that if the boy did well he should not want someone to bring him forward. Mrs. Pontifex had her son's interest too much at heart to refuse such an offer, so the matter was soon arranged and about a fortnight after the Fairlies had left, George was sent up by coach to London, where he was met by his uncle and aunt, with whom it was arranged that he should live.

This was George's great start in life. He now wore more fashionable clothes than he had yet been accustomed to, and any little rusticity of gait or pronunciation which he had brought from Paleham, was so quickly and completely lost that it was ere long impossible to detect that he had not been born and bred among people of what is commonly called education. The boy paid great attention to his work, and more than justified the favourable opinion which Mr. Fairlie had formed concerning him. Sometimes Mr. Fairlie would send him down to Paleham for a few days' holiday, and ere long his parents perceived that he had acquired an air and manner of talking different from any that he had taken with him from Paleham. They were proud of him, and soon fell into their proper places, resigning all appearance of a parental control, for which indeed there was no kind of necessity. In return, George was always kindly to them, and to the end of his life retained a more affectionate feeling towards his father and mother than I imagine him ever to have felt again for man, woman or child.

George's visits to Paleham were never long, for the distance from London was under fifty miles and there was a direct coach, so that the journey was easy; there was not time, therefore, for the novelty to wear off either on the part of the young man or of his parents. George liked the fresh country air and green fields after the darkness to which he had been so long accustomed in Paternoster Row, which then, as now, was a narrow gloomy lane rather than a street. Independently of the pleasure of seeing the familiar faces of the farmers and villagers, he liked also being seen and being congratulated on growing up such a fine-looking and fortunate young fellow, for he was not the youth to hide his light under a bushel. His uncle had had him taught Latin and Greek of an evening; he had taken kindly to these languages and had rapidly and easily mastered what many boys take years in acquiring. I suppose his knowledge gave him a self-confidence which made itself felt whether he intended it or not; at any rate, he soon began to pose as a judge of literature, and from this to being a judge of art, architecture, music and everything else, the path was easy. Like his father, he knew the value of money, but he was at once more ostentatious and less liberal than his father; while yet a boy he was a thorough little man of the world, and did well rather upon principles which he had tested by personal experiment, and recognized as principles, than from those profounder convictions which in his father were so instinctive that he could give no account concerning them.

His father, as I have said, wondered at him and let him alone. His son had fairly distanced him, and in an inarticulate way the father knew it perfectly well. After a few years he took to wearing his best clothes whenever his son came to stay with him, nor would he discard them for his ordinary ones till the young man had returned to London. I believe old Mr. Pontifex, along with his pride and affection, felt also a certain fear of his son, as though of something which he could not thoroughly understand, and whose ways, notwithstanding outward agreement, were nevertheless not as his ways. Mrs. Pontifex felt nothing of this; to her George was pure and absolute perfection, and she saw, or thought she saw, with pleasure, that he resembled her and her family in feature as well as in disposition rather than her husband and his.

When George was about twenty-five years old his uncle took him into partnership on very liberal terms. He had little cause to regret this step. The young man infused fresh vigour into a concern that was already vigorous, and by the time he was thirty found himself in the receipt of not less than £1500 a year as his share of the profits. Two years later he married a lady about seven years younger than himself, who brought him a handsome dowry. She died in 1805, when her youngest child Alethea was born, and her husband did not marry again.

CHAPTER THREE

IN the early years of the century five little children and a couple of nurses began to make periodical visits to Paleham. It is needless to say they were a rising generation of Pontifexes, towards whom the old couple, their grandparents, were as tenderly deferential as they would have been to the children of the Lord-Lieutenant of the County. Their names were Eliza, Maria, John, Theobald (who like myself was born in 1802), and Alethea. Mr. Pontifex always put the prefix 'master' or 'miss' before the names of his grandchildren, except in the case of Alethea, who was his favourite. To have resisted his grandchildren would have been as impossible for him as to have resisted his wife; even old Mrs. Pontifex yielded before her son's children, and gave them all manner of licence which she would never have allowed even to my sisters and myself, who stood next in her regard. Two regulations only they must attend to: they must wipe their shoes well on coming into the house, and they must not overfeed Mr. Pontifex's organ with wind, nor take the pipes out.

By us at the Rectory there was no time so much looked forward to as the annual visit of the little Pontifexes to Paleham. We came in for some of the prevailing licence; we went to tea with Mrs. Pontifex to meet her grandchildren, and then our young friends were asked to the Rectory to have tea with us, and we had what we considered great times. I fell desperately in love with Alethea, indeed we all fell in love with each other, plurality and exchange whether of wives or husbands being openly and unblushingly advocated in the very presence of our nurses. We were very merry, but it is so long ago that I have forgotten nearly everything save that we *were* very merry. Almost the only thing that remains with me as a permanent impression was the fact that Theobald one day beat his nurse and teased her, and when she said she should go away cried out, 'You shan't go away — I'll keep you on purpose to torment you.'

One winter's morning, however, in the year 1811, we heard the church bell tolling while we were dressing in the back nursery and were told it was for old Mrs. Pontifex. Our manservant John told us and added with grim levity that they were ringing the bell to come and take her away. She had had a fit of paralysis which had carried her off quite suddenly. It was very shocking, the more so because our nurse assured us that if God chose we might all have fits of paralysis ourselves that very day and be taken straight off to the Day of Judgment. The Day of Judgment indeed, according to the opinion of those who were most likely to know, would not under any circumstances be delayed more than a few years longer, and then the whole world would be burned, and we ourselves be consigned to an eternity of torture, unless we mended our ways more than we at present seemed at all likely to do. All this was so alarming that we fell to screaming and made such a hullabaloo that the nurse was obliged for her own peace to reassure us. Then we wept, but more composedly, as we remembered that there would be no more tea and cakes for us now at old Mrs. Pontifex's.

On the day of the funeral, however, we had a great excitement; old Mr. Pontifex sent round a penny loaf to every inhabitant of the village according to a custom still not uncommon at the beginning of the century; the loaf was called a dole. We had never heard of this custom before, besides, though we had often heard of penny loaves, we had never before seen one; moreover, they were presents to us as inhabitants of the village, and we were treated as grown-up people, for our father and mother and the servants had each one loaf sent them, but only one. We had never yet suspected that we were inhabitants at all; finally, the little loaves were new, and we were passionately fond of new bread, which we were seldom or never allowed to have, as it was supposed not to be good for us. Our affection, therefore, for our old friend had to stand against the combined attacks of archaeological interest , the rights of citizenship and property, the pleasantness to the eye and goodness for food of the little loaves themselves, and the sense of importance which was given us by our having been intimate with someone who had actually died. It seemed upon further inquiry that there was little reason to anticipate an early death for any one of ourselves, and this being so, we rather liked the idea of someone else's being put away into the churchyard; we passed, therefore, in a short time from extreme depression to a no less extreme exultation; a new heaven and a new earth had been revealed to us in our perception of the possibility of benefiting by the death of our friends, and I fear that for some time we took an interest in the health of everyone in the village whose position rendered a repetition of the dole in the least likely.

Those were the days in which all great things seemed far off, and we were astonished to find that Napoleon Buonaparte was an actually living person. We had thought such a great man could only have lived a very long time ago, and here he was after all almost as it were at our own doors. This lent colour to the view that the Day of Judgment might indeed be nearer than we had thought, but nurse said that was all right now, and she knew. In those days the snow lay longer and drifted deeper in the lanes than it does now, and the milk was sometimes brought in frozen in winter, and we were taken down into the back kitchen to see it. I suppose there are rectories up and down the country now where the milk comes in frozen sometimes in winter, and the children go down to wonder at it, but I never see any frozen milk in London, so I suppose the winters are warmer than they used to be.

About one year after his wife's death Mr. Pontifex also was gathered to his fathers. My father saw him the day before he died. The old man had a theory about sunsets, and had had two steps built up against a wall in the kitchen garden on which he used to stand and watch the sun go down whenever it was clear. My father came on him in the

THE WAY OF ALL FLESH

afternoon, just as the sun was setting, and saw him with his arms resting on the top of the wall looking towards the sun over a field through which there was a path on which my father was. My father heard him say 'Goodbye, sun; goodbye, sun,' as the sun sank, and saw by his tone and manner that he was feeling very feeble. Before the next sunset he was gone.

There was no dole. Some of his grandchildren were brought to the funeral and we remonstrated with them, but did not take much by doing so. John Pontifex, who was a year older than I was, sneered at penny loaves, and intimated that if I wanted one it must be because my papa and mamma could not afford to buy me one, whereon I believe we did something like fighting, and I rather think John Pontifex got the worst of it, but it may have been the other way. I remember my sister's nurse, for I was just outgrowing nurses myself, reported the matter to higher quarters, and we were all of us put to some ignominy, but we had been thoroughly awakened from our dream, and it was long enough before we could hear the words 'penny loaf' mentioned without our ears tingling with shame. If there had been a dozen doles afterwards we should not have deigned to touch one of them.

George Pontifex put up a monument to his parents, a plain slab in Paleham church, inscribed with the following epitaph:

SACRED TO THE MEMORY

OF

JOHN PONTIFEX

WHO WAS BORN AUGUST 16, 1727, AND DIED FEBRUARY 8, 1812
IN HIS 85TH YEAR,

AND OF

RUTH PONTIFEX, HIS WIFE

WHO WAS BORN OCTOBER 13, 1727, AND DIED JANUARY 10, 1811
IN HER 84TH YEAR.

THEY WERE UNOSTENTATIOUS BUT EXEMPLARY
IN THE DISCHARGE OF THEIR
RELIGIOUS, MORAL, AND SOCIAL DUTIES.
THIS MONUMENT WAS PLACED
BY THEIR ONLY SON.

MR. PONTIFEX was not the man to trouble himself much about his motives. People were not so introspective then as we are now; they lived more according to a rule of thumb. Dr. Arnold had not yet sown that crop of earnest thinkers which we are now harvesting, and men did not see why they should not have their own way if no evil consequences to themselves seemed likely to follow upon their doing so. Then as now, however, they sometimes let themselves in for more evil consequences than they had bargained for.

Like other rich men at the beginning of this century he ate and drank a good deal more than was enough to keep him in health. Even his excellent constitution was not proof against a prolonged course of overfeeding and what we should now consider overdrinking. His liver would not unfrequently get out of order, and he would come down to breakfast looking yellow about the eyes. Then the young people knew that they had better look out. It is not as a general rule the eating of sour grapes that causes the children's teeth to be set on edge. Well-to-do parents seldom eat many sour grapes; the danger to the children lies in the parents eating too many sweet ones.

I grant that at first sight it seems very unjust, that the parents should have the fun and the children be punished for it, but young people should remember that for many years they were part and parcel of their parents and therefore had a good deal of the fun in the person of their parents. If they have forgotten the fun now, that is no more than people do who have a headache after having been tipsy overnight. The man with a headache does not pretend to be a different person from the man who got drunk, and claim that it is his self of the preceding night and not his self of this morning who should be punished; no more should offspring complain of the headache which it has earned when in the person of its parents, for the continuation of identity though not so immediately apparent, is just as real in one case as in the other. What is really hard is when the parents have the fun after the children have been born, and the children are punished for this.

On these, his black days, he would take very gloomy views of things and say to himself that in spite of all his goodness to them his children did not love him. But who can love any man whose liver is out of order? How base, he would exclaim to himself, was such ingratitude! How especially hard upon himself, who had been such a model son, and always honoured and obeyed his parents though they had not spent one-hundredth part of the money upon him which he had lavished upon his own children. 'It is always the same story,' he would say to himself, 'the more young people have the more they want, and the less thanks one gets; I have made a great mistake; I have been far too lenient with my children; never mind, I have done my duty by them, and more; if they fail in theirs to me it is a matter between God and them. I, at any rate, am guiltless. Why, I might have married again and become the father of a second and perhaps more affectionate family,' etc. etc. He pitied himself for the expensive education which he was giving his children; he did not see that the education cost the children far more than it cost him, inasmuch as it cost them the power of earning their living easily rather than helped them towards it, and ensured their being at the mercy of their father for years after they had come to an age when they should be independent. A public school education cuts off a boy's retreat; he can no longer become a labourer or a mechanic, and these are the only people whose tenure of independence is not precarious — with the exception of course of those who are born inheritors of money or who are placed young in some safe and deep groove. Mr. Pontifex saw nothing of this; all he saw was that he was spending much more money upon his children than the law would have compelled him to do, and what more could you have? Might he not have apprenticed both his sons to greengrocers? Might he not even yet do so tomorrow morning if he were so minded? The possibility of this course being adopted was a favourite topic with him when he was out of temper; true, he never did apprentice either of his sons to greengrocers, but his boys comparing notes together had sometimes come to the conclusion that they wished he would.

At other times when not quite well he would have them in for the fun of shaking his will at them. He would in his imagination cut them all out one after another and leave his money to found almshouses, till at last he was obliged to put them back, so that he might have the pleasure of cutting them out again the next time he was in a passion.

Of course if young people allow their conduct to be in any way influenced by regard to the wills of living persons they are doing very wrong and must expect to be sufferers in the end, nevertheless the powers of will-dangling and will-shaking are so liable to abuse and are continually made so great an engine of torture that I would pass a law, if I could, to incapacitate any man from making a will for three months.

from the date of each offence in either of the above respects and let the bench of magistrates or judge, before whom he has been convicted, dispose of his property as they shall think right and reasonable if he dies during the time that his will-making power is suspended.

Mr. Pontifex would have the boys into the dining-room. 'My dear John, my dear Theobald,' he would say, 'look at me. I began life with nothing but the clothes with which my father and mother sent me up to London. My father gave me ten shillings and my mother five for pocket-money and I thought them munificent. I never asked my father for a shilling in the whole course of my life, nor took aught from him beyond the small sum he used to allow me monthly till I was in receipt of a salary. I made my own way and I shall expect my sons to do the same. Pray don't take it into your heads that I am going to wear my life out making money that my sons may spend it for me. If you want money you must make it for yourselves as I did, for I give you my word I will not leave a penny to either of you unless you show that you deserve it. Young people seem nowadays to expect all kinds of luxuries and indulgences which were never heard of when I was a boy. Why, my father was a common carpenter, and here you are both of you at public schools, costing me ever so many hundreds a year, while I at your age was plodding away behind a desk in my Uncle Fairlie's counting-house. What should I not have done if I had had one-half of your advantages? You should become dukes or found new empires in undiscovered countries, and even then I doubt whether you would have done proportionately so much as I have done. No, no, I shall see you through school and college and then, if you please, you will make your own way in the world.'

In this manner he would work himself up into such a state of virtuous indignation that he would sometimes thrash the boys then and there upon some pretext invented at the moment.

And yet, as children went, the young Pontifexes were fortunate; there would be ten families of young people worse off for one better; they ate and drank good wholesome food, slept in comfortable beds, had the best doctors to attend them when they were ill and the best education that could be had for money. The want of fresh air does not seem much to affect the happiness of children in a London alley: the greater part of them sing and play as though they were on a moor in Scotland. So the absence of a genial mental atmosphere is not commonly recognized by children who have never known it. Young people have a marvellous faculty of either dying or adapting themselves to circumstances. Even if they are unhappy — very unhappy — it is astonishing how easily they can be prevented from finding it out, or at any rate from attributing it to any other cause than their own sinfulness.

To parents who wish to lead a quiet life I would say: Tell your children that they are very naughty — much naughtier than most children. Point to the young people of some acquaintances as models of perfection and impress your own children with a deep sense of their own inferiority. You carry so many more guns than they do that they cannot fight you. This is called moral influence, and it will enable you to bounce them as much as you please. They think you know and they will not have yet caught you lying often enough to suspect that you are not the unworldly and scrupulously truthful person which you represent yourself to be; nor yet will they know how great a coward you are, nor how soon you will run away, if they fight you with persistency and judgment. You keep the dice and throw them both for your children and yourself. Load them then, for you can easily manage to stop your children from examining them. Tell them how singularly indulgent you are; insist on the incalculable benefit you conferred upon them, firstly in bringing them into the world at all, but more particularly in bringing them into it as your own children rather than anyone else's. Say that you have their highest interests at stake whenever you are out of temper and wish to make yourself unpleasant by way of balm to your soul. Harp much upon these highest interests. Feed them spiritually upon such brimstone and treacle as the late Bishop of Winchester's Sunday stories. You hold all the trump cards, or if you do not you can filch them; if you play them with anything like judgment you will find yourselves heads of happy, united, God-fearing families, even as did my old friend Mr. Pontifex. True, your children will probably find out all about it some day, but not until too late to be of much service to them or inconvenience to yourself.

Some satirists have complained of life inasmuch as all the pleasures belong to the fore part of it and we must see them dwindle till we are left, it may be, with the miseries of a decrepit old age.

To me it seems that youth is like spring, an overpraised season — delightful if it happen to be a favoured one, but in practice very rarely favoured and more remarkable, as a general rule, for biting east winds than genial breezes. Autumn is the mellower season, and what we lose in flowers we more than gain in fruits. Fontenelle at the age of ninety, being asked what was the happiest time of his life, said he did not know that he had ever been much happier than he then was, but that perhaps his best years had been those when he was between fifty-five and seventy-five, and Dr. Johnson placed the pleasures of old age far higher than those of youth. True, in old age we live under the shadow of Death, which, like a sword of Damocles, may descend at any moment, but we have so long found life to be an affair of being rather frightened than hurt that we have become like the people who live under Vesuvius, and chance it without much misgiving.

CHAPTER SEVEN

BEFORE he was well out of his frocks it was settled that he was to be a clergyman. It was seemly that Mr. Pontifex, the well-known publisher of religious books, should devote at least one of his sons to the Church; this might tend to bring business, or at any rate to keep it in the firm; besides, Mr. Pontifex had more or less interest with bishops and Church dignitaries and might hope that some preferment would be offered to his son through his influence. The boy's future destiny was kept well before his eyes from his earliest childhood and was treated as a matter which he had already virtually settled by his acquiescence. Nevertheless a certain show of freedom was allowed him. Mr. Pontifex would say it only right to give a boy his option, and was much too equitable to grudge his son whatever benefit he could derive from this. He had the greatest horror, he would exclaim, of driving any young man into a profession which he did not like. Far be it from him to put pressure upon a son of his as regards any profession and much less when so sacred a calling as the ministry was concerned. He would talk in this way when there were visitors in the house and when his son was in the room. He spoke so wisely and so well that his listening guests considered him a paragon of right-mindedness. He spoke, too, with such emphasis and his rosy gills and bald head looked so benevolent that it was difficult not to be carried away by his discourse. I believe two or three heads of families in the neighbourhood gave their sons absolute liberty of choice in the matter of their professions — and am not sure that they had not afterwards considerable cause to regret having done so. The visitors, seeing Theobald look shy and wholly unmoved by the exhibition of so much consideration for

190

his wishes, would remark to themselves that the boy seemed hardly likely to be equal to his father and would set him down as an unenthusiastic youth, who ought to have more life in him and be more sensible of his advantages than he appeared to be.

No one believed in the righteousness of the whole transaction more firmly than the boy himself; a sense of being ill at ease kept him silent, but it was too profound and too much without break for him to become fully alive to it, and come to an understanding with himself. He feared the dark scowl which would come over his father's face upon the slightest opposition. His father's violent threats, or coarse sneers, would not have been taken *au sérieux* by a stronger boy, but Theobald was not a strong boy, and rightly or wrongly, gave his father credit for being quite ready to carry his threats into execution. Opposition had never got him anything he wanted yet, nor indeed had yielding, for the matter of that, unless he happened to want exactly what his father wanted for him. If he had ever entertained thoughts of resistance, he had none now, and the power to oppose was so completely lost for want of exercise that hardly did the wish remain; there was nothing left save dull acquiescence as of an ass crouched between two burdens. He may have had an ill-defined sense of ideals that were not his actuals; he might occasionally dream of himself as a soldier or a sailor far away in foreign lands, or even as a farmer's boy upon the wolds, but there was not enough in him for there to be any chance of his turning his dreams into realities, and he drifted on with his stream, which was a slow, and, I am afraid, a muddy one.

I think the Church Catechism has a good deal to do with the unhappy relations which commonly even now exist between parents and children. That work was written too exclusively from the parental point of view; the person who composed it did not get a few children to come in and help him; he was clearly not young himself, nor should I say it was the work of one who likes children — in spite of the words 'my good child' which, if I remember rightly, are once put into the mouth of the catechist and, after all, carry a harsh sound with them. The general impression it leaves upon the mind of the young is that their wickedness at birth was but very imperfectly wiped out at baptism, and that the mere fact of being young at all has something with it that savours more or less distinctly of the nature of sin.

If a new edition of the work is ever required I should like to introduce a few words insisting on the duty of seeking all reasonable pleasure and avoiding all pain that can be honourably avoided. I should like to see children taught that they should not say they like things which they do not like, merely because certain other people say they like them, and how foolish it is to say they believe this or that when they understand nothing about it. If it be urged that these additions would make the Catechism too long I would curtail the remarks upon our duty towards our neighbour and upon the sacraments. In the place of the paragraph beginning 'I desire my Lord God our Heavenly Father' I would — but perhaps I had better return to Theobald, and leave the recasting of the Catechism to abler hands.

CHAPTER EIGHT

M R. PONTIFEX had set his heart on his son's becoming a fellow of a college before he became a clergyman. This would provide for him at once and would ensure his getting a living if none of his father's ecclesiastical friends gave him one. The boy had done just well enough at school to render this possible, so he was sent to one of the smaller colleges at Cambridge and was at once set to read with the best private tutors that could be found. A system of examination had been adopted a year or so before Theobald took his degree which had improved his chances of a fellowship, for whatever ability he had was classical rather than mathematical, and this system gave more encouragement to classical studies than had been given hitherto.

Theobald had the sense to see that he had a chance of independence if he worked hard, and he liked the notion of becoming a fellow. He therefore applied himself, and in the end took a degree which made his getting a fellowship in all probability a mere question of time. For a while Mr. Pontifex senior was really pleased, and told his son he would present him with the works of any standard writer whom he might select. The young man chose the works of Bacon, and Bacon accordingly made his appearance in ten nicely bound volumes. A little inspection, however, showed that the copy was a second-hand one.

Now that he had taken his degree the next thing to look forward to was ordination — about which Theobald had thought little hitherto beyond acquiescing in it as something that would come as a matter of course some day. Now, however, it had actually come and was asserting itself as a thing which should be only a few months off, and this rather frightened him inasmuch as there would be no way out of it when he was once in it. He did not like the near view of ordination as well as the distant one, and even made some feeble efforts to escape, as may be perceived by the following correspondence which his son Ernest found among his father's papers written on gilt-edged paper, in faded ink and tied neatly round with a piece of tape, but without any note or comment. I have altered nothing. The letters are as follows:

My Dear Father: I do not like opening up a question which has been considered settled, but as the time approaches I begin to be very doubtful how far I am fitted to be a clergyman. Not, I am thankful to say, that I have the faintest doubts about the Church of England, and I could subscribe cordially to every one of the thirty-nine articles which do indeed appear to me to be the *ne plus ultra* of human wisdom, and Paley, too, leaves no loophole for an opponent; but I am sure I should be running counter to your wishes if I were to conceal from you that I do not feel the inward call to be a minister of the gospel that I shall have to say I have felt when the Bishop ordains me. I try to get this feeling, I pray for it earnestly, and sometimes half think that I have got it, but in a little time it wears off, and though I have no absolute repugnance to being a clergyman and trust that if I am one I shall endeavour to live to the Glory of God and to advance His interests upon earth, yet I feel that something more than this is wanted before I am fully justified in going into the Church. I am aware that I have been a great expense to you in spite of my scholarships, but you have ever taught me that I should obey my conscience, and my conscience tells me I should do wrong if I became a clergyman. God may yet give me the spirit for which I assure you I have been and am continually praying, but He may not, and in that case would it not be better for me to try and look out for something else? I know that neither you nor John wish me to go into your business, nor do I understand anything about money matters, but is there nothing else that I can do? I do not like to ask you to maintain me while I go in for medicine or the bar; but when I get my fellowship, which should not be long first, I will endeavour to cost you nothing further, and I might make a little money by writing or taking pupils. I trust you will not think this letter improper; nothing is further from my wish than to cause you any uneasiness. I hope you will make allowance for my present feelings which, indeed, spring from nothing but from that respect for my conscience which no one has so often instilled into me as yourself. Pray let me have a few lines shortly. I hope your cold is better. With love to Eliza and Maria, I am your affectionate son,   THEOBALD PONTIFEX

Dear Theobald: I can enter into your feelings and have no wish to quarrel with your expression of them. It is quite right and natural that you should feel as you do except as regards one passage, the impropriety of which you will yourself doubtless feel upon reflection, and to which I will not further allude than to say that it has wounded me. You should not have said 'in spite of my scholarships'. It was only proper that if you could do anything to assist me in bearing the heavy burden of your education, the money should be, as it was, made over to myself. Every line in your letter convinces me that you are under the influence of a morbid sensitiveness which is one of the devil's favourite devices for luring people to their destruction. I have as you say, been at great expense with your education. Nothing has been spared by me to give you the advantages which, as an English gentle-man, I was anxious to afford my son, but I am not prepared to see that expense thrown away and to have to begin again from the beginning, merely because you have taken some foolish scruples into your head, which you should resist as no less unjust to yourself than to me.

Don't give way to that restless desire for change which is the bane of so many persons of both sexes at the present day.

Of course you needn't be ordained: nobody will compel you; you are perfectly free; you are twenty-three years of age, and should know your own mind; but why not have known it sooner, instead of never so much as breathing a hint of opposition until I have had all the expense of sending you to the University, which I should never have done unless I had believed you to have made up your mind about taking orders? I have letters from you in which you express the most perfect willingness to be ordained, and your brother and sisters will bear me out in saying that no pressure of any sort has been put upon you. You mistake your own mind, and are suffering from a nervous timidity which may be very natural but may not the less be pregnant with serious consequences to yourself. I am not at all well, and the anxiety occasioned by your letter is naturally preying upon me. May God guide you to a better judgment. Your affectionate father,

                                                                    G. PONTIFEX

On the receipt of this letter Theobald plucked up his spirits. 'My father,' he said to himself, 'tells me I need not be ordained if I do not like. I do not like, and therefore I will not be ordained. But what was the meaning of the words "pregnant with serious consequences to yourself"? Did there lurk a threat under these words — though it was impossible to lay hold of it or of them? Were they not intended to produce all the effect of a threat without being actually threatening?'

Theobald knew his father well enough to be little likely to misapprehend his meaning, but having ventured so far on the path of opposition, and being really anxious to get out of being ordained if he could, he determined to venture further. He accordingly wrote the following:

My Dear Father: You tell me — and I heartily thank you — that no one will compel me to be ordained. I knew you would not press ordination upon me if my conscience was seriously opposed to it; I have therefore resolved on giving up the idea, and believe that if you will continue to allow me what you do at present, until I get my fellowship, which should not be long, I will then cease putting you to further expense. I will make up my mind as soon as possible what profession I will adopt, and will let you know at once. Your affectionate son,

THEOBALD PONTIFEX

The remaining letter, written by return of post, must now be given. It has the merit of brevity.

Dear Theobald: I have received yours. I am at a loss to conceive its motive, but am very clear as to its effect. You shall not receive a single sixpence from me till you come to your senses. Should you persist in your folly and wickedness, I am happy to remember that I have yet other children whose conduct I can depend upon to be a source of credit and happiness to me. Your affectionate but troubled father,

G. PONTIFEX

I do not know the immediate sequel to the foregoing correspondence, but it all came perfectly right in the end. Either Theobald's heart failed him, or he interpreted the outward shove which his father gave him, as the inward call for which I have no doubt he prayed with great earnestness — for he was a firm believer in the efficacy of prayer. And so am I under certain circumstances. Tennyson has said that more things are wrought by prayer than this world dreams of, but he has wisely refrained from saying whether they are good things or bad things. It might perhaps be as well if the world were to dream of, or even become wide awake to, some of the things that are being wrought by prayer. But the question is avowedly difficult. In the end Theobald got his fellowship by a stroke of luck very soon after taking his degree, and was ordained in the autumn of the same year, 1825.

CHAPTER NINE

MR. ALLABY was rector of Crampsford, a village a few miles from Cambridge. He, too, had taken a good degree, had got a fellowship, and in the course of time had accepted a college living of about £400 a year and a house. His private income did not exceed £200 a year. On resigning his fellowship he married a woman a good deal younger than himself who bore him eleven children, nine of whom — two sons and seven daughters — were living. The two eldest daughters had married fairly well, but at the time of which I am now writing there were still five unmarried, of ages varying between thirty and twenty-two — and the sons were neither of them yet off their father's hands. It was plain that if anything were to happen to Mr. Allaby the family would be left poorly off, and this made both Mr. and Mrs. Allaby as unhappy as it ought to have made them.

Reader, did you ever have an income at best none too large, which died with you all except £200 a year? Did you ever at the same time have two sons who must be started in life somehow, and five daughters still unmarried for whom you would only be too thankful to find husbands — if you knew how to find them? If morality is that which, on the whole, brings a man peace in his declining years — if, that is to say, it is not an utter swindle, can you under these circumstances flatter yourself that you have led a moral life?

And this, even though your wife has been so good a woman that you have not grown tired of her, and has not fallen into such ill-health as lowers your own health in sympathy; and though your family has grown up vigorous, amiable and blessed with common sense. I know many old men and women who are reputed moral, but who are living with partners whom they have long ceased to love, or who have ugly disagreeable maiden daughters for whom they have never been able to find husbands — daughters whom they loathe and by whom they are loathed in secret, or sons whose folly or extravagance is a perpetual wear and worry to them. Is it moral for a man to have brought such things upon himself? Someone should do for morals what that old Pecksniff Bacon has obtained the credit of having done for science.

But to return to Mr. and Mrs. Allaby. Mrs. Allaby talked about having married two of her daughters as though it had been the easiest thing in the world. She talked in this way because she heard other mothers do so, but in her heart of hearts she did not know how she had done it, nor indeed, if it had been her doing at all. First there had been a young man in connection with whom she had tried to practise certain manœuvres which she had rehearsed in imagination over and over again, but which she found impossible to apply in practice. Then there had been weeks of a *wurra wurra* of hopes and fears and little stratagems which as often as not proved injudicious, and then somehow or other in the end, there lay the young man bound and with an arrow through his heart at her daughter's feet. It seemed to her to be all a fluke which she could have little or no hope of repeating. She had indeed repeated it once, and might perhaps with good luck repeat it yet once again — but five times over! It was awful: why, she would rather have three confinements than go through the wear and tear of marrying a single daughter.

Nevertheless it had got to be done, and poor Mrs. Allaby never looked at a young man without an eye to his being a future son-in-law. Papas and mammas sometimes ask young men whether their intentions are honourable towards their daughters. I think young men might occasionally ask papas and mammas whether their intentions are honourable before they accept invitations to houses where there are still unmarried daughters.

'I can't afford a curate, my dear,' said Mr. Allaby to his wife when the pair were discussing what was next to be done. 'It will be better to get some young man to come and help me for a time upon a Sunday. A guinea a Sunday will do this, and we can chop and change till we get someone who suits.' So it was settled that Mr. Allaby's health was not so strong as it had been, and that he stood in need of help in the performance of his Sunday duty.

Mrs. Allaby had a great friend — a certain Mrs. Cowey, wife of the celebrated Professor Cowey. She was what was called a truly spiritually-minded woman, a trifle portly, with an incipient beard, and an extensive connection among undergraduates, more especially among those who were inclined to take part in the great evangelical movement which was then at its height. She gave evening parties once a fortnight at which prayer was part of the entertainment. She was not only spiritually-minded, but, as enthusiastic Mrs. Allaby used to exclaim, she was a thorough woman of the world at the same time and had such a fund of strong masculine good sense. She, too, had daughters, but, as she used to say to Mrs. Allaby, she had been less fortunate than Mrs. Allaby herself, for one by one they had married and left her so that her old age would have been desolate indeed if her Professor had not been spared to her.

Mrs. Cowey, of course, knew the run of all the bachelor clergy in the University, and was the very person to assist Mrs. Allaby in finding an eligible assistant for her husband, so this last-named lady drove over one morning in the November of 1825, by arrangement, to take an early dinner with Mrs. Cowey and spend the afternoon. After dinner the two ladies retired together, and the business of the day began. How they fenced, how they saw through one another, with what loyalty they pretended not to see through one another, with what gentle dalliance they prolonged the conversation discussing the spiritual fitness of this or that deacon, and the other pros and cons connected with him after his spiritual fitness had been disposed of, all this must be left to the imagination of the reader. Mrs. Cowey had been so accustomed to scheming on her own account that she would scheme for anyone rather than not scheme at all. Many others turned to her in their hour of need and, provided they were spiritually-minded, Mrs. Cowey never failed to do her best for them; if the marriage of a young Bachelor of Arts was not made in Heaven, it was probably made, or at any rate attempted, in Mrs. Cowey's drawing-room. On the present occasion all the deacons of the University in whom there lurked any spark of promise were exhaustively discussed, and the upshot was that our friend Theobald was declared by Mrs. Cowey to be about the best thing she could do that afternoon.

'I don't know that he's a particularly fascinating young man, my dear,' said Mrs. Cowey, 'and he's only a second son, but then he's got his fellowship, and even the second son of such a man as Mr. Pontifex the publisher should have something very comfortable.'

'Why yes, my dear,' rejoined Mrs. Allaby complacently, 'that's what one rather feels.'

T H E next morning saw Theobald in his rooms coaching a pupil, and the Miss Allabys in the eldest Miss Allaby's bedroom playing at cards with Theobald for stakes.

The winner was Christina, the second unmarried daughter, then just twenty-seven years old and therefore four years older than Theobald. The younger sisters complained that it was throwing a husband away to let Christina try and catch him, for she was so much older that she had no chance; but Christina showed fight in a way not usual with her, for she was by nature yielding and good-tempered. Her mother thought it better to back her up, so the two dangerous ones were packed off then and there on visits to friends some way off, and those alone allowed to remain at home whose loyalty could be depended upon. The brothers did not even suspect what was going on and believed their father's getting assistance was because he really wanted it.

The sisters who remained at home kept their words and gave Christina all the help they could, for over and above their sense of fair play they reflected that the sooner Theobald was landed, the sooner another deacon might be sent for who might be won by themselves. So quickly was all managed that the two unreliable sisters were actually out of the house before Theobald's next visit — which was on the Sunday following his first.

This time Theobald felt quite at home in the house of his new friends — for so Mrs. Allaby insisted that he should call them. She took, she said, such a motherly interest in young men, especially in clergymen. Theobald believed every word she said, as he had believed his father and all his elders from his youth up. Christina sat next him at dinner and played her cards no less judiciously than she had played them in her sister's bedroom. She smiled (and her smile was one of her strong points) whenever he spoke to her; she went through all her little art-lessnesses and set forth all her little wares in what she believed to be their most taking aspect. Who can blame her? Theobald was not the ideal she had dreamed of when reading Byron upstairs with her sisters, but he was an actual within the bounds of possibility, and after all not a bad actual as actuals went. What else could she do? Run away? She dared not. Marry beneath her and be considered a disgrace to her family? She dared not. Remain at home and become an old maid and be laughed at? Not if she could help it. She did the only thing that could reasonably be expected. She was drowning; Theobald might be only a straw, but she could catch at him and catch at him she accordingly did.

If the course of true love never runs smooth, the course of true match-making sometimes does so. The only ground for complaint in the present case was that it was rather slow. Theobald fell into the part assigned to him more easily than Mrs. Cowey and Mrs. Allaby had dared to hope. He was softened by Christina's winning manners: he admired the high moral tone of everything she said; her sweetness towards her sisters and her father and mother, her readiness to undertake any small burden which no one else seemed willing to undertake, her sprightly manners, all were fascinating to one who, though unused to women's society, was still a human being. He was flattered by her unobtrusive but obviously sincere admiration for himself; she seemed to see him in a more favourable light, and to understand him better than anyone outside of this charming family had ever done. Instead of snubbing him as his father, brother and sisters did, she drew him out, listened attentively to all he chose to say, and evidently wanted him to say still more. He told a college friend that he knew he was in love now; he really was, for he liked Miss Allaby's society much better than that of his sisters.

Over and above the recommendations already enumerated, she had another in the possession of what was supposed to be a very beautiful contralto voice. Her voice was certainly contralto, for she could not reach higher than D in the treble; its only defect was that it did not go correspondingly low in the bass: in those days, however, a contralto voice was understood to include even a soprano if the soprano could not reach soprano notes, and it was not necessary that it should have the quality which we now assign to contralto. What her voice wanted in range and power was made up in the feeling with which she sang. She had transposed 'Angels ever bright and fair' into a lower key, so as to make it suit her voice, thus proving, as her mamma said, that she had a thorough knowledge of the laws of harmony; not only did she do this, but at every pause added an embellishment of arpeggios from one end to the other of the keyboard, on a principle which her governess had taught her; she thus added life and interest to an air which everyone — so she said — must feel to be rather heavy in the form in which Handel left it. As for her governess, she indeed had been a rarely accomplished musician; she was a pupil of the famous Dr. Clarke of Cambridge, and used to play the overture to *Atalanta*, arranged by Mazzinghi. Nevertheless, it was some time before Theobald could bring his courage to the sticking point of actually proposing. He made it quite clear that he believed himself to be much smitten, but month after month went by, during which there was still so much hope in Theobald that Mr. Allaby dared not discover that he was able to do his duty for himself, and was getting impatient at the number of half-guineas[1] he was disbursing — and yet there was no proposal. Christina's mother assured him that she was the best daughter in the whole world, and would be a priceless treasure to the man who married her. Theobald echoed Mrs. Allaby's sentiments with warmth, but still, though he visited the Rectory two or three times a week, besides coming over on Sundays — he did not propose. 'She is heart-whole yet, dear Mr. Pontifex,' said Mrs. Allaby, one day, 'at least I believe she is. It is not for want of admirers — oh! no — she has had her full share of these, but she is too, too difficult to please. I think, however, she would fall before a *great and good* man.' And she looked hard at Theobald, who blushed; but the days went by and still he did not propose.

Another time Theobald actually took Mrs. Cowey into his confidence, and the reader may guess what account of Christina he got from her. Mrs. Cowey tried the jealousy manœuvre and hinted at a possible rival. Theobald was, or pretended to be, very much alarmed; a little rudimentary pang of jealousy shot across his bosom and he began to believe with pride that he was not only in love, but desperately in love or he would never feel so jealous. Nevertheless, day after day still went by and he did not propose.

The Allabys behaved with great judgment. They humoured him till his retreat was practically cut off, though he still flattered himself that it was open. One day about six months after Theobald had become an almost daily visitor at the Rectory the conversation happened to turn upon long engagements. 'I don't like long engagements, Mr. Allaby, do you?' said Theobald imprudently. 'No,' said Mr. Allaby in appointed tone, 'nor long courtships,' and he gave Theobald a look which he could not pretend to misunderstand. He went back to Cambridge as fast as he could go, and in dread of the conversation with Mr. Allaby which he felt to be impending, composed the following letter which he dispatched that same afternoon

[1] The guinea mentioned on p. 197 was halved [Ed.].

by a private messenger to Crampsford. The letter was as follows:

Dearest Miss Christina: I do not know whether you have guessed the feelings that I have long entertained for you — feelings which I have concealed as much as I could through fear of drawing you into an engagement which, if you enter into it, must be prolonged for a considerable time, but, however this may be, it is out of my power to conceal them longer; I love you, ardently, devotedly, and send these few lines asking you to be my wife, because I dare not trust my tongue to give adequate expression to the magnitude of my affection for you.

I cannot pretend to offer you a heart which has never known either love or disappointment. I have loved already, and my heart was years in recovering from the grief I felt at seeing her become another's. That, however, is over, and having seen yourself I rejoice over a disappointment which I thought at one time would have been fatal to me. It has left me a less ardent lover than I should perhaps otherwise have been, but it has increased tenfold my power of appreciating your many charms and my desire that you should become my wife. Please let me have a few lines of answer by the bearer to let me know whether or not my suit is accepted. If you accept me I will at once come and talk the matter over with Mr. and Mrs. Allaby, whom I shall hope one day to be allowed to call father and mother.

I ought to warn you that in the event of your consenting to be my wife it may be years before our union can be consummated, for I cannot marry till a college living is offered me. If, therefore, you see fit to reject me, I shall be grieved rather than surprised. Ever most devotedly yours,   THEOBALD PONTIFEX

And this was all that his public school and University education had been able to do for Theobald! Nevertheless for his own part he thought his letter rather a good one, and congratulated himself in particular upon his cleverness in inventing the story of a previous attachment, behind which he intended to shelter himself if Christina should complain of any lack of fervour in his behaviour to her.

I need not give Christina's answer, which of course was to accept. Much as Theobald feared old Mr. Allaby I do not think he would have wrought up his courage to the point of actually proposing but for the fact of the engagement being necessarily a long one, during which a dozen things might turn up to break it off. However much he may have disapproved of long engagements for other people, I doubt whether he had any particular objection to them in his own case. A pair of lovers are like sunset and sunrise; there are such things every day but we very seldom see them. Theobald posed as the most ardent lover imaginable, but, to use the vulgarism for the moment in fashion, it was all 'side'. Christina was in love as indeed she had been twenty times already. But then Christina was impressionable and could not even hear the name 'Missolonghi' mentioned without bursting into tears. When Theobald accidentally left his sermon case behind him one Sunday, she slept with it in her bosom and was forlorn when she had as it were to disgorge it on the following Sunday; but I do not think Theobald ever took so much as an old toothbrush of Christina's to bed with him. Why, I knew a young man once who got hold of his mistress's skates and slept with them for a fortnight and cried when he had to give them up.

CHAPTER TWELVE

IN those days people believed with a simple downrightness which I do not observe among educated men and women now. It had never so much as crossed Theobald's mind to doubt the literal accuracy of any syllable in the Bible. He had never seen any book in which this was disputed, nor met with anyone who doubted it. True, there was just a little scare about geology, but there was nothing in it. If it was said that God made the world in six days, why He did make it in six days, neither in more nor less; if it was said that He put Adam to sleep, took out one of his ribs and made a woman of it, why it was so as a matter of course. He, Adam, went to sleep as it might be himself, Theobald Pontifex, in a garden, as it might be the garden at Cramps-ford Rectory during the summer months when it was so pretty, only that it was larger, and had some tame wild animals in it. Then God came up to him, as it might be Mr. Allaby or his father, dexterously took out one of his ribs without waking him, and miraculously healed the wound so that no trace of the operation remained. Finally, God had taken the rib perhaps into the greenhouse, and had turned it into just such another young woman as Christina. That was how it was done; there was neither difficulty nor shadow of difficulty about the matter. Could not God do anything He liked, and had He not in His own inspired Book told us that He had done this?

This was the average attitude of fairly educated young men and women towards the Mosaic cosmogony fifty, forty or even twenty years ago. The combating of infidelity, therefore, offered little scope for enterprising young clergymen, nor had the Church awakened to the activity which she has since displayed among the poor in our large towns. These were then left almost without an effort at resistance or co-operation to the labours of those who had succeeded Wesley. Missionary work indeed in heathen countries was being carried on with some energy, but Theobald did not feel any call to be a missionary. Christina suggested this to him more than once, and assured him of the unspeakable happiness it would be to her to be the wife of a missionary, and to share his dangers; she and Theobald might even be martyred; of course they would be martyred simultaneously, and martyrdom many years hence as regarded from the arbour in the Rectory garden was not painful; it would ensure them a glorious future in the next world, and at any rate posthumous renown in this — even if they were not miraculously restored to life again — and such things had happened ere now in the case of martyrs. Theobald, however, had not been kindled by Christina's enthusiasm, so she fell back upon the Church of Rome — an enemy more dangerous, if possible, than paganism itself. A combat with Romanism might even yet win for her and Theobald the crown of martyrdom. True, the Church of Rome was tolerably quiet just then, but it was the calm before the storm, of this she was assured, with a conviction deeper than she could have attained by any argument founded upon mere reason.

'We, dearest Theobald,' she exclaimed, 'will be ever faithful. We will stand firm and support one another even in the hour of death itself. God in His mercy may spare us from being burnt alive. He may or may not do so. O Lord' (and she turned her eyes prayerfully to Heaven), 'spare my Theobald, or grant that he may be beheaded.'

'My dearest,' said Theobald gravely, 'do not let us agitate ourselves unduly. If the hour of trial comes we shall be best prepared to meet it by having led a quiet unobtrusive life of self-denial and devotion to God's glory. Such a life let us pray God that it may please Him to enable us to pray that we may lead.'

'Dearest Theobald,' exclaimed Christina, drying the tears that had gathered in her eyes, 'you are always, always right. Let us be self-denying, pure, upright, truthful in word and deed.' She clasped her hands and looked up to Heaven as she spoke.

'Dearest,' rejoined her lover, 'we have ever hitherto endeavoured to be all of these things; we have not been worldly people; let us watch and pray that we may so continue to the end.'

The moon had risen and the arbour was getting damp, so they adjourned further aspirations for a more convenient season. At other times Christina pictured herself and Theobald as braving the scorn of almost every human being in the achievement of some mighty task which should redound to the honour of her Redeemer. She could face anything for this. But always towards the end of her vision there came a little coronation scene high up in the golden regions of the Heavens, and a diadem was set upon her head by the Son of Man Himself, amid a host of angels and archangels who looked on with envy and admiration — and here even Theobald himself was out of it. If there could be such a thing as the Mammon of Righteousness Christina would have assuredly made friends with it. Her papa and mamma were very estimable people and would in the course of time receive Heavenly Mansions in which they would be exceedingly comfortable; so doubtless would her sisters; so perhaps, even might her brothers; but for herself she felt that a higher destiny was preparing, which it was her duty never to lose sight of. The first step towards it would be her marriage with Theobald. In spite, however, of these flights of religious romanticism, Christina was a good-tempered, kindly-natured girl enough, who, if she had married a sensible layman — we will say a hotel-keeper — would have developed into a good landlady and been deservedly popular with her guests.

Such was Theobald's engaged life. Many a little present passed between the pair, and many a small surprise did they prepare pleasantly for one another. They never quarrelled, and neither of them ever flirted with anyone else. Mrs. Allaby and his future sisters-in-law idolized Theobald in spite of its being impossible to get another deacon to come and be played for as long as Theobald was able to help Mr. Allaby, which now of course he did free gratis and for nothing; two of the sisters, however, did manage to find husbands before Christina was actually married, and on each occasion Theobald played the part of decoy elephant. In the end only two out of the seven daughters remained single.

After three or four years, old Mr. Pontifex became accustomed to his son's engagement and looked upon it as among the things which had now a prescriptive right to toleration. In the spring of 1831, more than five years after Theobald had first walked over to Crampsford, one of the best livings in the gift of the College unexpectedly fell vacant, and was for various reasons declined by the two fellows senior to Theobald, who might each have been expected to take it. The living was then offered to and of course accepted by Theobald, being in value not less than £500 a year with a suitable house and garden. Old Mr. Pontifex then came down more handsomely than was expected and settled £10,000 on his son and daughter-in-law for life with remainder to such of their issue as they might appoint. In the month of July 1831, Theobald and Christina became man and wife.

CHAPTER THIRTEEN

A DUE number of old shoes had been thrown at the carriage in which the happy pair departed from the Rectory, and it had turned the corner at the bottom of the village. It could then be seen for two or three hundred yards creeping past a fir coppice, and after this was lost to view.

'John,' said Mr. Allaby to his manservant, 'shut the gate,' and he went indoors with a sigh of relief which seemed to say: 'I have done it, and I am alive.' This was the reaction after a burst of enthusiastic merriment during which the old gentleman had run twenty yards after the carriage to fling a slipper at it — which he had duly flung.

But what were the feelings of Theobald and Christina when the village was passed and they were rolling quietly by the fir plantation? It is at this point that even the stoutest heart must fail, unless it beat in the breast of one who is over head and ears in love. If a young man is in a small boat on a choppy sea, along with his affianced bride and both are sea-sick, and if the sick swain can forget his own anguish in the happiness of holding the fair one's head when she is at her worst — then he is in love, and his heart will be in no danger of failing him as he passes his fir plantation. Other people, and unfortunately by far the greater number of those who get married must be classed among the 'other people', will inevitably go through a quarter or half an hour of greater or less badness as the case may be. Taking numbers into account, I should think more mental suffering had been undergone in the streets leading from St. George's, Hanover Square, than in the condemned cells of Newgate. There is no time at which what the Italians call *la figlia della Morte* lays her cold hand upon a man more awfully

206

than during the first half-hour that he is alone with a woman whom he has married but never genuinely loved.

Death's daughter did not spare Theobald. He had behaved very well hitherto. When Christina had offered to let him go, he had stuck to his post with a magnanimity on which he had plumed himself ever since. From that time forward he had said to himself: 'I, at any rate, am the very soul of honour; I am not,' etc. etc. True, at the moment of magnanimity the actual cash payment, so to speak, was still distant; when his father gave formal consent to his marriage things began to look more serious; when the college living had fallen vacant and been accepted they looked more serious still; but when Christina actually named the day, then Theobald's heart fainted within him.

The engagement had gone on so long that he had got into a groove, and the prospect of change was disconcerting. Christina and he had got on, he thought to himself, very nicely for a great number of years; why — why — why should they not continue to go on as they were doing now for the rest of their lives? But there was no more chance of escape for him than for the sheep which is being driven to the butcher's back premises, and like the sheep he felt that there was nothing to be gained by resistance, so he made none. He behaved, in fact, with decency and was declared on all hands to be one of the happiest men imaginable.

Now, however, to change the metaphor, the drop had actually fallen, and the poor wretch was hanging in mid-air along with the creature of his affections. This creature was now thirty-three years old, and looked it: she had been weeping, and her eyes and nose were reddish; if 'I have done it and I am alive,' was written on Mr. Allaby's face after he had thrown the shoe, 'I have done it, and I do not see how I can possibly live much longer' was upon the face of Theobald as he was being driven along by the fir plantation. This, however, was not apparent at the Rectory. All that could be seen there was the bobbing up and down of the postilion's head, which just over-topped the hedge by the roadside as he rose in his stirrups, and the black and yellow body of the carriage.

For some time the pair said nothing: what they must have felt during their first half-hour, the reader must guess, for it is beyond my power to tell him; at the end of that time, however, Theobald had rummaged up a conclusion from some odd corner of his soul to the effect that now he and Christina were married the sooner they fell into their future mutual relations the better. If people who are in a difficulty will only do the first little reasonable thing which they can clearly recognize as reasonable, they will always find the next step more easy both to see and take. What, then, thought Theobald, was here at this moment the first and most obvious matter to be considered, and what would be an equitable view of his and Christina's relative positions in respect to it? Clearly their first dinner was their first joint entry into the duties and pleasures of married life. No less clearly it was Christina's duty to order it, and his own to eat it and pay for it.

The arguments leading to this conclusion, and the conclusion itself, flashed upon Theobald about three and a half miles after he had left Crampsford on the road to Newmarket. He had breakfasted early, but his usual appetite had failed him. They had left the vicarage at noon without staying for the wedding breakfast. Theobald liked an early dinner; it dawned upon him that he was beginning to be hungry; from this to the conclusion stated in the preceding paragraph the steps had been easy. After a few minutes' further reflection he broached the matter to his bride, and thus the ice was broken.

Mrs. Theobald was not prepared for so sudden an assumption of importance. Her nerves, never of the strongest, had been strung to their highest tension by the event of the morning. She wanted to escape observation; she was conscious of looking a little older than she quite liked to look as a bride who had been married that morning; she feared the landlady, the chambermaid, the waiter — everybody and everything; her heart beat so fast that she could hardly speak, much less go through the ordeal of ordering dinner in a strange hotel with a strange landlady. She begged and prayed to be let off. If Theobald would only order dinner this once, she would order it any day and every day in future.

But the inexorable Theobald was not to be put off with such absurd excuses. He was master now. Had not Christina less than two hours ago promised solemnly to honour and obey him, and was she turning restive over such a trifle as this? The loving smile departed from his face, and was succeeded by a scowl which that old Turk, his father, might have envied. 'Stuff and nonsense, my dearest Christina,' he exclaimed mildly, and stamped his foot upon the floor of the carriage. 'It is a wife's duty to order her husband's dinner; you are my wife, and I shall expect you to order mine.' For Theobald was nothing if he was not logical.

The bride began to cry, and said he was unkind; whereon he said nothing, but revolved unutterable things in his heart. Was this, then, the end of his six years of unflagging devotion? Was it for this that when Christina had offered to let him off, he had stuck to his engagement? Was this the outcome of her talks about duty and spiritual-mindedness — that now upon the very day of her marriage she should fail to see that the first step in obedience to God lay in obedience to himself? He would drive back to Crampsford; he would complain to Mr. and Mrs. Allaby; he didn't mean to have married Christina; he hadn't married her; it was all a hideous dream; he would — But a voice kept ringing in his ears which said: 'You CAN'T, CAN'T, CAN'T.'

'CAN'T I?' screamed the unhappy creature to himself.

'No,' said the remorseless voice, 'YOU CAN'T. YOU ARE A MARRIED MAN.'

He rolled back in his corner of the carriage and for the first time felt how iniquitous were the marriage laws of England. But he would buy Milton's prose works and read his pamphlet on divorce. He might perhaps be able to get them at Newmarket.

So the bride sat crying in one corner of the carriage; and the bridegroom sulked in the other, and he feared her as only a bridegroom can fear.

Presently, however, a feeble voice was heard from the bride's corner saying:

'Dearest Theobald — dearest Theobald, forgive me; I have been very, very wrong. Please do not be angry with me. I will order the — the —' but the word 'dinner' was checked by rising sobs.

When Theobald heard these words a load began to be lifted from his heart, but he only looked towards her, and that not too pleasantly.

'Please tell me,' continued the voice, 'what you think you would like, and I will tell the landlady when we get to Newmar —' but another burst of sobs checked the completion of the word.

The load on Theobald's heart grew lighter and lighter. Was it possible that she might not be going to henpeck him after all? Besides, had she not diverted his attention from herself to his approaching dinner?

He swallowed down more of his apprehensions and said, but still gloomily, 'I think we might have a roast fowl with bread sauce, new potatoes and green peas, and then we will see if they could let us have a cherry tart and some cream.'

After a few minutes more he drew her towards him, kissed away her tears, and assured her that he knew she would be a good wife to him.

'Dearest Theobald,' she exclaimed in answer, 'you are an angel.'

Theobald believed her, and in ten minutes more the happy couple alighted at the inn at Newmarket.

Bravely did Christina go through her arduous task. Eagerly did she beseech the landlady, in secret, not to keep her Theobald waiting longer than was absolutely necessary.'

'If you have any soup ready, you know, Mrs. Barber, it might save ten minutes, for we might have it while the fowl is browning.'

See how necessity had nerved her! But in truth she had a splitting headache, and would have given anything to have been alone.

The dinner was a success. A pint of sherry had warmed Theobald's heart, and he began to hope that, after all, matters might still go well with him. He had conquered in the first battle, and this gives great prestige. How easy it had been too! Why had he never treated his sisters in this way? He would do so next time he saw them; he might in time be able to stand up to his brother John, or even his father. Thus do we build castles in air when flushed with wine and conquest.

The end of the honeymoon saw Mrs. Theobald the most devotedly obsequious wife in all England. According to the old saying, Theobald had killed the cat at the beginning. It had been a very little cat, a mere kitten in fact, or he might have been afraid to face it, but such as it had been he had challenged it to mortal combat, and had held up its dripping head defiantly before his wife's face. The rest had been easy.

Strange that one whom I have described hitherto as so timid and easily put upon should prove such a Tartar all of a sudden on the day of his marriage. Perhaps I have passed over his years of courtship too rapidly. During these he had become a tutor of his college, and had at last been Junior Dean. I never yet knew a man whose sense of his own importance did not become adequately developed after he had held a resident fellowship for five or six years. True — immediately on arriving within a ten mile radius of his father's house, an enchantment fell upon him, so that his knees waxed weak, his greatness departed, and he again felt himself like an overgrown baby under a perpetual cloud; but then he was not often at Elmhurst, and as soon as he left it the spell was taken off again; once more he became the fellow and tutor of his college, the Junior Dean, the betrothed of Christina, the idol of the Allaby womankind. From all which it may be gathered that if Christina had been a Barbary hen, and had ruffled her feathers in any show of resistance Theobald would not have ventured to swagger with her, but she was not a Barbary hen, she was only a common hen, and that too with rather a smaller share of personal bravery than hens generally have.

CHAPTER FOURTEEN

I REMEMBER staying with Theobald some six or seven months after he was married, and while the old church was still standing. I went to church, and felt as Naaman must have felt on certain occasions when he had to accompany his master on his return after having been cured of his leprosy. I have carried away a more vivid recollection of this and of the people, than of Theobald's sermon. Even now I can see the men in blue smock-frocks reaching to their heels, and more than one old woman in a scarlet cloak; the row of stolid, dull, vacant ploughboys, ungainly in build, uncomely in face, lifeless, apathetic, a race a good deal more like the pre-revolution French peasant as described by Carlyle than is pleasant to reflect upon — a race now supplanted by a smarter, comelier and more hopeful generation, which has discovered that it too has a right to as much happiness as it can get, and with clearer ideas about the best means of getting it.

They shamble in one after another, with steaming breath, for it is winter, and loud clattering of hob-nailed boots; they beat the snow from off them as they enter, and through the opened door I catch a momentary glimpse of a dreary leaden sky and snow-clad tombstones. Somehow or other I find the strain which Handel has wedded to the words 'There the ploughman near at hand,' has got into my head and there is no getting it out again. How marvellously old Handel understood these people!

They bob to Theobald as they pass the reading-desk ('The people hereabouts are truly respectful,' whispered Christina to me, 'they know their betters'), and take their seats in a long row against the wall. The choir clamber up into the gallery with their instruments — a violoncello, a clarinet and a trombone. I see them and soon I hear them, for there is a hymn before the service, a wild strain, a remnant, if I mistake not, of some pre-Reformation litany. I have heard what I believe was its remote musical progenitor in the church of SS. Giovanni e Paolo at Venice not five years since; and again I have heard it far away in mid-

Atlantic upon a grey sea-Sabbath in June, when neither winds nor waves are stirring, so that the emigrants gather on deck, and their plaintive psalm goes forth upon the silver haze of the sky, and on the wilderness of a sea that has sighed till it can sigh no longer. Or it may be heard at some Methodist Camp Meeting upon a Welsh hillside, but in the churches it is gone for ever. If I were a musician I would take it as the subject for the *adagio* in a Wesleyan symphony.

Gone now are the clarinet, the violoncello and the trombone, wild minstrelsy as of the doleful creatures in Ezekiel, discordant, but infinitely pathetic. Gone is that scare-babe stentor, that bellowing bull of Bashan the village blacksmith, gone is the melodious carpenter, gone the brawny shepherd with the red hair, who roared more lustily than all, until they came to the words, 'Shepherds with your flocks abiding', when modesty covered him with confusion, and compelled him to be silent, as though his own health were being drunk. They were doomed and had a presentiment of evil, even when first I saw them, but they had still a little lease of choir life remaining, and they roared out:

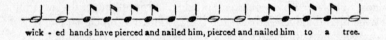

wick - ed hands have pierced and nailed him, pierced and nailed him to a tree.

but no description can give a proper idea of the effect. When I was last in Battersby church there was a harmonium played by a sweet-looking girl with a choir of school children around her, and they chanted the canticles to the most correct of chants, and they sang Hymns Ancient and Modern; the high pews were gone, nay, the very gallery in which the old choir had sung was removed as an accursed thing which might remind the people of the high places, and Theobald was old, and Christina was lying under the yew trees in the churchyard.

But in the evening later on I saw three very old men come chuckling out of a dissenting chapel, and surely enough they were my old friends the blacksmith, the carpenter and the shepherd. There was a look of content upon their faces which made me feel certain they had been singing; not doubtless with the old glory of the violoncello, the clarinet and the trombone, but still songs of Sion and no new-fangled papistry.

PERHAPS I have now said enough to indicate the kind of place in which Theobald's lines were cast, and the sort of woman he had married. As for his own habits, I see him trudging through muddy lanes and over long sweeps of plover-haunted pastures to visit a dying cottager's wife. He takes her meat and wine from his own table, and that not a little only but liberally. According to his lights also, he administers what he is pleased to call spiritual consolation.

'I am afraid I'm going to Hell, Sir,' says the sick woman with a whine. 'Oh, Sir, save me, save me, don't let me go there. I couldn't stand it, Sir, I should die with fear, the very thought of it drives me into a cold sweat all over.'

'Mrs. Thompson,' says Theobald gravely, 'you must have faith in the precious blood of your Redeemer; it is He alone who can save you.'

'But are you sure, Sir,' says she, looking wistfully at him, 'that He will forgive me — for I've not been a very good woman, indeed I haven't — and if God would only say "Yes" outright with His mouth when I ask whether my sins are forgiven me —'

'But they *are* forgiven you, Mrs. Thompson,' says Theobald with some sternness, for the same ground has been gone over a good many times already, and he has borne the unhappy woman's misgivings now for a full quarter of an hour. Then he puts a stop to the conversation by repeating prayers taken from the 'Visitation of the Sick', and overawes the poor wretch from expressing further anxiety as to her condition.

'Can't you tell me, Sir,' she exclaims piteously, as she sees that he is preparing to go away, 'can't you tell me that there is no Day of Judgment, and that there is no such place as Hell? I can do without the Heaven, Sir, but I cannot do with the Hell.' Theobald is much shocked.

'Mrs. Thompson,' he rejoins impressively, 'let me implore you to suffer no doubt concerning these two corner-stones of our religion to cross your mind at a moment like the present. If there is one thing more certain than another it is that we shall all appear before the Judgment Seat of Christ, and that the wicked will be consumed in a lake of everlasting fire. Doubt this, Mrs. Thompson, and you are lost.'

The poor woman buries her fevered head in the coverlet in a paroxysm of fear which at last finds relief in tears.

'Mrs. Thompson,' says Theobald, with his hand on the door, 'compose yourself, be calm; you must please to take my word for it that at the Day of Judgment your sins will be all washed white in the blood of the Lamb, Mrs. Thompson. Yea,' he exclaims frantically, 'though they be as scarlet, yet shall they be as white as wool,' and he makes off as fast as he can from the fetid atmosphere of the cottage to the pure air out-side. Oh, how thankful he is when the interview is over!

He returns home, conscious that he has done his duty, and administered the comforts of religion to a dying sinner. His admiring wife awaits him at the Rectory, and assures him that never yet was clergyman so devoted to the welfare of his flock. He believes her; he has a natural tendency to believe everything that is told him, and who should know the facts of the case better than his wife? Poor fellow! He has done his best, but what does a fish's best come to when the fish is out of water? He has left meat and wine — that he can do; he will call again and will leave more meat and wine; day after day he trudges over the same plover-haunted fields, and listens at the end of his walk to the same agony of forebodings, which day after day he silences, but does not remove, till at last a merciful weakness renders the sufferer careless of her future, and Theobald is satisfied that her mind is now peacefully at rest in Jesus.

CHAPTER SIXTEEN

WHO so *integer vitæ scelerisque purus*, it was asked, as Mr. Ponti-fex of Battersby? Who so fit to be consulted if any difficulty about parish management should arise? Who such a happy mixture of the sincere uninquiring Christian and of the man of the world? For so people actually called him. They said he was such an admirable man of business. Certainly if he had said he would pay a sum of money at a certain time, the money would be forthcoming on the appointed day, and this is saying a good deal for any man. His constitutional timidity rendered him incapable of an attempt to overreach when there was the remotest chance of opposition or publicity, and his correct bearing and somewhat stern expression were a great protection to him against being overreached. He never talked of money, and invariably changed the subject whenever money was introduced. His expression of unutterable horror at all kinds of meanness was a sufficient guarantee that he was not mean himself. Besides he had no business transactions save of the most ordinary butcher's book and baker's book description. His tastes

— if he had any — were, as we have seen, simple; he had £900 a year and a house; the neighbourhood was cheap, and for some time he had no children to be a drag upon him. Who was not to be envied, and if envied why then respected, if Theobald was not enviable?

Yet I imagine that Christina was on the whole happier than her husband. She had not to go and visit sick parishioners, and the management of her house and the keeping of her accounts afforded as much occupation as she desired. Her principal duty was, as she well said, to her husband — to love him, honour him and keep him in a good temper. To do her justice she fulfilled this duty to the uttermost of her power. It would have been better perhaps if she had not so frequently assured her husband that he was the best and wisest of mankind, for no one in his little world ever dreamed of telling him anything else, and it was not long before he ceased to have any doubt upon the matter. As for his temper, which had become very violent at times, she took care to humour it on the slightest sign of an approaching outbreak. She had early found that this was much the easiest plan. The thunder was seldom for herself. Long before her marriage even she had studied his little ways, and knew how to add fuel to the fire as long as the fire seemed to want it, and then to damp it judiciously down, making as little smoke as possible.

In money matters she was scrupulousness itself. Theobald made her a quarterly allowance for her dress, pocket money and little charities and presents. In these last items she was liberal in proportion to her income; indeed she dressed with great economy and gave away whatever was over in presents or charity. Oh, what a comfort it was to Theobald to reflect that he had a wife on whom he could rely never to cost him a sixpence of unauthorized expenditure! Letting alone her absolute submission, the perfect coincidence of her opinion with his own upon every subject and her constant assurances to him that he was right in everything which he took it into his head to say or do, what a tower of strength to him was her exactness in money matters! As years went by he became as fond of his wife as it was in his nature to be of any living thing, and applauded himself for having stuck to his engagement — a piece of virtue of which he was now reaping the reward. Even when Christina did outrun her quarterly stipend by some thirty shillings or a couple of pounds, it was always made perfectly clear to Theobald how the deficiency had arisen — there had been an unusually costly evening dress bought which was to last a long time, or somebody's unexpected wedding had necessitated a more handsome present than the quarter's balance would quite allow: the excess of expenditure was always repaid in the following quarter or quarters even though it were only ten shillings at a time.

I believe, however, that after they had been married some twenty years, Christina had somewhat fallen from her original perfection as regards money. She had got gradually in arrear during many successive quarters, till she had contracted a chronic loan, a sort of domestic national debt, amounting to between seven and eight pounds. Theobald at length felt that a remonstrance had become imperative, and took advantage of his silver wedding day to inform Christina that her indebtedness was cancelled, and at the same time to beg that she would endeavour henceforth to equalize her expenditure and her income. She burst into tears of love and gratitude, assured him that he was the best and most generous of men, and never during the remainder of her married life was she a single shilling behindhand.

Christina hated change of all sorts no less cordially than her husband. She and Theobald had nearly everything in this world that they could wish for; why, then, should people desire to introduce all sorts of changes of which no one could foresee the end? Religion, she was deeply convinced, had long since attained its final development, nor could it enter into the heart of reasonable man to conceive any faith more perfect than was inculcated by the Church of England. She could imagine no position more honourable than that of a clergyman's wife unless indeed it were a bishop's. Considering his father's influence it was not at all impossible that Theobold might be a bishop some day — and then — then would occur to her that one little flaw in the practice of the Church of England — a flaw not indeed in its doctrine, but in its policy, which she believed on the whole to be a mistaken one in this respect. I mean the fact that a bishop's wife does not take the rank of her husband.

This had been the doing of Elizabeth, who had been a bad woman, of exceedingly doubtful moral character, and at heart a Papist to the last. Perhaps people ought to have been above mere considerations of worldly dignity, but the world was as it was, and such things carried weight with them, whether they ought to do so or no. Her influence as plain Mrs. Pontifex, wife, we will say, of the Bishop of Winchester, would no doubt be considerable. Such a character as hers could not fail to carry weight if she were ever in a sufficiently conspicuous sphere for

THE WAY OF ALL FLESH

its influence to be widely felt; but as Lady Winchester — or the Bishopess — which would sound quite nicely — who could doubt that her power for good would be enhanced? And it would be all the nicer because if she had a daughter the daughter would not be a Bishopess unless indeed she were to marry a Bishop too, which would not be likely.

These were her thoughts upon her good days; at other times she would, to do her justice, have doubts whether she was in all respects as spiritually-minded as she ought to be. She must press on, press on, till every enemy to her salvation was surmounted and Satan himself lay bruised under her feet. It occurred to her on one of these occasions that she might steal a march over some of her contemporaries if she were to leave off eating black puddings, of which whenever they had killed a pig she had hitherto partaken freely; and if she were also careful that no fowls were served at her table which had had their necks wrung, but only such as had had their throats cut and been allowed to bleed. St. Paul and the Church of Jerusalem had insisted upon it as necessary that even Gentile converts should abstain from things strangled and from blood, and they had joined this prohibition with that of a vice about the abominable nature of which there could be no question; it would be well therefore to abstain in future and see whether any noteworthy spiritual result ensued. She did abstain, and was certain that from the day of her resolve she had felt stronger, purer in heart, and in all respects more spiritually-minded than she had ever felt hitherto. Theobald did not lay so much stress on this as she did, but as she settled what he should have at dinner she could take care that he got no strangled fowls; as for black puddings, happily, he had seen them made when he was a boy, and had never got over his aversion for them. She wished the matter were one of more general observance than it was; this was just a case in which as Lady Winchester she might have been able to do what as plain Mrs. Pontifex it was hopeless even to attempt.

And thus this worthy couple jogged on from month to month and from year to year. The reader, if he has passed middle life and has a clerical connection, will probably remember scores and scores of rectors and rectors' wives who differed in no material respect from Theobald and Christina. Speaking from a recollection and experience extending over nearly eighty years from the time when I was myself a child in the nursery of a vicarage, I should say I had drawn the better rather than the worse side of the life of an English country parson of some fifty years ago. I admit, however, that there are no such people to be found nowadays. A more united, or, on the whole, happier couple could not have been found in England. One grief only over-shadowed the early years of their married life: I mean the fact that no living children were born to them.

CHAPTER SEVENTEEN

IN the course of time this sorrow was removed. At the beginning of the fifth year of her married life Christina was safely delivered of a boy. This was on September 6th, 1835.

Word was immediately sent to old Mr. Pontifex, who received the news with real pleasure. His son John's wife had borne daughters only, and he was seriously uneasy lest there should be a failure in the male line of his descendants. The good news, therefore, was doubly welcome, and caused as much delight at Elmhurst as dismay in Woburn Square, where the John Pontifexes were then living.

Here, indeed, this freak of fortune was felt to be all the more cruel on account of the impossibility of resenting it openly; but the delighted grandfather cared nothing for what the John Pontifexes might feel or not feel; he had wanted a grandson and he had got a grandson, and this should be enough for everybody; and, now that Mrs. Theobald had taken to good ways, she might bring him more grandsons, which would be desirable, for he should not feel safe with fewer than three.

He rang the bell for the butler.

'Gelstrap,' he said solemnly, 'I want to go down into the cellar.'

Then Gelstrap preceded him with a candle, and he went into the inner vault where he kept his choicest wines.

He passed many bins: there was 1803 Port, 1792 Imperial Tokay, 1800 Claret, 1812 Sherry, these and many others were passed, but it was not for them that the head of the Pontifex family had gone down into his inner cellar. A bin, which had appeared empty until the full light of the candle had been brought to bear upon it, was now found to contain a single pint bottle. This was the object of Mr. Pontifex's search.

Gelstrap had often pondered over this bottle. It had been placed there by Mr. Pontifex himself about a dozen years previously on his return from a visit to his friend the celebrated traveller Dr. Jones — but there was no tablet above the bin which might give a clue to the nature of its contents. On more than one occasion when his master had gone out and left his keys accidentally behind him, as he sometimes did, Gelstrap had submitted the bottle to all the tests he could venture upon, but it was so carefully sealed that wisdom remained quite shut out from that entrance at which he would have welcomed her most gladly — and indeed from all other entrances, for he could make out nothing at all.

And now the mystery was to be solved. But alas! it seemed as though the last chance of securing even a sip of the contents was to be removed for ever, for Mr. Pontifex took the bottle into his own hands and held it up to the light after carefully examining the seal. He smiled and left the bin with the bottle in his hands.

Then came a catastrophe. He stumbled over an empty hamper; there was the sound of a fall — a smash of broken glass, and in an instant the cellar floor was covered with the liquid that had been preserved so carefully for so many years.

With his usual presence of mind Mr. Pontifex gasped out a month's warning to Gelstrap. Then he got up, and stamped as Theobald had done when Christina had wanted not to order his dinner.

'It's water from the Jordan,' he exclaimed furiously, 'which I have been saving for the baptism of my eldest grandson. Damn you, Gelstrap, how dare you be so infernally careless as to leave that hamper littering about the cellar?'

I wonder the water of the sacred stream did not stand upright as a heap upon the cellar floor and rebuke him. Gelstrap told the other servants afterwards that his master's language had made his backbone curdle.

The moment, however, that he heard the word 'water', he saw his way again, and flew to the pantry. Before his master had well noted his absence he returned with a little sponge and a basin, and had begun sopping up the waters of the Jordan as though they had been a common slop.

'I'll filter it, Sir,' said Gelstrap meekly. 'It'll come quite clean.'

Mr. Pontifex saw hope in this suggestion, which was shortly carried out by the help of a piece of blotting-paper and a funnel, under his own eyes. Eventually it was found that half a pint was saved, and this was held to be sufficient.

Then he made preparations for a visit to Battersby. He ordered goodly hampers of the choicest eatables, he selected a goodly hamper of choice drinkables. I say choice and not choicest, for although in his first exaltation he had selected some of his very best wine, yet on reflection he had felt that there was moderation in all things, and as he was parting with his best water from the Jordan, he would only send some of his second best wine.

Before he went to Battersby he stayed a day or two in London, which he now seldom did, being over seventy years old, and having practically retired from business. The John Pontifexes, who kept a sharp eye on him, discovered to their dismay that he had had an interview with his solicitors.

CHAPTER EIGHTEEN

FOR the first time in his life Theobald felt that he had done something right, and could look forward to meeting his father without alarm. The old gentleman, indeed, had written him a most cordial letter, announcing his intention of standing godfather to the boy — nay, I may as well give it in full, as it shows the writer at his best. It runs:

Dear Theobald: Your letter gave me very sincere pleasure, the more so because I had made up my mind for the worst; pray accept my most hearty congratulations for my daughter-in-law and for yourself.

I have long preserved a phial of water from the Jordan for the christening of my first grandson, should it please God to grant me one. It was given me by my old friend Dr. Jones. You will agree with me that though the efficacy of the sacrament does not depend upon the source of the baptismal waters, yet, *ceteris paribus*, there is a sentiment attaching to the waters of the Jordan which should not be despised. Small matters like this sometimes influence a child's whole future career.

I shall bring my own cook, and have told him to get everything ready for the christening dinner. Ask as many of your best neighbours as your table will hold. By the way, I have told Lesueur *not to get a lobster* — you had better drive over yourself and get one from Saltness [for Battersby was only fourteen or fifteen miles from the sea coast]: they are better there, at least I think so, than anywhere else in England.

I have put your boy down for something in the event of his attaining the age of twenty-one years. If your brother John continues to have nothing but girls I may do more later on, but I have many claims upon me, and am not as well off as you may imagine. Your affectionate father,   G. PONTIFEX

A few days afterwards the writer of the above letter made his appearance in a fly which had brought him from Gildenham to Battersby, a distance of fourteen miles. There was Lesueur, the cook, on the box with the driver, and as many hampers as the fly could carry were disposed upon the roof and elsewhere. Next day the John Pontifexes had to come, and Eliza and Maria, as well as Alethea, who, by her own special request, was godmother to the boy, for Mr. Pontifex had decided that they were to form a happy family party; so come they all must, and be happy they all must, or it would be the worse for them. Next day the author of all this hubbub was actually christened. Theobald had proposed to call him George after old Mr. Pontifex, but strange to say, Mr. Pontifex overruled him in favour of the name Ernest. The word 'earnest' was just beginning to come into fashion, and he thought the possession of such a name might, like his having been baptized in water from the Jordan, have a permanent effect upon the boy's character, and influence him for good during the more critical periods of his life.

I was asked to be his second godfather, and was rejoiced to have an opportunity of meeting Alethea, whom I had not seen for some few years, but with whom I had been in constant correspondence. She and I had always been friends from the time we had played together as children onwards. When the death of her grandfather and grandmother severed her connection with Paleham my intimacy with the Pontifexes was kept up by my having been at school and college with Theobald, and each time I saw her I admired her more and more as the best, kindest, wittiest, most lovable, and, to my mind, handsomest woman whom I had ever seen. None of the Pontifexes were deficient in good looks; they were a well-grown shapely family enough, but Alethea was the flower of the flock even as regards good looks, while in respect of all other qualities that make a woman lovable, it seemed as though the stock that had been intended for the three daughters, and would have been about sufficient for them, had all been allotted to herself, her sisters getting none, and she all.

It is impossible for me to explain how it was that she and I never married. We two knew exceedingly well, and that must suffice for the reader. There was the most perfect sympathy and understanding between us; we knew that neither of us would marry anyone else. I had asked her to marry me a dozen times over; having said this much I will say no more upon a point which is in no way necessary for the development of my story. For the last few years there had been difficulties in the way of our meeting, and I had not seen her, though, as I have said, keeping up a close correspondence with her. Naturally I was overjoyed to meet her again; she was now just thirty years old, but I thought she looked handsomer than ever.

Her father, of course, was the lion of the party, but seeing that we were all meek and quite willing to be eaten, he roared to us rather than at us. It was a fine sight to see him tucking his napkin under his rosy old gills, and letting it fall over his capacious waistcoat while the high light from the chandelier danced about the bump of benevolence on his bald old head like a star of Bethlehem.

The soup was real turtle; the old gentleman was evidently well pleased and he was beginning to come out. Gelstrap stood behind his master's chair. I sat next Mrs. Theobald on her left hand, and was thus just opposite her father-in-law, whom I had every opportunity of observing.

During the first ten minutes or so, which were taken up with the soup and the bringing in of the fish, I should probably have thought, if I had not long since made up my mind about him, what a fine old man he was and how proud his children should be of him; but suddenly as he was helping himself to lobster sauce, he flushed crimson, a look of extreme vexation suffused his face, and he darted two furtive but fiery glances to the two ends of the table, one for Theobald and one for Christina. They, poor simple souls, of course saw that something was exceedingly wrong, and so did I, but I couldn't guess what it was till I heard the old man hiss in Christina's ear: 'It was not made with a hen lobster. What's the use,' he continued, 'of my calling the boy Ernest, and getting him christened in water from the Jordan, if his own father does not know a cock from a hen lobster?'

This cut me too, for I felt that till that moment I had not so much as known that there were cocks and hens among lobsters, but had vaguely thought that in the matter of matrimony they were even as the angels in heaven, and grew up almost spontaneously from rocks and seaweed.

Before the next course was over Mr. Pontifex had recovered his temper, and from that time to the end of the evening he was at his best. He told us all about the water from the Jordan; how it had been brought by Dr. Jones along with some stone jars of water from the Rhine, the Rhone, the Elbe and the Danube, and what trouble he had had with them at the Custom Houses, and how the intention had been to make punch with waters from all the greatest rivers in Europe; and how he, Mr. Pontifex, had saved the Jordan water from going into the bowl, etc. etc. 'No, no, no,' he continued, 'it wouldn't have done at all, you know; very profane idea; so we each took a pint bottle of it home with us, and the punch was much better without it. I had a narrow escape with mine, though, the other day; I fell over a hamper in the cellar, when I was getting it up to bring to Battersby, and if I had not taken the greatest care the bottle would certainly have been broken, but I saved it.' And Gelstrap was standing behind his chair all the time!

Nothing more happened to ruffle Mr. Pontifex, so we had a delightful evening, which has often recurred to me while watching the after career of my godson.

I called a day or two afterwards and found Mr. Pontifex still at Battersby, laid up with one of those attacks of liver and depression to which he was becoming more and more subject. I stayed to luncheon. The old gentleman was cross and very difficult; he could eat nothing — had no appetite at all. Christina tried to coax him with a little bit of the fleshy part of a mutton chop. 'How in the name of reason can I be asked to eat a mutton chop?' he exclaimed angrily. 'You forget, my dear Christina, that you have to deal with a stomach that is totally disorganized,' and he pushed the plate from him, pouting and frowning like a naughty old child. Writing as I do by the light of a later knowledge, I suppose I should have seen nothing in this but the world's growing pains, the disturbance inseparable from transition in human things. I suppose in reality not a leaf goes yellow in autumn without ceasing to care about its sap and making the parent tree very uncomfortable by long growling and grumbling — but surely nature might find some less irritating way of carrying on business if she would give her mind to it. Why should the generations overlap one another at all? Why cannot we be buried as eggs in neat little cells with ten or twenty thousand pounds each wrapped round us in Bank of England notes, and wake up, as the sphex wasp does, to find that its papa and mamma have not only left ample provision at its elbow, but have been eaten by sparrows some weeks before it began to live consciously on its own account?

About a year and a half afterwards the tables were turned on Battersby — for Mrs. John Pontifex was safely delivered of a boy. A year or so later still, George Pontifex was himself struck down suddenly by a fit of paralysis, much as his mother had been, but he did not see the years of his mother. When his will was opened, it was found that an original bequest of £20,000 to Theobald himself (over and above the sum that had been settled upon him and Christina at the time of his marriage) had been cut down to £17,500 when Mr. Pontifex left 'something' to Ernest. The 'something' proved to be £2500, which was to accumulate in the hands of trustees. The rest of the property went to John Pontifex, except that each of the daughters was left with about £15,000 over and above £5000 a piece which they inherited from their mother.

Theobald's father then had told him the truth but not the whole truth. Nevertheless what right had Theobald to complain? Certainly it was rather hard to make him think that he and his were to be gainers, and get the honour and glory of the bequest, when all the time the money was virtually being taken out of Theobald's own pocket. On the other hand, the father doubtless argued that he had never told Theobald he was to have anything at all; he had a full right to do what he liked with his own money; if Theobald chose to indulge in unwarrantable expectations that was no affair of his; as it was he was providing for him liberally; and if he did take £2500 of Theobald's share he was still leaving it to Theobald's son, which, of course, was much the same thing in the end.

No one can deny that the testator had strict right upon his side; nevertheless the reader will agree with me that Theobald and Christina might not have considered the christening dinner so great a success if all the facts had been before them. Mr. Pontifex had during his own lifetime set up a monument in Elmhurst Church to the memory of his wife (a slab with urns and cherubs like illegitimate children of King George the Fourth, and all the rest of it), and had left space for his own epitaph underneath that of his wife. I do not know whether it was written by one of his children, or whether they got some friend to write it for them. I do not believe that any satire was intended. I believe that it was the intention to convey that nothing short of the Day of Judgment could give anyone an idea how good a man Mr. Pontifex had been, but at first I found it hard to think that it was free from guile.

The epitaph begins by giving dates of birth and death; then sets out that the deceased was for many years head of the firm of Fairlie and Pontifex, and also resident in the parish of Elmhurst. There is not a syllable of either praise or dispraise. The last lines run as follows:

HE NOW LIES AWAITING A JOYFUL RESURRECTION
AT THE LAST DAY
WHAT MANNER OF MAN HE WAS
THAT DAY WILL DISCOVER

CHAPTER NINETEEN

THIS much, however, we may say in the meantime, that having lived to be nearly seventy-three years old and died rich he must have been in very fair harmony with his surroundings. I have heard it said sometimes that such and such a person's life was a lie: but no man's life can be a very bad lie; as long as it continues at all it is at worst nine-tenths of it true.

Mr. Pontifex's life not only continued a long time, but was prosperous right up to the end. Is not this enough? Being in this world is it not our most obvious business to make the most of it — to observe what things do *bona fide* tend to long life and comfort, and to act accordingly? All animals, except man, know that the principal business of life is to enjoy it — and they do enjoy it as much as man and other circumstances will allow. He has spent his life best who has enjoyed it most; God will take care that we do not enjoy it any more than is good for us. If Mr. Pontifex is to be blamed it is for not having eaten and drunk less and thus suffered less from his liver, and lived perhaps a year or two longer.

Goodness is naught unless it tends towards old age and sufficiency of means. I speak broadly and *exceptis excipiendis*. So the psalmist says, 'The righteous shall not lack anything that is good.' Either this is mere poetical licence, or it follows that he who lacks anything that is good is not righteous; there is a presumption also that he who has passed a long life without lacking anything that is good has himself also been good enough for practical purposes.

Mr. Pontifex never lacked anything he much cared about. True, he might have been happier than he was if he had cared about things which he did not care for, but the gist of this lies in the 'if he had cared'. We have all sinned and come short of the glory of making ourselves as comfortable as we easily might have done, but in this particular case Mr. Pontifex did not care, and would not have gained much by getting what he did not want.

There is no casting of swine's meat before men worse than that which would flatter virtue as though her true origin were not good enough for her, but she must have a lineage, deduced as it were by spiritual heralds, from some stock with which she has nothing to do. Virtue's true lineage is older and more respectable than any that can be invented for her. She springs from man's experience concerning his own well-being — and this, though not infallible, is still the least fallible thing we have. A system which cannot stand without a better foundation than this must have something so unstable within itself that it will topple over on whatever pedestal we place it.

The world has long ago settled that morality and virtue are what bring men peace at the last. 'Be virtuous,' says the copybook, 'and you will be happy.' Surely if a reputed virtue fails often in this respect it is only an insidious form of vice, and if a reputed vice brings no very serious mischief on a man's later years it is not so bad a vice as it is said to be. Unfortunately, though we are all of a mind about the main opinion that virtue is what tends to happiness, and vice what ends in sorrow, we are not so unanimous about details — that is to say, as to whether any given course, such, we will say, as smoking, has a tendency to happiness or the reverse.

I submit it as the result of my own poor observation, that a good deal of unkindness and selfishness on the part of parents towards children is not generally followed by ill consequences to the parents themselves. They may cast a gloom over their children's lives for many years without having to suffer anything that will hurt them. I should say, then, that it shows no great moral obliquity on the part of parents if within certain limits they make their children's lives a burden to them.

Granted that Mr. Pontifex's was not a very exalted character, ordinary men are not required to have very exalted characters. It is enough if we are of the same moral and mental statute as the 'main' or 'mean' part of men — that is to say as the average.

It is involved in the very essence of things that rich men who die old shall have been mean. The greatest and wisest of mankind will be almost always found to be the meanest — the ones who have kept the 'mean' best between excess either of virtue or vice. They hardly ever have been prosperous if they have not done this, and, considering how many miscarry altogether, it is no small feather in a man's cap if he has been no worse than his neighbours. Homer tells us about someone who made it his business αἴεν ἀριστεύειν καὶ ὑπείροχον ἔμμεναι ἄλλων — always to excel and to stand higher than other people. What an uncompanionable, disagreeable person he must have been! Homer's heroes generally came to a bad end, and I doubt not that this gentleman, whoever he was, did so sooner or later.

A very high standard, again, involves the possession of rare virtues, and rare virtues are like rare plants or animals, things that have not been able to hold their own in the world. A virtue to be serviceable must, like gold, be alloyed with some commoner but more durable metal.

People divide off vice and virtue as though they were two things, neither of which had with it anything of the other. This is not so. There is no useful virtue which has not some alloy of vice, and hardly any vice, if any, which carries not with it a little dash of virtue; virtue and vice are like life and death, or mind and matter — things which cannot exist without being qualified by their opposite. The most absolute life contains death, and the corpse is still in many respects living; so also it has been said, 'If thou, Lord, wilt be extreme to mark what is done amiss', which shows that even the highest ideal we can conceive will yet admit so much compromise with vice as shall countenance the poor abuses of the time, if they are not too outrageous. That vice pays homage to virtue is notorious; we call this hypocrisy; there should be a word found for the homage which virtue not unfrequently pays, or at any rate would be wise in paying, to vice.

I grant that some men will find happiness in having what we all feel to be a higher moral standard than others. If they go in for this, however, they must be content with virtue as her own reward, and not grumble if they find lofty Quixotism an expensive luxury, whose rewards belong to a kingdom that is not of this world. They must not wonder if they cut a poor figure in trying to make the most of both worlds. Disbelieve as we may the details of the accounts which record the growth of the Christian religion, yet a great part of Christian teaching will remain as true as though we accepted the details. We cannot serve God and Mammon; strait is the way and narrow is the gate which leads to what those who live by faith hold to be best worth having, and there is no way of saying this better than the Bible has done. It is well there should be some who think thus, as it is well there should be speculators in commerce, who will often burn their fingers — but it is not well that the majority should leave the 'mean' and beaten path.

For most men, and most circumstances, pleasure — tangible material prosperity in this world — is the safest test of virtue. Progress has ever been through the pleasures rather than through the extreme sharp virtues, and the most virtuous have leaned to excess rather than to asceticism. To use a commercial metaphor, competition is so keen, and the margin of profits has been cut down so closely that virtue cannot afford to throw any *bona fide* chance away, and must base her action rather on the actual moneying out of conduct than on a flattering prospectus. She will not therefore neglect — as some do who are prudent and economical enough in other matters — the important factor of our chance of escaping detection, or at any rate of our dying first. A reasonable virtue will give this chance its due value, neither more nor less.

Pleasure, after all, is a safer guide than either right or duty. For hard as it is to know what gives us pleasure, right and duty are often still harder to distinguish and, if we go wrong with them, will lead us into just as sorry a plight as a mistaken opinion concerning pleasure. When men burn their fingers through following after pleasure they find out their mistake and get to see where they have gone wrong more easily than when they have burnt them through following after a fancied duty, or a fancied idea concerning right virtue. The Devil, in fact, when he dresses himself in angel's clothes, can only be detected by experts of exceptional skill, and so often does he adopt this disguise that it is hardly safe to be seen talking to an angel at all, and prudent people will follow after pleasure as a more homely but more respectable and on the whole much more trustworthy guide.

Returning to Mr. Pontifex, over and above his having lived long and prosperously, he left numerous offspring, to all of whom he communicated not only his physical and mental characteristics, with no more than the usual amount of modification, but also no small share of characteristics which are less easily transmitted — I mean his pecuniary characteristics. It may be said that he acquired these by sitting still and letting money run, as it were, right up against him; but against how many does not money run who do not take it when it does, or who, even if they hold it for a little while, cannot so incorporate it with themselves that it shall descend through them to their offspring? Mr. Pontifex did this. He kept what he may be said to have made, and money is like a reputation for ability — more easily made than kept.

Take them, then, for all in all, I am not inclined to be so severe upon him as my father was. Judge him according to any very lofty standard, and he is nowhere. Judge him according to a fair average standard, and there is not much fault to be found with him. I have said what I have said in the foregoing chapter once for all, and shall not break my thread to repeat it. It should go without saying in modification of the verdict which the reader may be inclined to pass too hastily, not only upon Mr. George Pontifex, but also upon Theobald and Christina. And now I will continue my story.

CHAPTER TWENTY

THE birth of his son opened Theobald's eyes to a good deal which he had but faintly realized hitherto. He had had no idea how great a nuisance a baby was. Babies come into the world so suddenly at the end, and upset everything so terribly when they do come: why cannot they steal in upon us with less of a shock to the domestic system? His wife, too, did not recover rapidly from her confinement; she remained an invalid for months; here was another nuisance and an expensive one, which interfered with the amount which Theobald liked to put by out of his income against, as he said, a rainy day, or to make provision for his family if he should have one. Now he was getting a family, so that it became all the more necessary to put money by, and here was the baby hindering him. Theorists may say what they like about a man's children being a continuation of his own identity, but it will generally be found that those who talk in this way have no children of their own. Practical family men know better.

About twelve months after the birth of Ernest there came a second, also a boy, who was christened Joseph, and in less than twelve months afterwards, a girl, to whom was given the name of Charlotte. A few months before this girl was born Christina paid a visit to the John Pontifexes in London, and, knowing her condition, passed a good deal of time at the Royal Academy exhibition looking at the types of female beauty portrayed by the Academicians, for she had made up her mind that the child this time was to be a girl. Alethea warned her not to do this, but she persisted, and certainly the child turned out plain, but whether the pictures caused this or no I cannot say.

Theobald had never liked children. He had always got away from them as soon as he could, and so had they from him; oh, why, he was inclined to ask himself, could not children be born into the world grown up? If Christina could have given birth to a few full-grown clergymen in priest's orders — of moderate views, but inclining rather to Evangelicalism, with comfortable livings and in all respects facsimiles of Theobald himself — why, there might have been more sense in it; or if people could buy ready-made children at a shop of whatever age and sex they liked, instead of always having to make them at home, and to begin at the beginning with them — that might do better, but as it was he did not like it. He felt as he had felt when he had been required to come and be married to Christina — that he had been going on for a long time quite nicely, and would much rather continue things on their present footing. In the matter of getting married he had been obliged to pretend he liked it; but times were changed, and if he did not like a thing now, he could find a hundred unexceptionable ways of making his dislike apparent.

It might have been better if Theobald in his younger days had kicked more against his father: the fact that he had not done so encouraged him to expect the most implicit obedience from his own children. He could trust himself, he said (and so did Christina), to be more lenient than perhaps his father had been to himself; his danger, he said (and so again did Christina), would be rather in the direction of being too indulgent; he must be on his guard against this, for no duty could be more important than that of teaching a child to obey its parents in all things.

He had read not long since of an Eastern traveller, who, while exploring somewhere in the more remote parts of Arabia and Asia Minor, had come upon a remarkably hardy, sober, industrious little Christian community — all of them in the best of health — who had turned out to be the actual living descendants of Jonadab, the son of Rechab; and two men in European costume, indeed, but speaking English with a broken accent, and by their colour evidently Oriental, had come begging to Battersby soon afterwards, and represented themselves as belonging to this people; they had said they were collecting funds to promote the conversion of their fellow tribesmen to the

English branch of the Christian religion. True, they turned out to be imposters, for when he gave them a pound and Christina five shillings from her private purse, they went and got drunk with it in the next village but one to Battersby; still, this did not invalidate the story of the Eastern traveller. Then there were the Romans — whose greatness was probably due to the wholesome authority exercised by the head of a family over all its members. Some Romans had even killed their children; this was going too far, but then the Romans were not Christians, and knew no better.

The practical outcome of the foregoing was a conviction in Theobald's mind, and if in his, then in Christina's, that it was their duty to begin training up their children in the way they should go, even from their earliest infancy. The first signs of self-will must be carefully looked for, and plucked up by the roots at once before they had time to grow. Theobald picked up this numb serpent of a metaphor and cherished it in his bosom.

Before Ernest could well crawl he was taught to kneel; before he could well speak he was taught to lisp the Lord's Prayer, and the general confession. How was it possible that these things could be taught too early? If his attention flagged or his memory failed him, here was an ill weed which would grow apace, unless it were plucked out immediately, and the only way to pluck it out was to whip him, or shut him up in a cupboard, or dock him of some of the small pleasures of childhood. Before he was three years old he could read and, after a fashion, write. Before he was four he was learning Latin, and could do rule of three sums.

As for the child himself, he was naturally of an even temper, he doted upon his nurse, on kittens and puppies, and on all things that would do him the kindness of allowing him to be fond of them. He was fond of his mother, too, but as regards his father, he has told me in later life he could remember no feeling but fear and shrinking. Christina did not remonstrate with Theobald concerning the severity of the tasks imposed upon their boy, nor yet as to the continual whippings that were found necessary at lesson times. Indeed, when during any absence of Theobald's the lessons were entrusted to her, she found to her sorrow that it was the only thing to do, and she did it no less effectually than Theobald himself, nevertheless she was fond of her boy, which Theobald never was, and it was long before she could destroy all affection for herself in the mind of her first-born. But she persevered.

CHAPTER TWENTY-ONE

STRANGE! for she believed she doted upon him, and certainly she loved him better than either of her other children. Her version of the matter was that there had never yet been two parents so self-denying and devoted to the highest welfare of their children as Theobald and herself. For Ernest, a very great future — she was certain of it — was in store. This made severity all the more necessary, so that from the first he might have been kept pure from every taint of evil. She could not allow herself the scope for castle building which, we read, was indulged in by every Jewish matron before the appearance of the Messiah, for the Messiah had now come, but there was to be a millennium shortly, certainly not later than 1866, when Ernest would be just about the right age for it, and a modern Elias would be wanted to herald its approach. Heaven would bear her witness that she had never shrunk from the idea of martyrdom for herself and Theobald, nor would she avoid it for her boy, if his life was required of her in her Redeemer's service. Oh, no! If God told her to offer up her first-born, as He had told Abraham, she would take him up to Pigbury Beacon and plunge the — no, that she could not do, but it would be unnecessary — someone else might do that. It was not for nothing that Ernest had been baptized in water from the Jordan. It had not been her doing, nor yet Theobald's. They had not sought it. When water from the sacred stream was wanted for a sacred infant, the channel had been found through which it was to flow from far Palestine over land and sea to the door of the house where the child was lying. Why, it was a miracle! It was! It was! She saw it all now. The Jordan had left its bed and flowed into her own house. It was idle to say that this was not a miracle. No miracle was effected without means of some kind; the difference between the faithful and the unbeliever consisted in the very fact that the former could see a miracle where the latter could not. The Jews could see no miracle even in the raising of Lazarus and the feeding of the five thousand. The John Pontifexes would see no miracle in this matter of the water from the Jordan. The essence of a miracle lay not in the fact that means had been dispensed with, but in the adoption of means to a great end that had not been available without interference; and no one would suppose that Dr. Jones would have brought the water unless he had been directed. She would tell this to Theobald, and get him to see it in the . . . and yet perhaps it would be better not.

The insight of women upon matters of this sort was deeper and more unerring than that of men. It was a woman and not a man who had been filled most completely with the whole fullness of the Deity. But why had they not treasured up the water after it was used? It ought never, never to have been thrown away, but it had been. Perhaps, however, this was for the best too — they might have been tempted to set too much store by it, and it might have become a source of spiritual danger to them — perhaps even of spiritual pride, the very sin of all others which she most abhorred. As for the channel through which the Jordan had flowed to Battersby, that mattered not more than the earth through which the river ran in Palestine itself. Dr. Jones was certainly worldly — very worldly; so, she regretted to feel, had been her father-in-law, though in a less degree; spiritual, at heart, doubtless, and becoming more and more spiritual continually as he grew older, still he was tainted with the world, till a very few hours, probably, before his death, whereas she and Theobald had given up all for Christ's sake. *They* were not worldly. At least Theobald was not. She had been, but she was sure she had grown in grace since she had left off eating things strangled and blood — this was as the washing in Jordan as against Abana and Pharpar, rivers of Damascus. Her boy should never touch a strangled fowl nor a black pudding — that, at any rate, she could see to. He should have a coral from the neighbourhood of Joppa — there were coral insects on those coasts, so that the thing could easily be done with a little energy; she would write to Dr. Jones about it, etc. And so on for hours together day after day for years. Truly, Mrs. Theobald loved her child according to her lights with an exceeding great fondness, but the dreams she had dreamed in sleep were sober realities in comparison with those she indulged in while awake.

When Ernest was in his second year, Theobald, as I have already said, began to teach him to read. He began to whip him two days after he had begun to teach him.

'It was painful,' as he said to Christina, but it was the only thing to do and it was done. The child was puny, white and sickly, so they sent continually for the doctor who dosed him with calomel and James's powder. All was done in love, anxiety, timidity, stupidity and impatience. They were stupid in little things; and he that is stupid in little will be stupid also in much.

Presently old Mr. Pontifex died, and then came the revelation of the little alteration he had made in his will simultaneously with his bequest to Ernest. It was rather hard to bear, especially as there was no way of conveying a bit of their minds to the testator now that he could no longer hurt them. As regards the boy himself anyone must see that the bequest would be an unmitigated misfortune to him. To leave him a small independence was perhaps the greatest injury which one could inflict upon a young man. It would cripple his energies, and deaden his desire for active employment. Many a youth was led into evil courses by the knowledge that on arriving at majority he would come into a few thousands. They might surely have been trusted to have their boy's interests at heart, and must be better judges of those interests than he, at twenty-one, could be expected to be: besides if Jonadab, the son of Rechab's father — or perhaps it might be simpler under the circumstances to say Rechab at once — if Rechab, then, had left handsome legacies to his grandchildren — why Jonadab might not have found those children so easy to deal with, etc. 'My dear,' said Theobald, after having discussed the matter with Christina for the twentieth time, 'my dear, the only thing to guide and console us under misfortunes of this kind is to take refuge in practical work. I will go and pay a visit to Mrs. Thompson.'

On those days Mrs. Thompson would be told that her sins were all washed white, etc., a little sooner and a little more peremptorily than on others.

CHAPTER TWENTY-TWO

I WAS there on a Sunday, and observed the rigour with which the young people were taught to observe the Sabbath; they might not cut out things, nor use their paint-box on a Sunday, and this they thought rather hard, because their cousins the John Pontifexes might do these things. Their cousins might play with their toy train on Sunday, but though they had promised that they would run none but Sunday trains, all traffic had been prohibited. One treat only was allowed them — on Sunday evenings they might choose their own hymns.

In the course of the evening they came into the drawing-room, and, as an especial treat, were to sing some of their hymns to me, instead of saying them, so that I might hear how nicely they sang. Ernest was to choose the first hymn, and he chose one about some people who were to come to the sunset tree. I am no botanist, and do not know what kind of tree a sunset tree is, but the words began, 'Come, come, come; come to the sunset tree for the day is past and gone.' The tune was rather pretty and had taken Ernest's fancy, for he was unusually fond of music and had a sweet little child's voice which he liked using.

He was, however, very late in being able to sound a hard 'c' or 'k', and, instead of saying 'Come', he said 'Tum, tum, tum'.

'Ernest,' said Theobald, from the armchair in front of the fire, where he was sitting with his hands folded before him, 'don't you think it would be very nice if you were to say "come" like other people, instead of "tum"?'

'I do say tum,' replied Ernest, meaning that he had said 'come'.

Theobald was always in a bad temper on Sunday evening. Whether it is that they are as much bored with the day as their neighbours, or whether they are tired, or whatever the cause may be, clergymen are seldom at their best on Sunday evening; I had already seen signs that evening that my host was cross, and was a little nervous at hearing Ernest say so promptly 'I do say tum', when his papa had said he did not say it as he should.

Theobald noticed the fact that he was being contradicted in a moment. He got up from his armchair and went to the piano.

'No, Ernest, you don't,' he said, 'you say nothing of the kind, you say "tum", not "come". Now say "come" after me, as I do.'

'Tum,' said Ernest, at once; 'is that better?' I have no doubt he thought it was, but it was not.

'Now, Ernest, you are not taking pains; you are not trying as you ought to do. It is high time you learned to say "come", why, Joey can say "come", can't you, Joey?'

'Yeth, I can,' replied Joey, and he said something which was not far off 'come'.

'There, Ernest, do you hear that? There's no difficulty about it, nor shadow of difficulty. Now, take your own time, think about it, and say "come" after me.'

The boy remained silent a few seconds and then said 'tum' again.

I laughed, but Theobald turned to me impatiently and said, 'Please do not laugh, Overton; it will make the boy think it does not matter, and it matters a great deal,' then turning to Ernest he said, 'Now, Ernest, I will give you one more chance, and if you don't say "come", I shall know that you are self-willed and naughty.'

He looked very angry, and a shade came over Ernest's face, like that which comes upon the face of a puppy when it is being scolded without understanding why. The child saw well what was coming now, was frightened, and, of course, said 'tum' once more.

'Very well, Ernest,' said his father, catching him angrily by the shoulder. 'I have done my best to save you, but if you will have it so, you will,' and he lugged the little wretch, crying by anticipation, out of the room. A few minutes more and we could hear screams coming from the dining-room, across the hall which separated the drawing-room from the dining-room, and knew that poor Ernest was being beaten.

'I have sent him up to bed,' said Theobald, as he returned to the drawing-room, 'and now, Christina, I think we will have the servants into prayers,' and he rang the bell for them, red-handed as he was.

CHAPTER TWENTY-THREE

NEXT day I was to go back to London, but before I went I said I should like to take some new-laid eggs back with me, so Theobald took me to the house of a labourer in the village who lived a stone's throw from the Rectory as being likely to supply me with them. Ernest, for some reason or other, was allowed to come too. I think the hens had begun to sit, but at any rate eggs were scarce, and the cottager's wife could not find me more than seven or eight, which we proceeded to wrap up in separate pieces of paper so that I might take them to town safely.

This operation was carried on upon the ground in front of the cottage door, and while we were in the midst of it the cottager's little boy, a lad much about Ernest's age, trod upon one of the eggs that was wrapped up in paper and broke it.

'There now, Jack,' said his mother, 'see what you've done, you've broken a nice egg and cost me a penny — Here, Emma,' she added, calling her daughter, 'take the child away, there's a dear.'

Emma came at once, and walked off with the youngster, taking him out of harm's way.

'Papa,' said Ernest, after we had left the house, 'why didn't Mrs. Heaton whip Jack when he trod on the egg?'

I was spiteful enough to give Theobald a grim smile which said as

236

plainly as words could have done that I thought Ernest had hit him rather hard.

Theobald coloured and looked angry. 'I dare say,' he said quickly, 'that his mother will whip him now that we are gone.'

I was not going to have this and said I did not believe it, and so the matter dropped, but Theobald did not forget it and my visits to Battersby were henceforth less frequent.

On our return to the house we found the postman had arrived and had brought a letter appointing Theobald to a rural deanery which had lately fallen vacant by the death of one of the neighbouring clergy who had held the office for many years. The bishop wrote to Theobald most warmly, and assured him that he valued him as among the most hardworking and devoted of his parochial clergy. Christina of course was delighted, and gave me to understand that it was only an instalment of the much higher dignities which were in store for Theobald when his merits were more widely known.

I did not then foresee how closely my godson's life and mine were in after years to be bound up together; if I had, I should doubtless have looked upon him with different eyes and noted much to which I paid no attention at the time. As it was, I was glad to get away from him, for I could do nothing for him, or chose to say that I could not, and the sight of so much suffering was painful to me. A man should not only have his own way as far as possible, but he should only consort with things that are getting their own way so far that they are at any rate comfortable. Unless for short times under exceptional circum-stances, he should not even see things that have been stunted or starved, much less should he eat meat that has been vexed by having been over-driven or under-fed, or afflicted with any disease; nor should he touch vegetables that have not been well grown. For all these things cross a man; whatever a man comes in contact with in any way forms a cross with him which will leave him better or worse, and the better things he is crossed with the more likely he is to live long and happily. All things must be crossed a little or they would cease to live — but holy things, such for example as Giovanni Bellini's saints, have been crossed with nothing but what is good of its kind.

CHAPTER TWENTY-FOUR

THE storm which I have described in the previous chapter was a sample of those that occurred daily for many years. No matter how clear the sky, it was always liable to cloud over, now in one quarter, now in another, and the thunder and lightning were upon the young people before they knew where they were.

'And then, you know,' said Ernest to me, when I asked him not long since to give me more of his childish reminiscences for the benefit of my story, 'we used to learn Mrs. Barbauld's hymns; they were in prose, and there was one about the lion which began. "Come, and I will show you what is strong. The lion is strong; when he raiseth himself from his lair, when he shaketh his mane, when the voice of his roaring is heard the cattle of the field fly, and the beasts of the desert hide themselves, for he is very terrible." I used to say this to Joey and Charlotte about my father himself when I got a little older, but they were always didactic, and said it was naughty of me.

'One great reason why clergymen's households are generally unhappy is because the clergyman is so much at home or close about the house. The doctor is out visiting patients half his time: the lawyer and the merchant have offices away from home, but the clergyman has no official place of business which shall ensure his being away from home for many hours together at stated times. Our great days were when my father went for a day's shopping to Gildenham. We were some miles from this place, and commissions used to accumulate on my father's list till he would make a day of it and go and do the lot. As soon as his back was turned the air felt lighter; as soon as the hall door opened to let him in again, the law with its all-reaching "touch not, taste not, handle not" was upon us again. The worst of it was that I could never trust Joey and Charlotte; they would go a good way with me and then turn back, or even the whole way and then their consciences would compel them to tell papa and mamma. They liked running with the hare up to a certain point, but their instinct was towards the hounds.

'It seems to me,' he continued, 'that the family is a survival of the principle which is more logically embodied in the compound animal — and the compound animal is a form of life which has been found incompatible with high development. I would do with the family among mankind what nature has done with the compound animal, and confine it to the lower and less progressive races. Certainly there is no inherent love for the family system on the part of nature herself. Poll the forms of life and you will find it in a ridiculously small minority. The fishes know it not, and they get along quite nicely. The ants and the bees, who far outnumber man, sting their fathers to death as a matter of course, and are given to the atrocious mutilation of nine-tenths of the offspring committed to their charge, yet where shall we find communities more universally respected? Take the cuckoo again — is there any bird which we like better?'

I saw he was running off from his own reminiscences and tried to bring him back to them, but it was no use.

'What a fool,' he said, 'a man is to remember anything that happened more than a week ago unless it was pleasant, or unless he wants to make some use of it.

'Sensible people get the greater part of their own dying done during their own lifetime. A man at five-and-thirty should no more regret not having had a happier childhood than he should regret not having been born a prince of the blood. He might be happier if he had been more fortunate in childhood, but, for aught he knows, if he had, something else might have happened which might have killed him long ago. If I had to be born again I would be born at Battersby of the same father and mother as before, and I would not alter anything that has ever happened to me.'

The most amusing incident that I can remember about his childhood was that when he was about seven years old he told me he was going to have a natural child. I asked him his reasons for thinking this, and he explained that papa and mamma had always told him that nobody had children till they were married, and as long as he had believed this of course he had had no idea of having a child, till he was grown up; but not long since he had been reading Mrs. Markham's *History of England* and had come upon the words 'John of Gaunt had several natural children'; he had therefore asked his governess what a natural child was — were not all children natural?

'Oh, my dear,' said she, 'a natural child is a child a person has before he is married.' On this it seemed to follow logically that if John of Gaunt had had children before he was married, he, Ernest Pontifex, might have them also, and he would be obliged to me if I would tell him what he had better do under the circumstances.

I inquired how long ago he had made this discovery. He said about a fortnight, and he did not know where to look for the child, for it might come at any moment. 'You know,' he said, 'babies come so suddenly; one goes to bed one night and next morning there is a baby. Why, it might die of cold if we are not on the look-out for it. I hope it will be a boy.'

'And you have told your governess about this?'

'Yes, but she puts me off and does not help me: she says it will not come for many years, and she hopes not then.'

'Are you quite sure that you have not made any mistake in all this?'

'Oh, no; because Mrs. Burne, you know, called here a few days ago, and I was sent for to be looked at. And mamma held me out at arm's length and said, "Is he Mr. Pontifex's child, Mrs. Burne, or is he mine?" Of course, she couldn't have said this if papa had not had some of the children himself. I did think the gentleman had all the boys and the lady all the girls; but it can't be like this, or else mamma would not have asked Mrs. Burne to guess; but then Mrs. Burne said, "Oh, he's Mr. Pontifex's child *of course*," and I didn't quite know what she meant by saying "of course": it seemed as though I was right in thinking that the husband has all the boys and the wife all the girls; I wish you would explain to me all about it.'

This I could hardly do, so I changed the conversation, after reassuring him as best I could.

CHAPTER TWENTY-FIVE

THREE or four years after the birth of her daughter, Christina had had one more child. She had never been strong since she married, and had a presentiment that she should not survive this last confinement. She accordingly wrote the following letter, which was to be given, as she endorsed upon it, to her sons when Ernest was sixteen years old. It reached him on his mother's death many years later, for it was the baby who died now, and not Christina. It was found among papers which she had repeatedly and carefully arranged, with the seal already broken. This, I am afraid, shows that Christina had read it and thought it too creditable to be destroyed when the occasion that had called it forth had gone by. It is as follows:

My two dear boys: When this is put into your hands will you try to
bring to mind the mother whom you lost in your childhood, and
whom, I fear, you will almost have forgotten? You, Ernest, will
remember her best, for you are past five years old, and the many,
many times that she has taught you your prayers and hymns and sums
and told you stories, and our happy Sunday evenings will not quite
have passed from your mind, and you, Joey, though only four, will
perhaps recollect some of these things. My dear, dear boys, for the sake
of that mother who loved you very dearly — and for the sake of your
own happiness for ever and ever — attend to and try to remember, and
from time to time read over again the last words she can ever speak to
you. When I think about leaving you all, two things press heavily
upon me: one, your father's sorrow (for you, my darlings, after missing
me a little while, will soon forget your loss), the other, the everlasting
welfare of my children. I know how long and deep the former will be,
and I know that he will look to his children to be almost his only earthly
comfort. You know (for I am certain that it will have been so) how
he has devoted his life to you and taught you and laboured to lead you
to all that is right and good. Oh, then, be sure that you *are* his comforts.
Let him find you obedient, affectionate and attentive to his wishes,
upright, self-denying and diligent; let him never blush for or grieve
over the sins and follies of those who owe him such a debt of gratitude,
and whose first duty it is to study his happiness. You have both of you
a name which must not be disgraced, a father and a grandfather of
whom to show yourselves worthy; your respectability and well-doing
in life rest mainly with yourselves, but far, far beyond earthly respectability and well-doing, and compared with which they are as nothing,
your eternal happiness rests with yourselves. You *know* your duty,
but snares and temptations from without beset you, and the nearer you
approach to manhood the more strongly will you feel this. With God's
help, with God's word, and with humble hearts you will stand in spite
of everything, but should you leave off seeking in earnest for the first,
and applying to the second, should you learn to trust in yourselves, or
to the advice and example of too many around you, you will, you must
fall. Oh, 'let God be true and every man a liar'. He says you *cannot*
serve Him and Mammon. He says that strait is the gate that leads to
eternal life. Many there are who seek to widen it; they will tell you

that such and such self-indulgences are but venial offences — that this and that wordly compliance is excusable and even necessary. The thing *cannot be*; for in a hundred and a hundred places He tells you so — look to your Bibles and seek there whether such counsel is true — and if not, oh, 'halt not between two opinions', if God is the Lord follow *Him*; only be strong and of a good courage, and He will never leave you nor forsake you. Remember, there is not in the Bible one law for the rich, and one for the poor — one for the educated and one for the ignorant. To *all* there is but one thing needful. *All* are to be living to God and their fellow-creatures, and not to themselves. *All* must seek first the Kingdom of God and His righteousness — must *deny themselves*, be pure and chaste and charitable in the fullest and widest sense — all, 'forgetting those things that are behind,' must 'press forward towards the mark, for the prize of the high calling of God'.

And now I will add but two things more. Be true through life to each other, love as only brothers should do, strengthen, warn, encourage one another, and let who will be against you, let each feel that in his brother he has a firm and faithful friend who will be so to the end; and, oh! be kind and watchful over your dear sister; without mother or sisters she will doubly need her brothers' love and tenderness and confidence. I am certain she will seek them, and will love you and try to make you happy; be sure then that you do not fail her, and remember, that were she to lose her father and remain unmarried, she would doubly need protectors. To you, then, I especially commend her. Oh! my three darling children, be true to each other, your Father, and your God. May He guide and bless you, and grant that in a better and happier world I and mine may meet again. Your most affectionate mother,   CHRISTINA PONTIFEX

From inquiries I have made, I have satisfied myself that most mothers write letters like this shortly before their confinements, and that fifty per cent. keep them afterwards, as Christina did.

I HAVE often thought that the Church of Rome does wisely in not allowing her priests to marry. Certainly it is a matter of common observation in England that the sons of clergymen are frequently unsatisfactory. The explanation is very simple, but is so often lost sight of that I may perhaps be pardoned for giving it here.

The clergyman is expected to be a kind of human Sunday. Things must not be done in him which are venial in the weekday classes. He is paid for this business of leading a stricter life than other people. It is his *raison d'être*. If his parishioners feel that he does this, they approve of him, for they look upon him as their own contribution towards what they deem a holy life. This is why the clergyman is so often called a vicar — he being the person whose vicarious goodness is to stand for that of those entrusted to his charge. But his home is his castle as much as that of any other Englishman, and with him, as with others, unnatural tension in public is followed by exhaustion when tension is no longer necessary. His children are the most defenceless things he can reach, and it is on them in nine cases out of ten that he will relieve his mind.

A clergyman, again, can hardly ever allow himself to look facts fairly in the face. It is his profession to support one side; it is impossible, therefore, for him to make an unbiased examination of the other.

We forget that every clergyman with a living or curacy, is as much a paid advocate as the barrister who is trying to persuade a jury to acquit a prisoner. We should listen to him with the same suspense of judgment, the same full consideration of the arguments of the opposing counsel, as a judge does when he is trying a case. Unless we know these, and can state them in a way that our opponents would admit to be a fair representation of their views, we have no right to claim that we have formed an opinion at all. The misfortune is that by the law of the land one side only can be heard.

Theobald and Christina were no exceptions to the general rule. When they came to Battersby they had every desire to fulfil the duties of their position, and to devote themselves to the honour and glory of God through the eyes of a Church which had lived three hundred years without finding reason to change a single one of its opinions.

I should doubt whether he ever got as far as doubting the wisdom of his Church upon any single matter. His scent for possible mischief was tolerably keen; so was Christina's, and it is likely that if either of them detected in him or herself the first faint symptoms of a want of faith they were nipped no less peremptorily in the bud, than signs of self-will in Ernest were — and I should imagine more successfully. Yet Theobald considered himself, and was generally considered to be, and indeed perhaps was, an exceptionally truthful person; indeed he was generally looked upon as an embodiment of all those virtues which make the poor respectable and the rich respected. In the course of time he and his wife became persuaded even to unconsciousness, that no one could even dwell under their roof without deep cause for thankfulness. Their children, their servants, their parishioners must be fortunate *ipso facto* that they were theirs. There was no road to happiness here or hereafter, but the road that they had themselves travelled, no good people who did not think as they did upon every subject, and no reasonable person who had wants the gratification of which would be inconvenient to them — Theobald and Christina.

This was how it came to pass that their children were white and puny; they were suffering from *home-sickness*. They were starving, through being over-crammed with the wrong things. Nature came down upon them, but she did not come down on Theobald and Christina. Why should she? They were not leading a starved existence. There are two classes of people in this world, those who sin, and those who are sinned against; if a man must belong to either, he had better belong to the first than to the second.

CHAPTER TWENTY-SEVEN

I WILL give no more of the details of my hero's earlier years. Enough that he struggled through them, and at twelve years old knew every page of his Latin and Greek Grammars by heart. He had read the greater part of Virgil, Horace and Livy, and I do not know how many Greek plays: he was proficient in arithmetic, knew the first four books of Euclid thoroughly, and had a fair knowledge of French. It was now time he went to school, and to school he was accordingly to go, under the famous Dr. Skinner of Roughborough.

Theobald had known Dr. Skinner slightly at Cambridge. He had been a burning and a shining light in every position he had filled from his boyhood upwards. He was a very great genius. Everyone knew this; they said, indeed, that he was one of the few people to whom the word genius could be applied without exaggeration. Had he not taken I don't know how many University Scholarships in his freshman's year? Had he not been afterwards Senior Wrangler, First Chancellor's Medallist and I do not know how many more things besides? And then, he was such a wonderful speaker; at the Union Debating Club he had been without a rival, and had, of course, been president; his moral character — a point on which so many geniuses were weak — was absolutely irreproachable; foremost of all, however, among his many great qualities, and perhaps more remarkable even than his genius was what biographers have called 'the simple-minded and childlike earnestness of his character', an earnestness which might be perceived by the solemnity with which he spoke even about trifles. It is hardly necessary to say he was on the Liberal side in politics.

His personal appearance was not particularly prepossessing. He was about the middle height, portly, and had a couple of fierce grey eyes, that flashed fire from beneath a pair of great bushy beetling eyebrows and overawed all who came near him. It was in respect of his personal appearance, however, that, if he was vulnerable at all, his weak place was to be found. His hair when he was a young man was red, but after he had taken his degree he had a brain fever which caused him to have his head shaved; when he reappeared he did so wearing a wig, and one which was a good deal further off red than his own hair had been. He not only had never discarded his wig, but year by year it had edged it-self a little more and a little more off red, till by the time he was forty, there was not a trace of red remaining, and his wig was brown.

When Dr. Skinner was a very young man, hardly more than five-and-twenty, the head-mastership of Roughborough Grammar School had fallen vacant, and he had been unhesitatingly appointed. The result justified the selection. Dr. Skinner's pupils distinguished them-selves at whichever University they went to. He moulded their minds after the model of his own, and stamped an impression upon them which was indelible in after-life; whatever else a Roughborough man might be, he was sure to make everyone feel that he was a God-fearing earnest Christian and a Liberal, if not a Radical, in politics. Some boys, of course, were incapable of appreciating the beauty and loftiness of Dr. Skinner's nature. Some such boys, alas! there will be in every school; upon them Dr. Skinner's hand was very properly a heavy one. His hand was against them, and theirs against him during the whole time of the connection between them. They not only disliked him, but they hated all that he more especially embodied, and throughout their lives disliked all that reminded them of him. Such boys, however, were in a minority, the spirit of the place being decidedly Skinnerian.

I once had the honour of playing a game of chess with this great man. It was during the Christmas holidays, and I had come down to Roughborough for a few days to see Alethea Pontifex (who was then living there) on business. It was very gracious of him to take notice of me, for if I was a light of literature at all it was of the very lightest kind.

The game had been a long one, and at half-past nine, when supper came in, we had each of us a few pieces remaining. 'What will you take for supper, Dr. Skinner?' said Mrs. Skinner in a silvery voice.

He made no answer for some time, but at last in a tone of almost superhuman solemnity, he said, first, 'Nothing,' and then 'Nothing whatever.'

By and by, however, I had a sense come over me as though I were nearer the consummation of all things than I had ever yet been. The room seemed to grow dark, as an expression came over Dr. Skinner's face, which showed that he was about to speak. The expression gathered force, the room grew darker and darker. 'Stay,' he at length added, and I felt that here at any rate was an end to a suspense which was rapidly becoming unbearable. 'Stay — I may presently take a glass of cold water — and a small piece of bread and butter.'

As he said the word 'butter' his voice sank to a hardly audible whisper, then there was a sigh as though of relief when the sentence was concluded, and the universe this time was safe.

Another ten minutes of solemn silence finished the game. The Doctor rose briskly from his seat and placed himself at the supper-table. 'Mrs. Skinner,' he exclaimed jauntily, 'what are those mysterious-looking objects surrounded by potatoes?'

'Those are oysters, Dr. Skinner.'

'Give me some, and give Overton some.'

And so on till he had eaten a good plate of oysters, a scallop shell of minced veal nicely browned, some apple tart, and a hunk of bread and cheese. This was the small piece of bread and butter.

The cloth was now removed and tumblers with teaspoons in them, a lemon or two and a jug of boiling water were placed upon the table. Then the great man unbent. His face beamed.

'And what shall it be to drink?' he exclaimed persuasively. 'Shall it be brandy and water? No. It shall be gin and water. Gin is the more wholesome liquor.'

So gin it was, hot and stiff too.

Who can wonder at him or do anything but pity him? Was he not head master of Roughborough School? To whom had he owed money at any time? Whose ox had he taken, whose ass had he taken, or whom had he defrauded? What whisper had ever been breathed against his moral character? If he had become rich it was by the most honourable of all means — his literary attainments; over and above his great works of scholarship, his *Meditations upon the Epistle and Character of St. Jude* had placed him among the most popular of English theologians; it was so exhaustive that no one who bought it need ever meditate upon the subject again — indeed it exhausted all who had anything to do with it. He had made £5000 by this work alone, and would very likely make another £5000 before he died. A man who had done all this and wanted a piece of bread and butter had a right to announce the fact with some pomp and circumstance. Nor should his words be taken without searching for what he used to call a 'deeper and more hidden meaning'. Those who searched for this even in his lightest utterances would not be without their reward. They would find that 'bread and butter' was Skinnerese for oyster-patties and apple tart, and 'gin hot' the true translation of water.

But independently of their money value, his works had made him a lasting name in literature. So probably Gallio was under the impression that his fame would rest upon the treatises on natural history which we gather from Seneca that he compiled, and which for aught we know may have contained a complete theory of evolution; but the treatises are all gone and Gallio has become immortal for the very last reason in the world that he expected, and for the very last reason that would have flattered his vanity. He has become immortal because he cared nothing about the most important movement with which he was ever brought into connection (I wish people who are in search of immortality would lay the lesson to heart and not make so much noise about important movements), and so, if Dr. Skinner becomes immortal, it will probably be for some reason very different from the one which he so fondly imagined.

Could it be expected to enter the head of such a man as this that in reality he was making his money by corrupting youth; that it was his paid profession to make the worse appear the better reason in the eyes of those who were too young and inexperienced to be able to find him out; that he kept out of the sight of those whom he professed to teach material points of the argument, for the production of which they had a right to rely upon the honour of anyone who made professions of sincerity; that he was a passionate half-turkey-cock, half-gander of a man whose sallow, bilious face and hobble-gobble voice could scare the timid, but who would take to his heels readily enough if he were met firmly; that his *Meditations on St. Jude*, such as they were, were cribbed without acknowledgment, and would have been beneath contempt if so many people did not believe them to have been written honestly? Mrs. Skinner might have perhaps kept him a little more in his proper place if she had thought it worth while to try, but she had enough to attend to in looking after her household and seeing that the boys were well fed and, if they were ill, properly looked after — which she took good care they were.

CHAPTER TWENTY-EIGHT

O SCHOOLMASTERS — if any of you read this book — bear in mind when any particularly timid drivelling urchin is brought by his papa into your study, and you treat him with the contempt which he deserves, and afterwards make his life a burden to him for years — bear in mind that it is exactly in the disguise of such a boy as this that your future chronicler will appear. Never see a wretched little heavy-eyed mite sitting on the edge of a chair against your study wall without saying to yourselves, 'Perhaps this boy is he who, if I am not careful, will one day tell the world what manner of man I was.' If even two or three schoolmasters learn this lesson and remember it, the preceding chapters will not have been written in vain.

CHAPTER TWENTY-NINE

SOON after his father and mother had left him Ernest dropped asleep over a book which Mrs. Jay had given him, and he did not awake till dusk. Then he sat down on a stool in front of the fire, which showed pleasantly in the late January twilight, and began to muse. He felt weak, feeble, ill at ease and unable to see his way out of the innumerable troubles that were before him. Perhaps, he said to himself, he might even die, but this, far from being an end of his troubles, would prove the beginning of new ones; for at the best he would only go to Grandpapa Pontifex and Grandmamma Allaby, and though they would perhaps be more easy to get on with than Papa and Mamma, yet they were undoubtedly not so really good and were more worldly; moreover, they were grown-up people — especially Grandpapa Pontifex, who so far as he could understand had been very much grown-up, and he did not know why, but there was always something that kept him from loving any grown-up people very much — except one or two of the servants, who had indeed been as nice as anything that he could imagine. Besides, even if he were to die and go to Heaven, he supposed he should have to complete his education somewhere.

In the meantime his father and mother were rolling along the muddy roads, each in his or her own corner of the carriage, and each revolving many things which were and were not to come to pass. Times have changed since I last showed them to the reader as sitting together silently in a carriage, but except as regards their mutual relations, they have altered singularly little. When I was younger I used to think the Prayer Book was wrong in requiring us to say the General Confession twice a week from childhood to old age without making provision for our not being quite such great sinners at seventy as we had been at seven; granted that we should go to the wash like tablecloths at least once a week, still I used to think a day ought to come when we should want rather less rubbing and scrubbing at. Now that I have grown older myself I have seen that the Church has estimated probabilities better than I had done.

The pair said not a word to one another, but watched the fading light and naked trees, the brown fields with here and there a melancholy cottage by the roadside, and the rain that fell fast upon the carriage windows. It was a kind of afternoon on which nice people for the most part like to be snug at home, and Theobald was a little snappish at reflecting how many miles he had to post before he could be at his own fireside again. However there was nothing for it, so the pair sat quietly and watched the roadside objects flit by them, and get greyer and grimmer as the light faded.

Though they spoke not to one another, there was one nearer to each of them with whom they could converse freely. 'I hope,' said Theobald

to himself, 'I hope he'll work — or else that Skinner will make him. I
don't like Skinner, I never did like him, but he is unquestionably a man
of genius, and no one turns out so many pupils who succeed at Oxford
and Cambridge, and that is the best test. I have done my share towards
starting him well. Skinner said he had been well grounded and was
very forward. I suppose he will presume upon it now and do nothing,
for his nature is an idle one. He is not fond of me, I'm sure he is not.
He ought to be, after all the trouble I have taken with him, but he is
ungrateful and selfish. It is an unnatural thing for a boy not to be fond
of his own father. If he was fond of me I should be fond of him, but I
cannot like a son who, I am sure, dislikes me. He shrinks out of my
way whenever he sees me coming near him. He will not stay five
minutes in the same room with me if he can help it. He is deceitful.
He would not want to hide himself away so much if he were not
deceitful. That is a bad sign and one which makes me fear he will grow
up extravagant. I am sure he will grow up extravagant. I should have
given him more pocket-money if I had not known this — but what is
the good of giving him pocket-money? It is all gone directly. If he
doesn't buy something with it he gives it away to the first little boy or
girl he sees who takes his fancy. He forgets that it's my money he is
giving away. I give him money that he may have money and learn to
know its uses, not that he may go and squander it immediately. I wish
he was not so fond of music, it will interfere with his Latin and Greek.
I will stop it as much as I can. Why, when he was translating Livy the
other day he slipped out Handel's name in mistake for Hannibal's, and
his mother tells me he knows half the tunes in the *Messiah* by heart.
What should a boy of his age know about the *Messiah*? If I had shown
half as many dangerous tendencies when I was a boy, my father would
have apprenticed me to a greengrocer, of that I'm very sure,' etc. etc.

Then his thoughts turned to Egypt and the tenth plague. It seemed
to him that if the little Egyptians had been anything like Ernest, the
plague must have been something very like a blessing in disguise. If
the Israelites were to come to England now he should be greatly
tempted not to let them go.

Mrs. Theobald's thoughts ran in a different current. 'Lord Lonsford's
grandson — it's a pity his name is Figgins; however, blood is blood as
much through the female line as the male, indeed, perhaps even more
so if the truth were known. I wonder who Mr. Figgins was. I think
Mrs. Skinner said he was dead; however, I must find out all about him.

250

It would be delightful if young Figgins were to ask Ernest home for the holidays. Who knows but he might meet Lord Lonsford himself, or at any rate some of Lord Lonsford's other descendants?'

Meanwhile the boy himself was still sitting moodily before the fire in Mrs. Jay's room. 'Papa and Mamma,' he was saying to himself, 'are much better and cleverer than anyone else, but, I, alas! shall never be either good or clever.'

Mrs. Pontifex continued:

'Perhaps it would be best to get young Figgins on a visit to ourselves first. That would be charming. Theobald would not like it, for he does not like children; I must see how I can manage it, for it would be so nice to have young Figgins — or stay! Ernest shall go and stay with Figgins and meet the future Lord Lonsford, who I should think must be about Ernest's age, and then if he and Ernest were to become friends Ernest might ask him to Battersby, and he might fall in love with Charlotte. I think we have done *most wisely* in sending Ernest to Dr. Skinner's. Dr. Skinner's piety is no less remarkable than his genius. One can tell these things at a glance, and he must have felt it about me no less strongly than I about him. I think he seemed much struck with Theobald and myself — indeed, Theobald's intellectual power must impress anyone, and I was showing, I do believe, to my best advantage. When I smiled at him and said I left my boy in his hands with the most entire confidence that he would be as well cared for as if he were at my own house, I am sure he was greatly pleased. I should not think many of the mothers who bring him boys can impress him so favourably, or say such nice things to him as I did. My smile *is* sweet when I desire to make it so. I never was perhaps exactly pretty, but I was always admitted to be fascinating. Dr. Skinner is a very handsome man — too good on the whole I should say for Mrs. Skinner. Theobald says he is not handsome, but men are no judges, and he has such a pleasant bright face. I think my bonnet became me. As soon as I get home I will tell Chambers to trim my blue and yellow merino with —' etc. etc.

All this time the letter which has been given above was lying in Christina's private little Japanese cabinet, read and re-read and approved of many times over, not to say, if the truth were known, rewritten more than once, though dated as in the first instance — and this, too, though Christina was fond enough of a joke in a small way.

Ernest, still in Mrs. Jay's room, mused onward. 'Grown-up people,' he said to himself, 'when they were ladies and gentlemen, never did naughty things, but he was always doing them. He had heard that some grown-up people were worldly, which of course was wrong, still this was quite distinct from being naughty, and did not get them punished or scolded. His own Papa and Mamma were not even worldly; they had often explained to him that they were exceptionally unworldly; he well knew that they had never done anything naughty since they had been children, and that even as children they had been nearly faultless. Oh! how different from himself! When should he learn to love his Papa and Mamma as they had loved theirs? How could he hope ever to grow up to be as good and wise as they, or even tolerably good and wise? Alas! never. It could not be. He did not love his Papa and Mamma, in spite of all their goodness both in themselves and to him. He hated Papa and did not like Mamma, and this was what none but a bad and ungrateful boy would do after all that had been done for him. Besides, he did not like Sunday; he did not like anything that was really good; his tastes were low and such as he was ashamed of. He liked people best if they sometimes swore a little, so long as it was not at him. As for his Catechism and Bible readings he had no heart in them. He had never attended to a sermon in his life. Even when he had been taken to hear Mr. Vaughan at Brighton, who, as everyone knew, preached such beautiful sermons for children, he had been very glad when it was all over, nor did he believe he could get through church at all if it was not for the voluntary upon the organ and the hymns and chanting. The Catechism was awful. He had never been able to understand what it was that he desired of his Lord God and Heavenly Father, nor had he yet got hold of a single idea in connection with the word Sacrament. His duty towards his neighbour was another bugbear. It seemed to him that he had duties towards everybody, lying in wait for him upon every side, but that nobody had any duties towards him. Then there was that awful and mysterious word "business". What did it all mean? What was "business"? His Papa was a wonderfully good man of business, his Mamma had often told him so — but he should never be one. It was hopeless, and very awful, for people were continually telling him that he would have to earn his own living. No doubt, but how — considering how stupid, idle, ignorant, self-indulgent, and physically puny he was? All grown-up people were clever, except servants — and even these were cleverer than ever he should be. Oh, why, why, why, could not people be born into the world as grown-up persons? Then he thought of Casabianca. He had been examined in that poem by his father not long before. "When only would he leave his position? To whom did he call? Did he get an answer? Why? How many times did he call upon his father? What happened to him? What was the noblest life that perished there? Do you think so? Why do you think so?" And all the rest of it. Of course he thought Casabianca's was the noblest life that perished there; there could be no two opinions about that; it never occurred to him that the moral of the poem was that young people cannot begin too soon to exercise discretion in the obedience they pay to their Papa and Mamma. Oh, no! the only thought in his mind was that he should never, never have been like Casabianca, and that Casabianca would have despised him so much, if he could have known him, that he would not have condescended to speak to him. There was nobody else in the ship worth reckoning at all: it did not matter how much they were blown up. Mrs. Hemans knew them all and they were a very indifferent lot. Besides, Casabianca was so good-looking and came of such a good family.'

And thus his small mind kept wandering on till he could follow it no longer, and again went off into a doze.

CHAPTER THIRTY

NEVERTHELESS, he was far from happy. Dr. Skinner was much too like his father. True, Ernest was not thrown in with him much yet, but he was always there; there was no knowing at what moment he might not put in an appearance, and whenever he did show, it was to storm about something. He was like the lion in the Bishop of Oxford's Sunday story — always liable to rush out from behind some bush and devour someone when he was least expected. He called Ernest 'an audacious reptile' and said he wondered the earth did not open and swallow him up because he pronounced Thalia with a short i. 'And this to me,' he thundered, 'who never made a false quantity in my life.' Surely he would have been a much nicer person if he had made false quantities in his youth like other people. Ernest could not imagine how the boys in Dr. Skinner's form continued to live; but yet they did, and even throve, and, strange as it may seem, idolized him, or professed to do so in after life. To Ernest it seemed like living on the crater of Vesuvius.

He was himself, as has been said, in Mr. Templer's form, who was snappish, but not downright wicked, and was very easy to crib under. Ernest used to wonder how Mr. Templer could be so blind, for he supposed Mr. Templer must have cribbed when he was at school, and would ask himself whether he should forget his youth when he got old, as Mr. Templer had forgotten his. He used to think he never could possibly forget any part of it.

Then there was Mrs. Jay, who was sometimes very alarming. A few days after the half-year had commenced, there being some little extra noise in the hall, she rushed in with her spectacles on her forehead and her cap strings flying, and called the boy whom Ernest had selected as his hero the 'rampingest-scampingest-rackety-tackety-tow-row-roaringest boy in the whole school'. But she used to say things that Ernest liked. If the Doctor went out to dinner, and there were no prayers, she would come in and say, 'Young gentlemen, prayers are excused this evening'; and, take her for all in all, she was a kindly old soul enough.

CHAPTER THIRTY-ONE

WITH the masters Ernest was ere long in absolute disgrace. He had more liberty now than he had known heretofore. The heavy hand and watchful eye of Theobald were no longer about his path and about his bed and spying out all his ways; and punishment by way of copying out lines of Virgil was a very different thing from the savage beatings of his father. The copying out in fact was often less trouble than the lesson. Latin and Greek had nothing in them which commended them to his instinct as likely to bring him peace even at the last; still less did they hold out any hope of doing so within some more reasonable time. The deadness inherent in these defunct languages themselves had never been artificially counteracted by a system of *bona fide* rewards for application. There had been any amount of punishments for want of application, but no good comfortable bribes had baited the hook which was to allure him to his good.

Indeed, the more pleasant side of learning to do this or that had always been treated as something with which Ernest had no concern. We had no business with pleasant things at all, at any rate very little business, at any rate not he, Ernest. We were put into this world not for pleasure but duty, and pleasure had in it something more or less sinful in its very essence. If we were doing anything we liked, we, or at any rate he, Ernest, should apologize and think he was being very mercifully dealt with, if not at once told to go and do something else. With what he did not like, however, it was different; the more he disliked a thing the greater the presumption that it was right. It never occurred to him that the presumption was in favour of the rightness of what was most pleasant, and that the onus of proving that it was not right lay with those who disputed its being so. I have said more than once that he believed in his own depravity; never was there a little mortal more ready to accept without cavil whatever he was told by those who were in authority over him: he thought, at least, that he believed it, for as yet he knew nothing of that other Ernest that dwelt within him, and was so much stronger and more real than the Ernest of which he was conscious. The dumb Ernest persuaded with inarticulate feelings too swift and sure to be translated into such debatable things as words, but practically insisted as follows:

'Growing is not the easy plain sailing business that it is commonly supposed to be: it is hard work — harder than any but a growing boy can understand; it requires attention, and you are not strong enough to attend to your bodily growth and to your lessons too. Besides, Latin and Greek are great humbug; the more people know of them the more odious they generally are; the nice people whom you delight in either never knew any at all or forgot what they had learned as soon as they could; they never turned to the classics after they were no longer forced to read them; therefore they are nonsense, all very well in their own time and country, but out of place here. Never learn anything until you find you have been made uncomfortable for a good long while by not knowing it; when you find that you have occasion for this or that knowledge, or foresee that you will have occasion for it shortly, the sooner you learn it the better, but till then spend your time in growing bone and muscle; these will be much more useful to you than Latin and Greek, nor will you ever be able to make them if you do not do so now, whereas Latin and Greek can be acquired at any time by those who want them.

'You are surrounded on every side by lies which would deceive even the elect, if the elect were not generally so uncommonly wide awake; the self of which you are conscious, your reasoning and reflecting self, will believe these lies and bid you act in accordance with them. This

255

conscious self of yours, Ernest, is a prig begotten of prigs and trained in priggishness; I will not allow it to shape your actions, though it will doubtless shape your words for many a year to come. Your papa is not here to beat you now; this is a change in the conditions of your existence, and should be followed by changed actions. Obey *me*, your true self, and things will go tolerably well with you, but only listen to that outward and visible old husk of yours which is called your father, and I will rend you in pieces even unto the third and fourth generation as one who has hated God; for I, Ernest, am the God who made you.'

How shocked Ernest would have been if he could have heard the advice he was receiving; what consternation too there would have been at Battersby; but the matter did not end here, for this same wicked inner self gave him bad advice about his pocket-money, the choice of his companions, and on the whole Ernest was attentive and obedient to its behests, more so than Theobald had been. The consequence was that he learned little, his mind growing more slowly and his body rather faster than heretofore; and when by and by his inner self urged him in directions where he met obstacles beyond his strength to combat, he took — though with passionate compunctions of conscience — the nearest course to the one from which he was debarred which circumstances would allow.

CHAPTER THIRTY-EIGHT

ERNEST was thus in disgrace from the beginning of the holidays, but an incident soon occurred which led him into delinquencies compared with which all his previous sins were venial.

Among the servants at the Rectory was a remarkably pretty girl named Ellen. She came from Devonshire, and was the daughter of a fisherman who had been drowned when she was a child. Her mother set up a small shop in the village where her husband had lived, and just managed to make a living. Ellen remained with her till she was fourteen, when she first went out to service. Four years later, when she was about eighteen, but so well-grown that she might have passed for twenty, she had been strongly recommended to Christina, who was then in want of a housemaid, and had now been at Battersby about twelve months.

As I have said, the girl was remarkably pretty; she looked the perfection of health and good temper, indeed there was a serene expression upon her face which captivated almost all who saw her; she looked as if matters had always gone well with her and were always going to do so, and as if no conceivable combination of circumstances could put her for long together out of temper either with herself or with anyone else. Her complexion was clear, but high; her eyes were grey and beautifully shaped; her lips were full and restful, with something of an Egyptian Sphinx-like character about them. When I learned that she came from Devonshire I fancied I saw a strain of far-away Egyptian blood in her, for I had heard, though I know not what foundation there was for the story, that the Egyptians made settlements on the coast of Devonshire and Cornwall long before the Romans conquered Britain. Her hair was a rich brown, and her figure — of about the middle height — perfect, but erring if at all on the side of robustness. Altogether she was one of those girls about whom one is inclined to wonder how they can remain unmarried a week or a day longer.

Her face (as indeed faces generally are, though I grant they lie sometimes) was a fair index to her disposition. She was good nature itself, and everyone in the house, not excluding, I believe, even Theobald himself after a fashion, was fond of her. As for Christina she took the very warmest interest in her, and used to have her into the dining-room twice a week, and prepare her for confirmation (for by some accident she had never been confirmed) by explaining to her the geography of Palestine and the routes taken by St. Paul on his various journeys in Asia Minor.

When Bishop Treadwell did actually come down to Battersby and hold a confirmation there (Christina had her wish, he slept at Battersby, and she had a grand dinner party for him, and called him 'My lord' several times), he was so much struck with her pretty face and modest demeanour when he laid his hands upon her that he asked Christina about her. When she replied that Ellen was one of her own servants, the bishop seemed, so she thought or chose to think, quite pleased that so pretty a girl should have found so exceptionally good a situation.

Ernest used to get up early during the holidays so that he might play the piano before breakfast without disturbing his papa and mamma — or rather, perhaps, without being disturbed by them. Ellen would generally be there sweeping the drawing-room floor and dusting while he was playing, and the boy, who was ready to make friends with most people, soon became very fond of her. He was not as a general rule sensitive to the charms of the fair sex, indeed he had hardly been thrown in with any women except his Aunts Allaby, and his Aunt Alethea, his mother, his sister Charlotte and Mrs. Jay; sometimes also he had had to take off his hat to the Miss Skinners, and had felt as if he should sink into the earth on doing so, but his shyness had worn off with Ellen, and the pair had become fast friends.

Perhaps it was well that Ernest was not at home for very long together, but as yet his affection though hearty was quite Platonic. He was not only innocent, but deplorably — I might even say guiltily — innocent. His preference was based upon the fact that Ellen never scolded him, but was always smiling and good-tempered; besides she used to like to hear him play, and this gave him additional zest in playing. The morning access to the piano was indeed the one distinct advantage which the holidays had in Ernest's eyes, for at school he could not get at a piano except quasi-surreptitiously at the shop of Mr. Pearsall, the music seller.

On returning this midsummer he was shocked to find his favourite looking pale and ill. All her good spirits had left her, the roses had fled from her cheek, and she seemed on the point of going into a decline. She said she was unhappy about her mother, whose health was failing, and was afraid she was herself not long for this world. Christina, of course, noticed the change. 'I have often remarked,' she said, 'that those very fresh-coloured, healthy-looking girls are the first to break up. I have given her calomel and James's powders repeatedly, and though she does not like it, I think I must show her to Dr. Martin when he next comes here.'

'Very well, my dear,' said Theobald, and so next time Dr. Martin came Ellen was sent for. Dr. Martin soon discovered what would probably have been apparent to Christina herself if she had been able to conceive of such an ailment in connection with a servant who lived under the same roof as Theobald and herself — the purity of whose married life should have preserved all unmarried people who came near them from any taint of mischief.

When it was discovered that in three or four months more Ellen would become a mother, Christina's natural good nature would have prompted her to deal as leniently with the case as she could, if she had not been panic-stricken lest any mercy on her and Theobald's part should be construed into toleration, however partial, of so great a sin; hereon she dashed off into the conviction that the only thing to do was to pay Ellen her wages, and pack her off on the instant bag and baggage out of the house which purity had more especially and particularly singled out for its abiding city. When she thought of the fearful contamination which Ellen's continued presence even for a week would occasion, she could not hesitate.

Then came the question — horrid thought! — as to who was the partner of Ellen's guilt? Was it, could it be, her own son, her darling Ernest? Ernest was getting a big boy now. She could excuse any young woman for taking a fancy to him; as for himself, why she was sure he was behind no young man of his age in appreciation of the charms of a nice-looking young woman. So long as he was innocent she did not mind this, but oh, if he were guilty!

She could not bear to think of it, and yet it would be mere cowardice not to look such a matter in the face — her hope was in the Lord, and she was ready to bear cheerfully and make the best of any suffering He might think fit to lay upon her. That the baby must be either a boy or girl — this much, at any rate, was clear. No less clear was it that the child, if a boy would resemble Theobald, and if a girl, herself. Resemblance, whether of body or mind, generally leaped over a generation. The guilt of the parents must not be shared by the innocent offspring of shame — oh! no — and such a child as this would be . . . She was off in one of her reveries at once.

The child was in the act of being consecrated Archbishop of Canterbury when Theobald came in from a visit in the parish, and was told of the shocking discovery.

Christina said nothing about Ernest, and I believe was more than half angry when the blame was laid upon other shoulders. She was easily consoled, however, and fell back on the double reflection, firstly, that her son was pure, and secondly, that she was quite sure he would not have been so had it not been for his religious convictions which had held him back — as, of course, it was only to be expected they would.

Theobald agreed that no time must be lost in paying Ellen her wages and packing her off. So this was done, and less than two hours after Dr. Martin had entered the house Ellen was sitting beside John the coachman, with her face muffled up so that it could not be seen, weeping bitterly as she was being driven to the station.

CHAPTER FORTY

WHEN Ernest got home and sneaked in through the back door, he heard his father's voice in its angriest tones, inquiring whether Master Ernest had already returned. He felt as Jack must have felt in the story of Jack and the Bean Stalk, when from the oven in which he was hidden he heard the ogre ask his wife what young children she had got for his supper. With much courage, and, as the event proved, with not less courage than discretion, he took the bull by the horns, and announced himself at once as having just come in after having met with a terrible misfortune. Little by little he told his story, and though Theobald stormed somewhat at his 'incredible folly and carelessness', he got off better than he expected. Theobald and Christina had indeed at first been inclined to connect his absence from dinner with Ellen's dismissal, but on finding it clear, as Theobald said — everything was always clear with Theobald — that Ernest had not been in the house all the morning, and could therefore have known nothing of what had happened, he was acquitted on this account for once in a way, without a stain upon his character. Perhaps Theobald was in a good temper; he may have seen from the paper that morning that his stocks had been rising; it may have been this or twenty other things, but whatever it was, he did not scold so much as Ernest had expected, and, seeing the boy look exhausted and believing him to be much grieved at the loss of his watch, Theobald actually prescribed a glass of wine after his dinner, which, strange to say, did not choke him, but made him see things more cheerfully than was usual with him.

That night when he said his prayers, he inserted a few paragraphs to the effect that he might not be discovered, an d that things might go well with Ellen, but he was anxious and ill at ease. His guilty conscience pointed out to him a score of weak places in his story, through any one of which detection might even yet easily enter. Next day and for many days afterwards he fled when no man was pursuing, and trembled each time he heard his father's voice calling for him. He had already so many causes of anxiety that he could stand little more, and in spite of all his endeavours to look cheerful, even his mother could see that something was preying upon his mind. Then the idea returned to her that, after all, her son might not be innocent in the Ellen matter — and this was so interesting that she felt bound to get as near the truth as she could.

'Come here, my poor, pale-faced, heavy-eyed boy,' she said to him one day in her kindest manner; 'come and sit down by me, and we will have a little quiet confidential talk together, will we not?'

The boy went mechanically to the sofa. Whenever his mother wanted what she called a confidential talk with him she always selected the sofa as the most suitable ground on which to open her campaign. All mothers do this; the sofa is to them what the dining-room is to fathers. In the present case the sofa was particularly well adapted for a strategic purpose, being an old-fashioned one with a high back, mattress, bolsters and cushions. Once safely penned into one of its deep corners, it was like a dentist's chair, not too easy to get out of again. Here she could get at him better to pull him about, if this should seem desirable, or if she thought fit to cry she could bury her head in the sofa cushion and abandon herself to an agony of grief which seldom failed to its effect. None of her favourite manœuvres were so easily adopted in her usual seat, the armchair on the right-hand side of the fireplace, and so well did her son know from his mother's tone that this was going to be a sofa conversation that he took his place like a lamb as soon as she began to speak and before she could reach the sofa herself.

'My dearest boy,' began his mother, taking hold of his hand and placing it within her own, 'promise me never to be afraid either of your dear papa or of me; promise me this, my dear, as you love me, promise it to me,' and she kissed him again and again and stroked his hair. But with her other hand she still kept hold of his; she had got him and she meant to keep him.

The lad hung down his head and promised. What else could he do?

'You know there is no one, dear, dear Ernest, who loves you so much as your papa and I do; no one who watches so carefully over your interests, or who is so anxious to enter into all your little joys and troubles as we are; but my dearest boy, it grieves me to think sometimes that you have not that perfect love for and confidence in us which you ought to have. You know, my darling, that it would be as much our pleasure as our duty to watch over the development of your moral and spiritual nature, but alas! you will not let us see your moral and spiritual nature. At times we are almost inclined to doubt whether you have a moral and spiritual nature at all. Of your inner life, my dear, we know nothing beyond such scraps as we can glean in spite of you, from little things which escape you almost before you know that you have said them.'

The boy winced at this. It made him feel hot and uncomfortable all over. He knew well how careful he ought to be, and yet, do what he could, from time to time his forgetfulness of the part betrayed him into unreserve. His mother saw that he winced, and enjoyed the scratch she had given him. Had she felt less confident of victory she had better have forgone the pleasure of touching as it were the eyes at the end of the snail's horns in order to enjoy seeing the snail draw them in again — but she knew that when she had got him well down into the sofa, and held his hand, she had the enemy almost absolutely at her mercy, and could do pretty much what she liked.

'Papa does not feel,' she continued, 'that you love him with that full-ness and unreserve which would prompt you to have no concealment from him, and to tell him everything freely and fearlessly as your most loving earthly friend next only to your Heavenly Father. Perfect love, as we know, casteth out fear: your father loves you perfectly, my darling, but he does not feel as though you loved him perfectly in return. If you fear him it is because you do not love him as he deserves, and I know it sometimes cuts him to the very heart to think that he has earned from you a deeper and more willing sympathy than you dis-play towards him. Oh, Ernest, Ernest, do not grieve one who is so good and noble-hearted by conduct which I can call by no other name than ingratitude.'

Ernest could never stand being spoken to in this way by his mother: for he still believed that she loved him, and that he was fond of her and had a friend in her — up to a certain point. But his mother was begin-ning to come to the end of her tether; she had played the domestic confidence trick upon him times without number already. Over and over again had she wheedled from him all she wanted to know, and afterwards got him into the most horrible scrape by telling the whole to Theobald. Ernest had remonstrated more than once upon these occasions, and had pointed out to his mother how disastrous to him his confidences had been, but Christina had always joined issue with him and showed him in the clearest possible manner that in each case she had been right, and that he could not reasonably complain. Generally it was her conscience that forbade her to be silent, and against this there was no appeal, for we are all bound to follow the dictates of our con-science. Ernest used to have to recite a hymn about conscience. It was to the effect that if you did not pay attention to its voice it would soon leave off speaking. 'My mamma's conscience has not left off speaking,' said Ernest to one of his chums at Roughborough, 'it's always jabbering.'

When a boy has once spoken so disrespectfully as this about his mother's conscience it is practically all over between him and her. Ernest through sheer force of habit, of the sofa, and of the return of the associated ideas, was still so moved by the siren's voice as to yearn to sail towards her, and fling himself into her arms, but it would not do; there were other associated ideas that returned also, and the mangled bones of too many murdered confessions were lying whitening round the skirts of his mother's dress, to allow him by any possibility to trust her further. So he hung his head and looked sheepish, but kept his own counsel.

'I see, my dearest,' continued his mother, 'either that I am mistaken, and that there is nothing on your mind, or that you will not unburden yourself to me: but oh, Ernest, tell me at least this much; is there nothing that you repent of, nothing which makes you unhappy in connection with that miserable girl Ellen?'

Ernest's heart failed him. 'I am a dead boy now,' he said to himself. He had not the faintest conception what his mother was driving at, and thought she suspected about the watch; but he held his ground.

I do not believe he was much more of a coward than his neighbours, only he did not know that all sensible people are cowards when they are off their beat, or when they think they are going to be roughly handled. I believe, that if the truth were known, it would be found that even the valiant St. Michael himself tried hard to shirk his famous combat with the dragon; he pretended not to see all sorts of misconduct on the dragon's part; shut his eyes to the eating up of I do not know how many hundreds of men, women and children whom he had promised to protect; allowed himself to be publicly insulted a dozen times over without resenting it; and in the end when even an angel could stand it no longer he shilly-shallied and temporized an unconscionable time before he would fix the day and hour for the encounter. As for the actual combat it was much such another *wurra-wurra* as Mrs. Allaby had had with the young man who had in the end married her eldest daughter, till after a time behold, there was the dragon lying dead, while he was himself alive and not very seriously hurt after all.

'I do not know what you mean, Mamma,' exclaimed Ernest anxiously and more or less hurriedly. His mother construed his manner into indignation at being suspected, and being rather frightened herself she turned tail and scuttled off as fast as her tongue could carry her.

'Oh!' she said, 'I see by your tone that you are innocent! Oh! oh! how I thank my heavenly Father for this; may He for His dear Son's sake keep you always pure. Your father, my dear' — (here she spoke hurriedly but gave him a searching look) — 'was as pure as a spotless angel when he came to me. Like him, always be self-denying, truly truthful both in word and deed, never forgetful whose son and grandson you are, nor of the name we gave you, of the sacred stream in whose waters your sins were washed out of you through the blood and blessing of Christ,' etc.

But Ernest cut this — I will not say short — but a great deal shorter than it would have been if Christina had had her say out, by extricating himself from his mamma's embrace and showing a clean pair of heels. As he got near the purlieus of the kitchen (where he was more at ease) he heard his father calling for his mother, and again his guilty conscience rose against him. 'He has found all out now,' it cried, 'and he is going to tell mamma — this time I am done for.' But there was nothing in it; his father only wanted the key of the cellaret. Then Ernest slunk off into a coppice or spinney behind the Rectory paddock, and consoled himself with a pipe of tobacco. Here in the wood with the summer sun streaming through the trees and a book and his pipe the boy forgot his cares and had an interval of that rest without which I verily believe his life would have been insupportable.

Of course, Ernest was made to look for his lost property, and a reward was offered for it, but it seemed he had wandered a good deal off the path, thinking to find a lark's nest, more than once, and looking for a watch and purse on Battersby piewipes was very like looking for a needle in a bundle of hay: besides, it might have been found and taken by some tramp, or by a magpie of which there were many in the neighbourhood, so that after a week or ten days the search was discontinued, and the unpleasant fact had to be faced that Ernest must have another watch, another knife and a small sum of pocket-money.

It was only right, however, that Ernest should pay half the cost of the watch; this should be made easy for him, for it should be deducted from his pocket-money in half-yearly instalments extending over two, or even it might be three years. In Ernest's own interests, then, as well as those of his father and mother, it would be well that the watch should cost as little as possible, so it was resolved to buy a second-hand one. Nothing was to be said to Ernest, but it was to be bought, and laid upon his plate as a surprise just before the holidays were over. Theobald would have to go to the county town in a few days, and could then find some second-hand watch which would answer sufficiently well. In the course of time, therefore, Theobald went, furnished with a long list of household commissions, among which was the purchase of a watch for Ernest.

Those, as I have said, were always happy times, when Theobald was away for a whole day certain; the boy was beginning to feel easy in his mind as though God had heard his prayers, and he was not going to be found out. Altogether the day had proved an unusually tranquil one, but, alas! it was not to close as it had begun; the fickle atmosphere in which he lived was never more likely to breed a storm than after such an interval of brilliant calm, and when Theobald returned Ernest had only to look in his face to see that a hurricane was approaching.

Christina saw that something had gone very wrong, and was quite frightened lest Theobald should have heard of some serious money loss; he did not, however, at once unbosom himself, but rang the bell and said to the servant, 'Tell Master Ernest I wish to speak to him in the dining-room.'

CHAPTER FORTY-ONE

LONG before Ernest reached the dining-room his ill-divining soul had told him that his sin had found him out. What head of a family ever sends for any of its members into the dining-room if his intentions are honourable?

When he reached it he found it empty — his father having been called away for a few minutes unexpectedly upon some parish business — and he was left in the same kind of suspense as people are in after they have been ushered into their dentist's ante-room.

Of all the rooms in the house he hated the dining-room worst. It was here that he had had to do his Latin and Greek lessons with his father. It had a smell of some particular kind of polish or varnish which was used in polishing the furniture and neither I nor Ernest can even now come within range of the smell of this kind of varnish without our hearts failing us.

Over the chimney-piece there was a veritable old master, one of the few original pictures which Mr. George Pontifex had brought from

Italy. It was supposed to be a Salvator Rosa, and had been bought as a great bargain. The subject was Elijah or Elisha (whichever it was) being fed by the ravens in the desert. There were the ravens in the upper right-hand corner with bread and meat in their beaks and claws, and there was the prophet in question in the lower left-hand corner looking longingly up towards them. When Ernest was a very small boy it had been a constant matter of regret to him that the food which the ravens carried never actually reached the prophet; he did not understand the limitation of the painter's art, and wanted the meat and the prophet to be brought into direct contact. One day, with the help of some steps which had been left in the room, he had clambered up to the picture and with a piece of bread and butter traced a greasy line right across it from the ravens to Elisha's mouth, after which he had felt more comfortable.

Ernest's mind was drifting back to this youthful escapade when he heard his father's hand on the door, and in another second Theobald entered.

'Oh, Ernest,' said he, in an off-hand, rather cheery manner, 'there's a little matter which I should like you to explain to me, as I have no doubt you very easily can.' Thump, thump, thump went Ernest's heart against his ribs; but his father's manner was so much nicer than usual that he began to think it might be after all only another false alarm.

'It had occurred to your mother and myself that we should like to set you up with a watch again before you went back to school' ('Oh, that's all,' said Ernest to himself, quite relieved), 'and I have been today to look out for a second-hand one which should answer every purpose so long as you are at school.'

Theobald spoke as if watches had half a dozen purposes besides timekeeping, but he could hardly open his mouth without using one or other of his tags, and 'answering every purpose' was one of them.

Ernest was breaking out into the usual expressions of gratitude, when Theobald continued, 'You are interrupting me,' and Ernest's heart thumped again.

'You are interrupting me, Ernest. I have not yet done.' Ernest was instantly dumb.

'I passed several shops with second-hand watches for sale, but I saw none of a description and price which pleased me, till at last I was shown one which had, so the shopman said, been left with him recently for sale, and which I at once recognized as the one which had been given you by your Aunt Alethea. Even if I had failed to recognize it, as perhaps I might have done, I should have identified it directly it reached my hands, inasmuch as it had "E. P., a present from A. P." engraved upon the inside. I need say no more to show that this was the very watch which you told your mother and me that you had dropped out of your pocket.'

Up to this time Theobald's manner had been studiously calm, and his words had been uttered slowly, but here he suddenly quickened and flung off the mask as he added the words, 'or some such cock and bull story, which your mother and I were too truthful to disbelieve. You can guess what must be our feelings now.'

Ernest felt that this last home-thrust was just. In his less anxious moments he had thought his papa and mamma 'green' for the readiness with which they believed him, but he could not deny that their credulity was a proof of their habitual truthfulness of mind. In common justice he must own that it was very dreadful for two such truthful people to have a son as untruthful as he knew himself to be.

'Believing that a son of your mother and myself would be incapable of falsehood I at once assumed that some tramp had picked the watch up and was now trying to dispose of it.'

This to the best of my belief was not accurate. Theobald's first assumption had been that it was Ernest who was trying to sell the watch, and it was an inspiration of the moment to say that his magnanimous mind had at once conceived the idea of a tramp.

'You may imagine how shocked I was when I discovered that the watch had been brought for sale by that miserable woman Ellen' — here Ernest's heart hardened a little, and he felt as near an approach to an instinct to turn as one so defenceless could be expected to feel; his father quickly perceived this and continued, 'who was turned out of this house in circumstances which I will not pollute your ears by more particularly describing.

'I put aside the horrid conviction which was beginning to dawn upon me, and assumed that in the interval between her dismissal and her leaving this house, she had added theft to her other sin, and having found your watch in your bedroom had purloined it. It even occurred to me that you might have missed your watch after the woman was gone, and, suspecting who had taken it, had run after the carriage in order to recover it; but when I told the shopman of my suspicions he assured me that the person who left it with him had declared most solemnly that it had been given her by her master's son, whose property it was, and who had a perfect right to dispose of it.

'He told me further that, thinking the circumstances in which the watch was offered for sale somewhat suspicious, he had insisted upon the woman's telling him the whole story of how she came by it, before he would consent to buy it of her.

'He said that at first — as women of that stamp invariably do — she tried prevarication, but on being threatened that she should at once be given into custody if she did not tell the whole truth, she described the way in which you had run after the carriage, till as she said you were black in the face, and insisted on giving her all your pocket-money, your knife and your watch. She added that my coachman John — whom I shall instantly discharge — was witness to the whole transaction. Now, Ernest, be pleased to tell me whether this appalling story is true or false?'

It never occurred to Ernest to ask his father why he did not hit a man his own size, or to stop him midway in the story with a remonstrance against being kicked when he was down. The boy was too much shocked and shaken to be inventive; he could only drift and stammer out that the tale was true.

'So I feared,' said Theobald, 'and now, Ernest, be good enough to ring the bell.'

When the bell had been answered, Theobald desired that John should be sent for, and when John came Theobald calculated the wages due to him and desired him at once to leave the house.

John's manner was quiet and respectful. He took his dismissal as a matter of course, for Theobald had hinted enough to make him understand why he was being discharged, but when he saw Ernest sitting pale and awestruck on the edge of his chair against the dining-room wall, a sudden thought seemed to strike him, and turning to Theobald he said in a broad northern accent which I will not attempt to reproduce:

'Look here, master, I can guess what all this is about — now before I goes I want to have a word with you.'

'Ernest,' said Theobald, 'leave the room.'

'No, Master Ernest, you shan't,' said John, planting himself against the door. 'Now, master,' he continued, 'you may do as you please about me. I've been a good servant to you, and I don't mean to say as you've been a bad master to me, but I do say that if you bear hardly on Master Ernest here I have those in the village as'll hear on't and let me know; and if I do hear on't I'll come back and break every bone in your skin, so there!'

John's breath came and went quickly, as though he would have been well enough pleased to begin the bone-breaking business at once. Theobald turned of an ashen colour — not, as he explained afterwards, at the idle threats of a detected and angry ruffian, but at such atrocious insolence from one of his own servants.

'I shall leave Master Ernest, John,' he rejoined proudly, 'to the reproaches of his own conscience.' ('Thank God and thank John,' thought Ernest.) 'As for yourself, I admit that you have been an excellent servant until this unfortunate business came on, and I shall have much pleasure in giving you a character if you want one. Have you anything more to say?'

'No more nor what I have said,' said John sullenly, 'but what I've said I means and I'll stick to — character or no character.'

'Oh, you need not be afraid about your character, John,' said Theobald kindly, 'and as it is getting late, there can be no occasion for you to leave the house before tomorrow morning.'

To this there was no reply from John, who retired, packed up his things, and left the house at once.

When Christina heard what had happened she said she could condone all except that Theobald should have been subjected to such insolence from one of his own servants through the misconduct of his son. Theobald was the bravest man in the whole world, and could easily have collared the wretch and turned him out of the room, but how far more dignified, how far nobler had been his reply! How it would tell in a novel or upon the stage, for though the stage as a whole was immoral, yet there were doubtless some plays which were improving spectacles. She could fancy the whole house hushed with excitement at hearing John's menace, and hardly breathing by reason of their interest and expectation of the coming answer. Then the actor — probably the great and good Mr. Macready — would say, 'I shall leave Master Ernest, John, to the reproaches of his own conscience.' Oh, it was sublime! What a roar of applause must follow! Then she should enter herself, and fling her arms about her husband's neck, and call him her lion-hearted husband. When the curtain dropped, it would be buzzed about the house that the scene just witnessed had been drawn from real life, and had actually occurred in the household of the Rev. Theobald Pontifex, who had married a Miss Allaby, etc. etc.

As regards Ernest the suspicions which had already crossed her mind were deepened, but she thought it better to leave the matter where it was. At present she was in a very strong position. Ernest's official purity was firmly established, but at the same time he had shown himself so susceptible that she was able to fuse two contradictory impressions concerning him into a single idea, and consider him as a kind of Joseph and Don Juan in one. This was what she had wanted all along, but her vanity being gratified by the possession of such a son, there was an end of it; the son himself was naught.

No doubt if John had not interfered, Ernest would have had to expiate his offence with ache, penury and imprisonment. As it was the boy was 'to consider himself' as undergoing these punishments, and as suffering pangs of unavailing remorse inflicted on him by his conscience into the bargain; but beyond the fact that Theobald kept him more closely to his holiday task, and the continued coldness of his parents, no ostensible punishment was meted out to him. Ernest, however, tells me that he looks back upon this as the time when he began to know that he had a cordial and active dislike for both his parents, which I suppose means that he was now beginning to be aware that he was reaching man's estate.

CHAPTER FORTY-TWO

ABOUT week before he went back to school his father again sent for him into the dining-room, and told him that he should restore him his watch, but that he should deduct the sum he had paid for it — for he had thought it better to pay a few shillings rather than dispute the ownership of the watch, seeing that Ernest had undoubtedly given it to Ellen — from his pocket-money, in payments which should extend over two half-years. He would therefore have to go back to Roughborough this half-year with only five shillings' pocket-money. If he wanted more he must earn more merit money.

Ernest was not so careful about money as a pattern boy should be. He did not say to himself, 'Now I have got a sovereign which must last me fifteen weeks, therefore I may spend exactly one shilling and fourpence in each week' — and spend exactly one and fourpence in each week accordingly. He ran through his money at about the same rate as other boys did, being pretty well cleaned out a few days after he had got back to school. When he had no more money, he got a little into debt, and when as far in debt as he could see his way to repaying, he went without luxuries. Immediately he got any money he would pay his debts; if there was any over he would spend it; if there was not — and there seldom was — he would begin to go on tick again.

His finance was always based upon the supposition that he should go back to school with £1 in his pocket — of which he owed say a matter of fifteen shillings. There would be five shillings for sundry school subscriptions — but when these were paid the weekly allowance of sixpence given to each boy in the hall, his merit money (which this half he was resolved should come to a good sum) and renewed credit, would carry him through the half.

The sudden failure of 15s. was disastrous to my hero's scheme of finance. His face betrayed his emotions so clearly that Theobald said he was determined 'to learn the truth at once, and *this time* without days and days of falsehood' before he reached it. The melancholy fact was not long in coming out, namely, that the wretched Ernest added debt to the vices of idleness, falsehood and possibly — for it was not impossible — immorality.

How had he come to get into debt? Did the other boys do so? Ernest reluctantly admitted that they did.

With what shops did they get into debt?

This was asking too much. Ernest said he didn't know!

'Oh, Ernest, Ernest,' exclaimed his mother, who was in the room, 'do not so soon a second time presume upon the forbearance of the tenderest-hearted father in the world. Give time for one stab to heal before you wound him with another.'

This was all very fine, but what was Ernest to do? How could he get the school shopkeepers into trouble by owning that they let some of the boys go on tick with them? There was Mrs. Cross, a good old soul, who used to sell hot rolls and butter for breakfast, or eggs and toast, or it might be the quarter of a fowl with bread sauce and mashed potatoes for which she would charge 6d. If she made a farthing out of the sixpence it was as much as she did. When the boys would come trooping into her shop after 'the hounds' how often had not Ernest heard her say to her servant girls, 'Now then, you wanches, git some cheers.' All the boys were fond of her, and was he, Ernest, to tell tales about her? It was horrible.

'Now look here, Ernest,' said his father with his blackest scowl, 'I am going to put a stop to this nonsense once for all. Either take me fully into your confidence, as a son should take a father, and trust me to deal with this matter as a clergyman and a man of the world — or understand distinctly that I shall take the whole story to Dr. Skinner, who, I imagine, will take much sterner measures than I should.'

'Oh, Ernest, Ernest,' sobbed Christina, 'be wise in time, and trust those who have already shown you that they know but too well how to be forbearing.'

No genuine hero of romance should have hesitated for a moment. Nothing should have cajoled or frightened him into telling tales out of school. Ernest thought of his ideal boys; they, he well knew, would have let their tongues be cut out of them before information could have been wrung from any word of theirs. But Ernest was not an ideal boy, and he was not strong enough for his surroundings; I doubt how far any boy could withstand the moral pressure which was brought to bear upon him; at any rate he could not do so, and after a little more writhing he yielded himself a passive prey to the enemy. He consoled himself with the reflection that his papa had not played the confidence trick on him quite as often as his mamma had, and that probably it was better he should tell his father, than that his father should insist on Dr. Skinner's making an inquiry. His papa's conscience 'jabbered' a good deal, but not as much as his mamma's. The little fool forgot that he had not given his father as many chances of betraying him as he had given to Christina.

Then it all came out. He owed this at Mrs. Cross's, and this to Mrs. Jones, and this at the 'Swan and Bottle' public-house, to say nothing of another shilling or sixpence or two in other quarters. Nevertheless, Theobald and Christina were not satiated, but rather the more they discovered the greater grew their appetite for discovery; it was their obvious duty to find out everything, for though they might rescue their own darling from this hotbed of iniquity without getting to know more than they knew at present, were there not other papas and mammas with darlings whom also they were bound to rescue if it were yet possible? What boys, then, owed money to these harpies as well as Ernest?

Here, again, there was a feeble show of resistance, but the thumbscrews were instantly applied, and Ernest, demoralized as he already was, recanted and submitted himself to the powers that were. He told only a little less than he knew or thought he knew. He was examined, re-examined, cross-examined, sent to the retirement of his own bedroom and cross-examined again; the smoking in Mrs. Jones's kitchen all came out; which boys smoked and which did not; which boys owed money and, roughly, how much and where; which boys swore and used bad language. Theobald was resolved that this time Ernest should, as he called it, take him into his confidence without reserve, so the school list which went with Dr. Skinner's half-yearly bills was brought out, and the most secret character of each boy was gone through *seriatim* by Mr. and Mrs. Pontifex, so far as it was in Ernest's power to give information concerning it, and yet Theobald had on the preceding Sunday preached a less feeble sermon than he commonly preached upon the horrors of the Inquisition. No matter how awful was the depravity revealed to them, the pair never flinched, but probed and probed, till they were on the point of reaching subjects more delicate than they had yet touched upon. Here Ernest's unconscious self took the matter up and made a resistance to which his conscious self was unequal, by tumbling him off his chair in a fit of fainting.

Dr. Martin was sent for and pronounced the boy to be seriously unwell; at the same time he prescribed absolute rest and absence from nervous excitement. So the anxious parents were unwillingly compelled to be content with what they had got already — being frightened into leading him a quiet life for the short remainder of the holidays. They were not idle, but Satan can find as much mischief for busy hands as for idle ones, so he sent a little job in the direction of Battersby which Theobald and Christina undertook immediately. It would be a pity, they reasoned, that Ernest should leave Roughborough, now that he had been there three years; it would be difficult to find another school for him, and to explain why he had left Roughborough. Besides, Dr. Skinner and Theobald were supposed to be old friends, and it would be unpleasant to offend him; these were all valid reasons for not removing the boy. The proper thing to do, then, would be to warn Dr. Skinner confidentially of the state of his school, and to furnish him with a school list annotated with the remarks extracted from Ernest, which should be appended to the name of each boy.

Theobald was the perfection of neatness; while his son was ill upstairs , he copied out the school list so that he could throw his comments into a tabular form, which assumed the following shape — only that of course I have changed the names. One cross in each square was to indicate occasional offence; two stood for frequent, and three for habitual delinquency.

	Smoking	Drinking beer at the 'Swan and Bottle'	Swearing and Obscene Language	Notes
Smith	o	o	× ×	Will smoke next half
Brown	× × ×	o	×	
Jones	×	× ×	× × ×	
Robinson	× ×	× ×	×	

And thus through the whole school.

Of course, in justice to Ernest, Dr. Skinner would be bound over to secrecy before a word was said to him, but, Ernest being thus protected, he could not be furnished with the facts too completely.

·

CHAPTER FORTY-FOUR

ONLY once in the whole course of his school life did he get praise from Dr. Skinner for any exercise, and this he has treasured as the best example of guarded approval which he has ever seen. He had had to write a copy of Alcaics on 'The dogs of the monks of St. Bernard', and when the exercise was returned to him he found the Doctor had written on it: 'In this copy of Alcaics — which is still excessively bad — I fancy that I can discern some faint symptoms of improvement.' Ernest says that if the exercise was any better than usual it must have been by a fluke, for he is sure that he always liked dogs, especially St. Bernard dogs, far too much to take any pleasure in writing Alcaics about them.

274

THE intention at Battersby was (for Dr. Skinner had said that Ernest could never get a fellowship) that he should take a sufficiently good degree to be able to get a tutorship or mastership in some school preparatory to taking orders. When he was twenty-one years old his money was to come into his own hands, and the best thing he could do with it would be to buy the next presentation to a living, the rector of which was now old, and live on his mastership or tutorship till the living fell in. He could buy a very good living for the sum which his grandfather's legacy now amounted to, for Theobald had never had any serious intention of making deductions for his son's maintenance and education, and the money had accumulated till it was now about five thousand pounds; he had only talked about making deductions in order to stimulate the boy to exertion as far as possible, by making him think that this was his only chance of escaping starvation — or perhaps from pure love of teasing.

When Ernest had a living of £600 or £700 a year with a house, and not too many parishioners — why, he might add to his income by taking pupils, or even keeping a school, and then, say at thirty, he might marry. It was not easy for Theobald to hit on any much more sensible plan. He could not get Ernest into business, for he had no business connections — besides, he did not know what business meant; he had no interest, again, at the Bar; medicine was a profession which subjected its students to ordeals and temptations which these fond parents shrank from on behalf of their boy; he would be thrown among companions and familiarized with details which might sully him, and though he might stand, it was 'only too possible' that he would fall. Besides, ordination was the road which Theobald knew and understood, and indeed the only road about which he knew anything at all, so not unnaturally it was the one he chose for Ernest.

The foregoing had been instilled into my hero from earliest boyhood, much as it had been instilled into Theobald himself, and with the same result — the conviction, namely, that he was certainly to be a clergyman, but that it was a long way off yet, and he supposed it was all right. As for the duty of reading hard, and taking as good a degree as he could, this was plain enough, so he set himself to work, as I have said, steadily, and to the surprise of everyone as well as himself got a college scholarship, of no great value, but still a scholarship, in his freshman's term. It is hardly necessary to say that Theobald stuck to the whole of this money, believing the pocket-money he allowed Ernest to be sufficient for him, and knowing how dangerous it was for young men to have money at command. I do not suppose it even occurred to him to try and remember what he had felt when his father took a like course in regard to himself.

CHAPTER FORTY-SEVEN

ERNEST returned to Cambridge for the May term of 1858, on the plea of reading for ordination, with which he was now face to face, and much nearer than he liked. Up to this time, though not religiously inclined, he had never doubted the truth of anything that had been told him about Christianity. He had never seen anyone who doubted, nor read anything that raised a suspicion in his mind as to the historical character of the miracles recorded in the Old and New Testaments.

It must be remembered that the year 1858 was the last of a term during which the peace of the Church of England was singularly unbroken. Between 1844, when *Vestiges of Creation* appeared, and 1859, when *Essays and Reviews* marked the commencement of that storm which raged until many years afterwards, there was not a single book published in England that caused serious commotion within the bosom of the Church. Perhaps Buckle's *History of Civilization* and Mill's *Liberty* were the most alarming, but they neither of them reached the substratum of the reading public, and Ernest and his friends were ignorant of their very existence. The Evangelical movement, with the exception to which I shall revert presently, had become almost a matter of ancient history. Tractarianism had subsided into a tenth day's wonder; it was at work, but it was not noisy. The *Vestiges* were forgotten before Ernest went up to Cambridge; the Catholic aggression scare had lost its terrors; Ritualism was still unknown by the general provincial public, and the Gorham and Hampden controversies were defunct some years since; Dissent was not spreading; the Crimean war was the one engrossing subject, to be followed by the Indian Mutiny and the Franco-Austrian war. These great events turned men's minds from speculative subjects, and there was no enemy to the faith which could arouse even a languid interest. At no time probably since the beginning of the century could an ordinary observer have detected less sign of coming disturbance than at that of which I am writing.

I need hardly say that the calm was only on the surface. Older men, who knew more than undergraduates were likely to do, must have seen that the wave of scepticism which had already broken over Germany was setting towards our own shores, nor was it long, indeed, before it reached them. Ernest had hardly been ordained before three works in quick succession arrested the attention even of those who paid least heed to theological controversy. I mean *Essays and Reviews*, Charles Darwin's *Origin of Species* and Bishop Colenso's *Criticisms on the Pentateuch*.

This, however, is a digression; I must revert to the one phase of spiritual activity which had any life in it during the time Ernest was at Cambridge, that is to say, to the remains of the Evangelical awakening of more than a generation earlier, which was connected with the name of Simeon.

There were still a good many Simeonites, or as they were more briefly called 'Sims' in Ernest's time. Every college contained some of them, but their headquarters were at Caius, whither they were attracted by Mr. Clayton, who was at that time senior tutor, and among the sizars of St. John's.

Behind the then chapel of this last-named college, there was a 'labyrinth' (this was the name it bore) of dingy, tumbledown rooms, tenanted exclusively by the poorest undergraduates, who were dependent upon sizarships and scholarships for the means of taking their degrees. To many, even at St. John's, the existence and whereabouts of the labyrinth in which the sizars chiefly lived was unknown; some men in Ernest's time, who had rooms in the first court, had never found their way through the sinuous passage which led to it.

In the labyrinth there dwelt men of all ages, from mere lads to grey-haired old men who had entered late in life. They were rarely seen except in hall or chapel or at lecture, where their manners of feeding, praying and studying were considered alike objectionable; no one knew whence they came, whither they went, nor what they did, for they never showed at cricket or the boats; they were a gloomy, seedy-looking *confrérie*, who had as little to glory in in clothes and manners as in the flesh itself.

Ernest and his friends used to consider themselves marvels of economy for getting on with so little money, but the greater number of dwellers in the labyrinth would have considered one-half of their expenditure to be an exceeding measure of affluence, and so doubtless any domestic tyranny which had been experienced by Ernest was a small thing to what the average Johnian sizar had had to put up with.

A few would at once emerge on its being found after their first examination that they were likely to be ornaments to the college; these would win valuable scholarships that enabled them to live in some degree of comfort, and would amalgamate with the more studious of those who were in a better social position, but even these, with few exceptions, were long in shaking off the uncouthness they brought with them to the University, nor would their origin cease to be easily recognizable till they had become dons and tutors. I have seen some of these men attain high position in the world of politics or science, and yet still retain a look of labyrinth and Johnian sizarship.

Unprepossessing then, in feature, gait and manners, unkempt and ill-dressed beyond what can be easily described, these poor fellows formed a class apart, whose thoughts and ways were not as the thoughts and ways of Ernest and his friends, and it was among them that Simeonism chiefly flourished.

Destined most of them for the Church (for in those days 'holy orders' were seldom heard of), the Simeonites held themselves to have received a very loud call to the ministry, and were ready to pinch themselves for years so as to prepare for it by the necessary theological courses. To most of them the fact of becoming clergymen would be the *entrée* into a social position from which they were at present kept out by barriers they well knew to be impassable; ordination, therefore, opened fields for ambition which made it the central point in their thoughts, rather than as with Ernest, something which he supposed would have to be done some day, but about which, as about dying, he hoped there was no need to trouble himself as yet.

By way of preparing themselves more completely they would have meetings in one another's rooms for tea and prayer and other spiritual exercises. Placing themselves under the guidance of a few well-known tutors they would teach in Sunday Schools, and be instant, in season and out of season, in imparting spiritual instruction to all whom they could persuade to listen to them.

But the soil of the more prosperous undergraduates was not suitable for the seed they tried to sow. The small pieties with which they larded their discourse, if chance threw them into the company of one whom they considered worldly, caused nothing but aversion in the minds of those for whom they were intended. When they distributed tracts, dropping them by night into good men's letter-boxes while they were asleep, their tracts got burnt, or met with even worse contumely; they were themselves also treated with the ridicule which they reflected proudly had been the lot of true followers of Christ in all ages. Often at their prayer meetings was the passage of St. Paul referred to in which he bids his Corinthian converts note concerning themselves that they were for the most part neither well-bred nor intellectual people. They reflected with pride that they too had nothing to be proud of in these respects, and like St. Paul, gloried in the fact that in the flesh they had not much to glory.

Ernest had several Johnian friends, and came thus to hear about the Simeonites and to see some of them, who were pointed out to him as they passed through the courts. They had a repellent attraction for him; he disliked them, but he could not bring himself to leave them alone. On one occasion he had gone so far as to parody one of the tracts they had sent round in the night, and to get a copy dropped into each of the leading Simeonites' boxes. The subject he had taken was 'Personal Cleanliness'. Cleanliness, he said, was next to godliness; he wished to know on which side it was to stand, and concluded by exhorting Simeonites to a freer use of the tub. I cannot commend my hero's humour in this matter; his tract was not brilliant, but I mention the fact as showing that at this time he was something of a Saul and took pleasure in persecuting the elect, not, as I have said, that he had any hankering after scepticism, but because, like the farmers in his father's village, though he would not stand seeing the Christian religion made light of, he was not going to see it taken seriously. Ernest's friends thought his dislike for Simeonites was due to his being the son of a clergyman who, it was known, bullied him; it is more likely, however, that it rose from an unconscious sympathy with them, which, as in St. Paul's case, in the end drew him into the ranks of those whom he had most despised and hated.

CHAPTER FORTY-EIGHT

ONCE, recently, when he was down at home after taking his degree, his mother had had a short conversation with him about his becoming a clergyman, set on thereto by Theobald, who shrank from the subject himself. This time it was during a turn taken in the garden, and not on the sofa — which was reserved for supreme occasions.

'You know, my dearest boy,' she said to him, 'that Papa' (she always called Theobald 'papa' when talking to Ernest) 'is so anxious you should not go into the Church blindly, and without fully realizing the difficulties of a clergyman's position. He has considered all of them himself, and has been shown how small they are, when they are faced boldly, but he wishes you, too, to feel them as strongly and completely as possible before committing yourself to irrevocable vows, so that you may never, never have to regret the step you will have taken.'

This was the first time Ernest had heard that there were any difficulties, and he not unnaturally inquired in a vague way after their nature.

'That, my dear boy,' rejoined Christina, 'is a question which I am not fitted to enter upon either by nature or education. I might easily unsettle your mind without being able to settle it again. Oh, no! Such questions are far better avoided by women, and, I should have thought, by men; but Papa wished me to speak to you upon the subject, so that there might be no mistake hereafter, and I have done so. Now, therefore, you know all.'

The conversation ended here, so far as this subject was concerned, and Ernest thought he did know all. His mother would not have told him he knew all — not about a matter of that sort — unless he actually did know it; well, it did not come to very much; he supposed there *were* some difficulties, but his father, who at any rate was an excellent scholar and a learned man, was probably quite right here, and he need not trouble himself more about them. So little impression did the conversation make on him, that it was not till long afterwards that, happening to remember it, he saw what a piece of sleight of hand had been practised upon him. Theobald and Christina, however, were satisfied that they had done their duty by opening their son's eyes to the difficulties of assenting to all a clergyman must assent to. This was enough; it was a matter for rejoicing that, though they had been put so fully and candidly before him, he did not find them serious. It was not in vain that they had prayed for so many years to be made 'truly honest and conscientious'.

'And now, my dear,' resumed Christina, after having disposed of all the difficulties that might stand in the way of Ernest's becoming a clergyman, 'there is another matter on which I should like to have a talk with you. It is about your sister Charlotte. You know how clever she is, and what a dear, kind sister she has been and always will be to yourself and Joey. I wish, my dearest Ernest, that I saw more chance of her finding a suitable husband than I do at Battersby, and I sometimes think you might do more than you do to help her.'

Ernest began to chafe at this, for he had heard it so often, but he said nothing.

'You know, my dear, a brother can do so much for his sister if he lays himself out to do it. A mother can do very little — indeed, it is hardly a mother's place to seek out young men; it is a brother's place to find a suitable partner for his sister; all that I can do is to try to make Battersby as attractive as possible to any of your friends whom you may invite. And in that,' she added, with a little toss of her head, 'I do not think I have been deficient hitherto.'

Ernest said he had already at different times asked several of his friends.

'Yes, my dear, but you must admit that they were none of them exactly the kind of young man whom Charlotte could be expected to take a fancy to. Indeed, I must own to having been a little disappointed that you should have yourself chosen any of these as your intimate friends.'

Ernest winced again.

'You never brought down Figgins when you were at Roughborough; now I should have thought Figgins would have been just the kind of boy whom you might have asked to come and see us.'

Figgins had been gone through times out of number already. Ernest had hardly known him, and Figgins, being nearly three years older than Ernest, had left long before he did. Besides, he had not been a nice boy, and had made himself unpleasant to Ernest in many ways.

'Now,' continued his mother, 'there's Towncley. I have heard you speak of Towncley as having rowed with you in a boat at Cambridge. I wish, my dear, you would cultivate your acquaintance with Towneley, and ask him to pay us a visit. The name has an aristocratic sound, and I think I have heard you say he is an eldest son.'

Ernest flushed at the sound of Towneley's name.

What had really happened in respect of Ernest's friends was briefly this. His mother liked to get hold of the names of the boys and especially of any who were at all intimate with her son; the more she heard, the more she wanted to know; there was no gorging her to satiety; she was like a ravenous young cuckoo being fed upon a grass plot by a water-wagtail, she would swallow all that Ernest could bring her, and yet be as hungry as before. And she always went to Ernest for her meals rather than to Joey, for Joey was either more stupid or more impenetrable — at any rate she could pump Ernest much the better of the two.

From time to time an actual live boy had been thrown to her, either by being caught and brought to Battersby or by being asked to meet her if at any time she came to Roughborough. She had generally made herself agreeable, or fairly agreeable as long as the boy was present, but as soon as she got Ernest to herself again she changed her note. Into whatever form she might throw her criticisms it came always in the end to this, that his friend was no good, that Ernest was not much better, and that he should have brought her someone else, for this one would not do at all.

The more intimate the boy had been or was supposed to be with Ernest the more he was declared to be naught, till in the end he had hit upon the plan of saying, concerning any boy whom he particularly liked, that he was not one of his especial chums, and that indeed he hardly knew why he had asked him; but he found he only fell on Scylla in trying to avoid Charybdis, for though the boy was declared to be more successful it was Ernest who was naught for not thinking more highly of him.

When she had once got hold of a name she never forgot it. 'And how is So-and-so?' she would exclaim, mentioning some former friend of Ernest's with whom he had either now quarrelled, or who had long since proved to be a mere comet and no fixed star at all. How Ernest wished he had never mentioned So-and-so's name, and vowed to himself that he would never talk about his friends in future, but in a few hours he would forget and would prattle away as imprudently as ever; then his mother would pounce noiselessly on his remarks as a barn-owl pounces upon a mouse, and would bring them up in a pellet six months afterwards when they were no longer in harmony with their surroundings.

Then there was Theobald. If a boy or college friend had been invited to Battersby, Theobald would lay himself out at first to be agreeable. He could do this well enough when he liked, and as regards the outside world he generally did like. His clerical neighbours, and indeed all his neighbours, respected him yearly more and more, and would have given Ernest sufficient cause to regret his imprudence if he had dared to hint that he had anything, however little, to complain of. Theobald's mind worked in this way: 'Now, I know Ernest has told this boy what a disagreeable person I am, and I will just show him that I am not disagreeable at all, but a good old fellow, a jolly old boy, in fact a regular old brick, and that it is Ernest who is in fault all through.'

So he would behave very nicely to the boy at first, and the boy would be delighted with him, and side with him against Ernest. Of course if Ernest had got the boy to come to Battersby he wanted him to enjoy his visit, and was therefore pleased that Theobald should behave so well, but at the same time he stood so much in need of moral support that it was painful to him to see one of his own familiar friends go over to the enemy's camp. For no matter how well we may know a thing — how clearly we may see a certain patch of colour, for example, as red, it shakes us and knocks us about to find another see it, or be more than half inclined to see it, as green.

Theobald had generally begun to get a little impatient before the end of the visit, but the impression formed during the earlier part was the one which the visitor had carried away with him. Theobald never discussed any of the boys with Ernest. It was Christina who did this. Theobald let them come, because Christina in a quiet, persistent way insisted on it; when they did come he behaved, as I have said, civilly, but he did not like it, whereas Christina did like it very much; she would have had half Roughborough and half Cambridge to come and stay at Battersby if she could have managed it, and if it would not have cost so much money: she liked their coming, so that she might make a new acquaintance, and she liked tearing them to pieces and flinging the bits over Ernest as soon as she had had enough of them.

The worst of it was that she had so often proved to be right. Boys and young men are violent in their affections, but they are seldom very constant; it is not till they get older that they really know the kind of friend they want; in their earlier essays young men are simply learning to judge character. Ernest had been no exception to the general rule. His swans had one after the other proved to be more or less geese even in his own estimation, and he was beginning almost to think that his mother was a better judge of character than he was; but I think it may be assumed with some certainty that if Ernest had brought her a real young swan she would have declared it to be the ugliest and worst goose of all that she had yet seen.

At first he had not suspected that his friends were wanted with a view to Charlotte; it was understood that Charlotte and they might perhaps take a fancy for one another; and that would be so very nice, would it not? But he did not see that there was any deliberate malice in the arrangement. Now, however, that he had awoke to what it all meant, he was less inclined to bring any friend of his to Battersby. It seemed to his silly young mind almost dishonest to ask your friend to come and see you when all you really meant was, 'Please, marry my sister.' It was like trying to obtain money under false pretences. If he had been fond of Charlotte it might have been another matter, but he thought her one of the most disagreeable young women in the whole circle of his acquaintance.

She was supposed to be very clever. All young ladies are either very pretty or very clever or very sweet; they may take their choice as to which category they will go in for, but go in for one of the three they must. It was hopeless to try and pass Charlotte off as either pretty or sweet. So she became clever as the only remaining alternative. Ernest never knew what particular branch of study it was in which she showed her talent, for she could neither play nor sing nor draw, but so astute are women that his mother and Charlotte really did persuade him into thinking that she, Charlotte, had something more akin to true genius than any other member of the family. Not one, however, of all the friends whom Ernest had been inveigled into trying to inveigle had shown the least sign of being so far struck with Charlotte's commanding powers as to wish to make them his own, and this may have had something to do with the rapidity and completeness with which Christina had dimissed them one after another and had wanted a new one.

And now she wanted Towneley. Ernest had seen this coming and had tried to avoid it, for he knew how impossible it was for him to ask Towneley, even if he had wished to do so.

Towneley belonged to one of the most exclusive sets in Cambridge, and was perhaps the most popular man among the whole number of undergraduates. He was big and very handsome — as it seemed to Ernest the handsomest man whom he ever had seen or ever could see, for it was impossible to imagine a more lively and agreeable countenance. He was good at cricket and boating, very good-natured, singularly free from conceit, not clever but very sensible, and, lastly, his father and mother had been drowned by the overturning of a boat when he was only two years old and had left him as their only child and heir to one of the finest estates in the South of England. Fortune every now and then does things handsomely by a man all round; Towneley was one of those to whom she had taken a fancy, and the universal verdict in this case was that she had chosen wisely.

Ernest had seen Towneley as everyone else in the University (except, of course, dons) had seen him, for he was a man of mark, and being very susceptible he had liked Towneley even more than most people did, but at the same time it never so much as entered his head that he should come to know him. He liked looking at him if he got a chance, and was very much ashamed of himself for doing so, but there the matter ended.

By a strange accident, however, during Ernest's last year, when the names of the crews for the scratch fours were drawn he had found himself coxswain of a crew, among whom was none other than his especial hero Towneley; the three others were ordinary mortals, but they could row fairly well, and the crew on the whole was rather a good one.

Ernest was frightened out of his wits. When, however, the two met, he found Towneley no less remarkable for his entire want of anything like 'side', and for his power of setting those whom he came across at their ease, than he was for outward accomplishments; the only difference he found between Towneley and other people was that he was so very much easier to get on with. Of course Ernest worshipped him more and more.

The scratch fours being ended the connection between the two came to an end, but Towneley never passed Ernest thenceforward without a nod and a few good-natured words. In an evil moment he had mentioned Towneley's name at Battersby, and now what was the result? Here was his mother plaguing him to ask Towneley to come down to Battersby and marry Charlotte. Why, if he had thought there was the remotest chance of Towneley's marrying Charlotte he would have gone down on his knees to him and told him what an odious young woman she was, and implored him to save himself while there was yet time.

But Ernest had not prayed to be made '*truly* honest and conscientious' for as many years as Christina had. He tried to conceal what he felt and thought as well as he could, and led the conversation back to the difficulties which a clergyman might feel to stand in the way of his being ordained — not because he had any misgivings, but as a diversion. His mother, however, thought she had settled all that, and he got no more out of her. Soon afterwards he found the means of escaping, and was not slow to avail himself of them.

CHAPTER FIFTY-ONE

ERNEST had been ordained to a curacy in one of the central parts of London. He hardly knew anything of London yet, but his instincts drew him thither. The day after he was ordained he entered upon his duties — feeling much as his father had done when he found himself boxed up in the carriage with Christina on the morning of his marriage. Before the first three days were over, he became aware that the light of the happiness which he had known during his four years at Cambridge had been extinguished, and he was appalled by the irrevocable nature of the step which he now felt that he had taken much too hurriedly.

His rector was a moderate High Churchman of no very pronounced views — an elderly man who had had too many curates not to have long since found out that the connection between rector and curate, like that between employer and employed in every other walk of life, was a mere matter of business. He had now two curates, of whom Ernest was the junior, the senior curate was named Pryer, and when this gentleman made advances, as he presently did, Ernest in his forlorn state was delighted to meet them.

Pryer was about twenty-eight years old. He had been at Eton and Oxford. He was tall, and passed generally for good-looking; I only saw him once for about five minutes, and then thought him odious both in manners and appearance. Perhaps it was because he caught me up in a way I did not like. I had quoted Shakespeare for lack of something better to fill up a sentence — and had said that one touch of nature makes the whole world kin. 'Ah,' said Pryer, in a bold, brazen way which displeased me, 'but one touch of the unnatural makes it more kindred still,' and he gave me a look as though he thought me an old bore and did not care two straws whether I was shocked or not. Naturally enough, after this I did not like him.

This, however, is anticipating, for it was not till Ernest had been three or four months in London that I happened to meet his fellow-curate, and I must deal here rather with the effect he produced upon my godson than upon myself. Besides being what was generally considered good-looking, he was faultless in his get-up, and altogether the kind of man whom Ernest was sure to be afraid of and yet be taken in by. The style of his dress was very High Church, and his acquaintances were exclusively of the extreme High Church party, but he kept his views a good deal in the background in his rector's presence, and that gentleman, though he looked askance on some of Pryer's friends, had no such ground of complaint against him as to make him sever the connection. Pryer, too, was popular in the pulpit, and, take him all round, it was probable that many worse curates would be found for one better. When Pryer called on my hero, as soon as the two were alone together, he eyed him all over with a quick penetrating glance and seemed not dissatisfied with the result — for I must say here that Ernest had improved in personal appearance under the more genial treatment he had received at Cambridge. Pryer, in fact, approved of him sufficiently to treat him civilly, and Ernest was immediately won by anyone who did this. It was not long before he discovered that the High Church party, and even Rome itself, had more to say for themselves than he had thought. This was his first snipe-like change of flight.

Pryer introduced him to several of his friends. They were all of them young clergymen, belonging as I have said to the highest of the High Church school, but Ernest was surprised to find how much they resembled other people when among themselves. This was a shock to him; it was ere long a still greater one to find that certain thoughts which he had warred against as fatal to his soul, and which he had imagined he should lose once for all on ordination, were still as troublesome to him as they had been; he also saw plainly enough that the young gentlemen who formed the circle of Pryer's friends were in much the same unhappy predicament as himself.

This was deplorable. The only way out of it that Ernest could see was that he should get married at once. But then he did not know anyone whom he wanted to marry. He did not know any woman, in fact, whom he would not rather die than marry. It had been one of

Theobald's and Christina's main objects to keep him out of the way of women, and they had so far succeeded that women had become to him mysterious, inscrutable objects to be tolerated when it was impossible to avoid them, but never to be sought out or encouraged. As for any man loving, or even being at all fond of any woman, he supposed it was so, but he believed the greater number of those who professed such sentiments were liars. Now, however, it was clear that he had hoped against hope too long, and that the only thing to do was to go and ask the first woman who would listen to him to come and be married to him as soon as possible.

He broached this to Pryer, and was surprised to find that this gentleman, though attentive to such members of his flock as were young and good-looking, was strongly in favour of the celibacy of the clergy, as indeed were the other demure young clerics to whom Pryer had introduced Ernest.

CHAPTER FIFTY-TWO

'YOU know, my dear Pontifex,' said Pryer to him, some few weeks after Ernest had become acquainted with him, when the two were taking a constitutional one day in Kensington Gardens, 'You know, my dear Pontifex, it is all very well to quarrel with Rome, but Rome has reduced the treatment of the human soul to a science, while our own Church, though so much purer in many respects, has no organized system either of diagnosis or pathology — I mean, of course, spiritual diagnosis and spiritual pathology. Our Church does not prescribe remedies upon any settled system, and, what is still worse, even when her physicians have according to their lights ascertained the disease and pointed out the remedy, she has no discipline which will ensure its being actually applied. If our patients do not choose to do as we tell them, we cannot make them. Perhaps really under all the circumstances this is as well, for we are spiritually mere horse doctors as compared with the Roman priesthood, nor can we hope to make much headway against the sin and misery that surround us, till we return in some respects to the practice of our forefathers and of the greater part of Christendom.'

Ernest asked in what respects it was that his friend desired a return to the practice of our forefathers.

'Why, my dear fellow, can you really be ignorant? It is just this, either the priest is indeed a spiritual guide, as being able to show people how they ought to live better than they can find out for themselves, or he is nothing at all — he has no *raison d'être*. If the priest is not as much a healer and director of men's souls as a physician is of their bodies, what is he? The history of all ages has shown — and surely you must know this as well as I do — that as men cannot cure the bodies of their patients if they have not been properly trained in hospitals under skilled teachers, so neither can souls be cured of their more hidden ailments without the help of men who are skilled in soul-craft — or in other words, of priests. What do one-half of our formularies and rubrics mean if not this? How in the name of all that is reasonable can we find out the exact nature of a spiritual malady, unless we have had experience of other similar cases? How can we get this without express training. At present we have to begin all experiments for ourselves, without profiting by the organized experience of our predecessors, inasmuch as that experience is never organized and co-ordinated at all. At the outset, therefore, each one of us must ruin many souls which could be saved by knowledge of a few elementary principles.'

Ernest was very much impressed.

'As for men curing themselves,' continued Pryer, 'they can no more cure their own souls than they can cure their own bodies, or manage their own law affairs. In these last two cases they see the folly of meddling with their own cases clearly enough, and go to a professional adviser as a matter of course; surely a man's soul is at once a more difficult and intricate matter to treat and at the same time it is more important to him that it should be treated rightly than that either his body or his money should be so. What are we to think of the practice of a Church which encourages people to rely on unprofessional advice in matters affecting their eternal welfare, when they would not think of jeopardizing their worldly affairs by such insane conduct?'

Ernest could see no weak place in this. These ideas had crossed his own mind vaguely before now, but he had never laid hold of them or set them in an orderly manner before himself. Nor was he quick at detecting false analogies and the misuse of metaphors; in fact, he was a mere child in the hands of his fellow curate.

'And what,' resumed Pryer, 'does all this point to? Firstly, to the duty of confession — the outcry against which is absurd as an outcry would be against dissection as part of the training of medical students.

Granted these young men must see and do a great deal we do not ourselves like even to think of, but they should adopt some other profession
unless they are prepared for this; they may even get inoculated with
poison from a dead body and lose their lives, but they must stand their
chance. So if we aspire to be priests in deed as well as name, we must
familiarize ourselves with the minutest and most repulsive details of all
kinds of sin, so that we may recognize it in all its stages. Some of us
must doubtless perish spiritually in such investigations. We cannot
help it; all science must have its martyrs, and none of these will deserve
better of humanity than those who have fallen in the pursuit of spiritual
pathology.'

Ernest grew more and more interested, but in the meekness of his
soul said nothing.

'I do not desire this martyrdom for myself,' continued the other, 'on
the contrary, I will avoid it to the very utmost of my power, but if it
be God's will that I should fall while studying what I believe most
calculated to advance His glory — then I say, not my will, O Lord, but
thine be done.'

This was too much even for Ernest. 'I heard of an Irishwoman once,'
he said, with a smile, 'who said she was a martyr to the drink.'

'And so she was,' rejoined Pryer with warmth; and he went on to
show that this good woman was an experimentalist whose experiment,
though disastrous in its effects upon herself, was pregnant with instruction to other people. She was thus a true martyr or witness to the
frightful consequences of intemperance, to the saving, doubtless, of
many who but for her martyrdom would have taken to drinking. She
was one of a forlorn hope whose failure to take a certain position went
to the proving it to be impregnable and therefore to the abandonment
of all attempt to take it. This was almost as great a gain to mankind as
the actual taking of the position would have been.

'Besides,' he added more hurriedly, 'the limits of vice and virtue are
wretchedly ill-defined. Half the vices which the world condemns most
loudly have seeds of good in them and require moderate use rather than
total abstinence.'

Ernest asked timidly for an instance.

'No, no,' said Pryer, 'I will give you no instance, but I will give you
a formula that shall embrace all instances. It is this, that no practice is
entirely vicious which has not been extinguished among the comeliest,
most vigorous, and most cultivated races of mankind in spite of cen-

turies of endeavour to extirpate it. If a vice in spite of such efforts can still hold its own among the most polished nations, it must be founded on some immutable truth or fact in human nature, and must have some compensatory advantage which we cannot afford altogether to dispense with.'

'But,' said Ernest timidly, 'is not this virtually doing away with all distinction between right and wrong, and leaving people without any moral guide whatever?'

'Not the people,' was the answer: 'it must be our care to be guides to these, for they are and always will be incapable of guiding themselves sufficiently. We should tell them what they must do, and in an ideal state of things should be able to enforce their doing it: perhaps when we are better instructed the ideal state may come about; nothing will so advance it as greater knowledge of spiritual pathology on our own part. For this, three things are necessary: firstly, absolute freedom in experiment for us the clergy; secondly, absolute knowledge of what the laity think and do, and of what thoughts and actions result in what spiritual conditions; and thirdly, a compacter organization among ourselves.

'If we are to do any good we must be a closely united body and must be sharply divided from the laity. Also we must be free from those ties which a wife and children involve. I can hardly express the horror with which I am filled by seeing English priests living in what I can only designate as "open matrimony". It is deplorable. The priest must be absolutely sexless — if not in practice, yet at any rate in theory, absolutely — and that too, by a theory so universally accepted that none shall venture to dispute it.'

'But,' said Ernest, 'has not the Bible already told people what they ought and ought not to do, and is it not enough for us to insist on what can be found here, and let the rest alone?'

'If you begin with the Bible,' was the rejoinder, 'you are three parts gone on the road to infidelity, and will go the other part before you know where you are. The Bible is not without its value to us the clergy, but for the laity it is a stumbling-block which cannot be taken out of their way too soon or too completely. Of course, I mean on the supposition that they read it, which, happily, they seldom do. If people read the Bible as the ordinary British Churchman or Churchwoman reads it, it is harmless enough; but if they read it with any care — which we should assume they will if we give it them at all — it is fatal to them.'

'What do you mean?' said Ernest, more and more astonished, but more and more feeling that he was at least in the hands of a man who had definite ideas.

'Your question shows me that you have never read your Bible. A more unreliable book was never put upon paper. Take my advice and don't read it, not till you are a few years older, and may do so safely.'

'But surely you believe the Bible when it tells you of such things as that Christ died and rose from the dead? Surely you believe this?' said Ernest, quite prepared to be told that Pryer believed nothing of the kind.

'I do not believe it, I know it.'

'But how — if the testimony of the Bible fails?'

'On that of the living voice of the Church, which I know to be infallible and to be informed of Christ Himself.'

CHAPTER FIFTY-SIX

BY and by a subtle, indefinable *malaise* began to take possession of him. I once saw a very young foal trying to eat some most objectionable refuse, and unable to make up its mind whether it was good or no. Clearly it wanted to be told. If its mother had seen what it was doing she would have set it right in a moment, and as soon as ever it had been told that what it was eating was filth, the foal would have recognized it and never have wanted to be told again; but the foal could not settle the matter for itself, or make up its mind whether it liked what it was trying to eat or no, without assistance from without. I suppose it would have come to do so by and by, but it was wasting time and trouble, which a single look from its mother would have saved, just as wort will in time ferment of itself, but will ferment much more quickly if a little yeast be added to it. In the matter of knowing what gives us pleasure we are all like wort, and if unaided from without can only ferment slowly and toilsomely.

CHAPTER FIFTY-SEVEN

ONE evening, however, about this time, whom should he see coming along a small street not far from his own but, of all persons in the world, Towneley, looking as full of life and good spirits as ever, and if possible even handsomer than he had been at

Cambridge. Much as Ernest liked him he found himself shrinking from speaking to him, and was endeavouring to pass him without doing so when Towneley saw him and stopped him at once, being pleased to see an old Cambridge face. He seemed for the moment a little confused at being seen in such a neighbourhood, but recovered himself so soon that Ernest hardly noticed it, and then plunged into a few kindly remarks about old times. Ernest felt that he quailed as he saw Towneley's eye wander to his white necktie and saw that he was being reckoned up, and rather disapprovingly reckoned up, as a parson. It was the merest passing shade upon Towneley's face, but Ernest had felt it.

Towneley said a few words of common form to Ernest about his profession as being what he thought would be most likely to interest him, and Ernest, still confused and shy, gave him for lack of something better to say his little threepenny-bit about poor people being so very nice. Towneley took this for what it was worth and nodded assent, whereon Ernest imprudently went further and said, 'Don't you like poor people very much yourself?'

Towneley gave his face a comical but good-natured screw, and said quietly, but slowly and decidedly, 'No, no, no,' and escaped.

It was all over with Ernest from that moment. As usual he did not know it, but he had entered none the less upon another reaction. Towneley had just taken Ernest's threepenny-bit into his hands, looked at it and returned it to him as a bad one. Why did he see in a moment that it was a bad one now, though he had been unable to see it when he had taken it from Pryer? Of course some poor people were very nice, and always would be so, but as though scales had fallen suddenly from his eyes he saw that no one was nicer for being poor, and that between the upper and lower classes there was a gulf which amounted practically to an impassable barrier.

CHAPTER FIFTY-NINE

BEFORE going down into the kitchen to convert the tinker Ernest ran hurriedly over his analysis of Paley's *Evidences*, and put into his pocket a copy of Archbishop Whately's *Historic Doubts*. Then he descended the dark, rotten old stairs and knocked at the tinker's door. Mr. Shaw was very civil; he said he was rather throng just now, but if Ernest did not mind the sound of hammering he should be very glad of a talk with him. Our hero, assenting to this, ere long led the conversation to Whately's *Historic Doubts* — a work which, as the reader may know, pretends to show that there never was any such person as Napoleon Buonaparte, and thus satirizes the arguments of those who have attacked the Christian miracles.

Mr. Shaw said he knew *Historic Doubts* very well.

'And what do you think of it?' said Ernest, who regarded the pamphlet as a masterpiece of wit and cogency.

'If you really want to know,' said Mr. Shaw, with a sly twinkle, 'I think that he who was so willing and able to prove that what was was not, would be equally able and willing to make a case for thinking that what was not was, if it suited his purpose.' Ernest was very much taken aback. How was it that all the clever people of Cambridge had never put him up to this simple rejoinder? The answer is easy: they did not develop it for the same reason that a hen has never developed webbed feet — that is to say, because they did not want to do so; but this was before the days of Evolution, and Ernest could not as yet know anything of the great principle that underlies it.

'You see,' continued Mr. Shaw, 'these writers all get their living by writing in a certain way, and the more they write in that way, the more they are likely to get on. You should not call them dishonest for this any more than a judge should call a barrister dishonest for earning his living by defending one in whose innocence he does not seriously believe; but you should hear the barrister on the other side before you decide upon the case.'

This was another facer. Ernest could only stammer that he had endeavoured to examine these questions as carefully as he could.

'You think you have,' said Mr. Shaw, 'you Oxford and Cambridge gentlemen think you have examined everything. I have examined very little myself except the bottoms of old kettles and saucepans, but if you will answer me a few questions, I will tell you whether or no you have examined much more than I have.'

Ernest expressed his readiness to be questioned.

'Then,' said the tinker, 'give me the story of the Resurrection of Jesus Christ as told in St. John's gospel.'

I am sorry to say that Ernest mixed up the four accounts in a deplorable manner; he even made the angel come down and roll away the stone and sit upon it. He was covered with confusion when the tinker first told him without the book of some of his many inaccuracies, and then verified his criticisms by referring to the New Testament itself.

'Now,' said Mr. Shaw good naturedly, 'I am an old man and you are a young one, so perhaps you'll not mind my giving you a piece of advice. I like you, for I believe you mean well, but you've been real bad brought up, and I don't think you have ever had so much as a chance yet. You know nothing of our side of the question, and I have just shown you that you do not know much more of your own, but I think you will make a kind of Carlyle sort of a man some day. Now go upstairs and read the accounts of the Resurrection correctly without mixing them up, and have a clear idea of what it is that each writer tells us, then if you feel inclined to pay me another visit I shall be glad to see you, for I shall know you have made a good beginning and mean business. Till then, Sir, I must wish you a very good morning.'

Ernest retreated abashed. An hour sufficed him to perform the task enjoined upon him by Mr. Shaw; and at the end of that hour the 'No, no, no,' which still sounded in his ears as he heard it from Towneley, came ringing up more loudly still from the very pages of the Bible itself, and in respect of the most important of all the events which are recorded in it.

CHAPTER SIXTY

ERNEST now went home and occupied himself till luncheon with studying Dean Alford's notes upon the various Evangelistic records of the Resurrection, doing as Mr. Shaw had told him, and trying to find out not that they were all accurate, but whether they were all accurate or no. He did not care which result he should arrive at, but he was resolved that he would reach one or the other. When he had finished Dean Alford's notes he found them come to this, namely, that no one yet had succeeded in bringing the four accounts into tolerable harmony with each other, and that the Dean, seeing no chance of succeeding better than his predecessors had done, recommended that the whole story should be taken on trust — and this Ernest was not prepared to do.

He got his luncheon, went out for a long walk, and returned to dinner at half-past six. While Mrs. Jupp was getting him his dinner — a steak and a pint of stout — she told him that Miss Snow would be very happy to see him in about an hour's time. This disconcerted him, for his mind was too unsettled for him to wish to convert anyone just then. He reflected a little, and found that, in spite of the sudden shock to his opinions, he was being irresistibly drawn to pay the visit as though nothing had happened. It would not look well for him not to go, for he was known to be in the house. He ought not to be in too great a hurry to change his opinions on such a matter as the evidence for Christ's Resurrection all of a sudden — besides, he need not talk to Miss Snow about this subject today — there were other things he might talk about. What other things? Ernest felt his heart beat fast and fiercely, and an inward monitor warned him that he was thinking of anything rather than of Miss Snow's soul.

What should he do? Fly, fly, fly — it was the only safety. But would Christ have fled? Even though Christ had not died and risen from the dead there could be no question that He was the model whose example we were bound to follow. Christ would not have fled from Miss Snow; he was sure of that, for He went about more especially with prostitutes and disreputable people. Now, as then, it was the business of the true Christian to call not the righteous but sinners to repentance. It would be inconvenient to him to change his lodgings, and he could not ask Mrs. Jupp to turn Miss Snow and Miss Maitland out of the house. Where was he to draw the line? Who would be just good enough to live in the same house with him, and who just not good enough?

Besides, where were these poor girls to go? Was he to drive them from house to house till they had no place to lie in? It was absurd; his duty was clear: he would go and see Miss Snow at once, and try if he could not induce her to change her present mode of life; if he found temptation becoming too strong for him he would fly then — so he went upstairs with his Bible under his arm, and a consuming fire in his heart.

He found Miss Snow looking very pretty in a neatly, not to say demurely, furnished room. I think she had bought an illuminated text or two, and pinned it up over her fireplace that morning. Ernest was very much pleased with her, and mechanically placed his Bible upon the table. He had just opened a timid conversation and was deep in blushes, when a hurried step came bounding up the stairs as though of one over whom the force of gravity had little power, and a man burst into the room saying, 'I'm come before my time.' It was Towneley.

His face dropped as he caught sight of Ernest. 'What, *you* here, Pontifex! Well, upon my word!'

I cannot describe the hurried explanations that passed quickly between the three — enough that in less than a minute Ernest, blushing more scarlet than ever, slunk off, Bible and all, deeply humiliated as he contrasted himself and Towneley. Before he had reached the bottom of the staircase leading to his own room he heard Towneley's hearty laugh through Miss Snow's door, and cursed the hour that he was born.

Then it flashed upon him that if he could not see Miss Snow he could at any rate see Miss Maitland. He knew well enough what he wanted now, and as for the Bible, he pushed it from him to the other end of his table. It fell over on to the floor, and he kicked it into a corner. It was the Bible given him at his christening by his affectionate aunt, Elizabeth Allaby. True, he knew very little of Miss Maitland, but ignorant young fools in Ernest's state do not reflect or reason closely. Mrs. Baxter had said that Miss Maitland and Miss Snow were birds of a feather, and Mrs. Baxter probably knew better than that old liar, Mrs. Jupp. Shakespeare says:

> O Opportunity, thy guilt is great!
> 'Tis thou that execut'st the traitor's treason:
> Thou set'st the wolf where he the lamb may get;
> Whoever plots the sin, thou 'point'st the season;
> 'Tis thou that spurn'st at right, at law, at reason;
>   And in thy shady cell, where none may spy him,
>   Sits Sin, to seize the souls that wander by him.

If the guilt of opportunity is great, how much greater is the guilt of that which is believed to be opportunity but in reality is no opportunity at all? If the better part of valour is discretion, how much more is not discretion the better part of vice?

About ten minutes after we last saw Ernest, a scared, insulted girl, flushed and trembling, was seen hurrying from Mrs. Jupp's house as fast as her agitated state would let her, and in another ten minutes two policemen were seen also coming out of Mrs. Jupp's, between whom there shambled rather than walked our unhappy friend Ernest, with staring eyes, ghastly pale, and with despair branded upon every line of his face.

CHAPTER SEVENTY-ONE

IT seems he had been patrolling the streets for the last three or four nights — I suppose in search of something to do — at any rate knowing better what he wanted to get than how to get it. Nevertheless, what he wanted was in reality so easily to be found that it took a highly educated scholar like himself to be unable to find it. But, however this may be, his determination had hardly been formed and he had not gone more than a hundred yards in the direction of Mrs. Jupp's house, when a woman accosted him.

He was turning from her, as he had turned from so many others, when she started back with a movement that aroused his curiosity. He had hardly seen her face, but being determined to catch sight of it, followed her as she hurried away, and passed her; then turning round he saw that she was none other than Ellen, the housemaid who had been dismissed by his mother eight years previously.

He ought to have assigned Ellen's unwillingness to see him to its true cause, but a guilty conscience made him think she had heard of his disgrace and was turning away from him in contempt. Brave as had been his resolutions about facing the world, this was more than he was prepared for. 'What! you too shun me, Ellen?' he exclaimed.

The girl was crying bitterly and did not understand him. 'Oh, Master Ernest,' she sobbed, 'let me go; you are too good for the likes of me to speak to now.'

'Why, Ellen,' said he, 'what nonsense you talk; you haven't been in prison, have you?'

'Oh, no, no, no, not so bad as that,' she exclaimed passionately.

'Well, I have,' said Ernest, with a forced laugh, 'I came out three or four days ago after six months with hard labour.'

Ellen did not believe him, but she looked at him with a 'Lor'! Master Ernest,' and dried her eyes at once. The ice was broken between them, for as a matter of fact Ellen had been in prison several times, and though she did not believe Ernest, his merely saying he had been in prison made her feel more at ease with him. For her there were two classes of people, those who had been in prison and those who had not. The first she looked upon as fellow-creatures and more or less Christians; the second, with few exceptions, she regarded with suspicion, not wholly unmingled with contempt.

298

Then Ernest told her what had happened to him during the last six months, and by and by she believed him.

'Master Ernest,' said she, after they had talked for a quarter of an hour or so, 'there's a place over the way where they sell tripe and onions. I know you was always very fond of tripe and onions, let's go over and have some, and we can talk better there.'

So the pair crossed the street and entered the tripe shop; Ernest ordered supper.

'And how is your pore dear mamma, and your dear papa, Master Ernest,' said Ellen, who had now recovered herself and was quite at home with my hero. 'Oh, dear, dear me,' she said, 'I did love your pa; he was a good gentleman, he was, and your ma too; it would do anyone good to live with her, I'm sure.'

Ernest was surprised and hardly knew what to say. He had expected to find Ellen indignant at the way she had been treated, and inclined to lay the blame of her having fallen to her present state at his father's and mother's door. It was not so. Her only recollection of Battersby was as of a place where she had had plenty to eat and drink, not too much hard work, and where she had not been scolded. When she heard that Ernest had quarrelled with his father and mother she assumed as a matter of course that the fault must lie entirely with Ernest.

'Oh, your pore, pore ma!' said Ellen. 'She was always so very fond of you, Master Ernest: you was always her favourite; I can't abear to think of anything between you and her. To think now of the way she used to have me into the dining-room and teach me my Catechism, that she did! Oh, Master Ernest, you really must go and make it all up with her; indeed you must.'

Ernest felt rueful, but he had resisted so valiantly already that the devil might have saved himself the trouble of trying to get at him through Ellen in the matter of his father and mother. He changed the subject, and the pair warmed to one another as they had their tripe and pots of beer. Of all people in the world Ellen was perhaps the one to whom Ernest could have spoken most freely at this juncture. He told her what he thought he could have told to no one else.

'You know, Ellen,' he concluded, 'I had learnt as a boy things that I ought not to have learnt, and had never had a chance of that which would have set me straight.'

'Gentlefolks is always like that,' said Ellen musingly.

CHAPTER SEVENTY-NINE

I HAD expected that he would now rapidly recover, and was disappointed to see him get as I thought decidedly worse. Indeed, before long I thought him looking so ill that I insisted on his going with me to consult one of the most eminent doctors in London. This gentleman said there was no acute disease but my young friend was suffering from nervous prostration, the result of long and severe mental suffering, from which there was no remedy except time, prosperity and rest.

He said that Ernest must have broken down later on, but that he might have gone on for some months yet. It was the suddenness of the relief from tension which had knocked him over now.

'Cross him,' said the doctor, 'at once. Crossing is the great medical discovery of the age. Shake him out of himself by shaking something else into him.'

I had not told him that money was no object to us and I think he had reckoned me up as not over rich. He continued:

'Seeing is a mode of touching, touching is a mode of feeding, feeding is a mode of assimilation, assimilation is a mode of re-creation and reproduction, and this is crossing — shaking yourself into something else and something else into you.'

He spoke laughingly, but it was plain he was serious. He continued:

'People are always coming to me who want crossing, or change, if you prefer it, and whom I know have not money enough to let them get away from London. This has set me thinking how I can best cross them even if they cannot leave home, and I have made a list of cheap London amusements which I recommend to my patients; none of them cost more than a few shillings or take more than half a day or a day.'

I explained that there was no occasion to consider money in this case.

'I am glad of it,' he said, still laughing. 'The homoeopathists use *aurum* as a medicine, but they do not give it in large doses enough; if you can dose your young friend with this pretty freely you will soon bring him round. However, Mr. Pontifex is not well enough to stand so great a change as going abroad yet; from what you tell me I should think he had had as much change lately as is good for him. If he were to go abroad now he would probably be taken seriously ill within a week. We must wait till he has recovered tone a little more. I will begin by ringing my London changes on him.'

He thought a little and then said:

'I have found the Zoological Gardens of service to many of my patients. I should prescribe for Mr. Pontifex a course of the larger mammals. Don't let him think he is taking them medicinally, but let him go to their house twice a week for a fortnight, and stay with the hippopotamus, the rhinoceros and the elephants, till they begin to bore him. I find these beasts do my patients more good than any others. The monkeys are not a wide enough cross; they do not stimulate sufficiently. The larger carnivora are unsympathetic. The reptiles are worse than useless, and the marsupials are not much better. Birds again, except parrots, are not very beneficial; he may look at them now and again, but with the elephants and the pig tribe generally he should mix just now as freely as possible.

'Then, you know, to prevent monotony I should send him say, to morning service at the Abbey before he goes. He need not stay longer than the *Te Deum*. I don't know why, but *Jubilates* are seldom satisfactory. Just let him look in at the Abbey, and sit quietly in Poet's Corner till the main part of the music is over. Let him do this two or three times, not more, before he goes to the Zoo.

'Then next day send him down to Gravesend by boat. By all means let him go to the theatres in the evenings — and then let him come to me again in a fortnight.'

CHAPTER EIGHTY-TWO

A FEW days, however, after Ernest had come into his property, I received a letter from Theobald enclosing one for Ernest which I could not withold.
The letter ran thus:

To my son Ernest: Although you have more than once rejected my overtures I appeal yet again to your better nature. Your mother, who has long been ailing, is, I believe, near her end; she is unable to keep anything on her stomach, and Dr. Martin holds out but little hopes of her recovery. She has expressed a wish to see you, and says she knows you will not refuse to come to her, which, considering her condition, I am unwilling to suppose you will.

I remit you a Post Office order for your fare, and will pay your return journey.

If you want clothes to come in, order what you consider suitable, and desire that the bill be sent to me; I will pay it immediately, to an amount not exceeding eight or nine pounds, and if you will let me know what train you will come by, I will send the carriage to meet you. Believe me, Your affectionate father,   T. PONTIFEX

Of course there could be no hesitation on Ernest's part. He could afford to smile now at his father's offering to pay for his clothes, and his sending him a Post Office order for the exact price of a second-class ticket, and he was of course shocked at learning the state his mother was said to be in, and touched at her desire to see him. He telegraphed that he would come down at once. I saw him a little before he started, and was pleased to see how well his tailor had done by him. Towneley himself could not have been appointed more becomingly. His portmanteau, his railway wrapper, everything he had about him, was in keeping. I thought he had grown much better-looking than he had been at two or three and twenty. His year and a half of peace had effaced all the ill-effects of his previous suffering, and now that he had become actually rich there was an air of *insouciance* and good humour upon his face, as of a man with whom everything was going perfectly right, which would have made a much plainer man good-looking. I was proud of him and delighted with him. 'I am sure,' I said to myself, 'that whatever else he may do, he will never marry again.'

The journey was a painful one. As he drew near to the station and caught sight of each familiar feature, so strong was the force of association that he felt as though his coming into his aunt's money had been a dream, and he were again returning to his father's house as he had returned to it from Cambridge for the vacations. Do what he would, the old dull weight of *home-sickness* began to oppress him, his heart beat fast as he thought of his approaching meeting with his father and mother, 'and I shall have,' he said to himself, 'to kiss Charlotte.'

Would his father meet him at the station? Would he greet him as though nothing had happened, or would he be cold and distant? How, again, would he take the news of his son's good fortune? As the train drew up to the platform, Ernest's eye ran hurriedly over the few people who were in the station. His father's well-known form was not among them, but on the other side of the palings which divided the station yard from the platform, he saw the pony carriage, looking, as he thought, rather shabby, and recognized his father's coachman. In a

few minutes more he was in the carriage driving towards Battersby.
He could not help smiling as he saw the coachman give a look of surprise at finding him so much changed in personal appearance. The
coachman was the more surprised because when Ernest had last been at
home he had been dressed as a clergyman, and now he was not only a
layman, but a layman who was got up regardless of expense. The
change was so great that it was not till Ernest actually spoke to him that
the coachman knew him.

'How are my father and mother?' he asked hurriedly, as he got into
the carriage. 'The Master's well, sir,' was the answer, 'but the Missis
is very sadly.' The horse knew that he was going home and pulled hard
at the reins. The weather was cold and raw — the very ideal of a
November day; in one part of the road the floods were out, and near
here they had to pass through a number of horsemen and dogs, for the
hounds had met that morning at a place near Battersby. Ernest saw
several people whom he knew, but they either, as is most likely, did not
recognize him, or did not know of his good luck. When Battersby
church tower drew near, and he saw the Rectory on the top of the hill,
its chimneys just showing above the leafless trees with which it was
surrounded, he threw himself back in the carriage and covered his face
with his hands.

It came to an end, as even the worst quarters of an hour do, and in a
few minutes more he was on the steps in front of his father's house.
His father, hearing the carriage arrive, came a little way down the steps
to meet him. Like the coachman he saw at a glance that Ernest was
appointed as though money were abundant with him, and that he was
looking robust and full of health and vigour.

This was not what he had bargained for. He wanted Ernest to return,
but he was to return as any respectable, well-regulated prodigal ought
to return — abject, broken-hearted, asking forgiveness from the
tenderest and most long-suffering father in the whole world. If he
should have shoes and stockings and whole clothes at all, it should be
only because absolute rags and tatters had been graciously dispensed
with, whereas here he was swaggering in a grey ulster and a blue and
white neck-tie, and looking better than Theobald had ever seen him in
his life. It was unprincipled. Was it for this that he had been generous
enough to offer to provide Ernest with decent clothes in which to come
and visit his mother's deathbed? Could any advantage be meaner than
the one which Ernest had taken? Well, he would not go a penny

beyond the eight or nine pounds which he had promised. It was fortunate he had given a limit. Why he, Theobald, had never been able to afford such a portmanteau in his life. He was still using an old one which his father had turned over to him when he went up to Cambridge. Besides, he had said clothes, not a portmanteau.

Ernest saw what was passing through his father's mind, and felt that he ought to have prepared him in some way for what he now saw; but he had sent his telegram so immediately on receiving his father's letter, and had followed it so promptly that it would not have been easy to do so even if he had thought of it. He put out his hand and said laughingly, 'Oh, it's all paid for — I am afraid you do not know that Mr. Overton has handed over to me Aunt Alethea's money.'

Theobald flushed scarlet. 'But why,' he said, and these were the first words that actually crossed his lips — 'If the money was not his to keep, did he not hand it over to my brother John and me?' He stammered a good deal and looked sheepish, but he got the words out.

'Because, my dear father,' said Ernest, still laughing, 'my aunt left it to him in trust for me, not in trust either for you or for my Uncle John — and it has accumulated till it is now over £70,000. But tell me how is my mother?'

'No, Ernest,' said Theobald excitedly, 'the matter cannot rest here, I must know that this is all open and above board.'

This had the true Theobald ring and instantly brought the whole train of ideas which in Ernest's mind were connected with his father. The surroundings were the old familiar ones, but the surrounded were changed almost beyond power of recognition. He turned sharply on Theobald in a moment. I will not repeat the words he used, for they came out before he had time to consider them, and they might strike some of my readers as disrespectful; there were not many of them, but they were effectual. Theobald said nothing, but turned almost of an ashen colour; he never again spoke to his son in such a way as to make it necessary for him to repeat what he had said on this occasion. Ernest quickly recovered his temper and again asked after his mother. Theobald was glad enough to take this opening now, and replied at once in the tone he would have assumed towards one he most particularly desired to conciliate, that she was getting rapidly worse in spite of all he had been able to do for her, and concluded by saying she had been the comfort and mainstay of his life for more than thirty years but that he could not wish it prolonged.

The pair then went upstairs to Christina's room, the one in which Ernest had been born. His father went before him and prepared her for her son's approach. The poor woman raised herself in bed as he came towards her, and weeping as she flung her arms around him, cried: 'Oh, I knew he would come, I knew, I knew he could come.'

Ernest broke down and wept as he had not done for years.

'Oh, my boy, my boy,' she said as soon as she could recover her voice. 'Have you never really been near us for all these years? Ah, you do not know how we have loved you and mourned over you, papa just as much as I have. You know he shows his feelings less, but I can never tell you how very, very deeply he has felt for you. Sometimes at night I have thought I have heard footsteps in the garden, and have got quietly out of bed lest I should wake him, and gone to the window to look out, but there has been only dark or the greyness of the morning, and I have gone crying back to bed again. Still I think you have been near us though you were too proud to let us know — and now at last I have you in my arms once more, my dearest, dearest boy.'

How cruel, how infamously unfeeling Ernest thought he had been.

'Mother,' he said, 'forgive me — the fault was mine, I ought not to have been so hard; I was wrong, very wrong'; the poor blubbering fellow meant what he said, and his heart yearned to his mother as he had never thought that it could yearn again. 'But have you never,' she continued, 'come although it was in the dark and we did not know it — oh, let me think that you have not been so cruel as we have thought you. Tell me that you came if only to comfort me and make me happier.'

Ernest was ready. 'I had no money to come with, Mother, till just lately.'

This was an excuse Christina could understand and make allowance for. 'Oh, then you would have come, and I will take the will for the deed — and now that I have you safe again, say that you will never, never leave me — not till — not till — not till — oh, my boy, have they told you I am dying?' She wept bitterly, and buried her head in her pillow.

CHAPTER EIGHTY-THREE

ON Sunday Ernest went to church as a matter of course, and noted that the ever-receding tide of Evangelicalism had ebbed many a stage lower, even during the few years of his absence. His father used to walk to the church through the Rectory garden, and across a small intervening field. He had been used to walk in a tall hat, his Master's gown, and wearing a pair of Geneva bands. Ernest noticed that the bands were worn no longer, and lo! greater marvel still, Theobald did not preach in his Master's gown, but in a surplice. The whole character of the service was changed; you could not say it was high even now, for High Church Theobald could never under any circumstances become, but the old easygoing slovenliness, if I may say so, was gone for ever. The orchestral accompaniments to the hymns had disappeared while my hero was yet a boy, but there had been no chanting for some years after the harmonium had been introduced. While Ernest was at Cambridge, Charlotte and Christina had prevailed on Theobald to allow the canticles to be sung; and sung they were to old-fashioned double chants by Lord Mornington and Dr. Dupuis and others. Theobald did not like it, but he did it, or allowed it to be done.

Then Christina said: 'My dear, do you know, I really think' (Christina always 'really' thought) 'that the people like the chanting very much, and that it will be a means of bringing many to church who have stayed away hitherto. I was talking about it to Mrs. Goodhew and to old Miss Wright only yesterday, and they *quite* agreed with me, but they all said that we ought to chant the "Glory be to the Father" at the end of each of the psalms instead of saying it.'

Theobald looked black — he felt the waters of chanting rising higher and higher upon him inch by inch; but he felt also, he knew not why, that he had better yield than fight. So he ordered the 'Glory be to the Father' to be chanted in future, but he did not like it.

'Really, Mamma dear,' said Charlotte, when the battle was won, 'you should not call it the "Glory be to the Father," you should say "Gloria".'

'Of course, my dear,' said Christina, and she said 'Gloria' for ever after. Then she thought what a wonderfully clever girl Charlotte was, and how she ought to marry no one lower than a bishop. By and by when Theobald went away for an unusually long holiday one summer, he could find no one but a rather High Church clergyman to take his duty. This gentleman was a man of weight in the neighbourhood, having considerable private means, but without preferment. In the summer he would often help his brother clergymen, and it was through his being willing to take the duty at Battersby for a few Sundays that Theobald had been able to get away for so long. On his return, however, he found that the whole psalms were being chanted as well as the Glorias. The influential clergyman, Christina and Charlotte took the bull by the horns as soon as Theobald returned, and laughed it all off; and the clergyman laughed and bounced, and Christina laughed and coaxed, and Charlotte uttered unexceptionable sentiments, and the thing was done now, and could not be undone, and it was no use grieving over spilt milk; so henceforth the psalms were to be chanted, but Theobald grizzled over it in his heart, and he did not like it.

During this same absence what had Mrs. Goodhew and old Miss Wright taken to doing but turning towards the east while repeating the Belief! Theobald disliked this even worse than chanting. When he said something about it in a timid way at dinner after service, Charlotte said, 'Really, Papa dear, you *must* take to calling it the "Creed" and not the "Belief",' and Theobald winced impatiently and snorted meek defiance, but the spirit of her aunts Jane and Eliza was strong in Charlotte, and the thing was too small to fight about, and he turned it off with a laugh. 'As for Charlotte,' thought Christina, 'I believe she knows *everything*.' So Mrs. Goodhew and old Miss Wright continued to turn to the east during the time the Creed was said, and by and by others followed their example, and ere long the few who had stood out yielded and turned eastward too; and then Theobald made as though he had thought it all very right and proper from the first, but like it he did not. By and by Charlotte tried to make him say 'Alleluia' instead of 'Hallelujah', but this was going too far and Theobald turned, and she got frightened and ran away.

And they changed the double chants for single ones, and altered them psalm by psalm, and in the middle of psalms, just where a cursory reader would see no reason why they should do so, they changed from major to minor and from minor back to major; and then they got 'Hymns Ancient and Modern', and, as I have said, they robbed him of his beloved bands, and they made him preach in a surplice, and he must have celebration of the Holy Communion once a month instead of only five times in the year as heretofore, and he struggled in vain against the unseen influence which he felt to be working in season and

307

out of season against all that he had been accustomed to consider most distinctive of his party. Where it was, or what it was, he knew not, nor exactly what it would do next, but he knew exceedingly well that go where he would it was undermining him; that it was too persistent for him; that Christina and Charlotte liked it a great deal better than he did, and that it could end in nothing but Rome. Easter decorations indeed! Christmas decorations — in reason — were proper enough, but Easter decorations! well, it might last his time.

This was the course things had taken in the Church of England during the last forty years. The set had been steadily in one direction. A few men who knew what they wanted made cats' paws of the Christinas and the Charlottes, and the Christinas and the Charlottes made cats' paws of the Mrs. Goodhews and the old Miss Wrights, and the Mrs. Goodhews and old Miss Wrights told the Mr. Goodhews and young Miss Wrights what they should do, and when the Mr. Goodhews and the young Miss Wrights did it the little Goodhews and the rest of the spiritual flock did as they did, and the Theobalds went for nothing; step by step, day by day, year by year, parish by parish, diocese by diocese this was how it was done. And yet the Church of England looks with no friendly eyes upon the theory of Evolution or Descent with Modification.

CHAPTER EIGHTY-FIVE

I REMEMBER soon after one of these books was published I happened to meet Mrs. Jupp to whom, by the way, Ernest made a small weekly allowance. It was at Ernest's chambers, and for some reason we were left alone for a few minutes. I said to her: 'Mr. Pontifex has written another book, Mrs. Jupp.'

'Lor' now,' said she, 'has he really? Dear gentleman! Is it about love?' And the old sinner threw up a wicked sheep's eye glance at me from under her aged eyelids. I forget what there was in my reply which provoked it — probably nothing — but she went rattling on at full speed to the effect that Bell had given her a ticket for the opera. 'So, of course,' she said, 'I went. I didn't understand one word of it, for it was all French, but I saw their legs. Oh dear, oh dear! I'm afraid I shan't be here much longer, and when dear Mr. Pontifex sees me in my coffin he'll say, "Poor old Jupp, she'll never talk broad any more," but bless you I m not so old as all that, and I'm taking lessons in dancing.'

At this moment Ernest came in and the conversation was changed. Mrs. Jupp asked if he was still going on writing more books now that this one was done. 'Of course I am,' he answered, 'I'm always writing books; here is the manuscript of my next,' and he showed her a heap of paper.

'Well now,' she exclaimed, 'dear, dear me, and is that manuscript? I've often heard talk about manuscripts, but I never thought I should live to see some myself. Well! well! So that is really manuscript?'

There were a few geraniums in the window and they did not look well. Ernest asked Mrs. Jupp if she understood flowers. 'I understand the language of flowers,' she said, with one of her most bewitching leers, and on this we sent her off till she should choose to honour us with another visit, which she knows she is privileged from time to time to do, for Ernest likes her.

CHAPTER EIGHTY-SIX

TALKING of music reminds me of a little passage that took place between Ernest and Miss Skinner, Dr. Skinner's eldest daughter, not so very long ago. Dr. Skinner had long left Roughborough, and had become Dean of a Cathedral in one of our Midland counties — a position which exactly suited him. Finding himself once in the neighbourhood Ernest called, for old acquaintance' sake, and was hospitably entertained at lunch.

Thirty years had whitened the Doctor's bushy eyebrows — his hair they could not whiten. I believe that but for that wig he would have been made a bishop.

His voice and manner were unchanged, and when Ernest remarking upon a plan of Rome which hung in the hall, spoke inadvertently of the Quirĭnal, he replied with all his wonted pomp: 'Yes, the Quirīnal — or as I myself prefer to call it, the Quirīnal.' After this triumph he inhaled a long breath through the corners of his mouth, and flung it back again into the face of Heaven, as in his finest form during his head mastership. At lunch he did indeed once say, 'next to impossible to think of anything else,' but he immediately corrected himself and substituted the words, 'next to impossible to entertain irrelevant ideas,' after which he seemed to feel a good deal more comfortable. Ernest saw the familiar volumes of Dr. Skinner's works upon the bookshelves in the Deanery dining-room, but he saw no copy of *Rome or the Bible — Which?*

'And are you still as fond of music as ever, Mr. Pontifex?' said Miss Skinner to Ernest during the course of lunch.

'Of some kinds of music, yes, Miss Skinner, but you know I never did like modern music.'

'Isn't that rather dreadful? — Don't you think you rather —' She was going to have added, 'ought to?' but she left it unsaid, feeling doubtless that she had sufficiently conveyed her meaning.

'I would like modern music, if I could; I have been trying all my life to like it, but I succeed less and less the older I grow.'

'And pray, where do you consider modern music to begin?'

'With Sebastian Bach.'

'And don't you like Beethoven?'

'No, I used to think I did, when I was younger, but I know now that I never really liked him.'

'Ah! how can you say so? You cannot understand him, you never could say this if you understood him. For me a simple chord of Beethoven is enough. This is happiness.'

Ernest was amused at her strong family likeness to her father — a likeness which had grown upon her as she had become older, and which extended even to voice and manner of speaking. He remembered how he had heard me describe the game of chess I had played with the doctor in days gone by, and with his mind's ear seemed to hear Miss Skinner saying, as though it were an epitaph:

Stay:
I may presently take
A simple chord of Beethoven,
Or a small semiquaver
From one of Mendelssohn's Songs without Words.

After luncheon when Ernest was left alone for half an hour or so with the Dean he plied him so well with compliments that the old gentleman was pleased and flattered beyond his wont. He rose and bowed. 'These expressions,' he said, *voce sua*, 'are very valuable to me.' 'They are but a small part, Sir,' rejoined Ernest, 'of what any one of your old pupils must feel towards you,' and the pair danced as it were a minuet at the end of the dining-room table in front of the old bay window that looked upon the smooth-shaven lawn. On this Ernest departed; but a few days afterwards, the Doctor wrote him a letter and told him that his critics were σκληροὶ καὶ ἀντίτυποι and at the same time ἀνέκπληκτοι. Ernest remembered σκληροί, and knew that the other words were something of like nature, so it was all right. A month or two afterwards, Dr. Skinner was gathered to his fathers.

'He was an old fool, Ernest,' said I, 'and you should not relent towards him.'

'I could not help it,' he replied, 'he was so old that it was almost like playing with a child.'

THE FAIR HAVEN

MEMOIR OF JOHN PICKARD OWEN

BY WILLIAM BICKERSTETH OWEN

[From *The Fair Haven*.]

EDITOR'S PREFACE

*T*HE *Fair Haven*, from which the following *Memoir* is taken, was published in 1873, the year after *Erewhon*, and ran almost at once into a second edition, including a Preface in which Butler acknowledged his authorship. He can indeed never have intended to make much mystery about it; for the book was based largely on a pamphlet which he had published in 1865, under the title *The Evidence for the Resurrection of Jesus Christ as given by the Four Evangelists critically examined*. The pamphlet had been a straightforward critical study, whereas in *The Fair Haven* Butler adopted an ironical form, casting the book, in the words of its sub-title, into *A Work in Defence of the Miraculous Element in Our Lord's Ministry upon Earth, both as against Rationalistic Impugners and certain Orthodox Defenders, by the late John Pickard Owen, with a Memoir of the Author by William Bickersteth Owen*. When *The Fair Haven*, despite the evident irony of the *Memoir* — to say nothing of the main part of the book — was quite widely taken as a serious defence of the case which Butler was setting out to attack, he at once put his name to the second edition. There is much excellent ironical writing in the book itself; but it can be represented here only by the *Memoir* of the supposed author, with its picture of the daydreams of John Pickard Owen's mother, foreshadowing Christina's day-dreaming in *The Way of All Flesh*.

THE subject of this Memoir, and Author of the work which follows it, was born in Goodge Street, Tottenham Court Road, London, on February 5th, 1832. He was my elder brother by about
eighteen months. Our father and mother had once been rich, but
through a succession of unavoidable misfortunes they were left with
but a very moderate income when my brother and myself were about
three and four years old. My father died some five or six years afterwards, and we only recollected him as a singularly gentle and
humorous playmate who doted upon us both and never spoke un-
kindly. The charm of such a recollection can never be dispelled; both
my brother and myself returned his love with interest, and cherished
his memory with the most affectionate regret, from the day on which
he left us till the time came that the one of us was again to see him face
to face. So sweet and winning was his nature that his slightest wish was
our law — and whenever we pleased him, no matter how little, he
never failed to thank us as though we had done him a service which we
should have had a perfect right to withhold. How proud were we upon
any of these occasions, and how we courted the opportunity of being
thanked! He did indeed well know the art of becoming idolized by his
children, and dearly did he prize the results of his own proficiency; yet
truly there was no art about it; all arose spontaneously from the well-
spring of a sympathetic nature which knew how to feel as others felt,
whether old or young, rich or poor, wise or foolish. On one point
alone did he neglect us — I refer to our religious education. On all
other matters he was the kindest and most careful teacher in the world.
Love and gratitude be to his memory!

My mother loved us no less ardently than my father, but she was of
a quicker temper, and less adept at conciliating affection. She must have
been exceedingly handsome when she was young, and was still comely
when we first remembered her; she was also highly accomplished, but
she felt my father's loss of fortune more keenly than my father himself,
and it preyed upon her mind, though rather for our sake than for her
own. Had we not known my father we should have loved her better
than anyone in the world, but affection goes by comparison, and my
father spoiled us for anyone but himself; indeed, in after life, I remember my mother's telling me, with many tears, how jealous she had often

been of the love we bore him, and how mean she had thought it of him to entrust all scolding or repression to her, so that he might have more than his due share of our affection. Not that I believe my father did this consciously; still, he so greatly hated scolding that I dare say we might often have got off scot free when we really deserved reproof had not my mother undertaken the *onus* of scolding us herself. We therefore naturally feared her more than my father, and fearing more we loved less. For as love casteth out fear, so fear love.

This must have been hard to bear, and my mother scarcely knew the way to bear it. She tried to upbraid us, in little ways, into loving her as much as my father; the more she tried this, the less we could succeed in doing it; and so on and so on in a fashion which need not be detailed. Not but what we really loved her deeply, while her affection for us was insurpassable; still, we loved her less than we loved my father, and this was the grievance.

My father entrusted our religious education entirely to my mother. He was himself, I am assured, of a deeply religious turn of mind, and a thoroughly consistent member of the Church of England; but he conceived, and perhaps rightly, that it is the mother who should first teach her children to lift their hands in prayer, and impart to them a knowledge of the One in whom we live and move and have our being. My mother accepted the task gladly, for in spite of a certain narrowness of view — the natural but deplorable result of her earlier surroundings — she was one of the most truly pious women whom I have ever known; unfortunately for herself and us she had been trained in the lowest school of Evangelical literalism — a school which in after life both my brother and myself came to regard as the main obstacle to the complete overthrow of unbelief; we therefore looked upon it with something stronger than aversion, and for my own part I still deem it perhaps the most insidious enemy which the cause of Christ has ever encountered. But of this more hereafter.

My mother, as I said, threw her whole soul into the work of our religious education. Whatever she believed she believed literally, and, if I may say so, with a harshness of realization which left very little scope for imagination or mystery. Her plans of Heaven and solutions of life's enigmas were direct and forcible, but they could only be reconciled with certain obvious facts — such as the omnipotence and all-goodness of God — by leaving many things absolutely out of sight. And this my mother succeeded effectually in doing. She never doubted that her opinions comprised the truth, the whole truth, and nothing but the truth; she therefore made haste to sow the good seed in our tender minds, and so far succeeded that when my brother was four years old he could repeat the Apostles' Creed, the General Confession and the Lord's Prayer without a blunder. My mother made herself believe that he delighted in them; but, alas! it was far otherwise; for, strange as it may appear concerning one whose later life was a continual prayer, in childhood he detested nothing so much as being made to pray and to learn his Catechism. In this I am sorry to say we were both heartily of a mind. As for Sunday, the less said the better.

I have already hinted (but as a warning to other parents I had better, perhaps, express myself more plainly), that this aversion was probably the result of my mother's undue eagerness to reap an artificial fruit of lip service, which could have little meaning to the heart of one so young. I believe that the severe check which the natural growth of faith experienced in my brother's case was due almost entirely to this cause, and to the school of literalism in which he had been trained; but, however this may be, we both of us hated being made to say our prayers — morning and evening it was our one bugbear, and we would avoid it, as indeed children generally will, by every artifice which we could employ. Thus we were in the habit of feigning to be asleep shortly before prayer time, and would gratefully hear my father tell my mother that it was a shame to wake us; whereon he would carry us up to bed in a state apparently of the profoundest slumber when we were really wide awake and in great fear of detection. For we knew how to pretend to be asleep, but we did not know how we ought to wake again; there was nothing for it therefore when we were once committed, but to go on sleeping till we were fairly undressed and put to bed, and could wake up safely in the dark. But deceit is never long successful, and we were at last ignominiously exposed.

It happened one evening that my mother suspected my brother John, and tried to open his little hands which were lying clasped in front of him. Now my brother was as yet very crude and inconsistent in his theories concerning sleep, and had no conception of what a real sleeper would do under these circumstances. Fear deprived him of his powers of reflection, and he thus unfortunately concluded that because sleepers, so far as he had observed them, were always motionless, therefore, they must be quite rigid and incapable of motion, and indeed that any movement, under any circumstances (for from his earliest childhood he liked to carry his theories to their legitimate conclusion), would be physically impossible for one who was really sleeping; forgetful, oh! unhappy one, of the flexibility of his own body on being carried upstairs, and, more unhappy still, ignorant of the art of waking. He, therefore, clenched his fingers harder and harder as he felt my mother trying to unfold them while his head hung listless, and his eyes were closed as though he were sleeping sweetly. It is needless to detail the agony of shame that followed. My mother begged my father to box his ears, which my father flatly refused to do. Then she boxed them herself, and there followed a scene and a day or two of disgrace for both of us.

Shortly after this there happened another misadventure. A lady came to stay with my mother, and was to sleep in a bed that had been brought into our nursery, for my father's fortunes had already failed, and we were living in a humble way. We were still but four and five years old, so the arrangement was not unnatural, and it was assumed that we should be asleep before the lady went to bed, and be downstairs before she would get up in the morning. But the arrival of this lady and her being put to sleep in the nursery were great events to us in those days, and being particularly wanted to go to sleep, we of course sat up in bed talking and keeping ourselves awake till she should come upstairs. Perhaps we had fancied that she would give us something, but if so we were disappointed. However, whether this was the case or not, we were wide awake when our visitor came to bed, and having no particular object to gain, we made no pretence of sleeping. The lady kissed us both, told us to lie still and go to sleep like good children, and then began doing her hair.

I remember that this was the occasion on which my brother discovered a good many things in connection with the fair sex which had hitherto been beyond his ken; more especially that the mass of petticoats and clothes which envelop the female form were not, as he expressed it to me, 'all solid woman', but that women were not in reality more substantially built than men, and had legs as much as he had, a fact which he had never yet realized. On this he for a long time considered them as impostors, who had wronged him by leading him to suppose that they had far more 'body in them' (so he said), than he now found they had. This was a sort of thing which he regarded with stern moral reprobation. If he had been old enough to have a solicitor I believe he would have put the matter into his hands, as well as certain other things which had lately troubled him. For but recently my mother had bought a fowl, and he had seen it plucked, and the inside taken out; his irritation had been extreme on discovering that fowls were not all solid flesh, but that their insides — and these formed, as it appeared to him, an enormous percentage of the bird — were perfectly useless. He was now beginning to understand that sheep and cows were also hollow as far as good meat was concerned; the flesh they had was only a mouthful in comparison with what they ought to have considering their apparent bulk — insignificant, mere skin and bone covering a cavern. What right had they, or anything else, to assert themselves as being so big, and prove so empty? And now this discovery of woman's falsehood was quite too much for him. The world itself was hollow, made up of shams and delusions, full of sound and fury signifying nothing.

Truly a prosaic young gentleman enough. Everything with him was to be exactly in all its parts what it appeared on the face of it, and everything was to go on doing exactly what it had been doing hitherto. If a thing looked solid, it was to be very solid; if hollow, very hollow; nothing was to be half and half, and nothing was to change unless he had himself already become accustomed to its times and manners of changing; there were to be no exceptions and no contradictions; all things were to be perfectly consistent, and all premises to be carried with extremist rigour to their legitimate conclusions. Heaven was to be very neat (for he was always tidy himself), and free from sudden shocks to the nervous system, such as those caused by dogs barking at him, or cows driven in the streets. God was to resemble my father, and the Holy Spirit to bear some sort of indistinct analogy to my mother.

Such were the ideal theories of his childhood — unconsciously formed, but very firmly believed in. As he grew up he made such modifications as were forced upon him by enlarged perceptions, but every modification was an effort to him, in spite of a continual and successful resistance to what he recognized as his initial mental defect.

I may perhaps be allowed to say here, in reference to a remark in the preceding paragraph, that both my brother and myself used to notice it as an almost invariable rule that children's earliest ideas of God are modelled upon the character of their father — if they have one. Should the father be kind, considerate, full of the warmest love, fond of showing it, and reserved only about his displeasure, the child, having learned to look upon God as His Heavenly Father through the Lord's Prayer and our Church Services, will feel towards God as he does towards his own father; this conception will stick to a man for years and years after he has attained manhood — probably it will never leave him. For all children love their fathers and mothers, if these last will only let them; it is not a little unkindness that will kill so hardy a plant as the love of a child for its parents. Nature has allowed ample margin for many blunders, provided there be a genuine desire on the parent's part to make the child feel that he is loved, and that his natural feelings are respected. This is all the religious education which a child should have. As he grows older he will then turn naturally to the waters of life, and thirst after them of his own accord by reason of the spiritual refreshment which they, and they only, can afford. Otherwise he will shrink from them, on account of his recollection of the way in which he was led down to drink against his will, and perhaps with harshness, when all the analogies with which he was acquainted pointed in the direction of their being unpleasant and unwholesome. So soul-satisfying is family affection to a child, that he who has once enjoyed it cannot bear to be deprived of the hope that he is possessed in Heaven of a parent who is like this earthly father — of a friend and counsellor who will never, never fail him. There is no such religious nor moral education as kindly genial treatment and a good example; all else may then be let alone till the child is old enough to feel the want of it. It is true that the seed will thus be sown late, but in what a soil! On the other hand, if a man has found his earthly father harsh and uncongenial, his conception of his Heavenly Parent will be painful. He will begin by seeing God as an exaggerated likeness of his father. He will therefore shrink from Him. The rottenness of stillborn love in the heart of a child poisons the blood of the soul, and hence, later, crime.

To return, however, to the lady. When she had put on her night-gown, she knelt down by her bedside and, to our consternation, began to say her prayers. This was a cruel blow to both of us; we had always been under the impression that grown-up people were not made to say their prayers, and the idea of anyone saying them of his or her own accord had never occurred to us as possible. Of course the lady would not say her prayers if she were not obliged; and yet she did say them; therefore she must be obliged to say them; therefore we should be obliged to say them, and this was a very great disappointment. Awestruck and open-mouthed we listened while the lady prayed in sonorous accents, for many things which I do not now remember, and finally for my father and mother and for both of us — shortly afterwards she rose, blew out the light and got into bed. Every word that she said had confirmed our worst apprehensions; it was just what we had been taught to say ourselves.

Next morning we compared notes and drew the most painful inferences; but in the course of the day our spirits rallied. We agreed that there were many mysteries in connection with life and things which it was high time to unravel, and that an opportunity was now afforded us which might not readily occur again. All we had to do was to be true to ourselves and equal to the occasion. We laid our plans with great astuteness. We would be fast asleep when the lady came up to bed, but our heads should be turned in the direction of her bed, and covered with clothes, all but a single peep-hole. My brother, as the eldest, had clearly a right to be nearest the lady, but I could see very well, and could depend on his reporting faithfully whatever should escape me.

There was no chance of her giving us anything — if she had meant to do so she would have done it sooner; she might, indeed, consider the moment of her departure as the most auspicious for this purpose, but then she was not going yet, and the interval was at our own disposal. We spent the afternoon in trying to learn to snore, but we were not certain about it, and in the end regretfully concluded that as snoring was not *de rigueur* we had better dispense with it.

We were put to bed; the light was taken away; we were told to go to sleep, and promised faithfully that we would do so; the tongue indeed swore, but the mind was unsworn. It was agreed that we should keep pinching one another to prevent our going to sleep. We did so at frequent intervals; at last our patience was rewarded with the heavy creak, as of a stout elderly lady labouring up the stairs, and presently our victim entered.

To cut a long story short, the lady on satisfying herself that we were asleep, never said her prayers at all; during the remainder of her visit whenever she found us awake she always said them, but when she thought we were asleep, she never prayed. It is needless to add that we had the matter out with her before she left, and that the consequences were unpleasant for all parties; they added to the troubles in which we were already involved as to our prayers, and were indirectly among the earliest causes which led my brother to look with scepticism upon religion.

For a while, however, all went on as though nothing had happened. An effect of distrust, indeed, remained after the cause had been forgotten, but my brother was still too young to oppose anything that my mother told him, and to all outward appearance he grew in grace no less rapidly than in stature.

For years we led a quiet and eventless life, broken only by the one great sorrow of our father's death. Shortly after this we were sent to a day school in Bloomsbury. We were neither of us very happy there, but my brother, who always took kindly to his books, picked up a fair knowledge of Latin and Greek; he also learned to draw, and to exercise himself a little in English composition. When I was about fourteen my mother capitalized a part of her income and started me off to America, where she had friends who could give me a helping hand; by their kindness I was enabled, after an absence of twenty years, to return with a handsome income, but not, alas, before the death of my mother.

Up to the time of my departure my mother continued to read the Bible with us and explain it. She had become deeply impressed with the millenarian fervour which laid hold of so many some twenty-five or thirty years ago. The Apocalypse was perhaps her favourite book in the Bible, and she was imbued with the fullest conviction that all the threatened horrors with which it teems were upon the eve of their accomplishment. The year eighteen hundred and forty-eight was to be (as indeed it was) a time of general bloodshed and confusion, while in eighteen hundred and sixty-six, should it please God to spare her, her eyes would be gladdened by the visible descent of the Son of Man with a shout, with the voice of the Archangel, with the trump of God; and the dead in Christ should rise first; then she, as one of them that were alive, would be caught up with other saints into the air, and would possibly receive while rising some distinguishing token of confidence and approbation which should fall with due impressiveness upon the surrounding multitude; then would come the consummation of all things, and she would be ever with the Lord. She died peaceably in her bed before she could know that a commercial panic was the nearest approach to the fulfilment of prophecy which the year eighteen hundred and sixty-six brought forth.

These opinions of my mother's were positively disastrous — injuring her naturally healthy and vigorous mind by leading her to indulge in all manner of dreamy and fanciful interpretations of Scripture, which any but the most narrow literalist would feel at once to be untenable. Thus several times she expressed to us her conviction that my brother and myself were to be the two witnesses mentioned in the eleventh chapter of the Book of Revelation, and dilated upon the gratification she should experience upon finding that we had indeed been reserved for a position of such distinction. We were as yet mere children, and naturally took all for granted that our mother told us; we therefore made a careful examination of the passage which threw light upon our future; but on finding that the prospect was gloomy and full of bloodshed we protested against the honours which were intended for us, more especially when we reflected that the mother of the two witnesses was not menaced in Scripture with any particular discomfort. If we were to be martyrs, my mother ought to wish to be a martyr too, whereas nothing was further from her intention. Her notion clearly was that we were to be massacred somewhere in the streets of London, in consequence of the anti-Christian machinations of the Pope; that after lying about unburied for three days and a half we were to come to life again; and, finally, that we should conspicuously ascend to heaven, in front, perhaps, of the Foundling Hospital.

She was not herself indeed to share either our martyrdom or our glorification, but was to survive us many years on earth, living in an odour of great sanctity and reflected splendour, as the central and most august figure in a select society. She would perhaps be able indirectly, through her sons' influence with the Almighty, to have a voice in most of the arrangements both of this world and of the next. If all this were to come true (and things seemed very like it), those friends who had neglected us in our adversity would not find it too easy to be restored to favour, however greatly they might desire it — that is to say, they would not have found it too easy in the case of one less magnanimous and spiritually-minded than herself. My mother said but little of the above directly, but the fragments which occasionally escaped her were pregnant, and on looking back it is easy to perceive that she must have been building one of the most stupendous aerial fabrics that have ever been reared.

I have given the above in its more amusing aspect, and am half afraid that I may appear to be making a jest of weakness on the part of one of the most devotedly unselfish mothers who have ever existed. But one can love while smiling, and the very wildness of my mother's dream serves to show how entirely her whole soul was occupied with the things which are above. To her, religion was all in all; the earth was but a place of pilgrimage — only so far important as it was a possible road to heaven. She impressed this upon both of us by every word and action — instant in season and out of season, so that she might fill us more deeply with a sense of God. But the inevitable consequences happened; my mother had aimed too high and had overshot her mark. The influence indeed of her guileless and unworldly nature remained impressed upon my brother even during the time of his extremest unbelief (perhaps his ultimate safety is in the main referable to this cause, and to the happy memories of my father, which had predisposed him to love God), but my mother had insisted on the most minute verbal accuracy of every part of the Bible, she had also dwelt upon the duty of independent research, and on the necessity of giving up everything rather than assent to things which our conscience did not assent to. No one could have more effectually taught us to try *to think* the truth, and we had taken her at her word because our hearts told us that she was right. But she required three incompatible things. When my brother grew older he came to feel that independent and unflinching examination, with a determination to abide by the results, would lead him to reject the point which to my mother was more important than any other — I mean the absolute accuracy of the Gospel records. My mother was inexpressibly shocked at hearing my brother doubt the authenticity of the Epistle to the Hebrews; and then, as it appeared to him, she tried to make him violate the duties of examination and candour which he had learnt too thoroughly to unlearn. Thereon came pain and an estrangement which was none the less profound for being mutually concealed.

This estrangement was the gradual work of some five or six years, during which my brother was between eleven and seventeen years old. At seventeen, I am told that he was remarkably well informed and clever. His manners were, like my father's, singularly genial, and his appearance very prepossessing. He had as yet no doubt concerning the soundness of any fundamental Christian doctrine, but his mind was too active to allow of his being contented with my mother's child-like faith. There were points on which he did not indeed doubt, but which it would none the less be interesting to consider; such for example as the perfectibility of the regenerate Christian, and the meaning of the mysterious central chapters of the Epistle to the Romans. He was engaged in these researches though still only a boy, when an event occurred which gave the first real shock to his faith.

He was accustomed to teach in a school for the poorest children every Sunday afternoon, a task for which his patience and good temper well fitted him. On one occasion, however, while he was explaining the effect of baptism to one of his favourite pupils, he discovered to his great surprise that the boy had never been baptized. He pushed his inquiries further, and found that out of the fifteen boys in his class only five had been baptized, and, not only so, but that no difference in disposition or conduct could be discovered between the regenerate boys and the unregenerate. The good and bad boys were distributed in proportions equal to the respective numbers of the baptized and unbaptized. In spite of a certain impetuosity of natural character, he was also of a matter-of-fact and experimental turn of mind; he therefore went through the whole school, which numbered about a hundred boys, and found out who had been baptized and who had not. The same results appeared. The majority had not been baptized; yet the good and bad dispositions were so distributed as to preclude all possibility of maintaining that the baptized boys were better than the unbaptized.

The reader may smile at the idea of anyone's faith being troubled by a fact of which the explanation is so obvious, but in truth my brother was seriously and painfully shocked. The teacher to whom he applied for a solution of the difficulty was not a man of any real power, and reported my brother to the rector for having disturbed the school by his inquiries. The rector was old and self-opinionated; the difficulty, indeed, was plainly as new to him as it had been to my brother, but instead of saying so at once, and referring to any recognized theological authority, he tried to put him off with words which seemed intended to silence him rather than to satisfy him; finally he lost his temper, and my brother fell under suspicion of unorthodoxy.

This kind of treatment might answer with some people, but not with my brother. He alludes to it resentfully in the introductory chapter of his book. He became suspicious that a preconceived opinion was being defended at the expense of honest scrutiny, and was thus driven upon his own unaided investigation. The result may be guessed: he began to go astray, and strayed further and further. The children of God, he reasoned, the members of Christ and inheritors of the kingdom of Heaven, were no more spiritually minded than the children of the world and the devil. Was then the grace of God a gift which left no trace whatever upon those who were possessed of it — a thing the presence or absence of which might be ascertained by consulting the parish registry, but was not discernible in conduct? The grace of man was more clearly perceptible than this. Assuredly there must be a screw loose somewhere, which, for aught he knew, might be jeopardizing the salvation of all Christendom. Where then was this loose screw to be found?

He concluded after some months of reflection that the mischief was caused by the system of sponsors and by infant baptism. He therefore, to my mother's inexpressible grief, joined the Baptists and was immersed in a pond near Dorking. With the Baptists he remained quiet about three months, and then began to quarrel with his instructors as to their doctrine of predestination. Shortly afterwards he came accidentally upon a fascinating stranger who was no less struck with my brother than my brother with him, and this gentleman, who turned out to be a Roman Catholic missionary, landed him in the Church of Rome, where he felt sure that he had now found rest for his soul. But here, too, he was mistaken; after about two years he rebelled against the stifling of all free inquiry; on this rebellion the flood-gates of scepticism were opened, and he was soon battling with unbelief. He then fell in with one who was a pure Deist, and was shorn of every shred of dogma which he had ever held, except a belief in the personality and providence of the Creator.

On reviewing his letters written to me about this time, I am painfully struck with the manner in which they show that all these pitiable vagaries were to be traced to a single cause — a cause which still exists to the misleading of hundreds of thousands, and which, I fear, seems likely to continue in full force for many a year to come — I mean, to a false system of training which teaches people to regard Christianity as a thing one and indivisible, to be accepted entirely in the strictest reading of the letter, or to be rejected as absolutely untrue. The fact is, that all permanent truth is as one of those coal measures, a seam of which lies near the surface, and even crops up above the ground, but which is generally of an inferior quality and soon worked out; beneath it there comes a layer of sand and clay, and then at last the true seam of precious quality and in virtually inexhaustible supply. The truth which is on the surface is rarely the whole truth. It is seldom until this has been worked out and done with — as in the case of the apparent flatness of the earth — that unchangeable truth is discovered. It is the glory of the Lord to conceal a matter: it is the glory of the king to find it out. If my brother, from whom I have taken the above illustration, had had some judicious and wide-minded friend to correct and supplement the mainly admirable principles which had been instilled into him by my mother, he would have been saved years of spiritual wandering; but, as it was, he fell in with one after another, each in his own way as literal and unspiritual as the other — each impressed with one aspect of religious truth, and with one only. In the end he became perhaps the widest-minded and most original thinker whom I have ever met; but no one from his early manhood could have augured this result; on the contrary, he showed every sign of being likely to develop into one of those who can never see more than one side of a question at a time, in spite of their seeing that side with singular clearness of mental vision. In after life, he often met with mere lads who seemed to him to be years and years in advance of what he had been at their age, and would say, smiling, 'With a great sum obtained I this freedom; but thou wast free-born.'

Yet when one comes to think of it, a late development and laborious growth are generally more fruitful than those which are over-early luxuriant. Drawing an illustration from the art of painting, with which he was well acquainted, my brother used to say that all the greatest painters had begun with a hard and precise manner from which they had only broken after several years of effort; and that in like manner all the early schools were founded upon definiteness of outline to the exclusion of truth of effect. This may be true; but in my brother's case there was something even more unpromising than this; there was a commonness, so to speak, of mental execution, from which no one could have foreseen his after-emancipation. Yet in the course of time he was indeed emancipated to the very uttermost, while his bonds will, I firmly trust, be found to have been of inestimable service to the whole human race.

For although it was so many years before he was enabled to see the Christian scheme *as a whole*, or even to conceive the idea that there was any whole at all, other than each one of the stages of opinion through which he was at the time passing; yet when the idea was at length presented to him by one whom I must not name, the discarded fragments of his faith assumed shape, and formed themselves into a consistently organized scheme. Then became apparent the value of his knowledge of the details of so many different sides of Christian verity. Buried in the details, he had hitherto ignored the fact that they were only the unessential developments of certain component parts. Awakening to the perception of the whole after an intimate acquaintance with the details, he was able to realize the position and meaning of all that he had hitherto experienced in a way which has been vouchsafed to few, if any others.

Thus he became truly a broad Churchman. Not broad in the ordinary and ill-considered use of the term (for the broad Churchman is as little able to sympathize with Romanists, extreme High Churchmen and Dissenters, as these are with himself — he is only one of a sect which is called by the name broad, though it is no broader than its own base), but in the true sense of being able to believe in the naturalness, legitimacy and truth *qua* Christianity even of those doctrines which seem to stand most widely and irreconcilably asunder.

CHAPTER TWO

BUT it was impossible that a mind of such activity should have gone over so much ground, and yet in the end returned to the same position as that from which it started.

So far was this from being the case, that the Christianity of his maturer life would be considered dangerously heterodox by those who belong to any of the more definite or precise schools of theological thought. He was as one who has made the circuit of a mountain, and yet been ascending during the whole time of his doing so: such a person finds himself upon the same side as at first, but upon a greatly higher level. The peaks which had seemed the most important when he was in the valley were now dwarfed to their true proportions by colossal cloud-capped masses whose very existence could not have been suspected from beneath: and again, other points which had seemed among the lowest turned out to be the very highest of all — as the Finster-Aarhorn, which hides itself away in the centre of the Bernese Alps, is never seen to be the greatest till one is high and far off.

Thus he felt no sort of fear or repugnance in admitting that the New Testament writings, as we now have them, are not by any means accurate records of the events which they profess to chronicle. This, which few English Churchmen would be prepared to admit, was to him so much of an axiom that he despaired of seeing any sound theological structure raised until it was universally recognized.

And here he would probably meet with sympathy from the more advanced thinkers within the body of the Church, but so far as I know, he stood alone as recognizing the wisdom of the Divine counsels in having ordained the wide and apparently irreconcilable divergencies of doctrine and character which we find assigned to Christ in the Gospels, and as finding his faith confirmed, not by the supposition that both the portraits drawn of Christ are objectively true, but *that both are objectively inaccurate, and that the Almighty intended they should be inaccurate*, inasmuch as the true spiritual conception in the mind of man could be indirectly more certainly engendered by a strife, a warring, a clashing, so to speak, of versions, all of them distorting slightly some one or other of the features of the original, than directly by the most absolutely correct impression which human language could convey. Even the most perfect human speech, as has been often pointed out, is a very gross and imperfect vehicle of thought. I remember once hearing him say that it was not till he was nearly thirty that he discovered 'what thick and sticky fluids were air and water,' how crass and dull in comparison with other more subtle fluids; he added that speech had no less deceived him, seeming, as it did, to be such a perfect messenger of thought, and being after all nothing but a shuffler and a loiterer.

With most men the Gospels are true in spite of their discrepancies and inconsistencies; with him Christianity, as distinguished from a bare belief in the objectively historical character of each part of the Gospels, was true because of these very discrepancies; as his conceptions of the Divine manner of working became wider, the very forces which had at one time shaken his faith to its foundations established it anew upon a firmer and broader base. He was gradually led to feel that the ideal presented by the life and death of our Saviour could never have been accepted by Jews at all, if its whole purport had been made intelligible during the Redeemer's lifetime; that in order to insure its acceptance by a nucleus of followers it must have been endowed with a more local aspect than it was intended afterwards to wear; yet that, for the sake of its subsequent universal value, the destruction of that local complexion was indispensable; that the corruptions inseparable from viva voce communication and imperfect education were the means adopted by the Creator to blur the details of the ideal, and give it that

breadth which could not be otherwise obtainable — and that thus the
value of the ideal was indefinitely enhanced, and *designedly enhanced*,
alike by the waste of time and by its incrustations; that all ideals gain by
a certain amount of vagueness, which allows the beholder to fill in the
details according to his own spiritual needs, and that no ideal can be
truly universal and permanent, unless it have an elasticity which will
allow of this process in the minds of those who contemplate it; that it
cannot become thus elastic unless by the loss of no inconsiderable
amount of detail, and that thus the half, as Dr. Arnold used to say,
'becomes greater than the whole', the sketch more preciously suggestive than the photograph. Hence far from deploring the fragmentary, confused and contradictory condition of the Gospel records, he
saw in this condition the means whereby alone the human mind could
have been enabled to conceive — not the precise nature of Christ — but
the highest ideal of which each individual Christian soul was capable. As
soon as he had grasped these conceptions, which will be found more
fully developed in one of the later chapters of his book, the spell of
unbelief was broken.

But, once broken, it was dissolved utterly and entirely; he could
allow himself to contemplate fearlessly all sorts of issues from which
one whose experiences had been less varied would have shrunk. He
was free of the enemy's camp, and could go hither and thither whithersoever he would. The very points which to others were insuperable
difficulties were to him foundation-stones of faith. For example, to the
objection that if in the present state of the records no clear conception
of the nature of Christ's life and teaching could be formed, we should
be compelled to take one for our model of whom we knew little or
nothing certain, I have heard him answer, 'And so much the better for
us all. The truth, if read by the light of man's imperfect understanding,
would have been falser to him than any falsehood. It would have been
truth no longer. *Better be led aright by an error which is so adjusted as to
compensate for the errors in man's powers of understanding, than be misled by
a truth which can never be translated from objectivity to subjectivity.* In such
a case, it is the error which is the truth and the truth the error.'

Fearless himself, he could not understand the fears felt by others;
and this was perhaps his greatest sympathetic weakness. He was
impatient of the subterfuges with which untenable interpretations of
Scripture were defended, and of the disingenuousness of certain
harmonists; indeed, the mention of the word harmony was enough to

kindle an outbreak of righteous anger, which would sometimes go to the utmost limit of righteousness. 'Harmonies!' he would exclaim, 'the sweetest harmonies are those which are most full of discords, and the discords of one generation of musicians become heavenly music in the hands of their successors. Which of the great musicians has not enriched his art not only by the discovery of new harmonies, but by proving that sounds which are actually inharmonious are nevertheless essentially and eternally delightful? What an outcry has there not always been against the "unwarrantable licence" with the rules of harmony whenever a Beethoven or a Mozart has broken through any of the trammels which have been regarded as the safeguards of the art, instead of in their true light of fetters, and how gratefully have succeeding musicians acquiesced in and adopted the innovation.' Then would follow a tirade with illustration upon illustration, comparison of this passage with that, and an exhaustive demonstration that one or other, or both could have had no sort of possible foundation in fact; he could only see that the persons from whom he differed were defending something which was untrue and which they ought to have known to be untrue, but he could not see that people ought to know many things which they do not know.

Had he himself seen all that he ought to have been able to see from his own standpoints? Can any of us do so? The force of early bias and education, the force of intellectual surroundings, the force of natural timidity, the force of dullness, were things which he could appreciate and make allowance for in any other age, and among any other people than his own; but as belonging to England and the nineteenth century they had no place in his theory of Nature; they were inconceivable, unnatural, unpardonable, whenever they came into contact with the subject of Christian evidences. Deplorable, indeed, they are, but this was just the sort of word to which he could not confine himself. The criticisms upon the late Dean Alford's notes, which will be given in the sequel, display this sort of temper; they are not entirely his own, but he adopted them and endorsed them with a warmth which we cannot but feel to be unnecessary, not to say more. Yet I am free to confess that whatever editorial licence I could venture to take has been taken in the direction of lenity.

On the whole, however, he valued Dean Alford's work very highly, giving him great praise for the candour with which he not unfrequently set the harmonists aside. For example, in his notes upon the discrepan-

cies between St. Luke's and St. Matthew's accounts of the early life of
our Lord, the Dean openly avows that it is quite beyond his purpose to
attempt to reconcile the two. 'This part of the Gospel history,' he
writes, 'is one where the harmonists, by their arbitrary reconcilement of
the two accounts, have given great advantage to the enemies of the
faith. *As the two accounts now stand*, it is wholly impossible to suggest
any satisfactory method of *uniting them*, everyone who has attempted
it has in some part or other of his hypothesis violated probability and
common sense,' but in spite of this, the Dean had no hesitation in
accepting both the accounts. With reference to this the author of *The
Jesus of History* (Williams and Norgate, 1866) — a work to which my
brother admitted himself to be under very great obligations, and which
he greatly admired, in spite of his utter dissent from the main conclusion arrived at — has the following note:

'Dean Alford, N.T. for English readers, admits that the narratives
as they stand are contradictory, but he believes both. He is even severe
upon the harmonists who attempt to frame schemes of reconciliation
between the two, on account of the triumph they thus furnish to the
"enemies of the faith", a phrase which seems to imply all who believe
less than he does. The Dean, however, forgets that the faith which can
believe two (apparently) contradictory propositions in matters of fact
is a very rare gift, and that for one who is so endowed there are
thousands who can be satisfied with a plausible though demonstrably
false explanation. To the latter class the despised harmonists render a
real service.'

Upon this note my brother was very severe. In a letter, dated
December 18th, 1866, addressed to a friend who had alluded to it, and
expressed his concurrence with it as in the main just, my brother wrote:
'You are wrong about the note in *The Jesus of History*, there is more of
the Christianity of the future in Dean Alford's indifference to the
harmony between the discordant accounts of Luke and Matthew than
there would have been *even in the most convincing and satisfactory*
explanation of the way in which they came to differ. No such
explanation is possible; both the Dean and the author of *The Jesus of
History* were very well aware of this, but the latter is unjust in assuming
that his opponent was not alive to the absurdity of appearing to believe
two contradictory propositions at one and the same time. The Dean
takes very good care that he shall not appear to do this, for it is perfectly plain to any careful reader that he must really believe that one or

both narratives are inaccurate, inasmuch as the differences between them are too great to allow of reconciliation by a supposed suppression of detail.

'This, though not said so clearly as it should have been, is yet virtually implied in the admission that no sort of fact which could by any possibility be admitted as reconciling them had ever occurred to human ingenuity; what, then, Dean Alford must have really felt was that the spiritual value of each account was no less precious for not being in strict accordance with the other; that the objective truth lies somewhere between them, and is of very little importance, being long dead and buried, and living in its results only, in comparison with the subjective truth conveyed by both the narratives, which lived in our hearts independently of precise knowledge concerning the actual facts. Moreover, that though both accounts may perhaps be inaccurate, yet that *a very little* natural inaccuracy on the part of each writer would throw them apparently very wide asunder, that such inaccuracies are easily to be accounted for, and would, in fact, be inevitable in the sixty years of oral communication which elapsed between the birth of our Lord and the writing of the first Gospel, and again in the eighty or ninety years prior to the third, so that the details of the facts connected with the conception, birth, genealogy and earliest history of our Saviour are irrecoverable — a general impression being alone possible, or indeed desirable.

'It might perhaps have been more satisfactory if Dean Alford had expressed the above more plainly; but if he had done this, who would have read his book? Where would have been that influence in the direction of truly liberal Christianity which has been so potent during the last twenty years? As it was, the freedom with which the Dean wrote was the cause of no inconsiderable scandal. Or, again, he may not have been fully conscious of his own position: few men are; he had taken the right one, but more perhaps by spiritual instinct than by conscious and deliberate exercise of his intellectual faculties. Finally, compromise is not a matter of good policy only, it is a solemn duty in the interests of Christian peace, and this not in minor matters only — we can all do this much — but in those concerning which we feel most strongly, for here the sacrifice is greatest and most acceptable to God. There are, of course, limits to this, and Dean Alford may have carried compromise too far in the present instance, but it is very transparent. The narrowness which leads the author of *The Jesus of History* to strain at such a gnat is the secret of his inability to accept the divinity and miracles of our Lord, and has marred the most exhaustively critical exegesis of the life and death of our Saviour with an impotent conclusion.'

It is strange that one who could write thus should occasionally have shown himself so little able to apply his own principles. He seems to have been alternately under the influence of two conflicting spirits — at one time writing as though there were nothing precious under the sun except logic, consistency and precision, and breathing fire and smoke against even very trifling deviations from the path of exact criticism — at another, leading the reader almost to believe that he disregarded the value of any objective truth, and speaking of endeavour after accuracy in terms that are positively contemptuous. Whenever he was in the one mood he seemed to forget the possibility of any other; so much so that I have sometimes thought that he did this deliberately and for the same reasons as those which led Adam Smith to exclude one set of premises in his *Theory of Moral Sentiments*, and another in his *Wealth of Nations*. I believe, however, that the explanation lies in the fact that my brother was inclined to underrate the importance of belief in the objective truth of any other individual features in the life of our Lord than his Resurrection and Ascension. All else seemed dwarfed by the side of these events. His whole soul was so concentrated upon the centre of the circle that he forgot the circumference, or left it out of sight. Nothing less than the strictest objective truth as to the main facts of the Resurrection and Ascension would content him; the other miracles and the life and teaching of our Lord might then be left open; whatever view was taken of them by each individual Christian was probably the one most desirable for the spiritual well-being of each.

Even as regards the Resurrection and Ascension, he did not greatly value the detail. Provided these facts were so established that they could never henceforth be controverted, he thought that the less detail the broader and more universally acceptable would be the effect. Hence, when Dean Alford's notes seemed to jeopardize the evidences for these things, he could brook no trifling; for unless Christ actually died and actually came to life again, he saw no escape from an utter denial of any but natural religion. Christ would have been no more to him than Socrates or Shakespeare, except in so far as his teaching was more spiritual. The triune nature of the Deity — the Resurrection from the dead — the hope of Heaven and salutary fear of Hell — all would go but for the Resurrection and Ascension of Jesus Christ; nothing would remain except a sense of the Divine as a substitute for God, and the current feeling of one's peers as the chief moral check upon misconduct. Indeed, we have seen this view openly advocated by a recent writer, and set forth in the very plainest terms. My brother did not live to see it, but if he had, he would have recognized the fulfilment of his own prophecies as to what must be the inevitable sequel of a denial of our Lord's Resurrection.

It will be seen therefore that he was in no danger of being carried away by a 'pet theory'. Where light and definition were essential, he would sacrifice nothing of either; but he was jealous for his highest light, and felt 'that the whole effect of the Christian scheme was indefinitely heightened by keeping all other lights subordinate' — this at least was the illustration which he often used concerning it. But as there were limits to the value of light and 'finding' — limits which had been far exceeded, with the result of an unnatural forcing of the lights, and an effect of garishness and unreality — so there were limits to the as yet unrecognized preciousness of 'losing' and obscurity; these limits he placed at the objectivity of our Lord's Resurrection and Ascension. Let there be light enough to show these things, and the rest would gain by being in half-tone and shadow.

His facility of illustration was simply marvellous. From his conversation any one would have thought that he was acquainted with all manner of arts and sciences of which he knew little or nothing. It is true, as has been said already, that he had had some practice in the art of painting, and was an enthusiastic admirer of the masterpieces of Raphael, Titian, Guido, Domenichino and others; but he could never have been called a painter; for music he had considerable feeling; I think he must have known thorough-bass, but it was hard to say what he did or did not know. Of science he was almost entirely ignorant, yet he had assimilated a quantity of stray facts, and whatever he assimilated seemed to agree with him and nourish his mental being. But though his acquaintance with any one art or science must be allowed to have been superficial only, he had an astonishing perception of the relative bearings of facts which seemed at first sight to be quite beyond the range of one another, and of the relations between the sciences generally; it was this which gave him his felicity and fecundity of illustration — a gift which he never abused. He delighted in its use for the purpose of carrying a clear impression of his meaning to the mind of another, but I never remember to have heard him mistake illustration for argument, nor endeavour to mislead an adversary by a fascinating but irrelevant simile. The subtlety of his mind was a more serious source of danger to him, though I do not know that he greatly lost by it in comparison with what he gained; his sense, however, of distinctions was so fine that it would sometimes distract his attention from points of infinitely greater importance in connection with his subject than the particular distinction which he was trying to establish at the moment.

The reader may be glad to know what my brother felt about retaining the unhistoric passages of Scripture. Would he wish to see them sought for and sifted out? Or, again, what would he propose concerning such of the parables as are acknowledged by every liberal Churchman to be immoral, as, for instance, the story of Dives and Lazarus and the Unjust Steward — parables which can never have been spoken by our Lord, at any rate not in their present shape? And here we have a remarkable instance of his moderation and truly English good sense. 'Do not touch one word of them,' was his often-repeated exclamation. 'If not directly inspired by the mouth of God they have been indirectly inspired by the force of events, and the force of events is the power and manifestation of God; they could not have been allowed to come into their present position if they had not been recognized in the counsels of the Almighty as being of indirect service to mankind; there is a subjective truth conveyed even by these parables to the minds of many, that enables them to lay hold of other and objective truths which they could not else have grasped.

'There can be no question that the communistic utterances of the third gospel, as distinguished from St. Matthew's more spiritual and doubtless more historic rendering of the same teaching, have been of inestimable service to Christianity. Christ is not for the whole only, but also for them that are sick, for the ill-instructed and what we are pleased to call "dangerous" classes, as well as for the more sober thinkers. To how many do the words, "Blessed be ye poor: for your's is the kingdom of Heaven" (Luke vi, 20), carry a comfort which could never be given by the "Blessed are the poor in spirit" of Matthew v, 3. In Matthew we find, "Blessed are the poor in spirit: for their's is the kingdom of Heaven. Blessed are they that mourn: for they shall be comforted. Blessed are the meek: for they shall inherit the earth. Blessed are they which do hunger and thirst after righteousness: for they shall be filled. Blessed are the merciful: for they shall obtain mercy. Blessed are the pure in heart: for they shall see God. Blessed are the peacemakers: for they shall be called the children of God. Blessed are they which are persecuted for righteousness' sake: for their's is the kingdom of heaven. Blessed are ye, when men shall revile you, and persecute you, and shall say all manner of evil against you falsely, for my sake. Rejoice, and be exceeding glad: for great is your reward in heaven: for so persecuted they the prophets which were before you." In Luke we read, "Blessed are ye that hunger now: for ye shall be filled. Blessed are ye that weep now: for ye shall laugh . . . But woe unto you that are rich! for ye have received your consolation. Woe unto you that are full! for ye shall hunger. Woe unto you that laugh now! for ye shall mourn and weep. Woe unto you, when all men shall speak well of you! for so did *their* fathers to the false prophets," where even the grammar of the last sentence, independently of the substance, is such as it is impossible to ascribe to our Lord himself.

'The "upper" classes naturally turn to the version of Matthew, but the "lower", no less naturally to that of Luke, nor is it likely that the ideal of Christ would be one-tenth part so dear to them had not this provision for them been made, not by the direct teaching of the Saviour, but by the indirect inspiration of such events as were seen by the Almighty to be necessary for the full development of the highest ideal of which mankind was capable. All that we have in the New Testament is the inspired word, directly or indirectly, of God, the unhistoric no less than the historic; it is for us to take spiritual sustenance from whatever meats we find prepared for us not to order the removal of this or that dish; the coarser meats are for the coarser natures; as they grow in grace they will turn from these to the finer: let us ourselves partake of that which we find best suited to us, but do not let us grudge to others the provision that God has set before them. There are many things which though not objectively true are nevertheless subjectively true to those who can receive them; and subjective truth is universally felt to be even higher than objective, as may be shown by the acknowledged duty of obeying our consciences (which is the right *to us*) rather than any dictate of man however much more objectively true. It is that which is true *to us* that we are bound each one of us to seek and follow.'

Having heard him thus far, and being unable to understand, much less to sympathize with teaching so utterly foreign to anything which I had heard elsewhere, I said to him, 'Either our Lord did say the words assigned to him by St. Luke or he did not. If he did, as they stand they are bad, and anyone who heard them for the first time would say that they were bad; if he did not, then we ought not to allow them to remain in our Bibles to the misleading of people who will thus believe that God is telling them what he never did tell them — to the misleading of the poor, whom even in low self-interest we are bound to instruct as fully and truthfully as we can.'

He smiled and answered, 'That is the Peter Bell view of the matter. I thought so once, as indeed, no one can know better than yourself.'

The expression upon his face as he said this was sufficient to show the clearness of his present perception, nevertheless I was anxious to get to the root of the matter, and said that if our Lord never uttered these words their being attributed to him must be due to fraud: to pious fraud, but still to fraud.

'Not so,' he answered, 'it is due to the weakness of man's powers of memory and communication, and perhaps in some measure to unconscious inspiration. Moreover, even though wrong of some sort may have had its share in the origin of certain of the sayings ascribed to our Saviour, yet their removal now that they have been consecrated by time would be a still greater wrong. Would you defend the spoliation of the monasteries, or the confiscation of the abbey lands? I take it no — still less would you restore the monasteries or take back the lands; a consecrated change becomes a new departure; accept it and turn it to the best advantage. These are things to which the theory of the Church concerning lay baptism is strictly applicable. *Fieri non debet, factum valet.* If in our narrow and unsympathetic strivings after precision we should remove the hallowed imperfections whereby time has set the glory of his seal upon the gospels as well as upon all other aged things, not for twenty generations will they resume that ineffable and inviolable aspect which our fussy meddlesomeness will have disturbed. Let them alone. It is as they stand that they have saved the world.

'No change is good unless it is imperatively called for. Not even the Reformation was good; it is good now; I acquiesce in it, as I do in anything which in itself not vital has received the sanction of many generations of my countrymen. It is sanction which sanctifieth in matters of this kind. I would no more undo the Reformation now than I would have helped it forward in the sixteenth century. Leave the historic, the unhistoric, and the doubtful to grow together until the

339

harvest: that which is not vital will perish and rot unnoticed when it has ceased to have vitality; it is living till it has done this. Note how the very passages which you would condemn have died out of the regard of any but the poor. Who quotes them? Who appeals to them? Who believes in them? Who indeed except the poorest of the poor attaches the smallest weight to them whatever? To us they are dead, and other passages will die to us in like manner, noiselessly and almost imperceptibly, as the services for the fifth of November died out of the Prayer Book. One day the fruit will be hanging upon the tree, as it has hung for months, the next it will be lying upon the ground. It is not ripe until it has fallen of itself, or with the gentlest shaking; use no violence towards it, confident that you cannot hurry the ripening, and that if shaken down unripe the fruit will be worthless. Christianity must have contained the seeds of growth within itself, even to the shedding of many of its present dogmas. If the dogmas fall quietly in their maturity, the precious seed of truth (which will be found in the heart of every dogma that has been able to take living hold upon the world's imagination) will quicken and spring up in its own time: strike at the fruit too soon and the seed will die.'

I should be sorry to convey an impression that I am responsible for, or that I entirely agree with, the defence of the unhistoric which I have here recorded. I have given it in my capacity of editor and in some sort biographer, but am far from being prepared to maintain that it is likely, or indeed ought, to meet with the approval of any considerable number of Christians. But, surely, in these days of self-mystification it is refreshing to see the boldness with which my brother thought, and the freedom with which he contemplated all sorts of issues which are too generally avoided. What temptation would have been felt by many to soften down the inconsistencies and contradictions of the Gospels. How few are those who will venture to follow the lead of scientific criticism, and admit what every scholar must well know to be indisputable. Yet if a man will not do this, he shows that he has greater faith in falsehood than in truth.

CHAPTER THREE

ON my brother's death I came into possession of several of his early commonplace books filled with sketches for articles; some of these are more developed than others, but they are all of them fragmentary. I do not think that the reader will fail to be interested with the insight into my brother's spiritual and intellectual progress which a few extracts from these writings will afford, and have therefore, after some hesitation, decided in favour of making them public, though well aware that my brother would never have done so. They are too exaggerated to be dangerous, being so obviously unfair as to carry their own antidote. The reader will not fail to notice the growth not only in thought but also in literary style which is displayed by my brother's later writings.

In reference to the very subject of the parables above alluded to, he had written during his time of unbelief: 'Why are we to interpret so literally all passages about the guilt of unbelief, and insist upon the historical character of every miraculous account, while we are indignant if anyone demands an equally literal rendering of the precepts concerning human conduct? He that hath two coats is not to give to him that hath none: this would be "visionary", "utopian", "wholly unpractical", and so forth. Or, again, he that is smitten on the one cheek is not to turn the other to the smiter, but to hand the offender over to the law; nor are the commands relative to indifference as to the morrow and a neglect of ordinary prudence to be taken as they stand; nor yet the warnings against praying in public; nor can the parables, any one of them, be interpreted strictly with advantage to human welfare, except perhaps that of the Good Samaritan; nor the Sermon on the Mount, save in such passages as were already the common property of mankind before the coming of Christ. The parables which everyone praises are in reality very bad: the Unjust Steward, the Labourers in the Vineyard, the Prodigal Son, Dives and Lazarus, the Sower and the Seed, the Wise and Foolish Virgins, the Marriage Garment, the Man who planted a Vineyard, are all either grossly immoral, or tend to engender a very low estimate of the character of God — an estimate far below the standard of the best earthly kings; where they are not immoral, or do not tend to degrade the character of God, they are the merest commonplaces imaginable, such as one is astonished to see people accept as having been first taught by Christ. Such maxims as those

341

which inculcate conciliation and a forgiveness of injuries (wherever practicable) are certainly good, but the world does not owe their discovery to Christ, and they have had little place in the practice of his followers.

'It is impossible to say that as a matter of fact the English people forgive their enemies more freely now than the Romans did, we will say in the time of Augustus. The value of generosity and magnanimity was perfectly well known among the ancients, nor do these qualities assume any nobler guise in the teaching of Christ than they did in that of the ancient heathen philosophers. On the contrary, they have no direct equivalent in Christian thought or phraseology. They are heathen words drawn from a heathen language, and instinct with the same heathen ideas of high spirit and good birth as belonged to them in the Latin language; they are no part or parcel of Christianity, and are not only independent of it, but savour distinctly of the flesh as opposed to the spirit, and are hence more or less antagonistic to it, until they have undergone a certain modification and transformation — until, that is to say, they have been mulcted of their more frank and genial elements. The nearest approach to them in Christian phrase is "self-denial", but the sound of this word kindles no smile of pleasure like that kindled by the ideas of generosity and nobility of conduct. At the thought of self-denial we feel good, but uncomfortable, and as though on the point of performing some disagreeable duty which we think we ought to pretend to like, but which we do not like. At the thought of generosity, we feel as one who is going to share in a delightfully exhilarating but arduous pastime — full of the most pleasurable excitement. On the mention of the word generosity we feel as if we were going out hunting; at the word "self-denial", as if we were getting ready to go to church. Generosity turns well-doing into a pleasure, self-denial into a duty, as of a servant under compulsion.

'There are people who will deny this, but there are people who will deny anything. There are some who will say that St. Paul would not have condemned the Falstaff plays, *Twelfth Night*, *The Tempest*, *A Midsummer Night's Dream*, and almost everything that Shakespeare ever wrote; but there is no arguing against this. "Every man," said Dr. Johnson, "has a right to his own opinion, and everyone else has a right to knock him down for it." But even granting that generosity and high spirit have made some progress since the days of Christ, allowance must be made for the lapse of two thousand years, during which time it is only reasonable to suppose that an advance would have been made in civilization — and hence in the direction of clemency and forbearance — whether Christianity had been preached or not, but no one can show that the modern English, if superior to the ancients in these respects, show any greater superiority than may be ascribed justly to centuries of established order and good government.'

'Again, as to the ideal presented by the character of Christ, about which so much has been written; is it one which would meet with all this admiration if it were presented to us now for the first time? Surely it offers but a peevish view of life and things in comparison with that offered by other highest ideals — the old Roman and Greek ideals, the Italian ideal, and the Shakespearian ideal.'

'As with the parables so with the Sermon on the Mount — where it is not commonplace it is immoral, and vice versa; the admiration which is so freely lavished upon the teachings of Jesus Christ turns out to be but of the same kind as that bestowed upon certain modern writers, who have made great reputations by telling people what they perfectly well knew and were in no particular danger of forgetting. There is, however, this excuse for those who have been carried away with such musical but untruthful sentences as "Blessed are they that mourn: for they shall be comforted," namely, that they have not come to the subject with unbiased minds. It is one thing to see no merit in a picture, and another to see no merit in a picture when one is told that it is by Raphael; we are few of us able to stand against the *prestige* of a great name; our self-love is alarmed lest we should be deficient in taste, or, worse still, lest we should be considered to be so; as if it could matter to any right-minded person whether the world considered him to be of good taste or not, in comparison with the keeping of his own soul truthful to itself.

'But if this holds good about things which are purely matters of taste, how much more does it do so concerning those who make a distinct claim upon us for moral approbation or the reverse? Such a claim is most imperatively made by the teaching of Jesus Christ: are we then content to answer in the words of others — words to which we have no title of our own — or shall we strip ourselves of preconceived opinion, and come to the question with minds that are truly candid? Whoever shrinks from this is a liar to his own self, and as such, the worst and most dangerous of liars. He is as one who sits in an impregnable citadel and trembles in a time of peace — so great a coward as not even to feel safe when he is in his own keeping. How loose of soul if he knows that his own keeping is worthless, how aspen-hearted if he fears lest others should find him out and hurt him for communing truthfully with himself!'

'That a man should lie to others if he hopes to gain something considerable — this is reckoned cheating, robbing, fraudulent dealing, or whatever it may be; but it is an intelligible offence in comparison with the allowing oneself to be deceived. So in like manner with being bored. The man who lets himself be bored is even more contemptible than the bore. He who puts up with shoddy pictures, shoddy music, shoddy morality, shoddy society, is more despicable than he who is the prime agent in any of these things. He has less to gain, and probably deceives himself more; so that he commits the greater crime for the less reward. And I say emphatically that the morality which most men profess to hold as a Divine revelation was a shoddy morality, which would neither wash nor wear, but was woven together from a tissue of dreams and blunders, and steeped in blood more virulent than the blood of Nessus.

'Oh! if men would but leave off lying to themselves! If they would but learn the sacredness of their own likes and dislikes, and exercise their moral discrimination, making it clear to themselves what it is that they really love and venerate. There is no such enemy to mankind as moral cowardice. A downright vulgar self-interested and unblushing liar is a higher being than the moral cur whose likes and dislikes are at the beck and call of bullies that stand between him and his own soul; such a creature gives up the most sacred of all his rights for something more unsubstantial than a mess of pottage — a mental serf too abject even to know that he is being wronged. Wretched emasculator of his own reason, whose jejune timidity and want of vitality are thus omnipresent in the most secret chambers of his heart!

'We can forgive a man for almost any falsehood provided we feel that he was under strong temptation and well knew that he was deceiving. He has done wrong — still we can understand it, and he may yet have some useful stuff about him — but what can we feel towards one who for a small motive tells lies even to himself, and does not know that he is lying? What useless rotten fig-wood lumber must not such a thing be made of, and what lies will there not come out of it, falling in every direction upon all who come within its reach. The common self-deceiver of modern society is a more dangerous and contemptible object than almost any ordinary felon, a matter upon which those who do not deceive themselves need no enlightenment.'

'But why insist so strongly on the literal interpretation of one part of the sayings of Christ, and be so elastic about that of the passages which inculcate more than those ordinary precepts which all had agreed upon as early as the days of Solomon and probably earlier? We have cut down Christianity so as to make it appear to sanction our own conventions; but we have not altered our conventions so as to bring them into harmony with Christianity. We do not give to him that asketh; we take good care to avoid him; yet if the precept meant only that we should be liberal in assisting others — it wanted no enforcing: the probability is that it had been enforced too much rather than too little already; the more literally it has been followed the more terrible has the mischief been; the saying only becomes harmless when regarded as a mere convention. So with most parts of Christ's teaching. It is only conventional Christianity which will stand a man in good stead to live by; true Christianity will never do so. Men have tried it and found it fail; or, rather, its inevitable failure was so obvious that no age or country has ever been mad enough to carry it out in such a manner as would have satisfied its founders. So said Dean Swift in his *Argument against abolishing Christianity.* "I hope," he writes,

no reader imagines me so weak as to stand up in defence of real Christianity, such as used in primitive times (if we may believe the authors of those ages) to have an influence upon men's beliefs and actions. To offer at the restoring of that would be, indeed, a wild project; it would be to dig up foundations, to destroy at one blow all the wit and half the learning of the kingdom, to break the entire frame and constitution of things, to ruin trade, extinguish arts and sciences, with the professors of them; in short, to turn our courts of exchange and shops into deserts; and would be full as absurd as the proposal of Horace where he advises the Romans all in a body to leave their city, and to seek a new seat in some remote part of the world by way of cure for the corruption of their manners.

Therefore, I think this caution was in itself altogether unnecessary (which I have inserted only to prevent all possibility of cavilling), since every candid reader will easily understand my discourse to be intended only in defence of nominal Christianity, the other having been for some time wholly laid aside by general consent as utterly inconsistent with our present schemes of wealth and power.

'Yet but for these schemes of wealth and power the world would relapse into barbarianism; it is they and not Christianity which have created and preserved civilization. And what if some unhappy wretch, with a serious turn of mind and no sense of the ridiculous, takes all this talk about Christianity in sober earnest, and tries to act upon it? Into what misery may he not easily fall, and with what life-long errors may he not embitter the lives of his children!'

'Again, we do not cut off our right hand nor pluck out our eyes if they offend us; we conventionalize our interpretations of these sayings at our will and pleasure; we do take heed for the morrow, and should be inconceivably wicked and foolish were we not to do so; we do gather up riches, and indeed we do most things which the experience of mankind has taught us to be to our advantage, quite irrespectively of any precept of Christianity for or against. But why say that it is Christianity which is our chief guide, when the words of Christ point in such a very different direction from that which we have seen fit to take? Perhaps it is in order to compensate for our laxity of interpretation upon these points that we are so rigid in stickling for accuracy upon those which make no demand upon our comfort or convenience? Thus, though we conventionalize practice, we never conventionalize dogma. Here, indeed, we stickle for the letter most inflexibly; yet one would have thought that we might have had greater licence to modify the latter than the former. If we say that the teaching of Christ is not to be taken according to its import — why give it so much importance? Teaching by exaggeration is not a satisfactory method, nor one worthy of a being higher than man; it might have been well once, and in the East, but it is not well now. It induces more and more of that jarring and straining of our moral faculties, of which much is unavoidable in the existing complex condition of affairs, but of which the less the better. At present the tug of professed principles in one direction, and

346

of necessary practice in the other, causes the same sort of wear and tear in our moral gear as is caused to a steam-engine by continually reversing it when it is going it at full speed. No mechanism can stand it.'

The above extracts (written when he was about twenty-three years old) may serve to show how utter was the subversion of his faith. His mind was indeed in darkness! Who could have hoped that so brilliant a day should have succeeded to the gloom of such mistrust? Yet as upon a winter's morning in November when the sun rises red through the smoke, and presently the fog spreads its curtain of thick darkness over the city, and then there comes a single breath of wind from some more generous quarter, whereupon the blessed sun shines again, and the gloom is gone; or, again, as when the warm south-west wind comes up breathing kindness from the sea, unheralded, unsuspected, when the earth is in her saddest frost, and on the instant all the lands are thawed and opened to the genial influences of a sweet springful whisper — so thawed his heart, and the seed which had lain dormant in its fertile soil sprang up, grew, ripened and brought forth an abundant harvest.

Indeed now that the result has been made plain we can perhaps feel that his scepticism was precisely of that nature which should have given the greatest ground for hope. He was a genuine lover of truth in so far as he could see it.

His lights were dim, but such as they were he walked according to them, and hence they burnt ever more and more clearly, till in later life they served to show him what is vouchsafed to such men and to such only — the enormity of his own mistakes. Better that a man should feel the divergence between Christian theory and Christian practice, that he should be shocked at it — even to the breaking away utterly from the theory until he has arrived at a wider comprehension of its scope — than that he should be indifferent to the divergence and make no effort to bring his principles and practice into harmony with one another. A true lover of consistency, it was intolerable to him to say one thing with his lips and another with his actions. As long as this is true concerning any man, his friends may feel sure that the hand of the Lord is with him, though the signs thereof be hidden from mortal eyesight.

CHAPTER FOUR

DURING the dark and unhappy time when he had, as it seems to me, bullied himself, or been bullied into infidelity, he had been utterly unable to realize the importance even of such a self-evident fact as that our Lord addressing an Eastern people would speak in such a way as Eastern people would best understand; it took him years to appreciate this. He could not see that modes of thought are as much part of a language as the grammar and words which compose it, and that before a passage can be said to be translated from one language into another it is often not the words only which must be rendered, but the thought itself which must be transformed; to a people habituated to exaggeration a saying which was not exaggerated would have been pointless — so weak as to arrest the attention of no one; in order to translate it into such words as should carry precisely the same meaning to colder and more temperate minds, the words would often have to be left out of sight altogether, and a new sentence or perhaps even simile or metaphor substituted; this is plainly out of the question, and therefore the best course is that which has been taken, i.e. to render the words as accurately as possible, and leave the reader to modify the meaning. But it was years before my brother could be got to feel this, nor did he ever do so fully, simple and obvious though it must appear to most people, until he had learned to recognize the value of a certain amount of inaccuracy and inconsistency in everything which is not comprehended in mechanics or the exact sciences. 'It is this,' he used to say, 'which gives artistic or spiritual value as contrasted with mechanical precision.'

In inaccuracy and inconsistency, therefore (within certain limits), my brother saw the means whereby our minds are kept from regarding things as rigidly and immutably fixed which are not yet fully understood, and perhaps may never be so while we are in our present state of probation. Life is not one of the exact sciences, living is essentially an art and not a science. Everything addressed to human minds at all must be more or less of a compromise; thus, to take a very old illustration, even the definitions of a point and a line — the fundamental things in the most exact of the sciences — are mere compromises. A point is supposed to have neither length, breadth nor thickness — this in theory but in practice unless a point have a little of all these things there is nothing there. So with a line; a line is supposed to have length, but no breadth, yet in practice we never saw a line which had not breadth. What inconsistency is there here, in requiring us to conceive something which we cannot conceive, and which can have no existence, before we go on to the investigation of the laws whereby the earth can alone be measured and the orbits of the planets determined. I do not think that this illustration was presented to my brother's mind while he was young, but I am sure that if it had been it would have made him miserable. He would have had no confidence in mathematics, and would very likely have made a furious attack upon Newton and Galileo, and been firmly convinced that he was discomfiting them. Indeed I cannot forget a certain look of bewilderment which came over his face when the idea was put before him, I imagine, for the first time. Fortunately he had so grown that the right inference was now in no danger of being missed. He did not conclude that because the evidences for mathematics were founded upon compromises and definitions which are inaccurate — therefore that mathematics were false, or that there were no mathematics, but he learnt to feel that there might be other things which were no less indisputable than mathematics, and which might also be founded on facts for which the evidences were not wholly free from inconsistencies and inaccuracies.

To some he might appear to be approaching too nearly to the 'Sed tu vera puta' argument of Juvenal. I greatly fear that an attempt may be made to misrepresent him as taking this line; that is to say, as accepting Christianity on the ground of the excellence of its moral teaching, and looking upon it as, indeed, a superstition, but salutary for women and young people. Hardly anything would have shocked him more profoundly. This doctrine with its plausible show of morality appeared to him to be, perhaps, the most gross of all immoralities, inasmuch as it cuts the ground from under the feet of truth, luring the world farther and farther from the only true salvation — the careful study of facts and of the safest inferences that may be drawn from them. Every fact was to him a part of nature, a thing sacred, pregnant with Divine teaching of some sort, as being the expression of Divine will. It was through facts that he saw God; to tamper with facts was, in his view, to deface the countenance of the Almighty. To say that such and such was so and so, when the speaker did not believe it, was to lead people to worship a false God instead of a true one; an εἴδωλον; setting them, to quote the words of the Psalmist, 'a-whoring after their own imaginations'. He saw the Divine presence in everything — the evil as well as the good; the evil being the expression of the Divine will that such and such courses should not go unpunished, but bring pain and misery which should deter others from following them, and the good being his sign of approbation. There was nothing good for man to know which could not be deduced from facts. This was the only sound basis of knowledge, and to found things upon fiction which could be made to stand upon facts was to try and build upon a quicksand.

He, therefore, loathed the reasoning of Juvenal with all the intensity of his nature. It was because he believed that the Resurrection and Ascension of our Lord were just as much matters of actual history as the assassination of Julius Cæsar, and that they happened precisely in the same way as every daily event happens at present — that he accepted the Christian scheme in its essentials. Then came the details. Were these also objectively true? He answered, 'Certainly not in every case.' He would not for the world have had anyone believe that he so considered them; but having made it perfectly clear that he was not going to deceive himself, he set himself to derive whatever spiritual comfort he could from them, just as he would from any noble fiction or work of art, which, while not professing to be historical, was instinct with the soul of genius. That there were unhistorical passages in the New Testament was to him a fact; therefore it was to be studied as an expression of the Divine will. What could be the meaning of it? That we should consider them as true? Assuredly not this. Then what else? This — that we should accept as subjectively true whatever we found spiritually precious, and be at liberty to leave all the rest alone — the unhistoric element having been introduced purposely for the sake of giving greater scope and latitude to the value of the ideal.

Of course one who was so firmly persuaded of the objective truth of the Resurrection and Ascension could be in no sort of danger of relapsing into infidelity as long as his reason remained. During the years of his illness his mind was clearly impaired, and no longer under his own control; but while his senses were his own it was absolutely impossible that he could be shaken by discrepancies and inconsistencies in the gospels. What small and trifling things are such discrepancies by the side of the great central miracle of the Resurrection! Nevertheless their existence was indisputable, and was no less indisputably a cause of stumbling to many, as it had been to himself. His experience of his own sufferings as an unbeliever gave him a keener sympathy with those who were in that distressing condition than could be felt by anyone who had not so suffered, and fitted him, perhaps, more than anyone who has yet lived to be the interpreter of Christianity to the Rationalist, and of Rationalism to the Christian. This, accordingly, was the task to which he set himself, having been singularly adapted for it by Nature, and as singularly disciplined by events.

It seemed to him that the first thing was to make the two parties understand one another — a thing which had never yet been done, but which was not at all impossible. For Protestantism is raised essentially upon a Rationalistic base. When we come to a definition of Rationalism nothing can be plainer than that it demands no scepticism from anyone which an English Protestant would not approve of. It is another matter with the Church of Rome. That Church openly declares it as an axiom that religion and reason have nothing to do with one another, and that religion, though in flat contradiction to reason, should yet be accepted from the hands of a certain order as an act of unquestioning faith. The line of separation therefore between the Romanist and the Rationalist is clear, and definitely bars any possibility of arrangement between the two. Not so with the Protestant, who as heartily as the Rationalist admits that nothing is required to be believed by man except such things as can be reasonably proved — i.e. proved to the satisfaction of the reason. No Protestant would say that the Christian scheme ought to be accepted in spite of its being contrary to reason; we say that Christianity is to be believed because it can be shown to follow as the necessary consequences of using our reason rightly. We should be shocked at being supposed to maintain otherwise. Yet this is pure Rationalism. The Rationalist would require nothing more; he demurs to Christianity because he maintains that if we bring our reason to bear upon the evidences which are brought forward in support of it, we are compelled to reject it; but he would accept it without hesitation if he believed that it could be sustained by arguments which ought to carry conviction to the reason. Thus both are agreed in principle that if the evidences of Christianity satisfy human reason, then Christianity should be received, but that on any other supposition it should be rejected.

Here then, he said, we have a common starting-point and the main principle of Rationalism turns out to be nothing but what we all readily admit, and with which we and our fathers have been as familiar for centuries as with the air we breathe. Every Protestant is a

Rationalist, or else he ought to be ashamed of himself. Does he want to be called an 'Irrationalist'? Hardly — yet if he is not a Rationalist what else can he be? No: the difference between us is one of detail, not of principle. This is a great step gained.

The next thing therefore was to make each party understand the view which the other took concerning the position which they had agreed to hold in common. There was no work, so far as he knew, which would be accepted both by Christians and unbelievers as containing a fair statement of the arguments of the two contending parties; every book which he had yet seen upon either side seemed written with the view of maintaining that its own side could hold no wrong, and the other no right: neither party seemed to think that they had anything to learn from the other, and neither that any considerable addition to their knowledge of the truth was either possible or desirable. Each was in possession of truth already, and all who did not see and feel this must be either wilfully blinded, or intensely stupid, or hypocrites.

So long as people carried on a discussion thus, what agreement was possible between them? Yet where, upon the Christian side, was the attempt to grapple with the real difficulties now felt by unbelievers? Simply nowhere. All that had been done hitherto was antiquated. Modern Christianity seemed to shrink from grappling with modern Rationalism, and displayed a timidity which could not be accounted for except by the supposition of secret misgiving that certain things were being defended which could not be defended fairly. This was quite intolerable; a misgiving was a warning voice from God, which should be attended to as a man valued his soul. On the other hand, the conviction reasonably entertained by unbelievers that they were right on many not inconsiderable details of the dispute, and that so-called orthodox Christians in their hearts knew it but would not own it — or that if they did not know it, they were only in ignorance because it suited their purpose to be so — this conviction gave an overweening self-confidence to infidels, as though they must be right in the whole because they were so in part; they therefore blinded themselves to all the more fundamental arguments in support of Christianity, because certain shallow ones had been put forward in the front rank, and been far too obstinately defended. They thus regarded the question too superficially, and had erred even more through pride of intellect and conceit than their opponents through timidity.

What then was to be done? Surely this; *to explain the two contending parties to one another*; to show to Rationalists that Christians are right upon Rationalistic principles in all the more important of their allegations; that is to say, to establish the Resurrection and Ascension of the Redeemer upon a basis which should satisfy the most imperious demands of modern criticism. This would form the first and most important part of the task. Then should follow a no less convincing proof that Rationalists are right in demurring to the historical accuracy of much which has been too obstinately defended by so-called orthodox writers. This would be the second part. Was there not reason to hope that when this was done the two parties might understand one another, and meet in a common Christianity? He believed that there was, and that the ground had been already cleared for such mutual compromise as might be accepted by both sides, not from policy but conviction. Therefore he began writing the book which it has devolved upon myself to edit, and which must now speak for itself. For him it was to suffer and to labour; almost on the very instant of his having done enough to express his meaning he was removed from all further power of usefulness.

The happy change from unbelief to faith had already taken place some three or four years before my return from America. With it had also come that sudden development of intellectual and spiritual power which so greatly astonished even those who had known him best. The whole man seemed changed — to have become possessed of an unusually capacious mind, instead of one which was acute, but acute only. On looking over the earlier letters which I received from him when I was in America, I can hardly believe that they should have been written by the same person as the one to whom, in spite of not a few great mental defects, I afterwards owed more spiritual enrichment than I have owed to any other person. Yet so it was. It came upon me imperceptibly that I had been very stupid in not discovering that my brother was a genius; but hardly had I made the discovery, and hardly had the fragment which follows this memoir received its present shape, when his overworked brain gave way and he fell into a state little better than idiocy. His originally cheerful spirits left him, and were succeeded by a religious melancholy which nothing could disturb. He became incapable either of mental or physical exertion, and was pronounced by the best physicians to be suffering from some obscure disease of the brain brought on by excitement and undue mental tension: in this state he continued for about four years, and died peacefully, but still as one in the profoundest melancholy, on March 15th, 1872, aged 40.

Always hopeful that his health would one day be restored, I never ventured to propose that I should edit his book during his own life-time. On his death I found his papers in the most deplorable confusion. The following chapters had alone received anything like a presentable shape — and these providentially are the most essential.

A dream is a dream only, yet sometimes there follows a fulfilment which bears a strange resemblance to the thing dreamt of. No one now believes that the Book of Revelation is to be taken as foretelling events which will happen in the same way as the massacre, for instance, of St. Bartholomew, indeed it is doubtful how far the whole is not to be interpreted as an allegory, descriptive of spiritual revolutions; yet surely my mother's dream as to the future of one, at least, of her sons has been strangely verified, and it is believed that the reader when he lays down this volume will feel that there have been few more potent witnesses to the truth of Christ than John Pickard Owen.

THE HUMOUR OF HOMER

AND OTHER ESSAYS

EDITOR'S PREFACE

'THE Deadlock in Darwinism' was first published in April, May and June, 1890, in three consecutive issues of the *Universal Review*. It was re-published, together with other contributions of Butler's to the same journal, in 1908, in a volume entitled *Essays on Life, Art and Science*, and was later re-issued in another volume of collected essays, entitled *The Humour of Homer and Other Essays*, edited by Mr. R. A. Streatfield in 1913. I have included it here because, in face of the sheer impracticability of giving a fair view of Butler's attitude on evolution by means of selections from his four substantial volumes on the subject, it seems to me to give, better than anything else I can find, a general impression of what he was driving at. This impression is necessarily lop-sided, and in particular fails to represent adequately Butler's view of the function of unconscious memory on the lives of succeeding generations. But it is the best I can manage, unless I am to reconcile myself to leaving out altogether a vital part of Butler's mind and of the notions about heredity which lie at the back of *The Way of All Flesh*; and that I positively cannot bring myself to do.

THE DEADLOCK IN DARWINISM

IT will be readily admitted that of all living writers Mr. Alfred Russel Wallace is the one the peculiar turn of whose mind best fits him to write on the subject of natural selection, or the accumulation of fortunate but accidental variations through descent and the struggle for existence. His mind in all its more essential characteristics closely resembles that of the late Mr. Charles Darwin himself, and it is no doubt due to this fact that he and Mr. Darwin elaborated their famous theory at the same time, and independently of one another. I shall have occasion in the course of the following article to show how misled and misleading both these distinguished men have been, in spite of their unquestionable familiarity with the whole range of animal and vegetable phenomena. I believe it will be more respectful to both of them to do this in the most outspoken way. I believe their work to have been as mischievous as it has been valuable, and as valuable as it has been mischievous; and higher, whether praise or blame, I know not how to give. Nevertheless I would in the outset, and with the utmost sincerity, admit concerning Messrs. Wallace and Darwin that neither can be held as the more profound and conscientious thinker; neither can be put forward as the more ready to acknowledge obligation to the great writers on evolution who had preceded him, or to place his own developments in closer and more conspicuous historical connection with earlier thought upon the subject; neither is the more ready to welcome criticism and to state his opponent's case in the most pointed and telling way in which it can be put; neither is the more quick to encourage new truth; neither is the more genial, generous adversary, or has the profounder horror of anything even approaching literary or scientific want of candour; both display the same inimitable power of putting their opinions forward in the way that shall best ensure their acceptance; both are equally unrivalled in the tact that tells them when silence will be golden, and when on the other hand a whole volume of facts may be advantageously brought forward. Less than the foregoing tribute both to Messrs. Darwin and Wallace I will not, and more I cannot pay.

Let us now turn to the most authoritative exponent of latter-day evolution — I mean to Mr. Wallace, whose work, entitled *Darwinism*, though it should have been entitled *Wallaceism*, is still so far Darwinistic that it develops the teaching of Mr. Darwin in the direction given to it by Mr. Darwin himself — so far, indeed, as this can be ascertained at all — and not in that of Lamarck. Mr. Wallace tells us, on the first page of his preface, that he has no intention of dealing even in outline with the vast subject of evolution in general, and has only tried to give such an account of the theory of natural selection as may facilitate a clear conception of Darwin's work. How far he has succeeded is a point on which opinion will probably be divided. Those who find Mr. Darwin's works clear will also find no difficulty in understanding Mr. Wallace; those, on the other hand, who find Mr. Darwin puzzling are little likely to be less puzzled by Mr. Wallace. He continues:

'The objections now made to Darwin's theory apply solely to the particular means by which the change of species has been brought about, not to the fact of that change.'

But 'Darwin's theory' — as Mr. Wallace has elsewhere proved that he understands — has no reference 'to the fact of that change' — that is to say, to the fact that species have been modified in course of descent from other species. This is no more Mr. Darwin's theory than it is the reader's or my own. Darwin's theory is concerned only with 'the particular means by which the change of species has been brought about'; his contention being that this is mainly due to the natural survival of those individuals that have happened by some accident to be born most favourably adapted to their surroundings, or, in other words, through accumulation in the common course of nature of the more lucky variations that chance occasionally purveys. Mr. Wallace's words, then, in reality amount to this, that the objections now made to Darwin's theory apply solely to Darwin's theory, which is all very well as far as it goes, but might have been more easily apprehended if he had simply said, 'There are several objections now made to Mr. Darwin's theory.'

It must be remembered that the passage quoted above occurs on the first page of a preface dated March 1889, when the writer had completed his task, and was most fully conversant with his subject. Nevertheless, it seems indisputable either that he is still confusing evolution with Mr. Darwin's theory, or that he does not know when his sentences have point and when they have none.

I should perhaps explain to some readers that Mr. Darwin did not modify the main theory put forward, first by Buffon, to whom it indisputably belongs, and adopted from him by Erasmus Darwin, Lamarck and many other writers in the latter half of the eighteenth century and the earlier years of the nineteenth. The early evolutionists maintained that all existing forms of animal and vegetable life, including man, were derived in course of descent with modification from forms resembling the lowest now known.

Mr. Darwin went as far as this, and farther no one can go. The point at issue between him and his predecessors involves neither the main fact of evolution, nor yet the geometrical ratio of increase, and the struggle for existence consequent thereon. Messrs. Darwin and Wallace have each thrown invaluable light upon these last two points, but Buffon, as early as 1756, had made them the keystone of his system. 'The movement of nature,' he then wrote, 'turns on two immovable pivots: one, the illimitable fecundity which she has given to all species: the other, the innumerable difficulties which reduce the results of that fecundity.' Erasmus Darwin and Lamarck followed in the same sense. They thus admit the survival of the fittest as fully as Mr. Darwin himself, though they do not make use of this particular expression. The dispute turns not upon natural selection, which is common to all writers on evolution, but upon the nature and causes of the variations that are supposed to be selected from and thus accumulated. Are these mainly attributable to the inherited effects of use and disuse, supplemented by occasional sports and happy accidents? Or are they mainly due to sports and happy accidents, supplemented by occasional inherited effects of use and disuse?

The Lamarckian system has all along been maintained by Mr. Herbert Spencer, who, in his *Principles of Biology*, published in 1865, showed how impossible it was that accidental variations should accumulate at all. I am not sure how far Mr. Spencer would consent to being called a Lamarckian pure and simple, nor yet how far it is strictly accurate to call him one; nevertheless, I can see no important difference in the main positions taken by him and by Lamarck.

The question at issue between the Lamarckians, supported by Mr. Spencer and a growing band of those who have risen in rebellion against the Charles Darwinian system on the one hand, and Messrs. Darwin and Wallace with the greater number of our more prominent biologists on the other, involves the very existence of evolution as a workable theory. For it is plain that what Nature can be supposed able to do by way of choice must depend on the supply of the variations from which she is supposed to choose. She cannot take what is not offered to her; and so again she cannot be supposed able to accumulate unless what is gained in one direction in one generation, or series of generations, is little likely to be lost in those that presently succeed. Now variations ascribed mainly to use and disuse can be supposed capable of being accumulated, for use and disuse are fairly constant for long periods among the individuals of the same species, and often over large areas; moreover, conditions of existence involving changes of habit, and thus of organization, come for the most part gradually; so that time is given during which the organism can endeavour to adapt itself in the requisite respects, instead of being shocked out of existence by too sudden change. Variations, on the other hand, that are ascribed to mere chance cannot be supposed as likely to be accumulated, for chance is notoriously inconstant, and would not purvey the variations in sufficiently unbroken succession, or in a sufficient number of individuals, modified similarly in all the necessary correlations at the same time and place to admit of their being accumulated. It is vital therefore to the theory of evolution, as was early pointed out by the late Professor Fleeming Jenkin and by Mr. Herbert Spencer, that variations should be supposed to have a definite and persistent principle underlying them, which shall tend to engender similar and simul-taneous modification, however small, in the vast majority of individuals composing any species. The existence of such a principle and its per-manence is the only thing that can be supposed capable of acting as rudder and compass to the accumulation of variations, and of making it hold steadily on one course for each species, till eventually many havens, far remote from one another, are safely reached.

It is obvious that the having fatally impaired the theory of his predecessors could not warrant Mr. Darwin in claiming, as he most fatuously did, the theory of evolution. That he is still generally believed to have been the originator of this theory is due to the fact that he claimed it, and that a powerful literary backing at once came for-ward to support him. It seems at first sight improbable that those who too zealously urged his claims were unaware that so much had been written on the subject, but when we find even Mr. Wallace himself as profoundly ignorant on this subject as he still either is, or affects to be, there is no limit assignable to the ignorance or affected ignorance of the kind of biologists who would write reviews in leading journals thirty years ago. Mr. Wallace writes:

'A few great naturalists, struck by the very slight difference between many of these species, and the numerous links that exist between the most different forms of animals and plants, and also observing that a great many species do vary considerably in their forms, colours and habits, conceived the idea that they might be all produced one from the other. The most eminent of these writers was a great French naturalist, Lamarck, who published an elaborate work, the *Philosophie Zoologique*, in which he endeavoured to prove that all animals whatever are descended from other species of animals. He attributed the change of species chiefly to the effect of changes in the conditions of life — such as climate, food, etc.; and especially to the desires and efforts of the animals themselves to improve their condition, leading to a modification of form or size in certain parts, owing to the well-known physiological law that all organs are strengthened by constant use, while they are weakened or even completely lost by disuse. . . .

'The only other important work dealing with the question was the celebrated *Vestiges of Creation*, published anonymously, but now acknowledged to have been written by the late Robert Chambers.'

None are so blind as those who will not see, and it would be waste of time to argue with the invincible ignorance of one who thinks Lamarck and Buffon conceived that all species were produced from one another, more especially as I have already dealt at some length with the early evolutionists in my work *Evolution, Old and New*, first published ten years ago, and not, so far as I am aware, detected in serious error or omission. If, however, Mr. Wallace still thinks it safe to presume so far on the ignorance of his readers as to say that the only two important works on evolution before Mr. Darwin's were Lamarck's *Philosophie Zoologique* and the *Vestiges of Creation*, how fathomable is the ignorance of the average reviewer likely to have been thirty years ago, when the *Origin of Species* was first published? Mr. Darwin claimed evolution as his own theory. Of course, he would not claim it if he had no right to it. Then by all means give him the credit of it. This was the most natural view to take, and it was generally taken. It was not, moreover, surprising that people failed to appreciate all the niceties of Mr. Darwin's 'distinctive feature' which, whether distinctive or no, was assuredly not distinct, and was never frankly contrasted with the older view, as it would have been by one who wished it to be understood and judged upon its merits. It was in consequence of this omission that people failed to note how fast and loose Mr. Darwin played with his distinctive feature, and how readily he dropped it on occasion.

It may be said that the question of what was thought by the predecessors of Mr. Darwin is, after all, personal, and of no interest to the general public, comparable to that of the main issue — whether we are to accept evolution or not. Granted that Buffon, Erasmus Darwin and Lamarck bore the burden and heat of the day before Mr. Charles Darwin was born, they did not bring people round to their opinion, whereas Mr. Darwin and Mr. Wallace did, and the public cannot be expected to look beyond this broad and indisputable fact.

The answer to this is, that the theory which Messrs. Darwin and Wallace have persuaded the public to accept is demonstrably false, and that the opponents of evolution are certain in the end to triumph over it. Paley, in his *Natural Theology*, long since brought forward far too much evidence of design in animal organization to allow of our setting down its marvels to the accumulation of fortunate accident, undirected by will, effort and intelligence. Those who examine the main facts of animal and vegetable organization without bias will, no doubt, ere long conclude that all animals and vegetables are derived ultimately from unicellular organisms, but they will not less readily perceive that the evolution of species without the concomitance and direction of mind and effort is as inconceivable as is the independent creation of every individual species. The two facts, evolution and design, are equally patent to plain people. There is no escaping from either. According to Messrs. Darwin and Wallace, we may have evolution, but are on no account to have it as mainly due to intelligent effort, guided by ever higher and higher range of sensations, perceptions and ideas. We are to set it down to the shuffling of cards, or the throwing of dice without the play, and this will never stand.

According to the older men, cards did indeed count for much, but play counted for more. They denied the teleology of the time — that is to say, the teleology that saw all adaptation to surroundings as part of a plan devised long ages since by a quasi-anthropomorphic being who schemed everything out much as a man would do, but on an infinitely vaster scale. This conception they found repugnant alike to intelligence and conscience, but, though they do not seem to have perceived it, they left the door open for a design more true and more demonstrable than that which they excluded. By making their variations mainly due to effort and intelligence, they made organic development run on all-fours with human progress, and with inventions which we have watched growing up from small beginnings. They made the development of man from the amœba part and parcel of the story that may be read, though on an infinitely smaller scale, in the development of our most powerful marine engines from the common kettle, or of our finest microscopes from the dew-drop.

The development of the steam-engine and the microscope is due to intelligence and design, which did indeed utilize chance suggestions, but which improved on these, and directed each step of their accumulation, though never foreseeing more than a step or two ahead, and often not so much as this. The fact, as I have elsewhere urged, that the man who made the first kettle did not foresee the engines of the *Great Eastern*, or that he who first noted the magnifying power of the dew-drop had no conception of our present microscopes — the very limited amount, in fact, of design and intelligence that was called into play at any one point — this does not make us deny that the steam-engine and microscope owe their development to design. If each step of the road was designed, the whole journey was designed, though the particular end was not designed when the journey was begun. And so is it, according to the older view of evolution, with the development of those living organs, or machines, that are born with us, as part of the perambulating carpenter's chest we call our bodies. The older view gives us our design, and gives us our evolution too. If it refuses to see a quasi-anthropomorphic God modelling each species from without as a potter models clay, it gives us God as vivifying and indwelling in all His creatures — He in them, and they in Him. If it refuses to see God outside the universe, it equally refuses to see any part of the universe as outside God. If it makes the universe the body of God, it also makes God the soul of the universe. The question at issue, then, between the Darwinism of Erasmus Darwin and the neo-Darwinism of his grandson, is not a personal one, nor anything like a personal one. It not only involves the existence of evolution, but it affects the view we take of life and things in an endless variety of most interesting and important ways. It is imperative, therefore, on those who take any interest in these matters, to place side by side in the clearest contrast the views of those who refer the evolution of species mainly to accumulation of variations that have no other inception than chance, and of that older school which makes design perceive and develop still further the goods that chance provides.

But over and above this, which would be in itself sufficient, the historical mode of studying any question is the only one which will enable us to comprehend it effectually. The personal element cannot be eliminated from the consideration of works written by living persons for living persons. We want to know who is who — whom we can depend upon to have no other end than the making things clear to himself and his readers, and whom we should mistrust as having an ulterior aim on which he is more intent than on the furthering of our better understanding. We want to know who is doing his best to help us, and who is only trying to make us help him, or to bolster up the system in which his interests are vested. There is nothing that will throw more light upon these points than the way in which a man behaves towards those who have worked in the same field with himself, and, again, than his style. A man's style, as Buffon long since said, is the man himself. By style, I do not, of course, mean grammar or rhetoric, but that style of which Buffon again said that it is like happiness, and *vient de la douceur de l'âme*. When we find a man concealing worse than nullity of meaning under sentences that sound plausibly enough, we should distrust him much as we should a fellow-traveller whom we caught trying to steal our watch. We often cannot judge of the truth or falsehood of facts for ourselves, but we most of us know enough of human nature to be able to tell a good witness from a bad one.

However this may be, and whatever we may think of judging systems by the directness or indirectness of those who advance them, biologists, having committed themselves too rashly, would have been more than human if they had not shown some pique towards those who dared to say, first, that the theory of Messrs. Darwin and Wallace was unworkable; and secondly, that even though it were workable it would not justify either of them in claiming evolution. When biologists show pique at all they generally show a good deal of pique, but pique or no pique, they shunned Mr. Spencer's objection above referred to with a persistency more unanimous and obstinate than I ever remember to have seen displayed even by professional truth-seekers. I find no rejoinder to it from Mr. Darwin himself, between 1865 when it was first put forward, and 1882 when Mr. Darwin died. It has been similarly 'ostrichized' by all the leading apologists of Darwinism, so far at least as I have been able to observe, and I have followed the matter closely for many years. Mr. Spencer has repeated and amplified it in his recent work *The Factors of Organic Evolution*, but it still remains without so much as an attempt at serious answer, for the perfunctory and illusory remarks of Mr. Wallace at the end of his *Darwinism* cannot be counted as such. The best proof of its irresistible weight is that Mr. Darwin, though maintaining silence in respect to it, retreated from his original position in the direction that would most obviate Mr. Spencer's objection.

Yet this objection has been repeatedly urged by the more prominent anti-Charles Darwinian authorities, and there is no sign that the British public is becoming less rigorous in requiring people either to reply to objection repeatedly urged by men of even moderate weight, or to let judgment go by default. As regards Mr. Darwin's claim to the theory of evolution generally, Darwinians are beginning now to perceive that this cannot be admitted, and either say with some hardihood that Mr. Darwin never claimed it, or after a few saving clauses to the effect that this theory refers only to the particular means by which evolution has been brought about, imply forthwith thereafter none the less that evolution is Mr. Darwin's theory. Mr. Wallace has done this repeatedly in his recent *Darwinism*. Indeed, I should be by no means sure that on the first page of his preface, in the passage about 'Darwin's theory', which I have already somewhat severely criticized, he was not intending evolution by 'Darwin's theory', if in his preceding paragraph he had not so clearly shown that he knew evolution to be a theory of greatly older date than Mr. Darwin's.

The history of science — well exemplified by that of the development theory — is the history of eminent men who have fought against light and have been worsted. The tenacity with which Darwinians stick to their accumulation of fortuitous variations is on a par with the like tenacity shown by the illustrious Cuvier, who did his best to crush evolution altogether. It always has been thus, and always will be; nor is it desirable in the interests of Truth herself that it should be otherwise. Truth is like money — lightly come, lightly go; and if she cannot hold her own against even gross misrepresentation, she is herself not worth holding. Misrepresentation in the long run makes Truth as much as it mars her; hence our law courts do not think it desirable that pleaders should speak their *bona fide* opinions, much less that they should profess to do so. Rather let each side hoodwink judge and jury as best it can, and let truth flash out from collision of defence and accusation. When either side will not collide, it is an axiom of controversy that it desires to prevent the truth from being elicited.

Let us now note the courses forced upon biologists by the difficulties of Mr. Darwin's distinctive feature. Mr. Darwin and Mr. Wallace, as is well known, brought the feature forward simultaneously and independently of one another, but Mr. Wallace always believed in it more firmly than Mr. Darwin did. Mr. Darwin as a young man did not believe in it. He wrote before 1839, 'Nature, by making habit omnipotent and its effects hereditary, has fitted the Fuegian for the climate and productions of his country,'[1] a sentence than which nothing can coincide more fully with the older view that use and disuse were the main purveyors of variations, or conflict more fatally with his own subsequent distinctive feature   Moreover, as I showed in my last work on evolution,[2] in the peroration to his *Origin of Species*, he discarded his accidental variations altogether, and fell back on the older theory, so that the body of the *Origin of Species* supports one theory, and the peroration another that differs from it *toto cœlo*. Finally, in his later editions, he retreated indefinitely from his original position, edging always more and more continually towards the theory of his grandfather and Lamarck. These facts convince me that he was at no time a thoroughgoing Darwinian, but was throughout an unconscious Lamarckian, though ever anxious to conceal the fact alike from himself and from his readers.

Not so with Mr. Wallace, who was both more outspoken in the first instance, and who has persevered along the path of Wallaceism just as Mr. Darwin with greater sagacity was ever on the retreat from Darwinism. Mr. Wallace's profounder faith led him in the outset to place his theory in fuller daylight than Mr. Darwin was inclined to do. Mr. Darwin just waved Lamarck aside, and said as little about him as he could, while in his earlier editions Erasmus Darwin and Buffon were not so much as named. Mr. Wallace, on the contrary, at once raised the Lamarckian spectre, and declared it exorcized. He said the Lamarckian hypothesis was 'quite unnecessary'. The giraffe did not 'acquire its long neck by desiring to reach the foliage of the more lofty shrubs, and constantly stretching its neck for this purpose, but because any varieties which occurred among its antitypes with a longer neck than

[1] *Voyages of the 'Adventure' and 'Beagle'*, iii, p. 237.
[2] *Luck or Cunning*, pp. 170, 180.

usual at once secured a fresh range of pasture over the same ground
as their shorter-necked companions, and on the first scarcity of food
were thus enabled to outlive them.'[1]

'Which occurred' is evidently 'which happened to occur' by some
chance of accident unconnected with use and disuse. The word
'accident' is never used, but Mr. Wallace must be credited with this
instance of a desire to give his readers a chance of perceiving that
according to his distinctive feature evolution is an affair of luck, rather
than of cunning. Whether his readers actually did understand this as
clearly as Mr. Wallace doubtless desired that they should, and whether
greater development at this point would not have helped them to fuller
apprehension, we need not now inquire. What was gained in distinctness might have been lost in distinctiveness, and after all he did
technically put us upon our guard.

Nevertheless, he too at a pinch takes refuge in Lamarckism. In
relation to the manner in which the eyes of soles, turbots, and other
flat-fish travel round the head so as to become in the end unsym-
metrically placed, he says:

'The eyes of these fish are curiously distorted in order that both eyes
may be upon the upper side, where alone they would be of any use . . .
Now if we suppose this process, which in the young is completed in a
few days or weeks, to have been spread over thousands of generations
during the development of these fish, those usually surviving *whose
eyes retained more and more of the position into which the young fish tried to
twist them* [italics mine], the change becomes intelligible.'[2] When it
was said by Professor Ray Lankester — who knows as well as most
people what Lamarck taught — that this was 'flat Lamarckism', Mr.
Wallace rejoined that it was the survival of the modified individuals
that did it all, not the efforts of the young fish to twist their eyes, and
the transmission to descendants of the effects of those efforts. But this,
as I said in my book *Evolution, Old and New*, is like saying that horses
are swift runners, not by reason of the causes, whatever they were,
that occasioned the direct line of their progenitors to vary towards ever
greater and greater swiftness, but because their more slow-going uncles
and aunts go away. Plain people will prefer to say that the main cause
of any accumulation of favourable modifications consists rather in that
which brings about the initial variations, and in the fact that these can

[1] *Journals of the Proceedings of the Linnean Society* (*Zoology*, vol. III), 1859, p. 62.
[2] *Darwinism* (Macmillan, 1889), p. 129.

be inherited at all, than in the fact that the unmodified individuals were not successful. People do not become rich because the poor in large numbers go away, but because they have been lucky, or provident, or more commonly both. If they would keep their wealth when they have made it they must exclude luck thenceforth to the utmost of their power and their children must follow their example, or they will soon lose their money. The fact that the weaker go to the wall does not bring about the greater strength of the stronger; it is the consequence of this last and not the cause — unless, indeed, it be contended that a knowledge that the weak go to the wall stimulates the strong to exertions which they would not otherwise so make, and that these exertions produce inheritable modifications. Even in this case, however, it would be the exertions, or use and disuse, that would be the main agents in the modification. But it is not often that Mr. Wallace thus backslides. His present position is that acquired (as distinguished from congenital) modifications are not inherited at all. He does not indeed put his faith prominently forward and pin himself to it as plainly as could be wished, but under the heading 'The Non-Heredity of Acquired Characters', he writes as follows on p. 440 of his recent work in reference to Professor Weismann's Theory of Heredity:

'Certain observations on the embryology of the lower animals are held to afford direct proof of this theory of heredity, but they are too technical to be made clear to ordinary readers. A logical result of the theory is the impossibility of the transmission of acquired characters, since the molecular structure of the germ-plasm is already determined within the embryo; and Weismann holds that there are no facts which really prove that acquired characters can be inherited, although their inheritance has, by most writers, been considered so probable as hardly to stand in need of direct proof.

'We have already seen in the earlier part of this chapter that many instances of change, imputed to the inheritance of acquired variations, are really cases of selection.'

And the rest of the remarks tend to convey the impression that Mr. Wallace adopts Professor Weismann's view, but, curiously enough, though I have gone through Mr. Wallace's book with a special view to this particular point, I have not been able to find him definitely committing himself either to the assertion that acquired modifications never are inherited, or that they sometimes are so. It is abundantly laid down that Mr. Darwin laid too much stress on use and disuse, and a residuary impression is left that Mr. Wallace is endorsing Professor Weismann's view, but I have found it impossible to collect anything that enables me to define his position confidently in this respect.

This is natural enough, for Mr. Wallace has entitled his book *Darwinism*, and a work denying that use and disuse produced any effect could not conceivably be called Darwinism. Mr. Herbert Spencer has recently collected many passages from *The Origin of Species* and from *Animals and Plants under Domestication*,'[1] which show how largely, after all, use and disuse entered into Mr. Darwin's system, and we know that in his later years he attached still more importance to them. It was out of the question, therefore, that Mr. Wallace should categorically deny that their effects were inheritable. On the other hand, the temptation to adopt Professor Weismann's view must have been overwhelming to one who had been already inclined to minimize the effects of use and disuse. On the whole, one does not see what Mr. Wallace could do, other than what he has done — unless, of course, he changed his title, or had been no longer Mr. Wallace.

Besides, thanks to the works of Mr. Spencer, Professor Mivart, Professor Semper and very many others, there has for some time been a growing perception that the Darwinism of Charles Darwin was doomed. Use and disuse must either do even more than is officially recognized in Mr. Darwin's later concessions, or they must do a great deal less. If they can do as much as Mr. Darwin himself said they did, why should they not do more? Why stop where Mr. Darwin did? And again, where in the name of all that is reasonable did he really stop? He drew no line, and on what principle can we say that so much is possible as effect of use and disuse, but so much more impossible? If, as Mr. Darwin contended, disuse can so far reduce an organ as to render it rudimentary, and in many cases get rid of it altogether, why cannot use create as much as disuse can destroy, provided it has anything, no matter how low in structure, to begin with? Let us know where we stand. If it is admitted that use and disuse can do a good deal, what does a good deal mean? And what is the proportion between the shares attributable to use and disuse and to natural selection respectively? If we cannot be told with absolute precision, let us at any rate have something more definite than the statement that natural selection is 'the most important means of modification'.

Mr. Darwin gave us no help in this respect; and worse than this, he

[1] See *Nature*, March 6th, 1890.

371

contradicted himself so flatly as to show that he had very little definite idea upon the subject at all. Thus in respect to the winglessness of the Madeira beetles he wrote:

'In some cases we might easily put down to disuse modifications of structure, which are wholly or mainly due to natural selection. Mr. Wollaston has discovered the remarkable fact that 200 beetles, out of the 550 species (but more are now known) inhabiting Madeira, are so far deficient in wings that they cannot fly; and that of the 29 endemic genera no less than 23 have all their species in this condition! Several facts — namely, that beetles in many parts of the world are frequently blown out to sea and perish; that the beetles in Madeira, as observed by Mr. Wollaston, lie much concealed until the wind lulls and the sun shines; that the proportion of wingless beetles is larger on the exposed Desertas than in Madeira itself; and especially the extraordinary fact, so strongly insisted on by Mr. Wollaston, that certain large groups of beetles, elsewhere excessively numerous, which absolutely require the use of their wings are here almost entirely absent — these several considerations make me believe that the wingless condition of so many Madeira beetles is mainly due to the action of natural selection, *combined probably with disuse* [italics mine]. For during many successive generations each individual beetle which flew least, either from its wings having been ever so little less perfectly developed or from indolent habit, will have had the best chance of surviving, from not being blown out to sea; and, on the other hand, those beetles which most readily took to flight would oftenest have been blown to sea, and thus destroyed.'[1]

We should like to know, first, somewhere about how much disuse was able to do after all, and moreover why, if it can do anything at all it should not be able to do all. Mr. Darwin says: 'Any change in structure and function which can be effected by small stages is within the power of natural selection.' 'And why not,' we ask, 'within the power of use and disuse?' Moreover, on a later page we find Mr. Darwin saying:

'*It appears probable that disuse has been the main agent in rendering organs rudimentary* [italics mine]. It would at first lead by slow steps to the more and more complete reduction of a part, until at last it has become rudimentary — as in the case of the eyes of animals inhabiting dark caverns, and of the wings of birds inhabiting oceanic islands, which have seldom been forced by beasts of prey to take flight, and have

[1] *Origin of Species*, sixth edition, 1888, vol. I, p. 168.

ultimately lost the power of flying. Again, an organ, useful under certain conditions, might become injurious under others, *as with the wings of beetles living on small and exposed islands*; and in this case natural selection will have aided in reducing the organ, until it was rendered harmless and rudimentary [italics mine.']¹

So that just as an undefined amount of use and disuse was introduced on the earlier page to supplement the effects of natural selection in respect of the wings of beetles on small and exposed islands, we have here an undefined amount of natural selection introduced to supplement the effects of use and disuse in respect of the identical phenomena. In the one passage we find that natural selection has been the main agent in reducing the wings, though use and disuse have had an appreciable share in the result; in the other, it is use and disuse that have been the main agents, though an appreciable share in the result must be ascribed to natural selection.

Besides, who has seen the uncles and aunts going away with the uniformity that is necessary for Mr. Darwin's contention? We know that birds and insects do often get blown out to sea and perish, but in order to establish Mr. Darwin's position we want the evidence of those who watched the reduction of the wings during the many generations in the course of which it was being effected, and who can testify that all, or the overwhelming majority, of the beetles born with fairly well-developed wings got blown out to sea while those alone survived whose wings were congenitally degenerate. Who saw them go, or can point to analogous cases so conclusive as to compel assent from any equitable thinker?

Darwinians of the stamp of Mr. Thiselton Dyer, Professor Ray Lankester or Mr. Romanes, insist on their pound of flesh in the matter of irrefragable demonstration. They complain of us for not bringing forward someone who has been able to detect the movement of the hour-hand of a watch during a second of time, and when we fail to do so, declare triumphantly that we have no evidence that there is any connection between the beating of a second and the movement of the hour-hand. When we say that rain comes from the condensation of moisture in the atmosphere, they demand of us a rain-drop from moisture not yet condensed. If they stickle for proof and cavil on the ninth part of a hair, as they do when we bring forward what we deem excellent instances of the transmission of an acquired characteristic, why

¹ *Origin of Species*, sixth edition, 1888, vol. II, p. 261.

may not we, too, demand at any rate some evidence that the un-modified beetles actually did always, or nearly always, get blown out to sea, during the reduction above referred to, and that it is to this fact, and not to the masterly inactivity of their fathers and mothers, that the Madeira beetles owe their winglessness? If we begin stickling for proof in this way, our opponents would not be long in letting us know that absolute proof is unattainable on any subject, that reasonable presumption is our highest certainty, and that crying out for too much evidence is as bad as accepting too little. Truth is like a photographic sensitized plate, which is equally ruined by over and by under exposure, and the just exposure for which can never be absolutely determined.

Surely if disuse can be credited with the vast powers involved in Mr. Darwin's statement that it has probably 'been the main agent in ren-dering organs rudimentary', no limits are assignable to the accumulated effects of habit, provided the effects of habit, or use and disuse, are supposed, as Mr. Darwin supposed them, to be inheritable at all. Dar-winians have at length woke up to the dilemma in which they are placed by the manner in which Mr. Darwin tried to sit on the two stools of use and disuse, and natural selection of accidental variations, at the same time. The knell of Charles Darwinism is rung in Mr. Wallace's present book, and in the general perception on the part of biologists that we must either assign to use and disuse such a pre-dominant share in modification as to make it the feature most proper to be insisted on, or deny that the modifications, whether of mind or body, acquired during a single lifetime, are ever transmitted at all. If they can be inherited at all, they can be accumulated. If they can be accumulated at all, they can be so, for anything that appears to the con-trary, to the extent of the specific and generic differences with which we are surrounded. The only thing to do is to pluck them out root and branch: they are as a cancer which, if the smallest fibre be left unex-cised, will grow again, and kill any system on to which it is allowed to fasten. Mr. Wallace, therefore, may well be excused if he casts longing eyes towards Weismannism.

And what was Mr. Darwin's system? Who can make head or tail of the inextricable muddle in which he left it? The *Origin of Species* in its latest shape is the reduction of hedging to an absurdity. How did Mr. Darwin himself leave it in the last chapter of the last edition of the *Origin of Species*? He wrote:

'I have now recapitulated the facts and considerations which have thoroughly convinced me that species have been modified during a long course of descent. This has been effected chiefly through the natural selection of numerous, successive, slight, favourable variations; aided in an important manner by the inherited effects of the use and disuse of parts, and in an unimportant manner — that is, in relation to adaptive structures whether past or present — by the direct action of external conditions, and by variations which seem to us in our ignorance to arise spontaneously. It appears that I formerly underrated the frequency and value of these latter forms of variation, as leading to permanent modifications of structure independently of natural selection.'

The 'numerous, successive, slight, favourable variations' above referred to are intended to be fortuitous, accidental, spontaneous. It is the essence of Mr. Darwin's theory that this should be so. Mr. Darwin's solemn statement, therefore, of his theory, after he had done his best or his worst with it, is, when stripped of surplusage, as follows:

'The modification of species has been mainly effected by accumulation of spontaneous variations; it has been aided in an important manner by accumulation of variations due to use and disuse, and in an unimportant manner by spontaneous variations; I do not even now think that spontaneous variations have been very important, but I used once to think them less important than I do now.'

It is a discouraging symptom of the age that such a system should have been so long belauded, and it is a sign of returning intelligence that even he who has been more especially the *alter ego* of Mr. Darwin should have felt constrained to close the chapter of Charles Darwinism as a living theory, and relegate it to the important but not very creditable place in history which it must henceforth occupy. It is astonishing, however, that Mr. Wallace should have quoted the extract from the *Origin of Species* just given, as he has done on p. 412 of his *Darwinism*, without betraying any sign that he has caught its driftlessness — for drift, other than a desire to hedge, it assuredly has not got. The battle now turns on the question whether modifications of either structure or instinct due to use or disuse are ever inherited, or whether they are not. Can the effects of habit be transmitted to progeny at all? We know that more usually they are not transmitted to any perceptible extent, but we believe also that occasionally, and indeed not infrequently, they are inherited and even intensified. What are our grounds for this opinion? It will be my object to put these forward in the following number of the *Universal Review*.

AT the close of my article in last month's number of the *Universal Review*, I said I would in this month's issue show why the opponents of Charles Darwinism believe the effects of habits acquired during the lifetime of a parent to produce an effect on their subsequent offspring, in spite of the fact that we can rarely find the effect in any one generation, or even in several, sufficiently marked to arrest our attention.

I will now show that offspring can be, and not very infrequently is, affected by occurrences that have produced a deep impression on the parent organism — the effect produced on the offspring being such as leaves no doubt that it is to be connected with the impression produced on the parent. Having thus established the general proposition, I will proceed to the more particular one — that habits, involving use and disuse of special organs, with the modifications of structure thereby engendered, produce also an effect upon offspring, which, though seldom perceptible as regards structure in a single, or even in several generations, is nevertheless capable of being accumulated in suc-

---

[1] Mr. J. T. Cunningham, of the Marine Biological Laboratory, Plymouth, has called my attention to the fact that I have ascribed to Professor Ray Lankester a criticism on Mr. Wallace's remarks upon the eyes of certain flat-fish, which Professor Ray Lankester was, in reality, only adopting — with full acknowledgment — from Mr. Cunningham. Mr. Cunningham has left it to me whether to correct my omission publicly or not, but he would so plainly prefer my doing so that I consider myself bound to insert this note. Curiously enough, I find that in my book *Evolution, Old and New* I gave what Lamarck actually said upon the eyes of flat-fish, and, having been led to return to the subject, I may as well quote his words. He wrote:

'Need — always occasioned by the circumstances in which an animal is placed, and followed by sustained efforts at gratification — cannot only modify an organ — that is to say, augment or reduce it — but can change its position when the case requires its removal.

'Ocean fishes have occasion to see what is on either side of them, and have their eyes accordingly placed on either side of their head. Some fishes, however, have their abode near coasts on submarine banks and inclinations, and are thus forced to flatten themselves as much as possible in order to get as near as they can to the shore. In this situation they receive more light from above than from below, and find it necessary to pay attention to whatever happens to be above them; this need has involved the displacement of their eyes, which now take the remarkable position which we observe in the case of soles, turbots, plaice, etc. The transfer of position is not even yet complete in the case of these fishes, and the eyes are not, therefore, symmetrically placed; but they are so with the skate, whose head and whole body are equally disposed on either side a longitudinal section. Hence the eyes of this fish are placed symmetrically upon the uppermost side.' — *Philosophie Zoologique*, tom. I, pp. 250, 251. Edition C. Martins. Paris, 1873.

cessive generations till it amounts to specific and generic difference. I have found the first point as much as I can treat within the limits of this present article, and will avail myself of the hospitality of the *Universal Review* next month to deal with the second.

The proposition which I have to defend is one which no one till recently would have questioned, and even now those who look most askance at it do not venture to dispute it unreservedly; they every now and then admit it as conceivable, and even in some cases probable; nevertheless they seek to minimize it, and to make out that there is little or no connection between the great mass of the cells of which the body is composed, and those cells that are alone capable of reproducing the entire organism. The tendency is to assign to these last a life of their own, apart from, and unconnected with that of the other cells of the body, and to cheapen all evidence that tends to prove any response on their part to the past history of the individual, and hence ultimately of the race.

Professor Weismann is the foremost exponent of those who take this line. He has naturally been welcomed by English Charles Darwinians; for if his view can be sustained, then it can be contended that use and disuse produce no transmissible effect, and the ground is cut from under Lamarck's feet; if, on the other hand, his view is unfounded, the Lamarckian reaction, already strong, will gain still further strength. The issue, therefore, is important, and is being fiercely contested by those who have invested their all of reputation for discernment in Charles Darwinian securities.

Professor Weismann's theory is, that at every new birth a part of the substance which proceeds from parents and which goes to form the new embryo is not used up in forming the new animal, but remains apart to generate the germ-cells — or perhaps I should say 'germ-plasm' — which the new animal itself will in due course issue.

Contrasting the generally received view with his own, Professor Weismann says that according to the first of these 'the organism produces germ-cells afresh again and again, and that it produces them entirely from its own substance'. While by the second 'the germ-cells are no longer looked upon as the product of the parent's body, at least as far as their essential part — the specific germ-plasm — is concerned; they are rather considered as something which is to be placed in contrast with the *tout ensemble* of the cells which make up the parent's body, and the germ-cells of succeeding generations stand in a similar relation

377

to one another as a series of generations of unicellular organisms arising by a continued process of cell-division'.[1]

On another page he writes:

'I believe that heredity depends upon the fact that a small portion of the effective substance of the germ, the germ-plasm, remains unchanged during the development of the ovum into an organism, and that this part of the germ-plasm serves as a foundation from which the germ-cells of the new organism are produced. There is, therefore, continuity of the germ-plasm from one generation to another. One might represent the germ-plasm by the metaphor of a long creeping root-stock from which plants arise at intervals, these latter representing the individuals of successive generations.'[2]

Mr. Wallace, who does not appear to have read Professor Weismann's essays themselves, but whose remarks are, no doubt, ultimately derived from the sequel to the passage just quoted from page 266 of Professor Weismann's book, contends that the impossibility of the transmission of acquired characters follows as a logical result from Professor Weismann's theory, inasmuch as the molecular structure of the germ-plasm that will go to form any succeeding generation is already predetermined within the still unformed embryo of its predecessor; 'and Weismann,' continues Mr. Wallace, 'holds that there are no facts which really prove that acquired characters can be inherited, although their inheritance has, by most writers, been considered so probable as hardly to stand in need of direct proof.'[3]

Professor Weismann, in passages too numerous to quote, shows that he recognizes this necessity, and acknowledges that the non-transmission of acquired characters 'forms the foundation of the views' set forth in his book, p. 291.

Professor Ray Lankester does not commit himself absolutely to this view, but lends it support by saying (*Nature*, December 12th, 1889): 'It is hardly necessary to say that it has never yet been shown experimentally that *anything* acquired by one generation is transmitted to the next (putting aside diseases).'

Mr. Romanes, writing in *Nature*, March 13th, 1890, and opposing certain details of Professor Weismann's theory, so far supports it as to say that 'there is the gravest possible doubt lying against the supposition that any really inherited decrease is due to the inherited effects of

[1] *Essays on Heredity*, etc., Oxford, 1889, p. 171. [2] Ibid., p. 266.
[3] *Darwinism*, 1889, p. 440.

disuse'. The 'gravest possible doubt' should mean that Mr. Romanes regards it as a moral certainty that disuse has no transmitted effect in reducing an organ, and it should follow that he holds use to have no transmitted effect in its development. The sequel, however, makes me uncertain how far Mr. Romanes intends this, and I would refer the reader to the article which Mr. Romanes has just published on Weismann in the *Contemporary Review* for this current month.

The burden of Mr. Thiselton Dyer's controversy with the Duke of Argyll (see *Nature*, January 16th, 1890, *et seq.*) was that there was no evidence in support of the transmission of any acquired modification. The orthodoxy of science, therefore, must be held as giving at any rate a provisional support to Professor Weismann, but all of them, including even Professor Weismann himself, shrink from committing themselves to the opinion that the germ-cells of any organisms remain in all cases unaffected by the events that occur to the other cells of the same organism, and until they do this they have knocked the bottom out of their case.

From among the passages in which Professor Weismann himself shows a desire to hedge I may take the following from page 170 of his book:

'I am also far from asserting that the germ-plasm which, as I hold, is transmitted as the basis of heredity from one generation to another, is absolutely unchangeable or totally uninfluenced by forces residing in the organism within which it is transformed into germ-cells. I am also compelled to admit it as conceivable that organisms may exert a modifying influence upon their germ-cells, and even that such a process is to a certain extent inevitable. The nutrition and growth of the individual must exercise some influence upon its germ-cells. . . .'

Professor Weismann does indeed go on to say that this influence must be extremely slight, but we do not care how slight the changes produced may be, provided they exist and can be transmitted. On an earlier page (p. 101) he said in regard to variations generally that we should not expect to find them conspicuous, their frequency would be enough, if they could be accumulated. The same applies here, if stirring events that occur to the somatic cells can produce any effect at all on offspring. A very small effect, provided it can be repeated and accumulated in successive generations, is all that even the most exacting Lamarckian will ask for.

Having now made the reader acquainted with the position taken by the leading Charles Darwinian authorities, I will return to Professor Weismann himself, who declares that the transmission of acquired characters 'at first sight certainly seems necessary', and that 'it appears rash to attempt to dispense with its aid'. He continues:

'Many phenomena only appear to be intelligible if we assume the hereditary transmission of such acquired characters as the changes which we ascribe to the use or disuse of particular organs, or to the direct influence of climate. Furthermore, how can we explain instinct as hereditary habit, unless it has gradually arisen by the accumulation, through heredity, of habits which were practised in succeeding generations?'[1]

I may say in passing that Professor Weismann appears to suppose that the view of instinct just given is part of the Charles Darwinian system, for on page 389 of his book he says 'that many observers had followed Darwin in explaining them [instincts] as inherited habits'. This was not Mr. Darwin's own view of the matter. He wrote:

'If we suppose any habitual action to become inherited — and I think it can be shown that this does sometimes happen — then the resemblance between what originally was a habit and an instinct becomes so close as not to be distinguished ... But it would be the most serious error to suppose that the greater number of instincts have been acquired by habit in one generation, and then transmitted by inheritance to succeeding generations. It can be clearly shown that the most wonderful instincts with which we are acquainted, namely, those of the hive-bee and of many ants, could not possibly have been thus acquired.' — [Origin of Species, ed. 1859, p. 209.]

Again we read: 'Domestic instincts are sometimes spoken of as actions which have become inherited solely from long-continued and compulsory habit, but this, I think, is not true.' — [Ibid., p. 214.]

Again: 'I am surprised that no one has advanced this demonstrative case of neuter insects, against the well-known doctrine of inherited habit, as advanced by Lamarck.' — [Origin of Species, ed. 1872, p. 233.]

I am not aware that Lamarck advanced the doctrine that instinct is inherited habit, but he may have done so in some work that I have not seen.

It is true, as I have more than once pointed out, that in the later editions of the Origin of Species it is no longer 'the most serious' error to refer instincts generally to inherited habit, but it still remains 'a serious error', and this slight relaxation of severity does not warrant Professor

[1] Page 83.

Weismann in ascribing to Mr. Darwin an opinion which he emphatically condemned. His tone, however, is so off-hand that those who have little acquaintance with the literature of evolution would hardly guess that he is not much better informed on this subject than themselves.

Returning to the inheritance of acquired characters, Professor Weismann says that this has never been proved either by means of direct observation or by experiment. 'It must be admitted', he writes, 'that there are in existence numerous descriptions of cases which tend to prove that such mutilations as the loss of fingers, the scars of wounds, etc., are inherited by the offspring, but in these descriptions the previous history is invariably obscure, and hence the evidence loses all scientific value.'

The experiments of M. Brown-Séquard throw so much light upon the question at issue that I will quote at some length from the summary given by Mr. Darwin in his *Variation of Animals and Plants under Domestication*.[1] Mr. Darwin writes:

'With respect to the inheritance of structures mutilated by injuries or altered by disease, it was until lately difficult to come to any definite conclusion.' [Then follow several cases in which mutilations practised for many generations are not found to be transmitted.] 'Notwithstanding', continues Mr. Darwin, 'the above several negative cases, we now possess conclusive evidence that the effects of operations are sometimes inherited. Dr. Brown-Séquard gives the following summary of his observations on guinea-pigs, and this summary is so important that I will quote the whole:

' "1st. Appearance of epilepsy in animals born of parents having been rendered epileptic by an injury to the spinal cord.

' "2nd. Appearance of epilepsy also in animals born of parents having been rendered epileptic by the section of the sciatic nerve.

' "3rd. A change in the shape of the ear in animals born of parents in which such a change was the effect of a division of the cervical sympathetic nerve.

' "4th. Partial closure of the eyelids in animals born of parents in which that state of the eyelids had been caused either by the section of the cervical sympathetic nerve or the removal of the superior cervical ganglion.

' "5th. Exophthalmia in animals born of parents in which an injury

[1] Vol. I, p. 466, etc. Ed. 1885.

381

to the restiform body had produced that protrusion of the eyeball. This interesting fact I have witnessed a good many times, and I have seen the transmission of the morbid state of the eye continue through four generations. In these animals modified by heredity, the two eyes generally protruded, although in the parents usually only one showed exophthalmia, the lesion having been made in most cases only on one of the corpora restiformia.

' "6th. Hæmatoma and dry gangrene of the ears in animals born of parents in which these ear-alterations had been caused by an injury to the restiform body near the nib of the calamus.

' "7th. Absence of two toes out of the three of the hind leg, and sometimes of the three, in animals whose parents had eaten up their hind-leg toes which had become anæsthetic from a section of the sciatic nerve alone, or of that nerve and also of the crural. Sometimes, instead of complete absence of the toes, only a part of one or two or three was missing in the young, although in the parent not only the toes but the whole foot was absent (partly eaten off, partly destroyed by inflammation, ulceration or gangrene).

' "8th. Appearance of various morbid states of the skin and hair oι the neck and face in animals born of parents having had similar alterations in the same parts, as effects of an injury to the sciatic nerve."

'It should be especially observed that Brown-Séquard had bred during thirty years many thousand guinea-pigs from animals which had not been operated upon, and not one of these manifested the epileptic tendency. Nor has he ever seen a guinea-pig born without toes, which was not the offspring of parents which had gnawed off their own toes owing to the sciatic nerve having been divided. Of this latter fact thirteen instances were carefully recorded, and a greater number were seen; yet Brown-Séquard speaks of such cases as one of the rarer forms of inheritance. It is a still more interesting fact, "That the sciatic nerve in the congenitally toeless animal has inherited the power of passing through all the different morbid states which have occurred in one of its parents from the time of its division till after its reunion with the peripheric end. It is not, therefore, simply the power of performing an action which is inherited, but the power of performing a whole series of actions, in a certain order."

'In most of the cases of inheritance recorded by Brown-Séquard only one of the two parents had been operated upon and was effected. He concludes by expressing his belief that "what is transmitted is the morbid state of the nervous system", due to the operation performed on the parents.'

Mr. Darwin proceeds to give other instances of inherited effects of mutilations:

'With the horse there seems hardly a doubt that exostoses on the legs, caused by too much travelling on hard roads, are inherited. Blumenbach records the case of a man who had his little finger on the right hand almost cut off, and which in consequence grew crooked, and his sons had the same finger on the same hand similarly crooked. A soldier, fifteen years before his marriage, lost his left eye from purulent ophthalmia, and his two sons were microphthalmic on the same side.'

The late Professor Rolleston, whose competence as an observer no one is likely to dispute, gave Mr. Darwin two cases as having fallen under his own notice, one of a man whose knee had been severely wounded, and whose child was born with the same spot marked or scarred, and the other of one who was severely cut upon the cheek, and whose child was born scarred in the same place. Mr. Darwin's conclusion was that 'the effects of injuries, especially when followed by disease, or perhaps exclusively when thus followed, are occasionally inherited.'

Let us now see what Professor Weismann has to say against this. He writes:

'The only cases worthy of discussion are the well-known experiments upon guinea-pigs conducted by the French physiologist, Brown-Séquard. But the explanation of his results is, in my opinion, open to discussion. In these cases we have to do with the apparent transmission of artificially produced malformations ... All these effects were said to be transmitted to descendants as far as the fifth or sixth generation.

'But we must inquire whether these cases are really due to heredity, and not to simple infection. In the case of epilepsy, at any rate, it is easy to imagine that the passage of some specific organism through the reproductive cells may take place, as in the case of syphilis. We are, however, entirely ignorant of the nature of the former disease. This suggested explanation may not perhaps apply to the other cases; but we must remember that animals which have been subjected to such severe operations upon the nervous system have sustained a great shock, and if they are capable of breeding, it is only probable that they will produce weak descendants, and such as are easily affected by disease.

Such a result does not, however, explain why the offspring should suffer from the same disease as that which was artificially induced in the parents. But this does not appear to have been by any means invariably the case. Brown-Séquard himself says: "The changes in the eye of the offspring were of a very variable nature, and were only occasionally exactly similar to those observed in the parents."

'There is no doubt, however, that these experiments demand careful consideration, but before they can claim scientific recognition they must be subjected to rigid criticism as to the precautions taken, the nature and number of the control experiments, etc.

'Up to the present time such necessary conditions have not been sufficiently observed. The recent experiments themselves are only described in short preliminary notices, which, as regards their accuracy, the possibility of mistake, the precautions taken, and the exact succession of individuals affected, afford no data on which a scientific opinion can be founded' (pp. 81, 82).

The line Professor Weismann takes, therefore, is to discredit the facts; yet on a later page we find that the experiments have since been repeated by Obersteiner, 'who has described them in a very exact and unprejudiced manner', and that 'the fact' — (I imagine that Professor Weismann intends 'the facts') — 'cannot be doubted.'

On a still later page, however, we read:

'If, for instance, it could be shown that artificial mutilation spontaneously reappears in the offspring with sufficient frequency to exclude all possibilities of chance, then such proof [i.e. that acquired characters can be transmitted] would be forthcoming. The transmission of mutilations has been frequently asserted, and has been even recently again brought forward, but all the supposed instances have broken down when carefully examined' (p. 390).

Here, then, we are told that proof of the occasional transmission of mutilations would be sufficient to establish the fact, but on p. 267 we find that no single fact is known which really proves that acquired characters can be transmitted, *for the ascertained facts which seem to point to the transmission of artificially produced diseases cannot be considered as proof*. [Italics mine.] Perhaps; but it was mutilation in many cases that Professor Weismann practically admitted to have been transmitted when he declared that Obersteiner had verified Brown-Séquard's experiments.

That Professor Weismann recognizes the vital importance to his

384

own theory of the question whether or no mutilations can be transmitted under any circumstances, is evident from a passage on p. 425 of his work, on which he says: 'It can hardly be doubted that mutilations are acquired characters; they do not arise from any tendency contained in the germ, but are merely the reaction of the body under certain external influences. They are, as I have recently expressed it, purely somatogenic characters — viz. characters which emanate from the body (*soma*) only, as opposed to the germ-cells; they are, therefore, characters that do not arise from the germ itself.

'If mutilations must necessarily be transmitted' [which no one that I know of has maintained], 'or even if they might occasionally be transmitted' [which cannot, I imagine, be reasonably questioned], 'a powerful support would be given to the Lamarckian principle, and the transmission of functional hypertrophy or atrophy would thus become highly probable.'

I have not found any further attempt in Professor Weismann's book to deal with the evidence adduced by Mr. Darwin to show that mutilations, if followed by diseases, are sometimes inherited; and I must leave it to the reader to determine how far Professor Weismann has shown reason for rejecting Mr. Darwin's conclusion. I do not, however, dwell upon these facts now as evidence of a transmitted change of bodily form, or of instinct due to use and disuse or habit; what they prove is that the germ-cells within the parent's body do not stand apart from the other cells of the body so completely as Professor Weismann would have us believe, but that, as Professor Hering, of Prague, has aptly said, they echo with more or less frequency and force to the profounder impressions made upon other cells.

I may say that Professor Weismann does not more cavalierly wave aside the mass of evidence collected by Mr. Darwin and a host of other writers, to the effect that mutilations are sometimes inherited, than does Mr. Wallace, who says that, 'as regards mutilations, it is generally admitted that they are not inherited, and there is ample evidence on this point'. It is indeed generally admitted that mutilations, when not followed by disease, are very rarely, if ever, inherited; and Mr. Wallace's appeal to the 'ample evidence' which he alleges to exist on this head, is much as though he should say that there is ample evidence to show that the days are longer in summer than in winter. 'Nevertheless,' he continues, 'a few cases of apparent inheritance of mutilations have been recorded, and these, if trustworthy, are difficulties in the way of the theory'

... 'The often quoted case of a disease induced by mutilation being inherited (Brown-Séquard's epileptic guinea-pigs) has been discussed by Professor Weismann and shown to be not conclusive. The mutilation itself—a section of certain nerves—was never inherited, but the resulting epilepsy, or a general state of weakness, deformity, or sores, was sometimes inherited. It is, however, possible that the mere injury introduced and encouraged the growth of certain microbes, which, spreading through the organism, sometimes reached the germ-cells, and thus transmitted a diseased condition to the offspring.'[1]

I suppose a microbe which made guinea-pigs eat their toes off was communicated to the germ-cells of an unfortunate guinea-pig which had been already microbed by it, and made the offspring bite its toes off too. The microbe has a good deal to answer for.

On the case of the deterioration of horses in the Falkland Islands after a few generations, Professor Weismann says:

'In such a case we have only to assume that the climate which is unfavourable, and nutriment which is insufficient for horses, effect not only the animal as a whole but also its germ-cells. This would result in the diminution in size of the germ-cells, the effects upon the offspring being still further intensified by the insufficient nourishment supplied during growth. But such results would not depend upon the transmission by the germ-cells of certain peculiarities due to the unfavourable climate, which only appear in the full-grown horse.'

But Professor Weismann does not like such cases, and admits that he cannot explain the facts in connection with the climatic varieties of certain butterflies, except 'by supposing the passive acquisition of characters produced by the direct influence of climate'.

Nevertheless, in his next paragraph but one he calls such cases 'doubtful', and proposes that for the moment they should be left aside. He accordingly leaves them, but I have not yet found what other moment he considered auspicious for returning to them. He tells us that 'new experiments will be necessary, and that he has himself already begun to undertake them'. Perhaps he will give us the results of these experiments in some future book — for that they will prove satisfactory to him can hardly, I think, be doubted. He writes:

'Leaving on one side, for the moment, these doubtful and insufficiently investigated cases, we may still maintain that the assumption that changes induced by external conditions in the organism as a

[1] *Darwinism*, p. 440.

whole are communicated to the germ-cells after the manner indicated in Darwin's hypothesis of pangenesis, is wholly unnecessary for the explanation of these phenomena. Still we cannot exclude the possibility of such a transmission occasionally occurring, for even if the greater part of the effects must be attributable to natural selection, there might be a smaller part in certain cases which depends on this exceptional factor.'

I repeatedly tried to understand Mr. Darwin's theory of pangenesis, and so often failed that I long since gave the matter up in despair. I did so with the less unwillingness because I saw that no one else appeared to understand the theory, and that even Mr. Darwin's warmest adherents regarded it with disfavour. If Mr. Darwin means that every cell of the body throws off minute particles that find their way to the germ-cells, and hence into the new embryo, this is indeed difficult of comprehension and belief. If he means that the rhythms or vibrations that go on ceaselessly in every cell of the body communicate themselves with greater or less accuracy or perturbation, as the case may be, to the cells that go to form offspring, and that since the characteristics of matter are determined by vibrations, in communicating vibrations they in effect communicate matter, according to the view put forward in the last chapter of my book *Luck or Cunning*, then we can better understand it. I have nothing, however, to do with Mr. Darwin's theory of pangenesis beyond avoiding the pretence that I understand either the theory itself or what Professor Weismann says about it; all I am concerned with is Professor Weismann's admission, made immediately afterwards, that the somatic cells may, and perhaps sometimes do, impart characteristics to the germ-cells.

'A complete and satisfactory refutation of such an opinion,' he continues, 'cannot be brought forward at present'; so I suppose we must wait a little longer, but in the meantime we may again remark that, if we admit even occasional communication of changes in the somatic cells to the germ-cells, we have let in the thin end of the wedge, as Mr. Darwin did when he said that use and disuse did a good deal towards modification. Buffon, in his first volume on the lower animals,[1] dwells on the impossibility of stopping the breach once made by admission of variation at all. 'If the point,' he writes, 'were once gained, that among animals and vegetables there had been, I do not say several species, but even a single one, which had been produced in the course of direct

[1] Tom. IV, p. 383. Ed. 1753.

descent from another species; if, for example, it could be once shown that the ass was but a degeneration from the horse — then there is no further limit to be set to the power of Nature, and we should not be wrong in supposing that with sufficient time she could have evolved all other organized forms from one primordial type.' So with use and disuse and transmission of acquired characteristics generally — once show that a single structure or instinct is due to habit in preceding generations, and we can impose no limit on the results achievable by accumulation in this respect, nor shall we be wrong in conceiving it as possible that all specialization, whether of structure or instinct, may be due ultimately to habit.

How far this can be shown to be probable is, of course, another matter, but I am not immediately concerned with this; all I am concerned with now is to show that the germ-cells not unfrequently become permanently affected by events that have made a profound impression upon the somatic cells, in so far that they transmit an obvious reminiscence of the impression to the embryos which they go subsequently towards forming. This is all that is necessary for my case, and I do not find that Professor Weismann, after all, disputes it.

But here, again, comes the difficulty of saying what Professor Weismann does, and what he does not, dispute. One moment he gives all that is wanted for the Lamarckian contention, the next he denies common sense the bare necessaries of life. For a more exhaustive and detailed criticism of Professor Weismann's position, I would refer the reader to an admirably clear article by Mr. Sidney H. Vines, which appeared in *Nature*, October 24th, 1889. I can only say that while reading Professor Weismann's book, I feel as I do when I read those of Mr. Darwin, and of a good many other writers on biology whom I need not name. I become like a fly in a window-pane. I see the sunshine and freedom beyond, and buzz up and down their pages, ever hopeful to get through them to the fresh air without, but ever kept back by a mysterious something, which I feel but cannot either grasp or see. It was not thus when I read Buffon, Erasmus Darwin and Lamarck; it is not thus when I read such articles as Mr. Vines's just referred to. Love of self-display, and the want of singleness of mind that it inevitably engenders — these, I suppose, are the sins that glaze the casements of most men's minds; and from these, no matter how hard he tries to free himself, nor how much he despises them, who is altogether exempt?

Finally, then, when we consider the immense mass of evidence referred to briefly, but sufficiently, by Mr. Charles Darwin, and referred to without other, for the most part, than off-hand dismissal by Professor Weismann in the last of the essays that have been recently translated, I do not see how anyone who brings an unbiased mind to the question can hesitate as to the side on which the weight of testimony inclines. Professor Weismann declares that 'the transmission of mutilations may be dismissed into the domain of fable'.[1] If so, then, whom can we trust? What is the use of science at all if the conclusions of a man as competent as I readily admit Mr. Darwin to have been, on the evidence laid before him from countless sources, is to be set aside lightly and without giving the clearest and most cogent explanation of the why and wherefore? When we see a person 'ostrichizing' the evidence which he has to meet, as clearly as I believe Professor Weismann to be doing, we shall in nine cases out of ten be right in supposing that he knows the evidence to be too strong for him.

PART THREE

N O W let me return to the recent division of biological opinion into two main streams — Lamarckism and Weismannism. Both Lamarckians and Weismannists, not to mention mankind in general, admit that the better adapted to its surroundings a living form may be, the more likely it is to outbreed its compeers. The world at large, again, needs not to be told that the normal course is not unfrequently deflected through the fortunes of war; nevertheless, according to Lamarckians and Erasmus Darwinians, habitual effort, guided by ever-growing intelligence — that is to say, by continued increase of power in the matter of knowing our likes and dislikes — has been so much the main factor throughout the course of organic development, that the rest, though not lost sight of, may be allowed to go without saying. According, on the other hand, to extreme Charles Darwinians and Weismannists, habit, effort and intelligence acquired during the experience of any one life goes for nothing. Not even a little fraction of it endures to the benefit of offspring. It dies with him in whom it is acquired, and the heirs of a man's body take no interest therein. To

[1] *Essays*, etc., p. 447.

state this doctrine is to arouse instinctive loathing; it is my fortunate task to maintain that such a nightmare of waste and death is as baseless as it is repulsive.

The split in biological opinion occasioned by the deadlock to which Charles Darwinism has been reduced, though comparatively recent, widens rapidly. Ten years ago Lamarck's name was mentioned only as a byword for extravagance; now, we cannot take up a number of *Nature* without seeing how hot the contention is between his followers and those of Weismann. This must be referred, as I implied earlier, to growing perception that Mr. Darwin should either have gone further towards Lamarckism or not so far. In admitting use and disuse as freely as he did, he gave Lamarckians leverage for the overthrow of a system based ostensibly on the accumulation of fortunate accidents. In assigning the lion's share of development to the accumulation of fortunate accidents, he tempted fortuitists to try to cut the ground from under Lamarck's feet by denying that the effects of use and disuse can be inherited at all. When the public had once got to understand what Lamarck had intended, and wherein Mr. Charles Darwin had differed from him, it became impossible for Charles Darwinians to remain where they were, nor is it easy to see what course was open to them except to cast about for a theory by which they could get rid of use and disuse altogether. Weismannism, therefore, is the inevitable outcome of the straits to which Charles Darwinians were reduced through the way in which their leader had halted between two opinions.

This is why Charles Darwinians, from Professor Huxley downwards, have kept the difference between Lamarck's opinions and those of Mr. Darwin so much in the background. Unwillingness to make this understood is nowhere manifested more clearly than in Dr. Francis Darwin's life of his father. In this work Lamarck is sneered at once or twice and told to go away, but there is no attempt to state the two cases side by side; from which, as from not a little else, I conclude that Dr. Francis Darwin has descended from his father with singularly little modification.

Proceeding to the evidence for the transmissions of acquired habits, I will quote two recently adduced examples from among the many that have been credibly attested. The first was contributed to *Nature* (March 14th, 1889) by Professor Marcus M. Hartog, who wrote:

'A. B. is moderately myopic and very astigmatic in the left eye; extremely myopic in the right. As the left eye gave such bad images for near objects, he was compelled in childhood to mask it, and acquired the habit of leaning his head on his left arm for writing, so as to blind that eye, or of resting the left temple and eye on the hand, with the elbow on the table. At the age of fifteen the eyes were equalized by the use of suitable spectacles, and he soon lost the habit completely and permanently. He is now the father of two children, a boy and a girl, whose vision (tested repeatedly and fully) is emmetropic in both eyes, so that they have not inherited the congenital optical defect of their father. All the same, they have both of them inherited his early acquired habit, and need constant watchfulness to prevent their hiding the left eye when writing, by resting the head on the left forearm or hand. Imitation is here quite out of the question.

'Considering that every habit involves changes in the proportional development of the muscular and osseous systems, and hence probably of the nervous system also, the importance of inherited habits, natural or acquired, cannot be overlooked in the general theory of inheritance. I am fully aware that I shall be accused of flat Lamarckism, but a nickname is not an argument.'

To this Professor Ray Lankester rejoined (*Nature*, March 21st, 1889):

'It is not unusual for children to rest the head on the left forearm or hand when writing, and I doubt whether much value can be attached to the case described by Professor Hartog. The kind of observation which his letter suggests is, however, likely to lead to results either for or against the transmission of acquired characters. An old friend of mine lost his right arm when a schoolboy, and has ever since written with his left. He has a large family and grandchildren, but I have not heard of any of them showing a disposition to left-handedness.'

From *Nature* (March 21st, 1889) I take the second instance communicated by Mr. J. Jenner-Weir, who wrote as follows:

'Mr. Marcus M. Hartog's letter of March 6th, inserted in last week's number (p. 462), is a very valuable contribution to the growing evidence that acquired characters may be inherited. I have long held the view that such is often the case, and I have myself observed several instances of the, at least I may say, apparent fact.

'Many years ago there was a very fine male of the *Capra megaceros* in the gardens of the Zoological Society. To restrain this animal from jumping over the fence of the enclosure in which he was confined, a long and heavy chain was attached to the collar round his neck. He was constantly in the habit of taking this chain up by his horns and moving it from one side to another over his back; in doing this he threw his head very much back, his horns being placed in a line with the back. The habit had become quite chronic with him, and was very tiresome to look at. I was very much astonished to observe that his offspring inherited the habit, and although it was not necessary to attach a chain to their necks, I have often seen a young male throwing his horns over his back and shifting from side to side an imaginary chain. The action was exactly the same as that of his ancestor. The case of the kid of this goat appears to me to be parallel to that of child and parent given by Mr. Hartog. I think at the time I made this observation I informed Mr. Darwin of the fact by letter, and he did not accuse me of "flat Lamarckism".'

To this letter there was no rejoinder. It may be said, of course, that the action of the offspring in each of these cases was due to accidental coincidence only. Anything can be said, but the question turns not on what an advocate can say, but on what a reasonably intelligent and disinterested jury will believe; granted they might be mistaken in accepting the foregoing stories, but the world of science, like that of commerce, is based on the faith or confidence which both creates and sustains them. Indeed the universe itself is but the creature of faith, for assuredly we know of no other foundation. There is nothing so generally and reasonably accepted — not even our own continued identity — but questions may be raised about it that will shortly prove unanswerable. We cannot so test every sixpence given us in change as to be sure that we never take a bad one, and had better sometimes be cheated than reduce caution to an absurdity. Moreover, we have seen from the evidence given in my preceding article that the germ-cells issuing from a parent's body can, and do, respond to profound impressions made on the somatic cells. This being so, what impressions are more profound, what needs engage more assiduous attention than those connected with self-protection, the procuring of food, and the continuation of the species? If the mere anxiety connected with an ill-healing wound inflicted on but one generation is sometimes found to have so impressed the germ-cells that they hand down its scars to offspring, how much more shall not anxieties that have directed action of all kinds from birth till death, not in one generation only but in a longer series of generations than the mind can realize to itself, modify and indeed control, the organization of every species?

I see Professor S. H. Vines, in the article on Weismann's theory referred to in my preceding article says, Mr. Darwin 'held that it was not the sudden variations due to altered external conditions which become permanent, but those slowly produced by what he termed "the accumulative action of changed conditions of life".' Nothing can be more soundly Lamarckian, and nothing should more conclusively show that, whatever else Mr. Darwin was, he was not a Charles Darwinian; but what evidence other than inferential can from the nature of the case be adduced in support of this, as I believe, perfectly correct judgment? None know better than they who clamour for direct evidence that their master was right in taking the position assigned to him by Professor Vines, that they cannot reasonably look for it. With us, as with themselves, modification proceeds very gradually, and it violates our principles as much as their own to expect visible permanent progress, in any single generation, or indeed in any number of generations of wild species which we have yet had time to observe. Occasionally we can find such cases, as in that of *Branchipus stagnalis*, quoted by Mr. Wallace, or in that of the New Zealand Kea whose skin, I was assured by the late Sir Julius von Haast, has already been modified as a consequence of its change of food. Here we can show that in even a few generations structure is modified under changed conditions of existence, but as we believe these cases to occur comparatively rarely, so it is still more rarely that they occur when and where we can watch them. Nature is eminently conservative, and fixity of type, even under considerable change of conditions, is surely more important for the well-being of any species than an over-ready power of adaption to, it may be, passing changes. There could be no steady progress if each generation were not mainly bound by the traditions of those that have gone before it. It is evolution and not incessant revolution that both parties are upholding; and this being so, rapid visible modification must be the exception, not the rule. I have quoted direct evidence adduced by competent observers, which is, I believe, sufficient to establish the fact that offspring can be and is sometimes modified by the acquired habits of a progenitor. I will now proceed to the still more, as it appears to me, cogent proof afforded by general considerations.

What, let me ask, are the principal phenomena of heredity? There must be physical continuity between parent, or parents, and offspring, so that the offspring is, as Erasmus Darwin well said, a kind of elongation of the life of the parent.

Erasmus Darwin put the matter so well that I may as well give his words in full; he wrote:

'Owing to the imperfection of language the offspring is termed a new animal, but is in truth a branch or elongation of the parent, since a part of the embryon animal is, or was, a part of the parent, and therefore, in strict language, cannot be said to be entirely new at the time of its production; and therefore it may retain some of the habits of the parent system.

'At the earliest period of its existence the embryon would seem to consist of a living filament with certain capabilities of irritation, sensation, volition and association, and also with some acquired habits or propensities peculiar to the parent; the former of these are in common with other animals; the latter seem to distinguish or produce the kind of animal, whether man or quadruped, with the similarity of feature or form to the parent.'[1]

Those who accept evolution insist on unbroken physical continuity between the earliest known life and ourselves, so that we both are and are not personally identical with the unicellular organism from which we have descended in the course of many millions of years, exactly in the same ways as an octogenarian both is and is not personally identical with the microscopic impregnate ovum from which he grew up. Everything both is and is not. There is no such thing as strict identity between any two things in any two consecutive seconds. In strictness they are identical and yet not identical, so that in strictness they violate a fundamental rule of strictness — namely, that a thing shall never be itself and not itself at one and the same time; we must choose between logic and dealing in a practical spirit with time and space; it is not surprising, therefore, that logic, in spite of the show of respect outwardly paid to her, is told to stand aside when people come to practice. In practice identity is generally held to exist where continuity is only broken slowly and piecemeal; nevertheless, that occasional periods of even rapid change are not held to bar identity, appears from the fact that no one denies this to hold between the microscopically small impregnate ovum and the born child that springs from it, nor yet, therefore, between the impregnate ovum and the octogenarian into which the child grows; for both ovum and octogenarian are held personally identical with the new-born baby, and things that are identical with the same are identical with one another.

[1] *Zoonomia*, 1794, vol. I, p. 480.

The first, then, and most important element of heredity is that there should be unbroken continuity, and hence sameness of personality, between parents and offspring, in neither more nor less than the same sense as that in which any other two personalities are said to be the same. The repetition, therefore, of its developmental stages by any offspring must be regarded as something which the embryo repeating them has already done once, in the person of one or other parent; and if once, then, as many times as there have been generations between any given embryo now repeating it, and the point in life from which we started — say, for example, the amœba. In the case of asexually and sexually produced organisms alike, the offspring must be held to continue the personality of the parent or parents, and hence on the occasion of every fresh development, to be repeating something which in the person of its parent or parents it has done once, and if once, then any number of times, already.

It is obvious, therefore, that the germ-plasm (or whatever the fancy word for it may be) of any one generation is as physically identical with the germ-plasm of its predecessor as any two things can be. The difference between Professor Weismann and, we will say, Heringians consists in the fact that the first maintains the new germ-plasm when on the point of repeating its developmental processes to take practically no cognisance of anything that has happened to it since the last occasion on which it developed itself; while the latter maintain that offspring takes much the same kind of account of what has happened to it in the persons of its parents since the last occasion on which it developed itself, as people in ordinary life take things that happen to them. In daily life people let fairly normal circumstances come and go without much heed as matters of course. If they have been lucky they make a note of it and try to repeat their success. If they have been unfortunate but have recovered rapidly they soon forget it; if they have suffered long and deeply they grizzle over it and are scared and scarred by it for a long time. The question is one of cognisance or non-cognisance on the part of the new germs, of the more profound impressions made on them while they were one with their parents, between the occasion of their last preceding development and the new course on which they are about to enter. Those who accept the theory put forward independently by Professor Hering of Prague (whose work on this subject is translated in my book *Unconscious Memory*) and by myself in *Life and Habit*, believe in cognisance as do Lamarckians generally. Weismannites, and with them the orthodoxy of English science, find non-cognisance more acceptable.

If the Heringian view is accepted, that heredity is only a mode of memory, and an extension of memory from one generation to another, then the repetition of its development by any embryo thus becomes only the repetition of a lesson learned by rote; and, as I have elsewhere said, our view of life is simplified by finding that it is no longer an equation of, say, a hundred unknown quantities, but of ninety-nine only, inasmuch as two of the unknown quantities prove to be sub-stantially identical. In this case the inheritance of acquired charac-teristics cannot be disputed, for it is postulated in the theory that each embryo takes note of, remembers and is guided by the profounder impressions made upon it while in the persons of its parents, between its present and last preceding development. To maintain this is to maintain use and disuse to be the main factors throughout organic development; to deny it is to deny that use and disuse can have any conceivable effect. For the detailed reasons which led me to my own conclusions I must refer the reader to my books *Life and Habit* and *Unconscious Memory*, the conclusions of which have been often adopted, but never, that I have seen, disputed. A brief résumé of the leading points in the argument is all that space will here allow me to give.

We have seen that it is a first requirement of heredity that there shall be physical continuity between parents and offspring. This holds good with memory. There must be continued identity between the person remembering and the person to whom the thing that is remembered happened. We cannot remember things that happened to someone else, and in our absence. We can only remember having heard of them. We have seen, however, that there is as much *bona fide* sameness of personality between parents and offspring up to the time at which the offspring quits the parent's body, as there is between the different states of the parent himself at any two consecutive moments; the offspring therefore, being one and the same person with its progenitors until it quits them, can be held to remember what happened to them within, of course, the limitations to which all memory is subject, as much as the progenitors can remember what happened earlier to themselves. Whether it does so remember can only be settled by observing whether it acts as living beings commonly do when they are acting under guidance of memory. I will endeavour to show that, though heredity and habit based on memory go about in different dresses, yet if we catch them separately — for they are never seen together — and strip them there is not a mole nor strawberry-mark nor trick nor leer of the one, but we find it in the other also.

What are the moles and strawberry-marks of habitual action, or actions remembered and thus repeated? First, the more often we repeat them the more easily and unconsciously we do them. Look at reading, writing, walking, talking, playing the piano, etc.; the longer we have practised any one of these acquired habits, the more easily, automatically and unconsciously, we perform it. Look, on the other hand, broadly, at the three points to which I called attention in *Life and Habit*:

I. That we are most conscious of and have most control over such habits as speech, the upright position, the arts and sciences — which are acquisitions peculiar to the human race, always acquired after birth, and not common to ourselves and any ancestor who had not become entirely human.

II. That we are less conscious of and have less control over eating and drinking (provided the food be normal), swallowing, breathing, seeing and hearing — which were acquisitions of our prehuman ancestry, and for which we had provided ourselves with all the necessary apparatus before we saw light, but which are still, geologically speaking, recent.

III. That we are most unconscious of and have least control over our digestion and circulation — powers possessed even by our invertebrate ancestry, and, geologically speaking, of extreme antiquity.

I have put the foregoing very broadly, but enough is given to show the reader the gist of the argument. Let it be noted that disturbance and departure, to any serious extent, from normal practice tends to induce resumption of consciousness even in the case of such old habits as breathing, seeing and hearing, digestion and the circulation of the blood. So it is with habitual actions in general. Let a player be never so proficient on any instrument, he will be put out if the normal conditions under which he plays are too widely departed from, and will then do consciously, if indeed he can do it at all, what he had hitherto been doing unconsciously. It is an axiom as regards actions acquired after birth, that we never do them automatically save as the result of long practice; the stages in the case of any acquired facility, the inception of which we have been able to watch, have invariably been from a nothingness of ignorant impotence to a little somethingness of highly self-conscious, arduous performance, and thence to the unself-consciousness of easy mastery. I saw one year a poor blind lad of about eighteen sitting on a wall by the wayside at Varese, playing the concertina with his whole body, and snorting like a child. The next year the boy no longer snorted, and he played with his fingers only; the year after that he seemed hardly to know whether he was playing or not, it came so easily to him. I know no exception to this rule. Where is the intricate and at one time difficult art in which perfect automatic ease has been reached except as the result of long practice? If, then, wherever we can trace the development of automatism we find it to have taken this course, is it not most reasonable to infer that it has taken the same even when it has risen in regions that are beyond our ken? Ought we not, whenever we see a difficult action performed automatically, to suspect antecedent practice? Granted that without the considerations in regard to identity presented above it would not have been easy to see where a baby of a day old could have had the practice which enables it to do as much as it does unconsciously, but even without these considerations it would have been more easy to suppose that the necessary opportunities had not been wanting, than that the easy performance could have been gained without practice and memory.

When I wrote *Life and Habit* (originally published in 1877) I said in slightly different words:

'Shall we say that a baby of a day old sucks (which involves the whole principle of the pump and hence a profound practical knowledge of the laws of pneumatics and hydrostatics), digests, oxygenizes its blood — millions of years before anyone had discovered oxygen— sees and hears, operations that involve an unconscious knowledge of the facts concerning optics and acoustics compared with which the conscious discoveries of Newton are insignificant — shall we say that a baby can do all these things at once, doing them so well and so regularly without being even able to give them attention, and yet without mistake, and shall we also say at the same time that it has not learnt to do them, and never did them before?

'Such an assertion would contradict the whole experience of mankind.'

I have met with nothing during the thirteen years since the foregoing was published that has given me any qualms about its soundness. From the point of view of the law courts and everyday life it is, of course, nonsense; but in the kingdom of thought, as in that of heaven, there are many mansions, and what would be extravagance in the cottage or farm-house, as it were, of daily practice, is but common decency in the palace of high philosophy, wherein dwells evolution. If we leave evolution alone, we may stick to common practice and the law courts; touch evolution and we are in another world; not higher, nor lower, but different as harmony from counterpoint. As, however, in the most absolute counterpoint there is still harmony, and in the most absolute harmony still counterpoint, so high philosophy should be still in touch with common sense, and common sense with high philosophy.

The common-sense view of the matter to people who are not over-curious and to whom time is money, will be that a baby is not a baby until it is born, and that when born it should be born in wedlock. Nevertheless, as a sop to high philosophy, every baby is allowed to be the offspring of its father and mother.

The high-philosophy view of the matter is that every human being is still but a fresh edition of the primordial cell with the latest additions and corrections; there has been no leap nor break in continuity anywhere; the man of today is the primordial cell of millions of years ago as truly as he is the himself of yesterday; he can only be denied to be the one on grounds that will prove him not to be the other. Everyone is both himself and all his direct ancestors and descendants as well; therefore, if we would be logical, he is one also with all his cousins, no matter how distant, for he and they are alike identical with the primordial cell, and we have already noted it as an axiom that things which are identical with the same are identical with one another. This is practically making him one with all living things, whether animal or vegetable, that ever have existed or ever will — something of all which may have been in the mind of Sophocles when he wrote:

Nor seest thou yet the gathering hosts of ill
That shall en-one thee both with thine own self
And with thine offspring.

And all this has come of admitting that a man may be the same person for two days running! As for sopping common sense it will be enough to say that these remarks are to be taken in a strictly scientific sense, and have no appreciable importance as regards life and conduct. True they deal with the foundations on which all life and conduct are based, but like other foundations they are hidden out of sight, and the sounder they are, the less we trouble ourselves about them.

What other main common features between heredity and memory may we note besides the fact that neither can exist without that kind of physical continuity which we call personal identity? First, the development of the embryo proceeds in an established order; so must all habitual actions based on memory. Disturb the normal order and the performance is arrested. The better we know 'God save the Queen', the less easily can we play or sing it backwards. The return of memory again depends on the return of ideas associated with the particular thing that is remembered — we remember nothing but for the presence of these, and when enough of these are presented to us we re-member everything. So, if the development of an embryo is due to memory, we should suppose the memory of the impregnate ovum to revert not to yesterday, when it was in the persons of its parents, but to the last occasion on which it was an impregnate ovum. The return of the old environment and the presence of old associations would at once involve recollection of the course that should be next taken, and the same should happen throughout the whole course of development. The actual course of development presents precisely the phenomena agreeable with this. For fuller treatment of this point I must refer the reader to the chapter on the abeyance of memory in my book *Life and Habit*, already referred to.

Secondly, we remember best our last few performances of any given kind, so our present performance will probably resemble some one or other of these; we remember our earlier performances by way of residuum only, but every now and then we revert to an earlier habit. This feature of memory is manifested in heredity by the way in which offspring commonly resembles most its nearer ancestors, but sometimes reverts to earlier ones. Brothers and sisters, each as it were giving their own version of the same story, but in different words, should generally resemble each other more closely than more distant relations. And this is what actually we find.

Thirdly, the introduction of slightly new elements into a method already established varies it beneficially; the new is soon fused with the old, and the monotony ceases to be oppressive. But if the new be too foreign, we cannot fuse the old and the new — nature seeming to hate equally too wide a deviation from ordinary practice and none at all. This fact reappears in heredity as the beneficial effects of occasional crossing on the one hand, and on the other, in the generally observed sterility of hybrids. If heredity be an affair of memory, how can an embryo, say of a mule, be expected to build up a mule on the strength of but two mule memories? Hybridism causes a fault in the chain of memory, and it is to this cause that the usual sterility of hybrids must be referred.

Fourthly, it requires many repeated impressions to fix a method firmly, but when it has been engrained into us we cease to have much recollection of the manner in which it came to be so, or indeed of any individual repetition, but sometimes a single impression if prolonged as well as profound, produces a lasting impression and is liable to return with sudden force, and then to go on returning to us at intervals. As a general rule, however, abnormal impressions cannot long hold their own against the overwhelming preponderance of normal authority. This appears in heredity as the normal non-inheritance of mutilations on the one hand, and on the other as their occasional inheritance in the case of injuries followed by disease.

Fifthly, if heredity and memory are essentially the same, we should expect that no animal would develop new structures of importance after the age at which its species begins ordinarily to continue its race; for we cannot suppose offspring to remember anything that happens to the parent subsequently to the parent's ceasing to contain the offspring within itself. From the average age, therefore, of reproduction, offspring should cease to have any further steady, continuous memory to fall back upon; what memory there is should be full of faults, and as such unreliable. An organism ought to develop as long as it is backed by memory — that is to say, until the average age at which reproduction begins; it should then continue to go for a time on the impetus already received, and should eventually decay through failure of any memory to support it, and tell it what to do. This corresponds absolutely with what we observe in organisms generally, and explains, on the one hand, why the age of puberty marks the beginning of completed development — a riddle hitherto not only unexplained but, so far as I have seen, unasked; it explains, on the other hand, the phenomena of old age — hitherto without even attempt at explanation.

Sixthly, those organisms that are the longest in reaching maturity should on the average be the longest-lived, for they will have received the most momentous impulse from the weight of memory behind them. This harmonizes with the latest opinion as to the facts. In his article of Weismann in the *Contemporary Review* for May 1890, Mr. Romanes writes: 'Professor Weismann has shown that there is throughout the metazoa a general correlation between the natural lifetime of individuals composing any given species, and the age at which they reach maturity or first become capable of procreation.' This, I believe, has been the conclusion generally arrived at by biologists for some years past.

Lateness, then, in the average age of reproduction appears to be the principle underlying longevity. There does not appear at first sight to be much connection between such distinct and apparently disconnected phenomena as 1, the orderly normal progress of development; 2, atavism and the resumption of feral characteristics; 3, the more ordinary resemblance *inter se* of nearer relatives; 4, the benefit of an occasional cross, and the usual sterility of hybrids; 5, the unconsciousness with which alike bodily development and ordinary physiological functions proceed, so long as they are normal; 6, the ordinary noninheritance, but occasional inheritance of mutilations; 7, the fact that puberty indicates the approach of maturity; 8, the phenomena of middle life and old age; 9, the principle underlying longevity. These phenomena have no conceivable bearing on one another until heredity and memory are regarded as part of the same story. Identify these two things, and I know no phenomenon of heredity that does not immediately become infinitely more intelligible. Is it conceivable that a theory which harmonizes so many facts hitherto regarded as without either connection or explanation should not deserve at any rate consideration from those who profess to take an interest in biology?

It is not as though the theory were unknown, or had been condemned by our leading men of science. Professor Ray Lankester introduced it to English readers in an appreciative notice of Professor Hering's address, which appeared in *Nature*, July 13th, 1876. He wrote to the *Athenæum*, March 24th, 1884, and claimed credit for having done so, but I do not believe he has ever said more in public about it than what I have here referred to. Mr. Romanes did indeed try to crush it in *Nature*, January 27th, 1881, but in 1883, in his *Mental Evolution in Animals*, he adopted its main conclusion without acknowledgment. The *Athenæum*, to my unbounded surprise, called him to task for this (March 1st, 1884), and since that time he has given the Heringian theory a sufficiently wide berth. Mr. Wallace showed himself favourably enough disposed towards the view that heredity and memory are part of the same story when he reviewed my book *Life and Habit* in *Nature*, March 27th, 1879, but he has never since betrayed any sign of being aware that such a theory existed. Mr. Herbert Spencer wrote to the *Athenæum* (April 5th, 1884), and claimed the theory for himself, but, in spite of his doing this, he has never, that I have seen, referred to the matter again. I have dealt sufficiently with his claim in my book *Luck or Cunning*. Lastly, Professor Hering himself has never that I know of touched his own theory since the single short address read in 1870, and translated by me in 1881. Everyone, even its originator, except myself, seems afraid to open his mouth about it. Of course the inference suggests itself that other people have more sense than I have. I readily admit it; but why have so many of our leaders shown such a strong hankering after the theory, if there is nothing in it?

The deadlock that I have pointed out as existing in Darwinism will, I doubt not, lead ere long to a consideration of Professor Hering's theory. English biologists are little likely to find Weismann satisfactory for long, and if he breaks down there is nothing left for them but Lamarck, supplemented by the important and elucidatory corollary on his theory proposed by Professor Hering. When the time arrives for this to obtain a hearing it will be confirmed, doubtless, by arguments clearer and more forcible than any I have been able to adduce; I shall then be delighted to resign the championship which till then I shall continue, as for some years past, to have much pleasure in sustaining. Heretofore my satisfaction has mainly lain in the fact that more of our prominent men of science have seemed anxious to claim the theory than to refute it; in the confidence thus engendered I leave it to any fuller consideration which the outline I have above given may incline the reader to bestow upon it.

THE NOTE-BOOKS: VERSES

'APSALM of Montreal' was first published in the *Spectator* on May 18th, 1878. Its origin goes back to the years (1874-75) which Butler spent in Canada in an attempt to retrieve some of the money he had been persuaded by his friend, Hoare, to invest in various speculative companies. Butler gave a number of copies of the 'Psalm' to friends; but it was not re-published in his lifetime. It appeared, with his sonnets, in a volume, *Seven Sonnets and A Psalm of Montreal*, privately printed at Cambridge in 1904, and was included in *The Note-Books of Samuel Butler*, edited by Henry Festing Jones in 1912.

A PSALM OF MONTREAL

The City of Montreal is one of the most rising and, in many respects, most agreeable on the American continent, but its inhabitants are as yet too busy with commerce to care greatly about the masterpieces of old Greek Art. In the Montreal Museum of Natural History I came upon two plaster casts, one of the Antinous and the other of the Discobolus — not the good one, but in my poem, of course, I intend the good one — banished from public view to a room where were all manner of skins, plants, snakes, insects, etc., and, in the middle of these, an old man stuffing an owl.

'Ah,' said I, 'so you have some antiques here; why don't you put them where people can see them?'

'Well, sir,' answered the custodian, 'you see they are rather vulgar.'

He then talked a great deal and said his brother did all Mr. Spurgeon's printing.

The dialogue — perhaps true, perhaps imaginary, perhaps a little of the one and a little of the other — between the writer and this old man gave rise to the lines that follow:

Stowed away in a Montreal lumber room
The Discobolus standeth and turneth his face to the wall;
Dusty, cobweb-covered, maimed and set at naught,
Beauty crieth in an attic and no man regardeth:
　　　　　　　O God! O Montreal!

Beautiful by night and day, beautiful in summer and winter,
Whole or maimed, always and alike beautiful —
He preacheth gospel of grace to the skin of owls
And to one who seasoneth the skins of Canadian owls:
O God! O Montreal!

When I saw him I was wroth and I said, 'O Discobolus!
Beautiful Discobolus, a Prince both among gods and men!
What doest thou here, how camest thou hither, Discobolus,
Preaching gospel in vain to the skins of owls?'
O God! O Montreal!

And I turned to the man of skins and said unto him, 'O thou man of
skins,
Wherefore hast thou done thus to shame the beauty of the Discobolus?'
But the Lord had hardened the heart of the man of skins
And he answered, 'My brother-in-law is haberdasher to Mr. Spurgeon.'
O God! O Montreal!

'The Discobolus is put here because he is vulgar —
He has neither vest nor pants with which to cover his limbs;
I, Sir, am a person of most respectable connections —
My brother-in-law is haberdasher to Mr. Spurgeon.'
O God! O Montreal!

Then I said, 'O brother-in-law to Mr. Spurgeon's haberdasher,
Who seasonest also the skins of Canadian owls,
Thou callest trousers "pants", whereas I call them "trousers",
Therefore thou art in hell-fire and may the Lord pity thee!'
O God! O Montreal!

'Preferrest thou the gospel of Montreal to the gospel of Hellas,
The gospel of thy connection with Mr. Spurgeon's haberdashery to the
gospel of the Discobolus?'
Yet none the less blasphemed he beauty saying, 'The Discobolus hath
no gospel,
But my brother-in-law is haberdasher to Mr. Spurgeon.'
O God! O Montreal!

'THE Righteous Man' was written in 1876, and was first published in the *Examiner* in 1879, in connection with the correspondence arising out of Butler's contributions entitled *A Clergyman's Doubts*. It was signed 'X. Y. Z.' Festing Jones reprinted it in his volume of extracts from Butler's note-books.

THE RIGHTEOUS MAN

The righteous man will rob none but the defenceless,
Whatsoever can reckon with him he will neither plunder nor kill;
He will steal an egg from a hen or a lamb from an ewe,
For his sheep and his hens cannot reckon with him hereafter —
They live not in any odour of defencefulness:
Therefore right is with the righteous man, and he taketh advantage righteously,
Praising God and plundering.

The righteous man will enslave his horse and his dog,
Making them serve him for their bare keep and for nothing further,
Shooting them, selling them for vivisection when they can no longer profit him,
Backbiting them and beating them if they fail to please him;
For his horse and his dog can bring no action for damages,
Wherefore, then, should he not enslave them, shoot them, sell them for vivisection?

But the righteous man will not plunder the defenceful —
Not if he be alone and unarmed — for his conscience will smite him;
He will not rob a she-bear of her cubs, nor an eagle of her eaglets —
Unless he have a rifle to purge him from the fear of sin:
Then may he shoot rejoicing in innocency — from ambush or a safe distance;
Or he will beguile them, lay poison for them, keep no faith with them;
For what faith is there with that which cannot reckon hereafter,
Neither by itself, nor by another, nor by any residuum of ill consequences?
Surely, where weakness is utter, honour ceaseth.

Nay, I will do what is right in the eye of him who can harm me,
And not in those of him who cannot call me to account.
Therefore yield me up thy pretty wings, O humming-bird!
Sing for me in a prison, O lark!
Pay me thy rent, O widow! for it is mine.
Where there is reckoning there is sin,
And where there is no reckoning sin is not.

'IN Memoriam H. R. F.' was first printed in the *Note-Books* and was also printed in Festing Jones's *Memoir*. H. R. F. was a young Swiss, Hans Rudolf Faesch, to whom Butler had become deeply attached. Faesch came to London from Basle in 1893, and was much with Butler and Jones during the next two years. His health was bad, and he left to take up a business appointment in Singapore, in the hope that the climate would do him good. Butler was much grieved at the parting, and wrote this poem in the conviction that he would never see Hans again. Actually, he revisited Europe twice, and met Butler, whom he outlived by more than a year, dying in 1903 in the Shan States, at the age of 32.

IN MEMORIAM

Feb. 14th, 1895

TO

H. R. F.

Out, out, out into the night,
With the wind bitter North East and the sea rough:
You have a racking cough and your lungs are weak,
But out, out into the night you go,
    So guide you and guard you Heaven and fare you well!

We have been three lights to one another and now we are two,
For you go far and alone into the darkness;
But the light in you was stronger and clearer than ours,
For you came straighter from God and, whereas we had learned,
You had never forgotten. Three minutes more and then
Out, out into the night you go,
    So guide you and guard you Heaven and fare you well!

Never a cross look, never a thought,
Never a word that had better been left unspoken;
We gave you the best we had, such as it was,
It pleased you well, for you smiled and nodded your head;
And now, out, out into the night you go,
    So guide you and guard you Heaven and fare you well!

You said we were a little weak that the three of us wept,
Are we then weak if we laugh when we are glad?
When men are under the knife let them roar as they will,
So that they flinch not.
Therefore let tears flow on, for so long as we live
No such second sorrow shall ever draw nigh us,
Till one of us two leaves the other alone
And goes out, out, out into the night,
     So guard the one that is left, O God, and fare him well!

Yet for the great bitterness of this grief
We three, you and he and I,
May pass into the hearts of like true comrades hereafter,
In whom we may weep anew and yet comfort them,
As they too pass out, out, out into the night,
     So guide them and guard them Heaven and fare them well!

The minutes have flown and he whom we loved is gone,
The like of whom we never again shall see;
The wind is heavy with snow and the sea rough,
He has a racking cough and his lungs are weak.
Hand in hand we watch the train as it glides
Out, out, out into the night.
     So take him into thy holy keeping, O Lord,
     And guide him and guard him ever, and fare him well!

'WE Were Two Lovers'. This sonnet was written in 1902 — the last Butler wrote. He gave it the title 'An Academic Exercise', and Festing Jones retained this when he printed it for the first time in the *Note-Books*, but appended a note discussing why Butler could have given it so inappropriate a title. An 'academic exercise' I think it clearly was not. It was written at a time when Butler was going over old papers and 'editing his remains', as Festing Jones says. Butler did not show Jones the sonnet, or discuss it with him. For my part, I feel pretty sure it refers, in an indirect way, to Butler's friendship with Pauli, and that the title was designed to disguise this.

WE WERE TWO LOVERS

We were two lovers standing sadly by
While our two loves lay dead upon the ground;
Each love had striven not to be first to die,
But each was gashed with many a cruel wound.
Said I: 'Your love was false while mine was true.'
Aflood with tears he cried: 'It was not so,
'Twas your false love my true love falsely slew —
For 'twas your love that was the first to go.'
Thus did we stand and said no more for shame
Till I, seeing his cheek so wan and wet,
Sobbed thus: 'So be it; my love shall bear the blame;
Let us inter them honourably.' And yet
    I swear by all truth human and divine
    'Twas his that in its death throes murdered mine.

'A PRAYER' was written in 1900 or 1901, and was first published in the *Note-Books*. Butler probably composed it when he had lighted on the following passage in going over his old note-books for 1883:

'Cleanse thou me from my secret sins.' I heard a man moralizing on this and shocked him by saying demurely that I did not mind these so much, if I could get rid of those that were obvious to other people.

A PRAYER

Searcher of souls, you who in heaven abide,
To whom the secrets of all hearts are open,
Though I do lie to all the world beside,
From me to these no falsehood shall be spoken.
Cleanse me not, Lord, I say, from secret sin
But from those faults which he who runs can see,
'Tis these that torture me, O Lord, begin
With these and let the hidden vices be;
If you must cleanse these too, at any rate
Deal with the seen sins first, 'tis only reason,
They being so gross, to let the others wait
The leisure of some more convenient season;
    And cleanse not all even then, leave me a few,
    I would not be — not quite — so pure as you.

'THE Life after Death' was Butler's first sonnet, written in 1898 while he was at work on his edition of Shakespeare's Sonnets (*Shakespeare's Sonnets Reconsidered and in part Re-arranged*, 1899). After writing it, Butler wrote to Festing Jones, saying that it was 'a poor innocent thing, but I was surprised to find how easily it came; if you like it I may write a few more'. He did.

THE LIFE AFTER DEATH

Not on sad Stygian shore, nor in clear sheen
Of far Elysian plain, shall we meet those
Among the dead whose pupils we have been,
Nor those great shades whom we have held as foes;
No meadow of asphodel our feet shall tread,
Nor shall we look each other in the face
To love or hate each other being dead,
Hoping some praise, or fearing some disgrace.
We shall not argue saying ''Twas thus' or 'Thus,'
Our argument's whole drift we shall forget;
Who's right, who's wrong, 'twill be all one to us;
We shall not even know that we have met.
      Yet meet we shall, and part, and meet again,
      Where dead men meet, on lips of living men.

'HANDEL'. This is the second, and much better, of two sonnets Butler wrote on this theme. In 1883 he had written in his
note-book:

Of all dead men Handel has had the largest place in my thoughts.
In fact I should say that he and his music have been the central
fact of my life ever since I was old enough to know of the existence
of either life or music. All day long — whether I am writing or
painting or walking, but always — I have his music in my head;
and if I lose sight of it and of him for an hour or two, as of course
I sometimes do, this is as much as I do. I believe I am not exaggerating when I say that I have never been a day since I was 13
without having Handel in my head many times over.

(*Note-Books*, p. 384)

HANDEL

Father of my poor music — if such small
Offspring as mine, so born out of due time,
So scorn'd, can be called fatherful at all,
Or dare to thy high sonship's rank to climb —
Best lov'd of all the dead whom I love best,
Though I love many another dearly too,
You in my heart take rank above the rest;
King of those kings that most control me, you,
You were about my path, about my bed
In boyhood always and, where'er I be,
Whate'er I think or do, you, in my head,
Ground-bass to all my thoughts, are still with me;
  Methinks the very worms will find some strain
  Of yours still lingering in my wasted brain.

BUTLER first began composing music in 1883, and was soon collaborating with Festing Jones, whom he had first met in 1876, in the series of pieces in the 'Handelian manner' which appeared in 1885 as *Gavottes, Minuets, Fugues, and other short pieces for the Piano*. This was followed in 1888 by *Narcissus: a Cantata in the Handelian Form*, from which the following verses are taken. Butler seems to have written most of the words for this, the music being shared fairly equally between him and Jones. The manner of the Cantata is pastoral burlesque. Narcissus and Amaryllis are lovers; but the nymph jilts him because he has no money, only to be speedily re-united to him when he unexpectedly inherits a fortune from his great aunt. Interwoven with this theme is an outbreak of financial speculation among the shepherds and shepherdesses, who, like Butler, lose their money when the bubble bursts. The moral is that it is virtuous to be rich and to invest in the safety of Consolidated Three Per Cents, keeping clear of 'Speculation, horrid fiend'.

Butler's remaining musical composition, in which he again collaborated with Festing Jones, was *Ulysses: an Oratorio*, published in 1904, two years after his death. Jones records that Butler had finished his part of this more serious Handelian work before he died, and that the delay in publication was due to his own tardiness in finishing the parts assigned to him.

CHORUS Oh! Speculation, horrid fiend,
    Full well we know thee now;
   The mask that once thy features screened
    Has fallen from thy brow.
   We'll listen to thy voice no more,
   We would be shepherds as of yore.

NARCISSUS So sing they now; but should some god restore
   The gold they've lost they'd try their luck again.
   Not so with me; I never more would touch
   Egyptian bonds, nor far Columbia's rails,
   Nor mines, nor any loans from foreign shores,
   No matter how attractive. . . .

O Return to your Home

MESSENGER

AIR. S.B.

Oh! re - turn to your home far a - way   By the
From the flow'rs that e - na - mel the ground   Ga - ther

side of its mur-mur-ing stream   There at   least you can feed night and
chap-lets for Beau-ty's fair brows   And when   these are suf - fi - cient - ly

1

day On fresh eggs, On fresh eggs vir-gin hon-ey and cream   On fresh
crown'd Go and crown Go and crown all your beau-ti-ful cows   Go and

eggs vir-gin hon-ey and cream___
crown all your beau-ti-ful cows___

Your too in-no-cent na-tures in
Make the best not the worst of your

vain   Try   to fi-gure as bulls and as   bears   Ne - ver
lot   And   your trou-bles will pre-sent-ly   cease   Your mis-

dream of as-sum-ing a - gain A - ny form A - ny form so fe - ro-cious as
-for-tunes will then be for - got And you'll end And you'll end your life's jour-ney in

theirs   A - ny form so fe - ro-cious as   theirs.
peace   And you'll end your life's jour-ney in   peace.

Dal Segno

3

RECIT. — "Who knocks?"

S. B.

4

NARCISSUS   Shall I to Egypt's dusky bonds
     A portion of my wealth confine,
Where Memnon's fabled voice responds
     To morning's ray o'er Nilus' tide?

Shall far Columbia's flattering field
     Attract my thousands to her shores,
Or shall unplundered caverns yield
     At my command their glittering ores?

AMARYLLIS   Though jewelled monarchs plead for aid
     Your trusting hand restrain;
Your loans would never be repaid,
     So let them plead in vain.

A maiden's words are little worth,
     But, as you must invest,
Of all securities on earth
     The English funds are best.

CHORUS   Of all securities on earth
     The English funds are best.

CHORUS   How blest the prudent man, the maiden pure,
Whose income is both ample and secure,
Arising from Consolidated Three
Per Cent Annuities, paid quarterly.

SONG FROM *ULYSSES*

The authorship is not distinguished as between the collaborators in *Ulysses*, though it had been in *Narcissus*; but Festing Jones says in his *Memoir* that 'Butler wrote nearly all the words'.

Penelope's Song

> From morn to eve, the whole day long,
> My web I weave and sing my song
> And I pray that heaven will send him home
> For he tarrieth long but he yet will come.
>
> And I ply my loom while the sun rides high
>   With threads of silver and threads of gold;
> And the days pass on and the years roll by
>   But the tale I weave is still untold.
>
> For at night I tear the fabric through
> And again I weave and again undo.
>
> Speeding least when most progressing,
> Yielding least when most professing,
> Doing still and still undoing,
> Thus I cheat them in their wooing.
>
> From morn to eve, the whole day long,
> My web I weave, and sing my song.
> The days may tell but the nights destroy
> The wondrous tale of the fate of Troy.

THE AUTHORESS OF THE ODYSSEY

T H E following short prose version of the story of the Odyssey is taken from Butler's book, *The Authoress of the Odyssey*, which he published in 1897. Before making this short version he had translated the whole of the Odyssey into modern prose, aiming at the production of a readable English version that would be appreciated by readers who did not know Greek. The complete translation was published by Butler at his own expense in 1900, after a number of publishers had refused it. In the meantime, he had also made and published (in 1898) a parallel translation of the Iliad. In his preface to the latter he explained his views upon the art of translation in the following passage:

> The genius of the language into which a translation is being made is the first thing to be considered; if the original was readable, the translation must be so also, or however good it may be as a construe, it is not a translation.
>
> It follows that a translation should depart hardly at all from the modes of speech current in the translator's own times, inasmuch as nothing is readable, for long, which affects any other diction than that of the age in which it is written. We know the charm of the Elizabethan translations, but he who would attempt one that shall vie with these must eschew all Elizabethanisms that are not good Victorianisms also.
>
> For the charm of the Elizabethans does not lie in their Elizabethanisms; these are but as the mosses and lichens which Time will grow upon our Victorian literature as surely as he has grown them upon the Elizabethan — upon such of it, at least, as has not been jerry-built. Shakespeare tells us that it is Time's glory to stamp the seal of time on aged things. No doubt; but he will have no hands stamp it save his own; he will rot an artificial ruin, but he will not glorify it; if he is to hallow any work it must be frankly secular when he deigns to take it in hand — by this I mean honestly after the manner of its own age and country. The Elizabethans probably knew this too well to know that they knew it, but whether they knew it or no they did not lard a crib with Chaucerisms and think that they were translating. They aimed fearlessly and without taint of affectation at making a dead author

living to a generation other than his own. To do this they transfused their blood into his cold veins, and quickened him with their own livingness.

Then the life is theirs not his? In part no doubt it is so; but if they have loved him well enough, his life will have entered into them and possessed them. They will have given him of their life, and he will have paid them in their own coin. If, however, the mouth of the ox who treads out the corn may not be muzzled, and if there is to be a certain give and take between a dead author and his translator, it follows that a translator should be allowed greater liberty when the work he is translating belongs to an age and country widely remote from his own. For a poem's prosperity is like a jest's — it is in the ear of him that hears it. It takes two people to say a thing — a sayee as well as a sayer — and by parity of reasoning a poem's original audience and environment are integral parts of the poem itself. Poem and audience are as *ego* and *non-ego*; they blend into one another. Change either, and some corresponding change, spiritual rather than literal, will be necessary in the other, if the original harmony between them is to be preserved.

Happily in the cases both of the Iliad and the Odyssey we can see clearly enough that the audiences did not differ so widely from ourselves as we might expect after an interval of some three thousand years. But they differ, especially in the case of the Iliad, and the difference necessitates a greater amount of freedom on the part of a translator than would be tolerable if it did not exist.

Freedom of another kind is further involved in the initial liberty of rendering in prose a work that was composed in verse. Prose differs from verse much as singing from speaking or dancing from walking, and what is right in the one is often wrong in the other. Prose, for example, does not permit that iteration of epithet and title, sometimes due merely to the requirements of metre, and sometimes otiose, which abounds in the Iliad without in any way disfiguring it. We look, indeed, for the iteration and enjoy it. We are never weary of being told that Juno is white-armed, Minerva grey-eyed and Agamemnon king of men; but had Homer written in prose he would not have told us these things so often. Therefore, though frequently allowing common form epithets and titles to recur, I have not less frequently suppressed them.

THE STORY OF THE ODYSSEY

BOOK ONE

THE COUNCIL OF THE GODS—
TELEMACHUS AND THE SUITORS
IN THE HOUSE OF ULYSSES

TELL me, O Muse, of that ingenious hero who met with many adventures while trying to bring his men home after the Sack of Troy. He failed in this, for the men perished through their own sheer folly in eating the cattle of the Sun, and he himself, though he was longing to get back to his wife, was now languishing in a lonely island, the abode of the nymph Calypso. Calypso wanted him to marry her, and kept him with her for many years, till at last all the gods took pity upon him except Neptune, whose son Polyphemus he had blinded.

Now it so fell out that Neptune had gone to pay a visit to the Ethiopians, who lie in two halves, one half looking on to the Atlantic and the other on to the Indian Ocean. The other gods, therefore, held a council, and Jove made them a speech about the folly of Ægisthus in wooing Clytemnestra and murdering Agamemnon; finally, yielding to Minerva, he consented that Ulysses should return to Ithaca.

'In that case,' said Minerva, 'we should send Mercury to Calypso to tell her what we have settled. I will also go to Ithaca and embolden Ulysses' son Telemachus to dismiss the suitors of his mother Penelope, who are ruining him by their extravagance. Furthermore, I will send him to Sparta and Pylos to seek news of his father, for this will get him a good name.'

The goddess then winged her way to the gates of Ulysses' house, disguised as an old family friend, and found the suitors playing draughts in front of the house and lording it in great style. Telemachus, seeing her standing at the gate, went up to her, led her within, placed her spear in the spear-stand against a strong bearing-post, brought her a seat, and set refreshments before her.

Meanwhile the suitors came trooping into the sheltered cloisters that ran round the inner court; here, according to their wont, they feasted; and when they had done eating they compelled Phemius, a famous bard, to sing to them. On this Telemachus began talking quietly to

Minerva; he told her how his father's return seemed now quite hopeless, and concluded by asking her name and country.

Minerva said she was Mentes, chief of the Taphians, and was on her way to Temesa with a cargo of iron, which she should exchange for copper. She told Telemachus that her ship was lying outside the town, under Mt. Neritum, in the harbour that was called Rheithron. 'Go,' she added, 'and ask old Laertes, who I hear is now living but poorly in the country and never comes into the town; he will tell you that I am an old friend of your father's.'

She then said, 'But who are all these people whom I see behaving so atrociously about your house? What is it all about? Their conduct is enough to disgust any right-minded person.'

'They are my mother's suitors,' answered Telemachus, 'and come from the neighbouring islands of Dulichium, Same and Zacynthus, as well as from Ithaca itself. My mother does not say she will not marry again and cannot bring her courtship to an end. So they are ruining me.'

Minerva was very indignant, and advised him to fit out a ship and go to Pylos and Sparta, seeking news of his father. 'If,' she said, 'you hear of his being alive, you can put up with all this extravagance for yet another twelve months. If on the other hand you hear of his death, return at once, send your mother to her father's, and by fair means or foul kill the suitors.'

Telemachus thanked her for her advice, promised to take it, and pressed her to prolong her visit. She explained that she could not possibly do so, and then flew off into the air, like an eagle.

Phemius was still singing: he had chosen for his subject the disastrous return of the Achæans from Troy. Penelope could hear him from her room upstairs, and came down into the presence of the suitors holding a veil before her face, and waited upon by two of her handmaids, one of whom stood on either side of her. She stood by one of the bearing-posts that supported the roof of the cloisters, and bade Phemius change his theme, which she found too painful as reminding her of her lost husband.

Telemachus reasoned with her, and ended by desiring her to go upstairs again. 'Go back,' he said, 'within the house and see to your daily duties, your loom, your distaff, and the ordering of your servants; for speech is man's matter, and mine above all others, for it is I who am master here.'

On this Penelope went back, with her women, wondering into the house, and as soon as she was gone Telemachus challenged the suitors to meet him next day in full assembly, that he might formally and publicly warn them to leave his house.

Antinous and Eurymachus, their two leaders, both rejoined; but presently night fell, and the whole body of suitors left the house for their own several abodes. When they were gone his old nurse Euryclea conducted Telemachus by torch light to his bedroom, in a lofty tower, which overlooked the outer courtyard and could be seen from far and near.

Euryclea had been bought by Laertes when she was quite young; he had given the worth of twenty oxen for her, and she was made as much of in the house as his own wife was, but he did not take her to his bed, for he respected his wife's displeasure. The good old woman showed Telemachus to his room, and waited while he undressed. She took his shirt from him, folded it carefully up, and hung it on a peg by his bed side. This done, she left him to dream all night of his intended voyage.

BOOK TWO

ASSEMBLY OF THE PEOPLE OF ITHACA— TELEMACHUS STARTS FOR PYLOS

NEXT morning, as soon as he was up and dressed, Telemachus sent the criers round the town to call the people in assembly. When they came together he told them of his misfortune in the death of his father, and of the still greater one that the suitors were making havoc of his estate. 'If anybody,' he concluded, 'is to eat me out of house and home I had rather you did it yourselves; for you are men of substance, so that if I sued you household by household I should recover from you; whereas there is nothing to be got by suing a number of young men who have no means of their own.'

To this Antinous rejoined that it was Penelope's own fault. She had been encouraging the suitors all the time by sending flattering messages to every single one of them. He explained how for nearly four years she had tricked them about the web, which she said was to be a pall for Laertes. 'The answer therefore,' said he, 'that we make you is this: "Send your mother away, and let her marry the man of her own and of her father's choice"; for we shall not go till she has married some one or other of us.'

Telemachus answered that he could not force his mother to leave against her will. If he did so he should have to refund to his grandfather Icarius the dowry that Ulysses had received on marrying Penelope, and this would bear hardly on him. Besides it would not be a creditable thing to do.

On this Jove sent two eagles from the top of a mountain, who flew and flew in their own lordly flight till they reached the assembly, over which they screamed and fought, glaring death into the faces of those who were below. The people wondered what it might all mean, till the old Soothsayer Halitherses told that it foreshadowed the immediate return of Ulysses to take his revenge upon the suitors.

Eurymachus made him an angry answer. 'As long,' he concluded, 'as Penelope delays her choice, we can marry no one else, and shall continue to waste Telemachus' estate.'

Telemachus replied that there was nothing more to be said, and asked the suitors to let him have a ship with a crew of twenty men, that he might follow the advice given him by Minerva.

Mentor now upbraided his countrymen for standing idly by when they could easily coerce the suitors into good behaviour, and after a few insolent words from Leocritus the meeting dispersed. The suitors then returned to the house of Ulysses.

But Telemachus went away all alone by the seaside to pray. He washed his hands in the grey waves, and implored Minerva to assist him; whereon the goddess came up to him in the form of Mentor. She discoursed to him about his conduct generally, and wound up by saying that she would not only find him a ship, but would come with him herself. He was therefore to go home and get the necessary provisions ready.

He did as she directed him and went home, where, after an angry scene with the suitors, in which he again published his intention of going on his voyage, he went down into the store room and told Euryclea to get the provisions ready; at the same time he made her take a solemn oath of secrecy for ten or twelve days, so as not to alarm Penelope. Meanwhile Minerva, still disguised as Mentor, borrowed a ship from a neighbour, Noëmon, and at nightfall, after the suitors had left as usual, she and Telemachus with his crew of twenty volunteers got the provisions on board and set sail, with a fair wind that whistled over the waters.

BOOK THREE

TELEMACHUS AT THE HOUSE OF NESTOR

THEY reached Pylos on the following morning, and found Nestor, his sons and all the Pylians celebrating the feast of Neptune. They were cordially received, especially by Nestor's son Pisistratus, and were at once invited to join the festivities. After dinner Nestor asked them who they were, and Telemachus, emboldened by Minerva, explained that they came from Ithaca under Neritum, and that he was seeking news of the death of his father Ulysses.

When he heard this, Nestor told him all about his own adventures on his way home from Troy, but could give him no news of Ulysses. He touched, however, on the murder of Agamemnon by Ægisthus, and the revenge taken by Orestes.

Telemachus said he wished he might be able to take a like revenge on the suitors of his mother, who were ruining him; 'but this,' he exclaimed, 'could not happen, not even if the gods wished it. It is too much even to think of.'

Minerva reproved him sharply. 'The hand of heaven,' she said, 'can reach far when it has a mind to save a man.' Telemachus then changed the conversation, and asked Nestor how Ægisthus managed to kill Agamemnon, who was so much the better man of the two. What was Menelaus doing?

'Menelaus,' answered Nestor, 'had not yet returned from his long wanderings. As for Clytemnestra, she was naturally of a good disposition, but was beguiled by Ægisthus, who reigned seven years in Mycene after he had killed Agamemnon. In the eighth year, however, Orestes came from Athens and killed him, and on the very day when Orestes was celebrating the funeral feast of Ægisthus and Clytemnestra, Menelaus returned. Go then to Sparta, and see if he can tell you anything.'

By this time the sun had set, and Minerva proposed that she and Telemachus should return to their ship, but Nestor would not hear of their doing so. Minerva therefore consented that Telemachus should stay on shore, and explained that she could not remain with him inasmuch as she must start on the following morning for the Cauconians, to recover a large debt that had been long owing to her.

Having said this, to the astonishment of all present she flew away in the form of an eagle. Whereon Nestor grasped Telemachus' hand and said he could see that he must be a very important person. He also at once vowed to gild the horns of a heifer and sacrifice her to the goddess. He then took Telemachus home with him and lodged him in his own house.

Next day Nestor fulfilled his vow; the heifer was brought in from the plains, her horns were gilded, and Nestor's wife Eurydice and her daughters shouted with delight at seeing her killed.

After the banquet that ensued Nestor sent Telemachus and his son Pisistratus off in a chariot and pair for Lacedæmon, which they reached on the following morning, after passing a night in the house of Diocles at Pheræ.

BOOK FOUR

TELEMACHUS AT THE HOUSE OF MENELAUS—THE SUITORS RESOLVE TO LIE IN WAIT FOR HIM AS HE RETURNS, AND MURDER HIM

WHEN the two young men reached Lacedæmon they drove straight to Menelaus' house [and found him celebrating the double marriage of his daughter Hermione and his son Megapenthes].

Menelaus (after a little demur on the part of his *major domo* Eteoneus, for which he was severely reprimanded by his master) entertained his guests very hospitably, and overhearing Telemachus call his friend's attention to the splendour of the house, he explained to them how much toil and sorrow he had endured, especially through the murder of his brother Agamemnon, the plundering of his house by Paris when he carried off Helen, and the death of so many of his brave comrades at Troy. 'There is one man, however,' he added, 'of whom I cannot even think without loathing both food and sleep. I mean Ulysses.'

When Telemachus heard his father thus mentioned he could not restrain his tears, and while Menelaus was in doubt what to say or not say, Helen came down (dinner being now half through) with her three attendant maidens, Adraste, Alcippe and Phylo, who set a seat for her and brought her her famous work box which ran on wheels, that she might begin to spin.

428

'And who pray,' said she to her husband, 'may these two gentlemen be who are honouring us with their presence? Shall I guess right or wrong, but I really must say what I think. I never saw such a likeness — neither in man nor woman. This young man can only be Telemachus, whom Ulysses left behind him a baby in arms when he set out for Troy.'

'I too,' answered Menelaus, 'have observed the likeness. It is unmistakable.'

On this Pisistratus explained that they were quite right, whereon Menelaus told him all he had meant doing for Ulysses, and this was so affecting that all the four who were at table burst into tears. After a little while Pisistratus complimented Menelaus on his great sagacity (of which indeed his father Nestor had often told him), and said that he did not like weeping when he was getting his dinner; he therefore proposed that the remainder of their lamentation should be deferred until next morning. Menelaus assented to this, and dinner was allowed to proceed. Helen mixed some Nepenthe with the wine, and cheerfulness was thus restored.

Helen then told how she had met Ulysses when he entered Troy as a spy, and explained that by that time she was already anxious to return home, and was lamenting the cruel calamity which Venus had inflicted on her in separating her from her little girl and from her husband, who was really not deficient either in person or understanding.

Menelaus capped her story with an account of the adventures of the Achæans inside the wooden horse. 'Do you not remember,' said he, 'how you walked all round it when we were inside, and patted it? You had Deiphobus with you, and you kept on calling out our names and mimicking our wives, till Minerva came and took you away. It was Ulysses' presence of mind that then saved us.'

When he had told this, Telemachus said it was time to go to rest, so he and Pisistratus were shown to their room in the vestibule, while Menelaus and Helen retired to the interior of the house.

When morning came Telemachus told Menelaus about the suitors, and asked for any information he could give him concerning the death of his father. Menelaus was greatly shocked, but could only tell him what he had heard from Proteus. He said that as he was coming from Egypt he had been detained some weeks, through the displeasure of the gods, in the island of Pharos, where he and his men would have been starved but for the assistance given him by a goddess Idothea, daughter to Proteus, who taught him how to ensnare her father, and compel him to say why heaven was detaining him.

'Idothea,' said Menelaus, 'disguised me and my three chosen comrades as seals; to this end she had brought four fresh-flayed seal-skins, under which she hid us. The strong smell of these skins was most distressing to us — Who would go to bed with a sea monster if he could help it? but Idothea put some ambrosia under each man's nostrils, and this afforded us great relief. Other seals (Halosydne's chickens as they call them) now kept coming up by hundreds, and lay down to bask upon the beach.

'Towards noon Proteus himself came up. First he counted all his seals to see that he had the right number, and he counted us in with the others; when he had so done he lay down in the midst of them, as a shepherd with his sheep, and as soon as he was asleep we pounced upon him and gripped him tight; at one moment he became a lion, the next he was running water, and then again he was a tree; but we never loosed hold, and in the end he grew weary, and told us what we would know.

'He told me also of the fate of Ajax, son of Oïleus, and of my brother Agamemnon. Lastly he told me about Ulysses, who he said was in the island of the nymph Calypso, unable to get away inasmuch as he had neither ship nor crew.

'Then he disappeared under the sea, and I, after appeasing heaven's anger as he had instructed me, returned quickly and safely to my own country.'

Having finished his story Menelaus pressed Telemachus to remain with him some ten or twelve days longer, and promised to give him a chariot and a pair of horses as a keepsake, but Telemachus said that he could not stay. 'I could listen to you,' said he, 'for a whole twelve months, and never once think about my home and my parents; but my men, whom I have left at Pylos, are already impatient for me to return. As for any present you may make me, let it be a piece of plate. I cannot take horses to Ithaca; it contains no plains nor meadow lands, and is more fit for breeding goats than horses. None of our islands are suited for chariot races, and Ithaca least among them all.'

Menelaus smiled, and said he could see that Telemachus came of good family. He had a piece of plate, of very great value, which was just the thing, and Telemachus should have it.

[Guests now kept coming to the king's house, bringing both wine and sheep, and their wives had put them up a provision of bread. Thus, then, did they set about cooking their dinner in the courts.]

Meanwhile, the suitors in Ithaca were playing at quoits, aiming spears at a mark and behaving with all their old insolence on the level ground in front of Ulysses' house. While they were thus engaged Noëman came up and asked Antinaus if he could say when Telemachus was likely to be back from Pylos, for he wanted his ship. On this everything came out, and the suitors, who had no idea that Telemachus had really gone (for they thought he was only away on one of his farms in Ithaca), were very angry. They therefore determined to lie in wait for him on his return, and made ready to start.

Medon, a servant, overheard their plot, and told all to Penelope, who, like the suitors, learned for the first time that her son had left home and gone to Pylos. She bitterly upbraided her women for not having given her a call out of her bed when Telemachus was leaving, for she said she was sure they knew all about it. Presently, however, on being calmed by Euryclea, she went upstairs and offered sacrifice to Minerva. After a time she fell into a deep slumber, during which she was comforted by a vision of her sister Ipthime, which Minerva had sent to her bedside.

When night fell the suitors set sail, intending to waylay Telemachus in the Strait between Same and Ithaca.

BOOK FIVE

ULYSSES IN THE ISLAND OF CALYPSO—HE LEAVES THE ISLAND ON A RAFT, AND AFTER GREAT SUFFERING REACHES THE LAND OF THE PHÆACIANS

THE gods now held a second council, at which Minerva and Jove both spoke.

When Jove had done speaking he sent Mercury to Calypso to tell her that Ulysses was to return home, reaching the land of the Phæacians in twenty days. The Phæacians would load him with presents and send him on to Ithaca.

Mercury, therefore, flew over the sea like a cormorant that fishes every hole and corner of the deep. In the course of time he reached

Calypso's cave and told his story. Calypso was very angry, but seeing there was no help for it promised obedience. As soon as Mercury was gone she went to look for Ulysses, whom she found weeping as usual and looking out ever sadly upon the sea; she told him to build himself a raft and sail home upon it, but Ulysses was deeply suspicious and would not be reassured till she had sworn a very solemn oath that she meant him no harm, and was advising him in all good faith.

The pair then returned to Calypso's cave. 'I cannot understand,' she said, 'why you will not stay quietly here with me, instead of all the time thinking about this wife of yours. I cannot believe that I am any worse looking than she is. If you only knew how much hardship you will have to undergo before you get back, you would stay where you are and let me make you immortal.'

'Do not be angry with me,' answered Ulysses, 'you are infinitely better looking than Penelope. You are a goddess, and she is but a mortal woman. There can be no comparison. Nevertheless, come what may, I have a craving to get back to my own home.'

The next four days were spent in making the raft. Calypso lent him her axe and auger and showed him where the trees grew which would be driest and whose timber would be the best seasoned, and Ulysses cut them down. He made the raft about as broad in the beam as people generally make a good big ship, and he gave it a rudder — that he might be able to steer it.

Calypso then washed him, gave him clean clothes, and he set out, steering his ship skilfully by means of the rudder. He steered towards the Great Bear, which is also called the Wain, keeping it on his left hand, for so Calypso had advised him.

All went well with him for seventeen days, and on the eighteenth he caught sight of the faint outlines of the Phæacian coast lying long and low upon the horizon.

Here, however, Neptune, who was on his way home from the Ethiopians, caught sight of him and saw the march that the other gods had stolen upon him during his absence. He therefore stirred the sea round with his trident, and raised a frightful hurricane, so that Ulysses could see nothing more, everything being dark as night; presently he was washed overboard, but managed to regain his raft.

He was giving himself up for lost when Ino, also named Leucothea, took pity on him and flew on to his raft like a sea gull; she reassured him and gave him her veil, at the same time telling him to throw it back into the sea as soon as he reached land, and to turn his face away from the sea as he did so.

The storm still raged, and the raft went to pieces under its fury, whereon Ulysses bound Ino's veil under his arms and began to swim. Neptune on seeing this was satisfied and went away.

As soon as he was gone Minerva calmed all the winds except the North, which blew strong for two days and two nights, so that Ulysses was carried to the South again. On the morning of the third day he saw land quite close, but was nearly dashed to pieces against the rocks on trying to leave the water. At last he found the mouth of a river, who, in answer to Ulysses' prayer, stayed his flow, so that Ulysses was able to swim inland and get on shore.

Nearly dead with exhaustion and in great doubt what to do, he first threw Ino's veil into the salt waters of the river, and then took shelter on the rising ground, inland. Here he covered himself with a thick bed of leaves and fell fast asleep.

BOOK SIX

THE MEETING BETWEEN ULYSSES AND NAUSICAA

WHILE Ulysses was thus slumbering, Minerva went to the land of the Phæacians, on which Ulysses had been cast.

Now the Phæacians used to live in Hypereia near the lawless Cyclopes, who were stronger than they were and plundered them; so their king Nausithous removed them to Scheria, where they were secure. Nausithous was now dead, and his son Alcinous was reigning.

Alcinous had an only daughter, Nausicaa, who was in her bedroom fast asleep. Minerva went to her bedside and appeared to her in a dream, having assumed the form of one Captain Dymas' daughter, who was a bosom friend of Nausicaa's. She reminded her of her approaching marriage (for which, however, the bridegroom had not yet been decided upon), and upbraided her for not making due preparation by the washing of her own and of the family linen. She proposed, therefore, that on the following morning Nausicaa should take all the unwashed clothes to the washing cisterns, and said that she would come and help her: the cisterns being some distance from the town, she advised Nausicaa to ask her father to let her have a waggon and mules.

Nausicaa, on waking, told her father and mother about her dream, 'Papa, dear,' said she, 'could you manage to let me have a good big waggon? I want to take all our dirty clothes to the river and wash them. You are the chief man here, so it is only proper that you should have a clean shirt when you attend meetings of the Council. Moreover you have five sons, two of them married, while the other three are good-looking young bachelors; you know they always like to have clean linen when they go out to a dance.

Her father promised her all she wanted. The waggon was made ready, her mother put her up a basket of provisions, and Nausicaa drove her maids to the bank of the river, where were the cisterns, through which there flowed enough clear water to wash clothes however dirty they might be. They washed their clothes in the pits by treading upon them, laid them out to dry upon the sea-beach, had their dinner as the clothes were drying, and then began to play at ball while Nausicaa sang to them.

In the course of time, when they were thinking about starting home, Minerva woke Ulysses, who was in the wood just above them. He sat up, heard the voices and laughter of the women, and wondered where he was.

He resolved on going to see, but remembering that he had no clothes on, he held a bough of olive before him, and then, all grim, naked and unkempt as he was, he came out and drew near to the women, who all of them ran away along the beach and the points that jutted into the sea. Nausicaa, however, stood firm, and Ulysses set himself to consider whether he should go boldly up to her and embrace her knees, or speak to her from a respectful distance.

On the whole he concluded that this would be the most prudent course; and having adopted it, he began by asking Nausicaa to inform him whether she was a goddess or no. If she was a goddess, it was obvious from her beauty that she could only be Diana. If on the other hand she was a mortal, how happy would he be whose proposals in the way of settlements had seemed most advantageous, and who should take her to his own home. Finally he asked her to be kind enough to give him any old wrapper which she might have brought with her to wrap the clothes in, and to show him the way to the town.

Nausicaa replied that he seemed really to be a very sensible person, but that people must put up with their luck whatever it might happen to be. She then explained that he had come to the land of the Phæacians, and promised to conduct him to their city.

Having so said, she told her maids not to be such cowards. 'The man,' she said, 'is quite harmless; we live away from all neighbours on a land's end, with the sea roaring on either side of us, and no one can hurt us. See to this poor fellow, therefore, and give him something to eat.'

When they heard this the maids came back and gave Ulysses a shirt and cloak; they also gave him a bottle of oil and told him to go and wash in the river, but he said, 'I will not wash myself while you keep standing there. I cannot bring myself to strip before a number of good-looking young women.' So they went and told their mistress.

When Ulysses had done washing, Minerva made him look much grander and more imposing, and gave him a thick head of hair which flowed down in hyacinthine curls about his shoulders. Nausicaa was very much struck with the change in his appearance. 'At first,' she said, 'I thought him quite plain, but now he is of godlike beauty. I wish I might have such a man as that for my husband, if he would only stay here. But never mind this; girls, give him something to eat and drink.'

The maids then set meat and drink before Ulysses, who was ravenously hungry. While he was eating, Nausicaa got the clothes folded up and put on to the cart; after which she gave him his instructions. 'Follow after the cart,' she said, 'along with the maids, till you get near the houses. As for the town, you will find it lying between two good harbours, and approached by a narrow neck of land, on either side of which you will see the ships drawn up — for every man has a place where he can let his boat lie. You will also see the walls, and the temple of Neptune standing in the middle of the paved market-place, with the ship-broker's shops all round it.

'When you get near the town drop behind, for the people here are very ill-natured, and they would talk about me. They would say, "Who is this fine looking stranger that is going about with Nausicaa? Where did she find him? I suppose she is going to marry him. Is he a sailor whom she has picked up from some foreign vessel, or has a god come down from heaven in answer to her prayers and he is going to marry her? It would be a good thing if she would go and find a husband somewhere else, for she will have nothing to say to any of the many excellent Phæacians who are in love with her." This is what people would say, and I could not blame them, for I should be scandalized myself if I saw any girl going about with a stranger, while her father and mother were yet alive, without being married to him in the face of all the world.

'Do then as I say. When you come to the grove of Minerva a little outside the town, wait till you think I and the maids must have got home. Then come after us, ask which is Alcinous' house, and when you reach it go straight through the outer and inner courts till you come to my mother. You will see her sitting with her back to a bearing-post, and spinning her purple yarn by the fire. My father will be sitting close by her; never mind about him, but go and embrace my mother's knees, for if she looks favourably on your suit you will probably get what you want.'

Nausicaa then drove on, and as the sun was about setting they came to the grove of Minerva, where Ulysses sat down and waited. He prayed Minerva to assist him, and she heard his prayer, but she would not manifest herself to him, for she did not want to offend her uncle Neptune.

BOOK SEVEN

THE SPLENDOURS OF THE HOUSE OF KING
ALCINOUS—QUEEN ARETE WANTS TO
KNOW WHERE ULYSSES GOT HIS SHIRT
AND CLOAK, FOR SHE KNOWS THEM AS
HER OWN WORK—ULYSSES EXPLAINS

WHEN Nausicaa reached home her brothers attended to the waggon and mules, and her waiting-woman Eurymedusa lit the fire and brought her supper for her into her own room.

Presently Ulysses considered it safe to come on, and entered the town enveloped in a thick mist which Minerva shed round him for his protection from any rudeness that the Phæacians might offer him. She also met him outside the town disguised as a little girl carrying a pitcher.

Ulysses saw her in spite of the mist, and asked her to show him the way to the house of Alcinous; this, she said, she could easily do, and when they reached the house she told Ulysses all about the king's family history, and advised him how he should behave himself.

'Be bold,' she said; 'boldness always tells, no matter where a man comes from. First find the mistress of the house. She is of the same family as her husband, and her descent is in this wise. Eurymedon was king of the giants, but he and his people were overthrown, and he lost his own life. His youngest daughter was Periboea, a woman of surpassing beauty, who gave birth by Neptune to Nausithous, king of the Phæacians. He had two sons, Rhexenor and Alcinous; Rhexenor died young, leaving an only daughter, Arēte, whom her uncle Alcinous married, and whom he honours as no other woman in the whole world is honoured by her husband. All her family and all her neighbours adore her as a friend and peacemaker, for she is a thoroughly good woman. If you can gain her good offices all will go well with you.'

Minerva then left him and went to Marathon and Athens, where she visited the house of Erechtheus, but Ulysses went on to the house of Alcinous, and he pondered much as he paused awhile before he reached the threshold of bronze, for the splendour of the palace was like that of the sun and moon. The walls on either side were of bronze from end to end, and the cornice was of blue enamel. The doors were of gold and hung on pillars of silver that rose from a floor of bronze, while the lintel was of silver and the hook of the door was of gold.

On either side there were gold and silver mastiffs which Vulcan with his consummate skill had fashioned expressly to keep watch over the palace of King Alcinous, so they were immortal and could never grow old. Seats were ranged here and there all along the wall, from one end to the other, with coverings of fine woven work, which the women of the house had made. Here the chief persons of the Phæacians used to sit and eat and drink, for there was abundance at all seasons; and there were golden figures of young men with lighted torches in their hands, raised on pedestals to give light to them that sat at meat.

There are fifty women servants in the house, some of whom are always grinding rich yellow grain at the mill, while others work at the loom and sit and spin, and their shuttles go backwards and forwards like the fluttering of aspen leaves, while the linen is so closely woven that it will turn oil. As the Phæacians are the best sailors in the world, so their women excel all others in weaving, for Minerva has taught them all manner of useful arts, and they are very intelligent.

Outside the gate of the outer court there is a large garden of about four acres, with a wall all round it. It is full of beautiful trees — pears, pomegranates and the most delicious apples. There are luscious figs also, and olives in full growth. The fruits never rot nor fail all the year round, neither winter nor summer, for the air is so soft that a new crop ripens before the old has dropped. Pear grows on pear, apple on apple and fig on fig, and so also with the grapes, for there is an excellent vineyard; on the level ground of a part of this, the grapes are being made into raisins; on another part they are being gathered; some are being trodden in the wine-tubs; others, further on, have shed their blossom and are beginning to show fruit; others, again, are just changing colour. In the furthest part of the ground there are beautifully arranged beds of flowers that are in bloom all the year round. Two streams go through it, the one turned in ducts throughout the whole garden, while the other is carried under the ground of the outer court to the house itself, and the townspeople drew water from it. Such, then, were the splendours with which heaven had endowed the house of King Alcinous.

So here Ulysses stood for a while and looked about him, but when he had looked long enough he crossed the threshold and went within the precincts of the house. He passed through the crowd of guests who were nightly visitors at the table of King Alcinous, and who were then making their usual drink offering to Mercury before going for the night. He was still shrouded in the mist of invisibility with which Minerva had invested him, and going up to Arēte he embraced her knees, whereon he suddenly became visible. Everyone was greatly surprised at seeing a man there, but Ulysses paid no attention to this, and at once implored the queen's assistance; he then sat down among the ashes on the hearth.

Alcinous did not know what to do or say, nor yet did anyone else till one of the guests Echeneüs told him it was not creditable to him that a suppliant should be left thus grovelling among the ashes. Alcinous ought to give him a seat and set food before him. This was accordingly done, and after Ulysses had finished eating Alcinous made a speech, in which he proposed that they should have a great banquet next day in their guest's honour, and then provide him an escort to take him to his own home. This was agreed to, and after a while the other guests went home to bed.

When they were gone Ulysses was left alone with Alcinous and Arēte sitting over the fire, while the servants were taking the things away after supper. Then Arēte said, 'Stranger, before we go any further there is a question I should like to put to you. Who are you? and who gave you those clothes?' for she recognized the shirt and cloak Ulysses was wearing as her own work, and that of her maids.

Ulysses did not give his name, but told her how he had come from Calypso's island, and been wrecked on the Phæacian coast. 'Next day,' he said, 'I fell in with your daughter, who treated me with much greater kindness than one could have expected from so young a person — for young people are apt to be thoughtless. It was she who gave me the clothes.'

Alcinous then said he wished the stranger would stay with them for good and all and marry Nausicaa. They would not, however, press this, and if he insisted on going they would send him, no matter where. 'Even though it be further than Eubœa, which they say is further off than any other place, we will send you, and you shall be taken so easily that you may sleep the whole way if you like.'

To this Ulysses only replied by praying that the king might be as good as his word. A bed was then made for him in the gate-house and they all retired for the night.

BOOK EIGHT

THE PHÆACIAN GAMES AND BANQUET IN HONOUR OF ULYSSES

WHEN morning came Alcinous called an assembly of the Phæacians, and Minerva went about urging everyone to come and see the wonderful stranger. She also gave Ulysses a more imposing presence that he might impress the people favourably. When the Phæacians were assembled Alcinous said:

'I do not know who this stranger is, nor where he comes from; but he wants us to send him to his own home, and no guest of mine was ever yet able to complain that I did not send him home quickly enough. Let us therefore fit out a new ship with a crew of fifty-two men, and send him. The crew shall come to my house and I will find them in food which they can cook for themselves. The aldermen and councillors shall be feasted inside the house. I can take no denial, and we will have Demodocus to sing to us.'

439

The ship and crew were immediately found, and the sailors with all the male part of the population swarmed to the house of Alcinous till the yards and barns and buildings were crowded. The king provided them with twelve sheep, eight pigs and two bullocks, which they killed and cooked.

The leading men of the town went inside the inner courtyard; Pontonous, the *major domo*, conducted the blind bard Demodocus to a seat which he set near one of the bearing-posts that supported the roof of the cloisters, hung his lyre on a peg over his head, and showed him how to feel for it with his hands. He also set a table close by him with refreshments on it, to which he could help himself whenever he liked.

As soon as the guests had done eating Demodocus began to sing the quarrel between Ulysses and Achilles before Troy, a lay which at the time was famous. This so affected Ulysses that he kept on weeping as long as the bard sang, and though he was able to conceal his tears from the company generally, Alcinous perceived his distress and proposed that they should all now adjourn to the athletic sports — which were to consist mainly of boxing, wrestling, jumping and foot racing.

Demodocus, therefore, hung the lyre on its peg and was led out to the place where the sports were to be held. The whole town flocked to see them. Clytoneüs won the foot race, Euryalus took the prize for wrestling, Amphialus was the best jumper, Elatreus the best disc-thrower, and Alcinous' son Laodamas the best boxer.

Laodamas and Euryalus then proposed that Ulysses should enter himself for one of the prizes. Ulysses replied that he was a stranger and a suppliant; moreover, he had lately gone through great hardships, and would rather be excused.

Euryalus on this insulted Ulysses, and said that he supposed he was some grasping merchant who thought of nothing but his freights. 'You have none of the look,' said he, 'of an athlete about you.'

Ulysses was furious, and told Euryalus that he was a good-looking young fool. He then took up a disc far heavier than those which the Phæacians were in the habit of throwing. The disc made a hurtling sound as it passed through the air, and easily surpassed any throw that had been made yet. Thus encouraged he made another long and very angry speech, in which he said he would compete with any Phæacian in any contest they chose to name, except in running, for he was still so much pulled down that he thought they might beat him here. 'Also,' he said, 'I will not compete in anything with Laodamas. He is my host's son, and it is a most unwise thing for a guest to challenge any member of his host's family. A man must be an idiot to think of such a thing.'

'Sir,' said Alcinous, 'I understand that you are displeased at some remarks that have fallen from one of our athletes, who has thrown doubt upon your prowess in a way that no gentleman would do. I hear that you have also given us a general challenge. I should explain that we are not famous for our skill in boxing or wrestling, but are singularly fleet runners and bold mariners. We are also much given to song and dance, and we like warm baths and frequent changes of linen. So now come forward some of you who are the nimblest dancers, and show the stranger how much we surpass other nations in all graceful accomplishments. Let someone also bring Demodocus' lyre from my house where he has left it.'

The lyre was immediately brought, the dancers began to dance, and Ulysses admired the merry twinkling of their feet.

While they were dancing Demodocus sang the intrigue between Mars and Venus in the house of Vulcan, and told how Vulcan took the pair prisoners. All the gods came to see them; but the goddesses were modest and would not come.

Alcinous then made Halius and Laodamus have a game at ball, after which Ulysses expressed the utmost admiration of their skill. Charmed with the compliment Ulysses had paid his sons, the king said that the twelve aldermen (with himself, which would make thirteen) must at once give Ulysses a shirt and cloak and a talent of gold, so that he might eat his supper with a light heart. As for Euryalus, he must not only make a present, but apologize as well, for he had been rude.

Euryalus admitted his fault, and gave Ulysses his sword with its scabbard, which was of new ivory. He said Ulysses would find it worth a great deal of money to him.

Ulysses thanked him, wished him all manner of good fortune, and said he hoped Euryalus would not feel the want of the sword which he had just given him along with his apology.

Night was now falling, they therefore adjourned to the house of Alcinous. Here the presents began to arrive, whereon the king desired Arête to find Ulysses a chest in which to stow them, and to put a shirt and clean cloak in it as his own contribution; he also declared his intention of giving him a gold cup. Meanwhile, he said that Ulysses had better have a warm bath.

The bath was made ready. Arēte packed all the gold and presents which the Phæacian aldermen had sent, as also the shirt and tunic from Alcinous. Arēte told Ulysses to see to the fastening, lest someone should rob him while he was asleep on the ship; Ulysses therefore fastened the lid on to the chest with a knot which Circe had taught him. He then went into the bath room — very gladly, for he had not had a bath since he left Calypso, who as long as he was with her had taken as good care of him as though he had been a god.

As he came from the bath room Nausicaa was standing by one of the bearing-posts that supported the roof of the cloisters and bade him farewell, reminding him at the same time that it was she who had been the saving of him — a fact which Ulysses in a few words gracefully acknowledged.

He then took his seat at table, and after dinner, at his request, Demodocus sang the Sack of Troy and the Sally of the Achæans from the Wooden Horse. This again so affected him that he could not restrain his tears, which, however, Alcinous again alone perceived.

The king, therefore, made a speech in which he said that the stranger ought to tell them his name. He must have one, for people always gave their children names as soon as they were born. He need not be uneasy about his escort. All he had to do was to say where he wanted to go, and the Phæacian ships were so clever that they would take him there of their own accord. Nevertheless he remembered hearing his father Nausithous say, that one day Neptune would be angry with the Phæacians for giving people escorts so readily, and had said he would wreck one of their ships as it was returning, and would also bury their city under a high mountain.

BOOK NINE

THE VOYAGES OF ULYSSES—THE CICONS, LOTUS EATERS AND THE CYCLOPS POLYPHEMUS

THEN Ulysses rose. 'King Alcinous,' said he, 'you ask my name and I will tell you. I am Ulysses, and dwell in Ithaca, an island which contains a high mountain called Neritum. In its neighbourhood there are other islands near to one another, Dulichium, Same and Zacynthus. It lies on the horizon all highest up in the sea towards the West, while the other islands lie away from it to the East. This is the island which I would reach, for however fine a house a man may have in a land where his parents are not, there will still be nothing sweeter to him than his home and his own father and mother.

'I will now tell you of my adventures. On leaving Troy we first made a descent on the land of the Cicons, and sacked their city but were eventually beaten off, though we took our booty with us.

'Thence we sailed South with a strong North wind behind us, till we reached the island of Cythera, where we were driven off our course by a continuance of North wind which prevented my doubling Cape Malea.

'Nine days was I driven by foul winds, and on the tenth we reached the land of the lotus eaters, where the people were good to my men but gave them to eat of the lotus, which made them lose all desire to return home, so that I had a great work to get those who had tasted it on board again.

'Thence we were carried farther, till we came to the land of the savage Cyclopes. Off their coast, but not very far, there is a wooded island abounding with wild goats. It is untrodden by the foot of man; even the huntsmen, who as a general rule will suffer any hardship in forest or on mountain top, never go there; it is neither tilled nor fed down, but remains year after year uninhabited save by goats only. For the Cyclopes have no ships, and cannot therefore go from place to place as those who have ships can do. If they had ships they would have colonized the island, for it is not at all a bad one and would bring forth all things in their season. There is meadow land, well watered and of good quality, that stretches down to the water's edge. Grapes would do wonderfully well there; it contains good arable land, which would yield heavy crops, for the soil is rich; moreover it has a convenient port — into which some god must have taken us, for the night was so dark that we could see nothing. There was a thick darkness all round the ships, neither was there any moon, for the sky was covered with clouds. No one could see the island, nor yet waves breaking upon the shore till we found ourselves in the harbour. Here, then, we moored our ships and camped down upon the beach.

'When morning came we hunted the wild goats, of which we killed over a hundred, and all day long to the going down of the sun we feasted on them and the store of wine we had taken from the Cicons. We kept looking also on the land of the Cyclopes over against us, which was so near that we could see the smoke of their stubble fires, and almost fancy we heard the bleating of their sheep and goats.

'We camped a second night upon the beach, and at daybreak, having called a council, I said I would take my own ship and reconnoitre the country, but would leave the other ships at the island. Thereon I started, but when we got near the mainland we saw a great cave in the cliff, not far from the sea, and there were large sheep yards in front of it. On landing I chose twelve men and went inland, taking with me a goat skin full of a very wondrous wine that Maron, priest of Apollo, had given me when I spared his life and that of his family at the time that we were sacking the city of the Cicons. The rest of my crew were to wait my return by the sea side.

'We soon reached the cave, and finding that the owner was not at home we examined all that it contained; we saw vessels brimful of whey, and racks loaded with cheeses: the yards also were full of lambs and kids. My men implored me to let them steal some cheeses, drive off some of the lambs and kids, and sail away, but I would not, for I hoped the owner might give me something.

'We lit a fire in the cave, sacrificed some of the cheeses to the gods, and ate others ourselves, waiting till the owner should return. When he came we found him to be a huge monster, more like a peak standing out against the sky on some high mountain than a human being. He brought in with him a great bundle of firewood, which he flung down upon the floor with such a noise that we were scared and hid ourselves. He drove all his female goats and ewes into the cave, but left the males outside; and then he closed the door with a huge stone which not even two and twenty waggons could carry. He milked his goats and ewes all orderly, and gave each one her own young [for these had been left in the yard all day]; then he drank some of the milk, and put part by for his supper. Presently he lit his fire and caught sight of us, whereon he asked us who we were.

'I told him we were on our way home from Troy, and begged him in heaven's name to do us no hurt; but as soon as I had answered his question he gripped up two of my men, dashed them on the ground, and ate them raw, blood, bones and bowels, like a savage lion of the wilderness. Then he lay down on the ground of the cave and went to sleep: on which I should have crept up to him and plunged my sword into his heart while he was sleeping had I not known that if I did we should never be able to shift the stone. So we waited till dawn should come.

'When day broke the monster again lit his fire, milked his ewes all orderly and gave each one her own young. Then he gripped up two more of my men, and as soon as he had eaten them he rolled the stone from the mouth of the cave, drove out his sheep, and put the stone back again. He had, however, left a large and long piece of olive wood in the cave, and when he had gone I and my men sharpened this at one end, and hid it in the sheep dung of which there was much in the cave. In the evening he returned, milked his ewes, and ate two more men; whereon I went up to him with the skin of wondrous wine that Maron had given me and gave him a bowl full of it. He asked for another, and then another, so I gave them to him, and he was so much delighted that he inquired my name and I said it was Noman.

'The wine now began to take effect, and in a short time he fell dead drunk upon the ground. Then my men and I put the sharp end of the piece of olive wood in the fire till it was well burning, and drove it into the wretch's eye, turning it round and round as though it were an auger. After a while he plucked it out, flung it from him, and began crying to his neighbours for help. When they came, they said, "What ails you? Who is harming you?" and he answered, "No man is harming me." They then said that he must be ill, and had better pray to his father Neptune; so they went away, and I laughed at the success of my stratagem.

'Then I hid my men by binding them under the sheep's bellies. The Cyclops, whose name was Polyphemus, groped his way to the stone, rolled it away, and sat at the mouth of the cave feeling the sheep's backs as they went out; but the men were under their bellies so he did not find one of them. Nor yet did he discover me, for I was ensconced in the thick belly-fleece of a ram which by some chance he had brought in with the ewes. But he was near finding me, for the ram went last, and he kept it for a while and talked to it.

'When we were outside, I dropped from under the ram and unbound my companions. We drove the ewes down to my ship, got them on board and rowed out to sea. When we were a little way out I jeered at the Cyclops, whereon he tore up a great rock and hurled it after us; it fell in front of the ship and all but hit the rudder; the wash, moreover, that it made nearly carried us back to the land, but I kept the ship off it with a pole.

'When we had got about twice as far off as we were before, I was for speaking to the Cyclops again, and though my men tried to stay me, I shouted out to him "Cyclops, if you would know who it is that has blinded you, learn that it is I, Ulysses, son of Laertes, who live in Ithaca."

' "Alas," he cried in answer, "then the old prophecy about me is coming true. I knew that I was to lose my sight by the hand of Ulysses, but I was looking for some man of great stature and noble mien, whereas he has proved to be a mere whippersnapper. Come here, then, Ulysses that I may offer you gifts of hospitality and pray my father Neptune, who shall heal my eye, to escort you safely home."

' "I wish," said I, "that I could be as sure of killing you body and soul as I am that not even Neptune will be able to cure your eye."

'Then he prayed to Neptune saying "Hear me Neptune, if I am indeed your son, and vouchsafe me that Ulysses son of Laertes may never reach his home. Still, if he must do so, and get back to his friends, let him lose all his men, and though he get home after all, let it be late, on another man's ship, and let him find trouble in his house."

'So saying he tore up a still larger rock and flung it this time a little behind the ship, but so close that it all but hit the rudder: the wash, however, that it made carried us forward to the island from which we had set out.

'There we feasted on the sheep that we had taken, and mourned the loss of our comrades whom Polyphemus had eaten.

BOOK TEN

ÆOLUS—THE LÆSTRYGONIANS—CIRCE

'SO we sailed on and reached the island where dwells Æolus with his wife and family of six sons and six daughters, who live together amid great and continuous plenty. I staid with him a whole month and when I would go, he tied all the winds up (for he was their keeper) in a leather sack, which he gave me; but he left the West wind free, for this was the one I wanted.

'Nine days did we sail, and on the tenth we could see our native land with the stubble fires burning thereon. I had never let the rudder out of my hands till then, but being now close in shore I fell asleep. My men, thinking I had treasure in the sack, opened it to see, on which the winds came howling out and took us straight back to the Æolian island. So I went to the house of Æolus and prayed him to help me, but he said, "Get you gone, abhorred of heaven: him whom heaven hates will I in no wise help." So I went full sadly away.

'Six days thence did we sail onward, worn out in body and mind, and on the seventh we reached the stronghold of King Lamus, the Læstrygonian city Telepylus, where the shepherd who drives his flock into the town salutes another who is driving them out, and the other returns his salute. A man in that country could earn double wages if he could do without sleep, for they work much the same by night as they do by day. Here we landed, and I climbed a high rock to look round, but could see no signs of man or beast, save only smoke rising from the ground.

'Then I sent two of my crew with an attendant, to see what manner of men the people might be, and they met a young woman who was coming down to fetch water from the spring Artacia, whence the people drew their water. This young woman took my men to the house of her father Antiphates, whereon they discovered the people to be giants and ogres like Polyphemus. One of my men was gripped up and eaten, but the other two escaped and reached the ships. The Læstrygonians raised a hue and cry after them, and rushing to the harbour, within which all my ships were moored except my own, they dashed my whole fleet in pieces with the rocks that they threw. I and my own ship alone escaped them, for we were outside, and I bade the men row for their lives.

'On and on did we sail, till we reached the island of Circe, where heaven guided us into a harbour. Here I again climbed a rock and could see the smoke from Circe's house rising out of a thick wood; I then went back to the ship, and while on my way had the good fortune to kill a noble stag, which gave us a supply of meat on which we feasted all the rest of the day. Next morning I held a council and told my men of the smoke that I had seen.

'Eurylochus and twenty-two men then went inland to reconnoitre, and found Circe's house made of squared stones and standing on high ground in the middle of the forest. This forest was full of wild beasts, poor dazed creatures whom Circe had bewitched, but they fawned upon my men and did not harm them. When the men got to the door of her house they could hear her singing inside most beautifully, so they called her down, and when she came she asked them in, gave them a drugged drink, and then turned them into pigs — all except Eurylochus who had remained outside.

'Eurylochus made all haste back to tell me, and I started for Circe's house. When I was in the wood where the wild beasts were, Mercury met me and gave me an herb called Moly, which would protect me from Circe's spells; he also told me how I should treat her. Then I went to her house, and called her to come down.

'She asked me in, and tried to bewitch me as she had the others, but the herb which Mercury had given me protected me; so I rushed at her with my drawn sword. When she saw this, she said she knew I must be Ulysses, and that I must marry her at once. But I said, "Circe, you have just turned my men into pigs, and have done your best to bewitch me into the bargain; how can you expect me to be friendly with you? Still, if you will swear to take no unfair advantage of me, I will consent." So she swore, and I consented at once.

'Then she set the four maid servants of her house to wash me and feast me, but I was still moody and would not eat till Circe removed her spells from off my men, and brought them back safe and sound in human form. When she had done this she bade me go back to my ship and bring the rest of my men — which I presently did, and we staid with her for a whole twelve months, feasting continually and drinking an untold quantity of wine. At last, however, my men said that if I meant going home at all it was time I began to think of starting.

'That night, therefore, when I was in bed with Circe, I told her how my men were murmuring, and asked her to let me go. This she said she would do; but I must first go down into the house of Hades, and consult the blind Theban prophet Tiresias. And she directed me what I should do.

'On the following morning I told my men, and we began to get ready; but we had an accident before we started, for there was a foolish and not very valiant young man in my ship named Elpenor, who had got drunk and had gone on to the roof of Circe's house to sleep off his liquor in the cool. The bustle my men made woke him, and in his flurry he forgot all about coming down by the staircase, and fell right off the roof; whereby he broke his neck and was killed. We started, however, all the same, and Circe brought us a lamb and a black sheep to offer to the Shades below. She passed in and out among us, but we could not see her; who, indeed, can see the gods, when they are in no mind to be seen?

448

BOOK ELEVEN

ULYSSES IN THE HOUSE OF HADES

'WHEN we were at the water side we got the lamb and the ewe on board and put out to sea, running all that day before a fair wind which Circe had sent us, and at nightfall entering the deep waters of the river Oceanus. Here is the land of the Cimmerians, who dwell in darkness which the sun's rays never pierce; we therefore made our ship fast to the shore and came out of her, going along the beach till we reached the place of which Circe had told us.

'Perimedes and Eurylochus then held the victims, while I followed the instructions of Circe and slaughtered them, letting their blood flow into a trench which I had dug for it. On this, the ghosts came up in crowds from Erebus, brides, young bachelors, old men, maids who had been crossed in love and warriors with their armour still smirched with blood. They cried with a strange screaming sound that made me turn pale with fear, but I would let none of them taste of the blood till Tiresias should have come and answered my questions.

'The first ghost I saw was that of Elpenor whose body was still lying unburied at Circe's house. Then I said, "How now, Elpenor? you have got here sooner by land than I have done by water." The poor fellow told me how he had forgotten about the stairs, and begged me to give him all due rites when I returned to Circe's island — which I promised faithfully that I would do.

'Then I saw the ghost of my mother Anticlea, but in all sadness I would not let her taste of the blood till Tiresias should have come and answered my questions.

'Presently Tiresias came with his golden sceptre in his hand, bade me let him taste of the blood, and asked me why I had come.

'I told him I would learn how I was to get home to Ithaca, and he said I should have much difficulty: "Still," he continued, "you will reach your home if you can restrain your men when you come to the Thrinacian island, where you will find the cattle of the Sun. If you leave these unharmed, after much trouble you will yet reach Ithaca; but if you harm them, you will lose your men, and though you may get home after all, it will be late, [on another man's ship, and you will find your house full of riotous men who are wasting your substance and wooing your wife.

' "When you have got back you will indeed kill these men either by treachery or in fair fight, and you must then take an oar, which you must carry till you have reached a people who know nothing about the sea and do not mix salt with their bread. These people have never heard of ships, nor of oars that are the wings with which ships fly; I will tell you how you may know them; you will meet a man by the way who will ask you whether it is a winnowing shovel that you have got upon your shoulder; when you hear this you must fix your oar in the ground, and offer sacrifice to Neptune, a ram, a bull and a boar; then go home again, and offer hecatombs to the gods that dwell in heaven. As for your own end, death shall come to you very gently from the sea, and shall take you when you are full of years and peace of mind, and your people shall bless you."]

'Having thus said he went back within the house of Hades. Then I let my mother's ghost draw near and taste of the blood, whereon she knew me, and asked me what it was that had brought me though still alive into the abode of death. So I told her, and asked her how she had come by her end. "Tell me, also," I continued, "about my father, and the son whom I left behind me. Is my property still safe in their hands, or does another hold it who thinks that I shall not return? Of what mind, again, is my wife? Does she still live with her son and keep watch over his estate, or is she already married to the best man among the Achæans?"

' "Your wife," answered my mother, "is still at home, but she spends her life in tears both night and day. Telemachus holds your estate, and sees much company, for he is a magistrate and all men invite him. Your father lives a poor hard life in the country and never goes near the town. As for me, I died of nothing but sheer grief on your account. And now, return to the upper world as fast as you can, that you may tell all that you have seen to your wife."

'Then Proserpine sent up the ghosts of the wives and daughters of great kings and heroes of old time, and I made each of them tell me about herself. There were Tyro, Antiope, Alcmena, Epicaste the mother of Œdipus, Chloris, Leda, Iphimedea, Phædra, Procris, Ariadne and hateful Eriphyle; with all these did I discourse, nor can I tell you with how many more noble women, for it is now late, and time to go to rest.'

Here Ulysses ceased, and from one end of the covered cloisters to the other his listeners sat entranced with the charm of his story.

Then Arēte said, 'What think you of this man now, Phæacians, both as regards his personal appearance and his abilities? True he is my guest, but his presence is an honour to you all. Be not niggardly, therefore, in the presents that you will make him, for heaven has endowed you all with great abundance.' Alcinous also spoke urging Ulysses to tell still more of his adventures, and to say whether he met any of the heroes who had fought together with him at Troy. Thus pressed Ulysses resumed his story.

'When Proserpine,' said he, 'had dismissed the female ghosts, the ghost of Agamemnon drew near, surrounded by those of the men who had fallen with him in the house of Ægisthus. He was weeping bitterly, and I asked him how he met his end; whereon he detailed to me the treachery of Clytemnestra, which he said threw disgrace upon all women, even on the good ones. "Be sure," he continued, "that you never be too open with your wife; tell her a part only, and keep the rest to yourself. Not that you need have any fear about Penelope for she is an admirable woman. You will meet your son, too, who by this time must be a grown man. Nevertheless, do not let people know when you are coming home, but steal a march upon them. And now give me what news you can about my son Orestes." To which I answered that I could tell him nothing.

'While we were thus holding sad talk with one another, the ghost of Achilles came up and asked me for news of his father Peleus, and of his son. I said I could tell him nothing about Peleus, but his son Neoptolemus was with me in the Wooden Horse, and though all the others were trembling in every limb and wiping the tears from their cheeks, Neoptolemus did not even turn pale, nor shed a single tear. Whereon Achilles strode away over a meadow full of asphodel, exulting in the prowess of his son.

'Other ghosts then came up and spoke with me but that of Ajax alone held aloof, for he was still brooding over the armour of Achilles which had been awarded to me and not to him. I spoke to him but he would not answer; nevertheless I should have gone on talking to him till he did, had I not been anxious to see yet other ghosts.

'I saw Minos with his golden sceptre passing sentence on the dead; Orion also, driving before him over a meadow full of asphodel the ghosts of the wild beasts whom he had slain upon the mountains. I saw Tityus with the vulture ever digging its beak into his liver, Tantalus also, in a lake whose waters reached his neck but fled him when he

451

would drink, and Sisyphus rolling his mighty stone uphill till the sweat ran off him and the steam rose from him.

'Then I saw mighty Hercules. The ghosts were screaming round him like scared birds, flying all whithers. He looked black as night with his bare bow in his hand and his arrow on the string, glaring round as though ever on the point of taking aim. About his breast there was a wondrous golden belt marvellously enriched with bears, wild boars and lions with gleaming eyes; there were also war, battle and death.

'And I should have seen yet others of the great dead had not the ghosts come about me in so many thousands that I feared Proserpine might send up the Gorgon's head. I therefore bade my men make all speed back to their ship; so they hastened on board and we rowed out on to the waters of Oceanus, where before long we fell in with a fair wind.

BOOK TWELVE

THE SIRENS—SCYLLA AND CHARYBDIS— THE CATTLE OF THE SUN

'AS soon as we were clear of the river Oceanus, we got out into the open and reached the Æaean island, where there is dawn and sunrise. There we landed, camped down upon the beach and waited till morning came. At daybreak I sent my men to fetch the body of Elpenor, which we burned and buried. We built a barrow over him, and in it we fixed the oar with which he had been used to row.

'When Circe heard that we had returned, she came down with her maids, bringing bread and wine. "Today," she said, "eat and drink, and tomorrow go on your way."

'We agreed to this, and feasted the live-long day to the going down of the sun, but at nightfall Circe took me aside, and told me of the voyage that was before us. "You will first," said she, "come to the island of the two Sirens, who sit in a field of flowers, and warble all who draw near them to death with the sweetness of their song. Dead men's bones are lying strewn all round them; still, if you would hear them, you can stop your men's ears with wax and bid them bind you to a cross-plank on the mast.

' "As regards the next point that you will reach I can give you no definite instructions as to which of two courses you must take. You must do the best you can. I can only put the alternatives before you. I refer to the cliffs which the gods call 'the wanderers', and which close in on anything that would pass through them — even upon the doves that are bringing ambrosia to Father Jove. The sea moreover is strewn with wreckage from ships which the waves and hurricanes of fire have destroyed.

' "Of the two rocks, the one rises in a peak to heaven, and is overhung at all times with a dark cloud that never leaves it. It looks towards the West, and there is a cave in it, higher than an arrow can reach. In this sits Scylla yelping with a squeaky voice like that of a young hound, but she is an awful monster with six long necks and six heads with three rows of teeth in each; whenever a ship passes, she springs out and snatches up a man in each mouth.

' "The other rock is lower, but they are so close that you can shoot an arrow from the one to the other. [On it there is a fig-tree in full leaf.] Underneath it is the terrible whirlpool of Charybdis, which sucks the water down and vomits it out again three times a day. If you are there when she is sucking, not even Neptune can save you; so hug the Scylla side, for you had better lose six men than your whole crew.

' "You will then arrive at the Thrinacian island, where you will see the cattle of the Sun (and also his sheep) in charge of the two nymphs Lampetie and Phaëthusa. If you leave these flocks unharmed, after much trouble you will yet reach Ithaca; but if you harm them, you will lose your men, and though you may get home after all, it will be late.'

'Here she ended, and at break of day we set out, with a fair wind which Circe sent us. I then told my men about the two Sirens, but had hardly done so before we were at the island itself, whereon it fell a dead calm. I kneaded wax and stopped the men's ears; they bound me to a cross-plank on the mast; I heard the Sirens sing, and when I struggled to free myself they bound me still tighter. So we passed the island by.

'Shortly after this I saw smoke and a great wave ahead and heard a dull thumping sound. The sea was in an uproar, and my men were so frightened that they loosed hold of their oars, till I put heart into them, bade them row their hardest, and told the steersman to hug the Scylla side. But I said nothing about Scylla, though I kept straining my eyes all over her rock to see if I could espy her.

'So there we were, with Scylla on the one hand and dread Charybdis on the other. We could see the sea seething as in a cauldron, and the black ooze at the bottom with a wall of whirling waters careering round it. While my men were pale with fear at this awful sight, Scylla shot out her long necks and swooped down on six of them. I could see their poor hands and feet struggling in the air as she bore them aloft, and hear them call out my name in one last despairing cry. This was the most horrid sight that I saw in all my voyages.

'Having passed the cliffs, and Scylla and Charybdis, we came to the Thrinacian island, and from my ship I could hear the cattle lowing, and the sheep bleating. Then, remembering the warning that Tiresias and Circe had given me, I bade my men give the island a wide berth. But Eurylochus was insolent, and sowed disaffection among them, so that I was forced to yield and let them land for the night, after making them swear most solemnly that they would do the cattle no harm. We camped, therefore, on the beach near a stream.

'But in the third watch of the night there came up a great gale, and in the morning we drew our ship ashore and left her in a large cave wherein the sea nymphs meet and hold their dances. I then called my men together, and again warned them.

'It blew a gale from the South for a whole month, except when the wind shifted to the East, and there was no other wind save only South and East. As long as the corn and wine which Circe had given us held out, my men kept their word, but after a time they began to feel the pangs of hunger, and I went apart to pray heaven to take compassion upon us. I washed my hands and prayed, and when I had done so, I fell asleep.

'Meanwhile Eurylochus set my men on to disobey me, and they drove in some of the cattle and killed them. When I woke, and had got nearly back to the ship, I began to smell roast meat and knew full well what had happened.

'The nymph Lampetie went immediately and told the Sun what my men had done. He was furious, and threatened Jove that if he was not revenged he would never shine in heaven again but would go down and give his light among the dead. "All day long," said he, "whether I was going up heaven or down, there was nothing I so dearly loved to look upon as those cattle."

'Jove told him he would wreck our ship as soon as it was well away from land, and the Sun said no more. I know all this because Calypso told me, and she had it from Mercury.

'My men feasted six days — alarmed by the most awful prodigies;

for the skins of the cattle kept walking about, and the joints of meat lowed while they were being roasted. On the seventh day the wind dropped and we got away from the island, but as soon as we were out of sight of land a sudden squall sprang up, during which Jove struck our ship with his thunderbolts and broke it up. All my men were drowned, and so too should I have been, had I not made myself a raft by lashing the mast (which I found floating about) and the ship's keel together.

['The wind, which during the squall came from the West, now changed to the South, and blew all night, so that by morning I was back between Scylla and Charybdis again. My raft got carried down the whirlpool, but I clung on to the boughs of the fig tree, for a weary weary while, during which I felt as impatient as a magistrate who is detained in court by troublesome cases when he wants to get home to dinner. But in the course of time my raft worked its way out again, and when it was underneath me I dropped on to it and was carried out of the pool. Happily for me Jove did not let Scylla see me.]

'Thence I was borne along for nine days in the sea, and was taken to the Ogygian island of Calypso. I told you about this yesterday and will not repeat it, for I hate saying the same thing twice over.'

BOOK THIRTEEN

ULYSSES IS TAKEN BACK TO ITHACA
BY THE PHÆACIANS

THUS did Ulysses speak, and Alcinous immediately proposed that they should make him still further presents. The expense, however, of these, he said, should be borne by a levy or rate upon the public at large. The guests assented, and then went home to bed.

Next morning they brought their presents of hardware down to the ship, and Alcinous saw them so stowed that they should not incommode the rowers. There was then a second banquet at Alcinous' house, but Ulysses kept looking at the sun all the time, longing for it to set that he might start on his way. At last he rose and addressed the Phæacians; after thanking them, he concluded by saying that he hoped he should find his wife on his return living among her friends in peace and quietness, and that the Phæacians would continue to give satisfaction to their wives and children. He also bade farewell to Arēte, and wished her all happiness with her children, her people and with King Alcinous.

When Ulysses reached the ship, a rug and sail were spread for him, on which he lay down, and immediately fell into a deep sleep — so deep as to resemble death itself. The ship sped on her way faster than a falcon's flight and with the break of day they reached Ithaca.

Now in Ithaca there is a sheltered harbour in which a ship can ride without being even moored. At the head of this there is a large olive tree, near which there is a cave sacred to the Naiads, where you may find their cups and amphoræ of stone, and the stone looms whereon they weave their robes of sea-purple — very curious. The wild bees, too, build their nests in it. There is water in it all the year round, and it has two entrances, one looking North, by which mortals can go down into the cave, and the other towards the South, but men cannot enter by it — it is the way taken by gods.

The sailors knew this harbour, and took the ship into it. They were rowing so hard that they ran half her length on to the shore, and when they had got out of her they took Ulysses off, still fast asleep on his rug and sail, and laid him down on the ground. Hard by him they also laid all the presents the Phæacians had made him; they left them by the roots of the olive tree, a little out of the path, that no passer-by might steal them, and then went back to Scheria.

Neptune now saw what the Phæacians had done, and went to consult Jove how he should be revenged. It was arranged that he should go to Scheria, turn the ship into stone just as it was coming into port, and root it in the sea. So he did this, and the Phæacians said, 'Alack, who has rooted the ship in the sea just as it was coming in? We could see all of it a minute ago.'

Then Alcinous told them how Neptune had long ago threatened to do this to some Phæacian ship on its return from giving an escort, and also to bury their city under a high mountain as a punishment for giving escorts so freely. The Phæacians, therefore, made ready great sacrifices to Neptune, that he might have mercy upon them.

While they were thus standing round the altar of the god, Ulysses woke in his own land, but he had been away so long that he did not know it. Minerva, too, had shed a thick mist round him so that he might remain unseen while she told him how things were going on; for she did not want his wife or anyone else to know of his return until

he had taken his revenge upon the suitors. Therefore she made everything look strange to him — the long straight paths, the harbours with
their shipping, the steep precipices and the trees.

Ulysses now stood up and wondered where he was. He did not
believe he was in Ithaca and complained bitterly of the Phæacians for
having brought him wrong. Then he counted all the tripods, caul-
drons, gold and raiment, that they had given him, to see if he had been
robbed; but everything was there, and he was in dismay as to what he
should do with them. As he was thus in doubt Minerva came up to
him disguised as a young shepherd, so he asked her what country he was
in, and she answered that he was in Ithaca.

Ulysses said he had heard that there was such a place; he told Minerva
a long lying story as to how he had come to be where she saw him, and
on this the goddess assumed the form of a woman, fair, stately and
wise, and laughed at him for not knowing her. Ulysses answered that
she was not an easy person to recognize for she was continually
changing her appearance. Moreover, though she had been very good
to him at Troy, she had left him in the lurch ever since, until she had
taken him into the city of the Phæacians. 'Do not,' he said, 'deceive
me any further, but tell me whether or no this is really Ithaca.'

'You are always cunning and suspicious,' replied the goddess, 'and
that is why I cannot find it in my heart to leave you. Anyone else on
returning from a long voyage would have at once gone up to his house
to see his wife and children, but you do not seem to care about knowing
anything about them, and only think of testing your wife's fidelity.
As for my having left you in the lurch, I knew all the time that you
would get home safely in the end, and I did not want to quarrel with
my uncle Neptune. I will now prove to you that you are in Ithaca —
Here is the harbour of the old merman Phorcys, with the large olive
tree at the head of it; near it is the cave which is sacred to the Naiads;
here, again, is the overarching cavern in which you have sacrificed
many a hecatomb to the nymphs, and this is the wooded mountain of
Neritum.'

The goddess then dispersed the mist and let the prospect be seen.
Ulysses was thus convinced, and Minerva helped him to hide the
treasure which the Phæacians had given him, by concealing it in the
cave. Having done this she bade Ulysses consider how he should kill
the wicked suitors. 'They have been lording it,' she said, 'in your house
this three years, paying court to your wife and making her gifts of

wooing, while she, poor woman, though she flatters them, and holds out hopes to every man of them by sending him messages, is really plunged in the deepest grief on your account, and does not mean a word of what she says.'

'Great heavens,' replied Ulysses, 'what a narrow escape I have had from meeting the fate of Agamemnon. Stand by me, goddess, and advise me how I shall be revenged.'

'I will disguise you,' said Minerva, 'as a miserable old beggar so that no one shall know you. When I have done so, go to your swineherd, who has been always loyal to you and yours. You will find him with his pigs by the fountain Arethusa near the rock that is called Raven. Meantime I will go to Sparta and fetch Telemachus, who is gone thither to try and get news of you.'

'But why,' Ulysses answered, 'did you not tell him, for you knew all about it?'

'Do not be uneasy about him,' she answered, 'he is in the midst of great abundance. I sent him, that he might get himself a good name by having gone.'

Minerva then disguised Ulysses beyond all possible recognition, and the two separated — she going to Sparta, and Ulysses to the abode of his swineherd.

BOOK FOURTEEN

ULYSSES IN THE HUT OF EUMÆUS

ULYSSES followed a steep path that led from the harbour through the forest and over the top of the mountain, till he reached the hut of Eumæus, who was the most thrifty servant he had, and had built a number of fine yards and pigstyes during his master's absence.

Ulysses found him sitting at the door of his hut, which had been built high up in a place that could been seen from far; he had his four fierce dogs about him, and was cutting himself out a pair of sandal shoes.

The dogs flew at Ulysses, and it was all Eumæus could do to check them; 'They were like,' said he, 'to have made an end of you, which would have got me into a scrape, and I am in sorrow enough already through the loss, which I deplore without ceasing, of the best of masters. But come in, have something to eat, and then tell me your story.'

On this he brought him inside, threw some brushwood on the floor, and spread a goat's skin over it for Ulysses to lie on. 'I cannot do much for you,' he said; 'servants go in fear when they have young lords over them, as I now have, for my good old master went to Troy with Agamemnon and I shall never see him again.'

He then went out and killed two sucking pigs, singed them, cut them up, put the pieces of meat on skewers to roast on the embers, and brought them smoking hot, skewers and all, to Ulysses, who floured them. 'Eat,' said the swineherd, 'a dish of servant's pork; the fuller grown meat has to go down to the suitors.' He then explained how rich Ulysses was.

'And who, pray,' said Ulysses, 'was this noble master of yours? You say that he fell at Troy, and in that case I might be able to give you news of him.'

'That,' answered Eumæus, 'may not be: people are always coming and flattering my poor mistress with false hopes, but they are all liars. My master Ulysses is dead and gone, and I shall never see another like him. I cannot bear even to mention his name.'

'My friend,' replied Ulysses, 'do not be too hard of belief. I swear by this hearth to which I am now come, that Ulysses will return before the present month is over. If he comes you shall give me a shirt and cloak, but I will take nothing till then.'

'My friend,' said Eumæus, 'say not another word. You will never get your shirt and cloak. Now, moreover, I am as anxious about his son Telemachus as I have been about Ulysses himself; for he is gone to Pylos, and the suitors are lying in wait for him on his return. Let us, however, say no more about him now; tell me, rather, about yourself, who you are and how you came here.'

Then Ulysses told him a long lying story about his adventures in Crete: how he was compelled to go to Troy in joint command with Idomeneus over the Cretan forces; how he made a descent on Egypt, got taken prisoner, acquired wealth, and afterwards was inveigled into going to Libya; how on the voyage thither, after leaving Crete, the ship was wrecked and he was cast on the coast of Thesprotia. 'Here it was,' he continued, 'that I heard of Ulysses from King Pheidon, who was expecting him back daily from Dodona, where he had been to consult the oracle; he told me Ulysses was to return to Ithaca immediately, but there was a ship bound for Dulichium, and the king sent me on board it before Ulysses returned from Dodona. The sailors on this ship resolved to sell me as a slave, and bound me; but they landed on the coast of Ithaca, where I gave them the slip, and found my way to your hut.'

'Poor man,' answered the swineherd, 'but you will never get me to believe about Ulysses. Why should you tell me such lies? I have heard these stories too often, and will never believe them again.'

Ulysses tried still further to convince him, but it was no use, and presently the under-swineherds came back with the pigs that had been out feeding, and Eumæus told them to kill the best pig they had, and get supper ready, which they accordingly did. He was a good man and mindful of his duties to the gods, so when the pig was killed he threw some of its bristles into the fire and prayed heaven for the return of Ulysses. Then they supped and went to bed.

Now it was a wild rough night, and after they had lain down, Ulysses, fearing that he might be cold, told another lying story of an adventure he had had at Troy in company with Ulysses, by means of which Eumæus was induced to cover him over with a spare cloak of his own. Then the swineherd went out to pass the night with the pigs — and Ulysses was pleased at seeing how well he looked after his property, though he believed his master to be absent. First he slung his sword over his shoulders, and put on a thick cloak to keep out the wind; he also took the skin of a well-fed goat, and a javelin in case of attack from men or dogs. Thus equipped he went to his rest where the pigs were camped under an overhanging rock that sheltered them from the North Wind.

BOOK FIFTEEN

TELEMACHUS RETURNS FROM PYLOS, AND ON LANDING GOES TO THE HUT OF EUMÆUS

MINERVA now went to Lacedæmon and found Telemachus and Pisistratus fast asleep. She appeared to Telemachus in a dream, and told him that he was to return at once to Ithaca, for his mother was about to marry Eurymachus, and would probably go off with some of his property. She also told him how the suitors were lying in wait for him in the straits between Ithaca and Samos. She said that as soon as he reached Ithaca he was to leave the ship before sending it on to the town, and go to the swineherd's hut. 'Sleep there,' she said, 'and in the morning send the swineherd to tell Penelope that you have returned safely.'

Then she went away and Telemachus woke up. He kicked Pisistratus to wake him, and said that they must start at once. Pisistratus answered that this was impossible; it was still dark, and they must say goodbye to Menelaus, who, if Telemachus would only wait, would be sure to give him a present.

At break of day, seeing Menelaus up and about, Telemachus flung on his shirt and cloak, and told him that they must go.

Menelaus said he would not detain them, but on the score alike of propriety and economy, they must have something to eat before starting, and also receive the presents that were waiting Telemachus' acceptance. 'I will tell the servants,' said he, 'to get something ready for you of what there may be in the house, and if you would like to make a tour of the principal cities of the Peloponnese, I will conduct you. No one will send us away empty handed. Everyone will give us something.'

But Telemachus said he must start at once, for he had left property behind him that was insecurely guarded.

When Menelaus heard this he told his wife and servants to get dinner ready at once. Eteoneus, who lived at no great distance, now came up, and Menelaus told him to light the fire and begin cooking; and he did as he was told.

Menelaus then went down into his store-room together with Megapenthes, and brought up a double cup and a silver mixing bowl, while Helen fetched a dress of wondrous beauty, the work of her own hands. Menelaus presented the cup and mixing bowl, and then Helen said, 'Take this, my son, as a keepsake from the hand of Helen, and let your bride wear it on her wedding day. Till then let your dear mother keep it for you. Thus may you go on your way with a light heart.'

Telemachus thanked her; Pisistratus stowed the presents in the chariot, and they all sat down to dinner. Eteoneus carved, and Megapenthes served round the wine. When they had done eating the two young men prepared to set out.

As they were on the point of starting, an eagle flew upon their right hand, with a goose in its talons which it had carried off from the farm yard. This omen was so good that everyone was delighted to see it, and Pisistratus said, 'Say, King Menelaus, is the omen for us or for yourself?'

Menelaus was in doubt how to answer, but Helen said that as the eagle had come from a mountain and seized the goose, so Ulysses should return and take vengeance on the suitors. Telemachus said he only hoped it might prove so, and the pair then drove on. They reached Pylos on the following day, and Telemachus urged Pisistratus to drive him straight to his ship, for fear Nestor should detain him if he went to his house.

'I know,' said Pisistratus, 'how obstinate he is. He would come down to your ship, if he knew you were there, and would never go back without you. But he will be very angry.' He then drove to the ship, and Telemachus told the crew to get her under way as fast as they could.

Now as he was attending to everything and sacrificing to Minerva, there came to him a man of the race of Melampus who was flying from Argos because he had killed a man. His name was Theoclymenus and he came of an old and highly honourable family, his father and grand-father having been celebrated prophets and divines. He besought Telemachus to take him to Ithaca and thus save him from enemies who were in pursuit. Telemachus consented, took Theoclymenus on board, and laid his spear down on the deck.

Then they sailed away, and next day they got among the flying islands, whereon Telemachus wondered whether he should be taken or should escape.

All this time Ulysses was in the hut with Eumæus, and after supper Ulysses said he should like to go down to the town next day, and see if the suitors would take him into their service. Eumæus at once ex-plained to him that any such idea was out of the question. 'You do not know,' he said, 'what men these suitors are; their insolence reaches heaven; the young men who wait on them have good looking faces and well kempt heads; the tables are always clean and loaded with abundance. The suitors would be the death of you; stay here, then, where you are in nobody's way, till Telemachus returns from Pylos.'

Ulysses thanked Eumæus for his information, and then began to ask whether his father and mother were still living; he was told that Anticlea was dead, and that Laertes, though still alive, would be glad to follow her. Eumæus said he had been brought up in their service, and was better off formerly, for there was no getting a good word out of his mistress now, inasmuch as the suitors had turned the house upside down. 'Servants,' he said, 'like to have a talk with their mistress and hear things from her own lips; they like being told to eat and drink, and being allowed to take something back with them into the country. This is what will keep servants cheerful and contented.'

On being further questioned by Ulysses, Eumæus told how he had been kidnapped as a child by some Phœnician traders who had seduced his nurse (also a Phœnician) and persuaded her to go away with them, and bring him with her.

'I was born,' he said, 'in the island of Syra over against Ortygia, where the sun turns. It is not populous, but contains two cities which occupy the whole land between them, and my father was king over them both. A few days after my nurse had kidnapped me, and while we were on our voyage, Diana killed her, and she was flung overboard, but I was taken to Ithaca where Laertes bought me.'

Ulysses and Eumæus spent the greater part of the night talking with one another, and at dawn Telemachus' crew drew near to land, furled their sails and rowed into the harbour. There they threw out their mooring stones, made their ship fast, landed and ate their dinner on the shore. When they had done, Telemachus said, 'Now take the ship on to the city; I will go to look after my farm and will come down in the evening. Tomorrow morning I will give you all a hearty meal to reward you for your trouble.'

'But what,' said Theoclymenus, 'is to become of me? To whose house am I to go?'

'At any other time,' answered Telemachus, 'I should take you to my own house, but you would not find it convenient now, for I shall not be there, and my mother will not see you. I shall therefore send you to the house of Eurymachus, who is one of the first men we have, and is most eager in his suit for my mother's hand.'

As he spoke a hawk flew on Telemachus' right hand, with a dove whose feathers it was plucking while it flew. Theoclymenus assured Telemachus that this was an omen which boded most happily for the prosperity of his house. It was then settled that Theoclymenus should go to the house of Piræus the son of Clytius.

The crew now loosed the ship from her moorings and went on as they had been told to do, while Telemachus wended his way in all haste to the pig farm where Eumæus lived.

BOOK SIXTEEN

ULYSSES AND TELEMACHUS BECOME KNOWN TO ONE ANOTHER

ULYSSES and Eumæus prepared their meal at daybreak. When Telemachus was reaching the hut, Ulysses observed that the dogs did not bark, though he heard footsteps, and inquired whether the visitor was some acquaintance of the swineherd's. He had hardly done speaking when Telemachus entered, and was welcomed by Eumæus.

'Is my mother still at the house,' said he, 'or has she left it with another husband, so that the bed of Ulysses is festooned with cobwebs?'

'She is still there,' answered Eumæus, 'spending her time in tears both night and day.'

Eumæus set refreshments before him and when he had done eating he asked who the stranger might be.

When Telemachus heard that Ulysses was a ship-wrecked suppliant he was much displeased. 'I am as yet too young,' he said, 'to be able to hold my own in the house; what sufficient support, then, can I give this man? Still, as he has come to you I will send him clothes and all necessary food; and let him stay with you; I will not have him go near the suitors, for harm would be sure to come of it.'

Ulysses expressed his surprise and indignation about the suitors, whereon Telemachus explained still further, and wound up by telling Eumæus to go at once and inform Penelope of his return. Eumæus asked if he should turn a little out of his way and tell Laertes, but Telemachus said he was not to do so. Penelope would send him word all in due course.

As soon as Eumæus was gone Minerva came to the hut. Ulysses knew her, and so did the dogs, for they went whining away to the other end of the yards, but Telemachus did not see her. She made a sign to Ulysses that he was to come outside, and when he had done so she told him he was to reveal himself to his son — whereon she struck him with her wand, endowed him with a noble presence and clothed him in goodly raiment.

Then he went back into the hut and told his son who he was; but for a long while Telemachus would not believe. At last, however, when he was convinced, the pair flung their arms about each other's neck, and

THE STORY OF THE ODYSSEY

wept like eagles or vultures who had been robbed of their young.
Indeed they would have wept till sundown had it not occurred to
Telemachus to ask his father in what ship he had come to Ithaca, and
whose crew it was that had brought him.

Ulysses told him about the Phæacians, and how he had hidden the
presents they had given him. 'I am now come,' he said, 'by Minerva's
advice, to consult with you as to how we shall take vengeance on the
suitors. I would therefore learn how many there are of them, and
consider whether we two can kill them, or whether we must get help
from outside.'

Telemachus said it was hopeless to think of attacking the suitors
without assistance. There were fifty-two from Dulichium, with six
followers, twenty-four from Same, twenty from Zacynthus and
twelve from Ithaca.

Ulysses explained that he could rely on help from Jove and from
Minerva, and thought that this would be enough. 'They will not be
long in joining us,' said he, 'when the fight has begun in good earnest.
Go, then, tomorrow to the town, and join the suitors; let the swineherd
bring me later, disguised as a poor miserable beggar. Never mind how
much violence you may see the suitors do me. Look on and say
nothing, beyond asking them in a friendly way to leave me alone.
Also, find some pretext for removing the armour from the walls. Say
it is taking harm with the smoke, and that the sight of armour sometimes sets men fighting, so that it is better away — but leave two
swords, shields and spears for you and me to snatch up.'

As they were thus conversing, the ship that had brought Telemachus
from Pylos reached the harbour of Ithaca, and the crew took the
presents which Menelaus had given him to the house of Clytius. They
sent a man to tell Penelope that Telemachus was at the farm, and had
sent the ship on to allay her anxiety. This man and the swineherd met,
at the house of Ulysses, and the man said, in the presence of the maids,
'Madam, your son is returned from Pylos;' but Eumæus stood by her
and told her all that her son had bidden him. Then he went back to his
pig farm.

The suitors were very angry, and were about sending a ship to fetch
those who had been lying in wait for Telemachus, when Amphinomus,
a suitor, happened to turn round and saw their ship coming into harbour. So he laughed and said, 'We have no need to send, for the men
are here.' On this they all went to meet the ship, and Antinous said

465

that as Telemachus had escaped them in spite of their great vigilance, they must kill him, either at the farm or as he was coming thence. Otherwise he would expose their plot, and they would have the people rise against them. 'If,' he concluded, 'this does not please you, and you would let him live, we cannot eat up his estate any longer, but must go home, urge our suit each from his own house, and let the one among us take Penelope who will give most for her, or whose lot it may happen to be.'

Amphinomus, who came from the well-grassed and grain-growing island of Dulichium, then spoke. He was a man of good natural disposition, and his conversation was more pleasing to Penelope than that of any of the other suitors; 'I will only consent to kill Telemachus,' said he, 'if the gods give us their approval. It is a serious thing to kill a man who is of royal race. If they sanction it, I will be with you; otherwise I am for letting it alone.'

The rest assented, and they went back to the house. But Medon told Penelope of this new plot, so she went attended by her gentlewomen, stood by one of the bearing-posts that supported the roof of the cloister, and bitterly rebuked Antinous for his ingratitude in forgetting how Ulysses in old days had saved the life of his father Eupeithes.

Eurymachus then made a fair but false speech vowing eternal friendship to Telemachus, and Penelope returned to her own room to mourn her husband till Minerva closed her eyes in slumber.

In the evening Eumæus got back to his hut just as the others had killed a yearling pig and were getting supper ready. Meanwhile Minerva had again disguised Ulysses as an old beggar.

'What news from the town, Eumæus?' said Telemachus. 'Have the suitors got back with their ship?'

'I did not ask,' answered Eumæus, 'for when I had given my message I turned straight home; but I met the messenger from your own crew, who told your mother of your return before I could do so. As I was coming here, and was on the hill of Mercury above the town, I saw a ship with many men and much armour coming into port; so I suppose it was the suitors, but I cannot be sure.'

Telemachus gave his father a look, but so that the swineherd could not see him. Then they all got their supper and went to bed.

BOOK SEVENTEEN

TELEMACHUS GOES TO THE TOWN, AND IS FOLLOWED BY EUMÆUS AND ULYSSES, WHO IS MALTREATED BY THE SUITORS

WHEN morning came Telemachus told Eumæus that he would now go to the town and show himself to his mother, who would never be comforted till she saw him with her own eyes. 'As for this miserable stranger,' he continued, 'take him to the town, that he may beg there and get what he can; if this does not please him, so much the worse for him, but I like to say what I mean.'

Ulysses said he should be glad to go, for a beggar could do much better in town than country; but he must warm himself first, and wait till the sun had got some heat in it; his clothes were very bad, and he should perish with cold, for the town was some way off.

Telemachus then left, and when he reached the house he set his spear against a strong bearing-post, crossed the stone pavement and went inside. He found Euryclea putting the sheep skins on to the seats. She and all the other maids ran up to him as soon as they saw him, and kissed him on the head and shoulders. Then Penelope came weeping from her room, embraced him, and told him to tell her all that he had seen.

Telemachus bade her go back to her room and pray to Minerva that they might be revenged on the suitors. 'I must go,' said he, 'to the place of assembly, to look after a guest whom I have brought with me, and whom I have left with Piræus.'

Penelope did as her son had said, while Telemachus went to the place of assembly, and his two dogs with him. The suitors, who had not yet gone to the house of Ulysses for the day, gathered round him, and made him fair speeches, but he knew their falsehood and went to sit with his old friends Mentor, Antiphus and Halitherses. Presently Piræus came up, bringing Theoclymenus with him, and said, 'I wish you would send some of your women to my house to take away the presents that Menelaus gave you.'

Telemachus said he did not know what might happen; if the suitors killed him, he had rather Piræus kept the presents than that the suitors should have them. If, on the other hand, he killed the suitors he should be much obliged if Piræus would let him have the presents.

Then he took Theoclymenus to his own house, where they had a bath, and refreshments were set before them. Penelope sat near them, spinning, while they were at table, and then said she should go up stairs and lie down on that couch which she had never ceased to water with her tears from the day her husband left her. 'But you had not the patience,' she added, 'to tell me, before the suitors came, whether you had been able to hear anything about your father.'

Telemachus told her how good Nestor had been to him, and how he had sent him on to Menelaus, who had assured him that Ulysses was still alive, but was detained by Calypso, from whom he could not get away for want of a ship. Penelope was very much agitated, but Theoclymenus reassured her by telling her about the omen which had greeted Telemachus on his return to Ithaca.

While they were thus conversing, the suitors were playing at quoits and aiming javelins at a mark on the level ground in front of Ulysses' house. But when it was near dinner time and the flocks were coming in from all the country round with their shepherds as usual [to be milked], Medon, who was a great favourite with the suitors, called them to come in and set about getting their dinner ready. They therefore came in and began to butcher some sheep, goats, pigs and a heifer.

Meanwhile Eumæus told Ulysses that it was time to make a start, for the day was well up and if he waited till afternoon he would find the cold more severe. 'At any rate,' said Ulysses, 'let me have a staff if you have one, for the path is rugged.' Eumæus gave him one, and they set out along the steep path leading to the town. When they were nearly there they came to the fountain which Ithacus, Neritus and Polyctor had made, and from which the people drew their water; here they fell in with Melanthius son of Dolius, who was bringing goats for the suitors' dinner, he and his two under-shepherds.

Melanthius heaped all kinds of insult on Ulysses and Eumæus, and tried to kick Ulysses off the path, but could not do so. Ulysses restrained himself, and prayed to the nymphs, whereon Melanthius said he would put him on board ship and sell him in some foreign country. He then hurried on, leaving the swineherd and his master to follow at their own pace.

When they got near the house they could hear the sound of Phemius' lyre, and his voice as he sang to the suitors. They could also smell the savour of roast meats. Eumæus said that he would go in first, but that Ulysses had better follow him soon, for if he was seen standing about in the outer court people might throw things at him.

As they were thus talking the old hound Argus who was lying on the dunghill, very full of fleas, caught sight of Ulysses, recognized him, wagged his tail and tried to come to him, but could not do so. Thereon Ulysses wiped a tear from his eyes, and asked Eumæus whether the dog was of any use, or whether he was kept only for his good looks. Eumæus said what a noble hound Argus had been, but the dog, having seen his master, died just as Eumæus went inside the house.

Telemachus saw him enter and beckoned him to a seat at his own table. Ulysses followed him shortly, and sat down on the floor of ash wood inside the doorway, leaning against a bearing-post of well-squared cypress wood. Telemachus noted him and said to Eumæus, 'Take the stranger this handful of bread and meat, tell him also to go round and beg from the others, for a beggar must not be shamefaced.' Eumæus gave him both the message and the bread and meat.

Then Ulysses began to go round begging, for he wanted to exploit the suitors. He went from left to right, and some took compassion on him while others began asking who he might be; Melanthius then said that he had come with the swineherd. Antinous, therefore, asked Eumæus what he meant by bringing such a man to plague them.

'I did not ask him to come,' answered Eumæus. 'Who was likely to ask a man of that sort? One would ask a divine, a physician, a carpenter or a bard. You are always hardest of all the suitors on Ulysses' servants, and especially upon me, but I do not care so long as I have Penelope and Telemachus on my side.'

'Hush,' said Telemachus, 'Antinous has the bitterest tongue of them all, and he makes the others worse.' Then he turned towards Antinous and said, 'Give him something: I do not grudge it. Never mind my mother or any of the servants — not you — but you are fonder of eating than of giving.'

Antinous said, 'You are a swaggering upstart; if all the suitors will give him as much as I will, he will not come near the house again this three months.'

As he spoke he menaced Ulysses with the footstool from under his table. The other suitors all gave him something; and he was about to leave, when he determined to again beg from Antinous and trumped him up a story of the misfortunes that had befallen him in Egypt.

'Get out,' said Antinous, 'into the open part of the court, and away from my table, or I will give you Egypt over again.'

Ulysses drew back, and said, 'Your looks are better than your under-

THE AUTHORESS OF THE ODYSSEY

standing. I can see that if you were in your own house you would not spare a poor man so much as a pinch of salt.'

Antinous scowled at him. 'Take that,' he cried, 'and be off out of the court.' As he spoke he threw a footstool at him which hit him on the right shoulder, but Ulysses stood firm as a rock, and prayed that if there was a god, or an avenger of beggars, Antinous might be a corpse before he was a bridegroom.

'Have a care,' replied Antinous, 'and hold your peace, or we will flay you alive.'

The others reproved Antinous. 'You did ill,' they said, 'to strike the man. Who knows but he may be one of the gods who go about the world in disguise to redress wrong, and chastise the insolence of mankind?'

Penelope from her room upstairs heard what had been going on, and spoke with her women bitterly about the suitors. The housekeeper Eurynome answered that if her prayers were heard, not a single one of them would live till morning. 'Nurse,' replied Penelope, 'I hate them all, but Antinous is the worst.' Then she sent for Eumæus and said, 'Tell the stranger that I want to see him; he looks like a man who has travelled, and he may have seen or heard something of Ulysses.'

'He has been three days and three nights at my hut, Madam,' replied Eumæus, 'and the most accomplished bard could not have given me better entertainment. He told me that Ulysses was among the Thesprotians and would return shortly, bringing much treasure with him.'

'Then call him to me,' said Penelope, 'and as for the others, let them dine at their own expense for the future or how they best may, so long as they leave off coming here.'

Telemachus, who was down below, gave a great sneeze as she spoke, which echoed over the whole house. Penelope explained to Eumæus that this was a most favourable omen, and added that if she was satisfied of the truth of what the stranger told her she would give him a shirt and cloak.

Eumæus gave Penelope's message to Ulysses, but he feared the violence of the suitors, and told him to say that she must wait till nightfall, when the suitors would be gone. 'Then,' he said, 'let her set me down in a warm seat by the fire, and I will tell her about her husband; for my clothes are in a very bad state; you know they are, for yours was the first house I came to.'

Penelope was displeased at his delay, and asked Eumæus whether his fears were reasonable, or whether it was only that he was shamefaced. Eumæus explained that he was quite reasonable, whereon Penelope was satisfied; he then went back to where the suitors were, and told Telemachus that he would return to his pigs.

Telemachus said that he had better get something to eat first, and was to come back to the town on the following morning, bringing the pigs that were to be killed for dinner. It was now afternoon, and the suitors had turned to their singing and dancing.

BOOK EIGHTEEN

THE FIGHT BETWEEN ULYSSES AND IRUS —THE SUITORS MAKE PRESENTS TO PENELOPE—AND ILL-TREAT ULYSSES

NOW there came a common tramp to Ulysses' house, begging — a great hulking fellow with no stay in him — whose name was Arnæus; but people called him Irus, because he would run errands for anyone who would send him on them. This man began to threaten Ulysses, and said the suitors had urged him to turn him away from the house.

Ulysses said there was room enough for both of them, and that it should be a case of live-and-let-live between them. 'If, however,' he continued, 'it comes to blows, I will deluge your mouth and chest with blood, and I shall have the place to myself, for you will not come back again.'

Irus retorted angrily, and Antinous, hearing them wrangle, told the other suitors that Irus and the stranger were about to have a fight. 'It is the finest piece of sport,' he said, 'that heaven ever sent into this house. We are to have goat's paunches stuffed with blood and fat for supper; whichever of the two beats in this fight shall have his pick of the lot of them.'

The preliminaries being arranged, and fair play bargained for by Ulysses, he began to strip. When Irus saw his muscles his heart misgave him; but Antinous kept him up to it, and the fight began. Ulysses forthwith nearly killed Irus and dragged him by the heels into the outer court, where he put his staff in his hand and propped him up against the wall more dead than alive. Antinous then gave Ulysses a great goat's paunch, and Amphinomus drank his health.

Ulysses made Amphinomus a very grave and impressive speech, warning him to leave the house, inasmuch as Ulysses would return shortly. 'You seem,' said he, 'to be a man of good understanding, as indeed you may well be, seeing whose son you are. I have heard your father well spoken of; he is Nisus of Dulichium, a man both brave and wealthy. They tell me you are his son and you seem to be a considerable person; listen, therefore, and take heed to what I am saying. Man is the vainest of all creatures that live and move upon the earth; as long as heaven vouchsafes him health and strength he thinks that he shall come to no harm hereafter, and even when the blessed gods bring sorrow upon him, he bears it as he needs must and makes the best of it, for God Almighty gives men their daily minds day by day. I know all about it, for I was a rich man once, and did much wrong in the stubbornness of my pride and in the confidence that my father and my brothers would support me; therefore let a man fear God in all things always, and take the good that heaven may see fit to send him without vainglory.' But Amphinomus, though his heart boded ill, would not be persuaded.

Minerva then put it in Penelope's mind to get some presents out of the suitors. 'I hate them,' said she to Eurynome, 'but still for once in a way I will see them; I want to warn my son against them.'

'Certainly, my dear child,' answered Eurynome, 'but you must wash your face first. You cannot be seen with the stain of tears upon your cheeks.'

'Eurynome,' replied her mistress, 'do not try to persuade me. Heaven robbed me of all my beauty on the day when my husband sailed for Troy; but send Autonoë and Hippodamia to attend me, for I cannot think of seeing the suitors unattended.' The old woman then went through the house to fetch the women; and as soon as she was gone, Minerva sent Penelope into a deep sleep during which she endowed her with the most dazzling beauty, washing her face with the ambrosial loveliness which Venus wears when she goes out dancing with the Graces, and giving her a statelier and more imposing presence. When the two maids came, the noise of their coming woke her. 'What a delicious sleep,' she exclaimed, 'has overshadowed me. Would that it had been the sleep of death, which had thus ended all my sorrows.'

She then went down stairs, and the suitors were dazzled with her beauty. She began by upbraiding Telemachus for having allowed the fight to take place. Telemachus admitted his fault, but pleaded the extreme difficulty of his situation and the fact that after all Ulysses had thrashed Irus.

Eurymachus broke in upon their conversation by telling Penelope how very beautiful she was; and Penelope answered that heaven had robbed her of all her beauty on the day when her husband sailed for Troy. 'Moreover,' she added, 'I have another great sorrow— your suitors are not wooing me in the usual way. When men are suing for the hand of one who they think will make them a good wife, they generally bring oxen and sheep for her relations to feast upon, and make rich presents to the lady herself, instead of sponging upon other people's property.'

When Ulysses heard her say this, he was delighted at seeing his wife trying to get presents out of the suitors, and hoodwinking them.

Then Antinous said, 'Penelope, take all the presents you can get, but we will not go till you have married the best man among us.' On this they all made Penelope magnificent presents, and she went back to her own room, followed by the women, who carried the presents for her.

The suitors now turned to singing and dancing, lighted by large braziers that were placed in the court, and also by torches, which the maids held up by turns. Ulysses after a while told them to go inside, saying that he would hold the torches himself. The maids laughed at this, and Melantho, who was one of them, began to gibe at him. She was daughter to Dolius but Penelope had brought her up from childhood, and used to give her toys; she showed no consideration, however, for Penelope's sorrows, but misconducted herself with Eurymachus. 'Are you drunk?' she said to Ulysses. 'Are you always like this?'

Ulysses scowled at her, and said he would tell Telemachus, who would have her cut up into mincemeat. The women, therefore, were frightened and went away, so Ulysses was left holding up the flaming torches — looking upon all the suitors and brooding over his revenge.

Presently Eurymachus began to jeer at him, and taunt him by saying he preferred begging to working. Ulysses answered, 'If you and I, Eurymachus, were matched one against the other in early summer, when the days are at their longest — give us each a good scythe, and see whether you or I will mow the stronger or fast the longer, from dawn till dark when the mowing grass is about. Or let us be in a four acre field with a couple of tawny full fed oxen each, and see which of us can drive the straighter furrow. Again, let war break out this day — give me armour and you will find me fighting among the foremost. You are insolent and cruel, and think yourself a great man because you live in a little world, and that a bad one.'

Eurymachus was furious, and seized a stool; but Ulysses sat down by the knees of Amphinomus of Dulichium, for he was afraid; the stool hit the cupbearer and knocked him down, whereon there was a general uproar, amid which Telemachus said that he would compel no man, but he thought it would be better if they would all go home to bed. To this they assented, and shortly afterwards left the house.

BOOK NINETEEN

ULYSSES CONVERSES WITH PENELOPE, AND IS RECOGNIZED BY EURYCLEA

ULYSSES and Telemachus were left alone in the cloister, and Ulysses said, 'We must take the armour down from the walls; if the suitors are surprised, say what I told you when we were in Eumæus' hut.'

Telemachus called Euryclea, and bade her shut the women up in their room, for he was going to take the armour down into the store-room. 'Who,' asked Euryclea, 'will show you a light if the women are all shut up?' 'The stranger,' answered Telemachus; 'I will not have people doing nothing about my premises.'

He and Ulysses then began removing the armour, and Minerva went before them, shedding a strange lambent light that played on walls and rafters. Telemachus was lost in wonder, but Ulysses said, 'Hush, this is the manner of the gods. Get you to bed, and leave me to talk with your mother and the maids.' So Telemachus crossed the court and went to the room in which he always slept, leaving Ulysses in the cloister.

Penelope now came down, and they set a seat for her by the fire; the maids also were let out, and came to take away the meats on which the suitors had been feasting, and to heap fresh wood upon the braziers after they had emptied the ashes on to the ground. Melantho again began scolding at Ulysses for stopping in the house to spy on the women. Penelope heard her and said, 'Bold hussy, I hear you, and you shall smart for it; I have already told you that I wish to see the stranger and inquire from him about my husband. Eurynome, bring a seat for him, and spread a fleece on it.'

Eurynome did as she was told, and when Ulysses had sat down Penelope wanted to know who he was. Ulysses implored her not to ask this, for it would make him weep, and she or the servants might then think he had been drinking.

'Stranger,' answered Penelope, 'heaven robbed me of all my beauty when the Argives set out for Troy and Ulysses with them.' She then told about the suitors, and her web, and said that she was now at the very end of her resources. Her parents were urging her to marry again, and so also was her son, who chafed under the heavy burden of expense which her long courtship had caused him. 'In spite of all this, however,' she continued, 'I want to know who you are; for you cannot be the son of a rock or of an oak.'

Thus pressed, Ulysses said that his name was Æthon and that he came from Crete, where he had entertained Ulysses and his men for many days when they were on their way to Troy. Penelope wept bitterly as she listened, and it was all Ulysses could do to restrain his own tears — but he succeeded. 'I will now prove you,' said she; 'tell me how my husband was dressed. Tell me also what manner of man he was, and about the men who were with him.'

'I will tell you,' replied Ulysses, 'as nearly as I can remember after so long a time. He wore a mantle of purple wool, double lined, and it was fastened by a gold brooch with two catches for the pin. On the face of this there was a device that showed a dog holding a spotted fawn between its fore paws, and watching it as it lay panting on the ground. Everyone marvelled at the way in which these things had been done in gold — the dog looking at the fawn and strangling it, while the fawn was struggling convulsively to escape. As for his shirt, it fitted him like the skin of an onion, and glistened in the sunlight to the admiration of all the women who beheld it. He had a servant with him, a little older than himself, whose shoulders were hunched; he was dark, and had thick curly hair. His name was Eurybates.'

Penelope was deeply moved. 'You shall want for nothing,' she said. 'It was I who gave him the clothes and the brooch you speak of, but I shall never see him again.'

'Be not too dejected, Madam,' answered Ulysses. 'When I was with the Thesprotians I heard for certain that he was alive and well. Indeed he would have been here ere now, had he not deemed it better to amass great wealth before returning. Before this month is out I swear most solemnly that he will be here.'

'If you say truly,' replied Penelope, 'you shall indeed be rewarded richly, but he will not come. Still, you women, take the stranger and wash him; make him a comfortable bed, and in the morning wash him again and anoint him, that he may sit at the same table with Telemachus; if any of the suitors molest him, he shall rue it, for fume as he may, he shall have no more to do in this house. How indeed, Sir, can you know how much I surpass all other women in goodness and discretion unless I see that you are well clothed and fed?'

'Make me no bed, Madam,' said Ulysses, 'I will lie on the bare ground as I am wont to do. Nor do I like having my feet washed. I will not allow any of your serving women to touch my feet; but if you have any respectable old woman who has gone through as much as I have, I will let her wash them.'

'Stranger,' answered Penelope, 'your sense of propriety exceeds that of any foreigner who has ever come here. I have exactly the kind of person you describe; she was Ulysses' nurse from the day of his birth, and is now very old and feeble, but she shall wash your feet. Euryclea, come and wash the stranger's feet. He is about the same age as your master would be.'

Euryclea spoke compassionately to Ulysses, and ended by saying that he was very like her master. To which Ulysses replied that many other people had observed the likeness.

Then the old woman got a large foot bath and put some cold water into it, adding hot water until it was the right heat. As soon, however, as she got Ulysses' leg in her hands, she recognized a scar on it as one which her master had got from being ripped by a boar when he was hunting on Mt. Parnassus with his mother's father Autolycus, whom Mercury had endowed with the gift of being the most accomplished thief and perjurer in the whole world, for he was very fond of him. She immediately dropped the leg, which made a loud noise against the side of the bath and upset all the water. Her eyes filled with tears, and she caught Ulysses by the beard and told him that she knew him.

She looked towards Penelope to tell her; but Minerva had directed Penelope's attention elsewhere, so that she had observed nothing of what had been going on. Ulysses gripped Euryclea's throat, and swore he would kill her, nurse to him though she had been, unless she kept his return secret — which she promised to do. She also said that if heaven delivered the suitors into his hands, she would give him a list of all the women in the house who had misconducted themselves.

'You have no need,' said Ulysses, 'I shall find that out for myself. See that you keep my counsel and leave the rest to heaven.'

Euryclea now went to fetch some more water, for the first had been all spilt. When she had brought it, and had washed Ulysses, he turned his seat round to the fire to dry himself, and drew his rags over the scar that Penelope might not see it.

Then Penelope detailed her sorrows to Ulysses. Others, she said, could sleep, but she could not do so, neither night nor day. She could not rest for thinking what her duty might be. Ought she to stay where she was and stand guard over her son's estate, or ought she to marry one of the suitors and go elsewhere? Her son, while he was a boy, would not hear of her doing this, but now that he was grown up and realized the havoc that the suitors were making of his property, he was continually urging her to go. Besides, she had had a strange dream about an eagle that had come from a mountain and swooped down on her favourite geese as they were eating mash out of a tub, and had killed them all. Then the eagle came back and told her he was Ulysses, while the geese were the suitors; but when she woke the geese were still feeding at the mash tub. Now, what did all this mean?

Ulysses said it could only mean the immediate return of her husband, and his revenge upon the suitors.

But Penelope would not believe him. 'Dreams,' she said, 'are very curious things. They come through two gates, one of horn, and the other of ivory. Those that come through the gate of ivory have no significance. It is the others that alone are true, and my dream came through the gate of ivory. Tomorrow, therefore, I shall set Ulysses' bow before the suitors, and I will leave this house with him who can draw it most easily and send an arrow through the twelve holes whereby twelve axeheads are fitted into their handles.'

'You need not defer this competition,' said Ulysses, 'for your husband will be here before any one of them can draw the bow and shoot through the axes.'

'Stranger,' replied Penelope, 'I could stay talking with you the whole night through, but there is a time for everything, and I will now go to lie down upon that couch which I have never ceased to water with my tears from the day my husband set out for the city with an ill-omened name. You can sleep within the house, either on the ground or on a bedstead, whichever you may prefer.'

Then she went upstairs and mourned her dear husband till Minerva shed sweet sleep over her eyes.

BOOK TWENTY

ULYSSES CONVERSES WITH EUMÆUS, AND WITH HIS HERDSMAN PHILŒTIUS— THE SUITORS AGAIN MALTREAT HIM— CLYMENUS FORETELLS THEIR DOOM AND LEAVES THE HOUSE

ULYSSES made himself a bed of an untanned ox-hide in the vestibule and covered himself with sheep skins; then Eurynome threw a cloak over him. He saw the women who misbehaved themselves with the suitors go giggling out of the house, and was sorely tempted to kill them then and there, but he restrained himself. He kept turning round and round, as a man turns a paunch full of blood and fat before a hot fire to cook it, and could get no rest till Minerva came to him and comforted him, by reminding him that he was now in Ithaca.

'That is all very well,' replied Ulysses, 'but suppose I do kill these suitors, pray consider what is to become of me then? Where am I to fly to from the revenge their friends will take upon me?'

'One would think,' answered Minerva, 'that you might trust even a feebler aid than mine; go to sleep; your troubles shall end shortly.'

Ulysses then slept, but Penelope was still wakeful, and lamented her impending marriage, and her inability to sleep, in such loud tones that Ulysses heard her, and thought she was close by him.

It was now morning and Ulysses rose, praying the while to Jove. 'Grant me,' he cried, 'a sign from one of the people who are now waking in the house, and another sign from outside it.'

Forthwith Jove thundered from a clear sky. There came also a miller woman from the mill-room, who, being weakly, had not finished her appointed task as soon as the others had done. As she passed Ulysses he heard her curse the suitors and pray for their immediate death. Ulysses was thus assured that he should kill them.

The other women of the house now lit the fire, and Telemachus came down from his room.

'Nurse,' said he, 'I hope you have seen that the stranger has been duly fed and lodged. My mother, in spite of her many virtues, is apt to be too much impressed by inferior people, and to neglect those who are more deserving.'

'Do not find fault, child,' said Euryclea, 'when there is no one to find fault with. The stranger sat and drank as much wine as he liked. Your mother asked him if he would take any more bread, but he said he did not want any. As for his bed, he would not have one, but slept in the vestibule on an untanned hide, and I threw a cloak over him myself.'

Telemachus then went out to the place of assembly, and his two dogs with him. 'Now, you women,' said Euryclea, 'be quick and clean the house down. Put the cloths on the seats, sponge down the tables; wash the cups and mixing bowls, and go at once, some of you, to fetch water from the fountain. It is a feast day, and the suitors will be here directly.' So twenty of them went for water, and others busied themselves setting things straight about the house.

The men servants then came and chopped wood. The women came back from the fountain, and Eumæus with them, bringing three fine pigs, which he let feed about the yards. When he saw Ulysses he asked him how he was getting on, and Ulysses prayed that heaven might avenge him upon the suitors.

Then Melanthius came with the best goats he had, and made them fast in the gate-house. When he had done this he gibed at Ulysses, but Ulysses made him no answer.

Thirdly came Philœtius with a barren heifer and some fat goats for the suitors. These had been brought over for him by the boatman who plied for all comers. When he saw Ulysses, he asked Eumæus who he was, and said he was very like his lost master. Then he told Ulysses how well his old master had treated him, and how well also he had served his old master. Alas! that he was no longer living. 'We are fallen,' said he, 'on evil times, and I often think that though it would not be right of me to drive my cattle off, and put both myself and them under some other master while Telemachus is still alive, yet even this would be better than leading the life I have to lead at present. Indeed I should have gone off with them long ago, if I did not cling to the hope that Ulysses may still return.'

'I can see,' said Ulysses, 'that you are a very honest and sensible person. Therefore I will swear you a solemn oath that Ulysses will be here immediately, and if you like you shall see him with your own eyes kill the suitors.'

While they were thus conversing the suitors were again plotting the murder of Telemachus, but there appeared an unfavourable omen, so Amphinomus said they had better go to the house and get dinner ready, which they accordingly did. When they were at table, Eumæus gave them their cups, Philœtius handed round the bread and Melanthius poured them out their wine. Telemachus purposely set Ulysses at a little table on the part of the cloister that was paved with stone, and told the suitors that it should be worse for any of them who molested him. 'This,' he said, 'is not a public house, but it is mine, for it has come to me from Ulysses.'

The suitors were very angry but Antinous checked them. 'Let us put up with it,' said he; 'if Jove had permitted, we should have been the death of him ere now.' Meanwhile, it being the festival of Apollo, the people of the town were bearing his holy hecatomb about the streets.

The servants gave Ulysses an equal portion with what they gave the others, for Telemachus had so bidden them. Presently one of the suitors named Ctesippus observed this and said, 'I see the stranger has as good a portion as anyone else. I will give him a better, that he may have something to give the bath-woman or some other of the servants in the house' — and with this he flung a cow's heel at Ulysses' head.

Ulysses smiled with a grim Sardinian smile, and bowed his head so that the heel passed over it and hit the wall. Telemachus rebuked Ctesippus very fiercely, and all were silent till Agelaus tried to calm them saying, 'What Telemachus has said is just: let us not answer. Nevertheless I would urge him to talk quietly with his mother and tell her that as long as there was any chance of Ulysses coming back there was nothing unreasonable in her deferring a second marriage; but there is now no hope of his return, and if you would enjoy your own in peace, tell her to marry the best man among us and the one who will make her the most advantageous offer.'

'Nay,' answered Telemachus, 'it is not I that delay her marriage. I urge her to it, but I cannot and will not force her.'

Then Minerva made the suitors break out into a forced hysterical laughter, and the meats which they were eating became all smirched with blood. Their eyes were filled with tears and their hearts were oppressed with terrible forebodings. Theoclymenus saw that all was wrong, and said, 'Unhappy men, what is it that ails you? There is a shroud of darkness drawn over you from head to foot, your cheeks are wet with tears; the air is alive with wailing voices; the walls and roof beams drip blood; the gate of the cloisters, and the yard beyond them are full of ghosts trooping down into the night of hell; the sun is blotted out from heaven, and a blighting gloom is over all the land.'

The suitors laughed at him, and Eurymachus said, 'If you find it so dark here, we had better send a man with you to take you out into the open.'

'I have eyes,' he answered, 'that can guide, and feet that can take me from the doom that I see overhanging every single one of you.' On this he left them and went back to the house of Piræus.

Then one of the suitors said, 'Telemachus, you are very unfortunate in your guests. You had better ship both the stranger and this man off to the Sicels and sell them.' Telemachus made no answer, but kept his eye on his father for any signal that he might make him.

Penelope had had a seat placed for her overlooking the cloister, and heard all that had passed. The dinner had been good and plentiful and there had been much laughter, for they had slaughtered many victims, but little did they guess the terrible supper which the goddess and a strong man were preparing for them.

BOOK TWENTY-ONE

THE TRIAL OF THE BOW AND OF THE AXES

THEN Minerva put it in Penelope's mind to let the suitors compete for the bow and for a prize of iron. So she went upstairs and got the key of the store-room, where Ulysses' treasures of gold, copper and iron were kept, as also the mighty bow which Iphitus son of Eurytus had given him, and which had been in common use by Eurytus as long as he was alive. Hither she went attended by her women, and when she had unlocked the door she took the bow down from its peg and carried it, with its quiver full of deadly arrows, to the suitors, while her maids brought the chest in which were the many prizes of iron that Ulysses had won. Then, still attended by her two maidens, she stood by one of the bearing-posts that supported the roof of the cloister, and told the suitors she would marry the man among them who could string Ulysses' bow most easily, and send an arrow through the twelve holes by which twelve axe-heads were fastened on to their handles.

So saying she gave the bow into the hands of Eumæus and bade him let the suitors compete as she had said. Eumæus wept as he took it, and so did Philœtius who was looking on, whereon Antinous scolded them for a couple of country bumpkins.

Telemachus said that he too should compete, and that if he was successful he should certainly not allow his mother to leave her home with a second husband, while he remained alone. So saying he dug a long trench quite straight, set the axes in a line within it, and stamped the earth about them to keep them steady; everyone was surprised to see how accurately he fixed them, considering that he had never seen anything of the kind before. Having set the axes duly, he stood on the stone pavement, and tried to string the bow, but failed three times. He would, however, have succeeded the fourth time, if Ulysses had not made him a sign that he was not to try any more. So he laid both bow and arrow down and took his seat.

'Then,' said Antinous, 'begin at the place where the cup-bearer begins, and let each take his turn, going from left to right.' On this Leiodes came forward. He was their sacrificial priest, and sat in the angle of the wall hard by the mixing bowl; but he had always set his face against the wicked conduct of the suitors. When he had failed to string the bow he said it was so hard to string that it would rob many a man among them of life and heart — for which saying Antinous rebuked him bitterly.

'Bring some fire, Melantheus, and a wheel of fat from inside the house,' said he to Melanthius [sic], 'that we may warm the bow and grease it.' So they did this, but though many tried they could none of them string it. There remained only Antinous and Eurymachus who were their ringleaders.

The swineherd and the stockman Philœtius then went outside the forecourt, and Ulysses followed them; when they had got beyond the outer yard Ulysses sounded them, and having satisfied himself that they were loyal he revealed himself and showed them the scar on his leg. They were overjoyed, and Ulysses said, 'Go back one by one after me, and follow these instructions. The other suitors will not be for letting me have the bow, but do you, Eumæus, when you have got it in your hands, bring it to me, and tell the women to shut themselves into their room. If the sound of groaning or uproar reaches any of them when they are inside, tell them to stick to their work and not come out. I leave it to you, Philœtius, to fasten the gate of the outer court securely.' He then went inside, and resumed the seat that he had left.

Eurymachus now tried to string the bow but failed. 'I do not so much mind,' he said, 'about not marrying Penelope, for there are plenty of other women in Ithaca and elsewhere. What grieves me is the fact of our being such a feeble folk as compared with our forefathers.'

Antinous reminded him that it was the festival of Apollo. 'Who,' said he, 'can shoot on such a day as this? Let us leave the axes where they are — no one will take them; let us also sacrifice to Apollo the best goats Melanthius can bring us, and resume the contest tomorrow.'

Ulysses then cunningly urged that he might be allowed to try whether he was as strong a man as he used to be, and that the bow should be placed in his hands for this purpose. The suitors were very angry, but Penelope insisted that Ulysses should have the bow; if he succeeded in stringing it she said it was absurd to suppose that she would marry him; but she would give him a shirt and cloak, a javelin, sword and a pair of sandals, and she would send him wherever he might want to go.

'The bow, mother, is mine,' said Telemachus, 'and if I choose to give it this man out and out I shall give it him. Go within the house and mind your own proper duties.'

Penelope went back, with her women, wondering into the house, and going upstairs into her room she wept for her dear husband till Minerva shed sweet sleep over her eyes.

Eumæus was about to take the bow to Ulysses, but the suitors frightened him and he was for putting it down, till Telemachus threatened to stone him back to his farm if he did not bring it on at once; he therefore gave the bow to Ulysses. Then he called Euryclea aside and told her to shut the women up, and not to let them out if they heard any groans or uproar. She therefore shut them up.

At this point Philœtius slipped out and secured the main gate of the outer court with a ship's cable of Byblus fibre that happened to be lying beside it. This done, he returned to his seat and kept his eye on

Ulysses, who was examining the bow with great care to see whether it was sound in all its parts.

'This man,' said the suitors, 'is some old bow-fancier; perhaps he has got one like it at home, or wants to make one, so cunningly does the old rascal handle it.'

Ulysses, having finished his scrutiny, strung the bow as easily as a bard puts a new string on to his lyre. He tried the string and it sang under his hand like the cry of a swallow. He took an arrow that was lying out of its quiver by his table, placed the notch on the string, and from his seat sent the arrow through the handle-holes of all the axes and outside into the yard.

'Telemachus,' said he, 'your guest has not disgraced you. It is now time for the suitors to have their supper, and to take their pleasure afterwards with song and playing on the lyre.' So saying he made a sign to Telemachus, who girded on his sword, grasped his spear and stood armed beside his father's seat.

BOOK TWENTY-TWO

THE KILLING OF THE SUITORS

ULYSSES tore off his rags, and sprang on the broad pavement, with his bow and his quiver full of arrows. He shed the arrows on to the ground at his feet and said, 'The contest is at an end. I will now see whether Apollo will vouchsafe me to hit another mark which no man has yet aimed at.'

He took aim at Antinous as he spoke. The arrow struck him in the throat, so that he fell over and a thick stream of blood gushed from his nostrils. He kicked his table from him and upset the things on it, whereby the bread and meats were all soiled as they fell over on to the ground. The suitors were instantly in an uproar, and looked towards the walls for armour, but there was none. 'Stranger,' they cried, 'you shall pay dearly for shooting people down in this way. You are a doomed man.' But they did not yet understand that Ulysses had killed Antinous on purpose.

Ulysses glared at them and said, 'Dogs, did you think that I should not return from Troy? You have wasted my substance, you have violated the women of my house, you have wooed my wife while I was still alive, you have feared neither god nor man, and now you shall die.'

Eurymachus alone answered. 'If you are Ulysses,' said he, 'we have done you great wrong. It was all Antinous' doing. He never really wanted to marry Penelope: he wanted to kill your son and to be chief man in Ithaca. He is no more; then spare the lives of your people and we will pay you all.'

Ulysses again glared at him and said, 'I will not stay my hand till I have slain one and all of you. You must fight, or fly as you can, or die — and fly you neither can nor shall.'

Eurymachus then said, 'My friends, this man will give us no quarter. Let us show fight. Draw your swords and hold the tables up in front of you as shields. Have at him with a rush, and drive him from the pavement and from the door. We could then get through into the town and call for help.'

While he spoke and was springing forward, Ulysses sent an arrow into his heart and he fell doubled up over his table. The cup and all the meats went over on to the ground as he smote the earth with his fore-head in the agonies of death.

Amphinomus then made for Ulysses to try and dislodge him from the door, but Telemachus got behind him, and struck him through. He left his spear in the body and flew back to his father's side; 'Father,' said he, 'let me bring armour for you and me, as well as for Eumæus and Philœtius.' 'Run and fetch it,' answered Ulysses, 'while my arrows hold out; be quick, or they may get me away from the door when I am single-handed.'

Telemachus went to the store-room and brought four shields, eight spears and four helmets. He armed himself, as did also Eumæus and Philœtius, who then placed themselves beside Ulysses. As long as his arrows held out Ulysses shot the suitors down thick and threefold, but when they failed him he stood the bow against the end wall of the house hard by the doorway, and armed himself.

Now there was a trap-door on the wall, while at one end of the pavement there was an exit, closed by a good strong door and leading out into a narrow passage; Ulysses told Philœtius to stand by this door and keep it, for only one person could attack it at a time. Then Agelaus shouted out, 'Go up, somebody, to the trap-door and tell the people what is going on; they would come in and help us.'

'This may not be,' answered Melanthius, 'the mouth of the narrow passage is dangerously near the entrance from the street into the outer court. One brave man could prevent any number from getting in, but I will bring you arms from the store-room, for I am sure it is there that they have put them.' As he spoke he went back by passages to the store-room, and brought the suitors twelve shields and the same number of helmets; when Ulysses saw the suitors arming his heart began to fail him, and he said to Telemachus, 'Some of the women inside are helping the suitors — or else it is Melanthius.'

Telemachus said that is was his fault, for he had left the store-room door open. 'Go, Eumæus,' he added, 'and close it; see whether it is one of the women, or Melanthius, son of Dolius.'

Melanthius was now going back for more armour when Eumæus saw him and told Ulysses, who said, 'Follow him, you and Philœtius; bind his hands and feet behind him, and throw him into the store-room; then string him up to a bearing-post till he is close to the rafters, that he may linger on in agony.'

The men went to the store-room and caught Melanthius. They bound him in a painful bond and strung him up as Ulysses had told them. Eumæus wished him a good night and the two men returned to the side of Ulysses. Minerva also joined them, having assumed the form of Mentor; but Ulysses felt sure it was Minerva. The suitors were very angry when they saw her; 'Mentor,' they cried, 'you shall pay for this with your life, and we will confiscate all you have in the world.'

This made Minerva furious, and she rated Ulysses roundly. 'Your prowess,' said she, 'is no longer what it was at Troy. How comes it that you are less valiant now that you are on your own ground? Come on, my good fellow, and see how Mentor will fight for you and requite you for your many kindnesses.' But she did not mean to give him the victory just yet, so she flew up to one of the rafters and sat there in the form of a swallow.

The struggle still continued. 'My friends,' said Agelaus, 'he will soon have to leave off. See how Mentor has left him after doing nothing for him except brag. Do not aim at him all at once, but six of you throw your spears first.'

They did so, but Minerva made all their spears take no effect. Ulysses and the other three then threw, and each killed his man. The suitors drew back in fear into a corner, whereon the four sprang forward and regained their weapons. The suitors again threw, and this time Amphimedon really did take a piece of the top skin from Telemachus' wrist, and

Ctesippus just grazed Eumæus' shoulder above his shield. It was now the turn of Ulysses and his men, and each of their spears killed a man.

Then Minerva from high on the roof held up her deadly ægis, and struck the suitors with panic, whereon Ulysses and his men fell upon them and smote them on every side. They made a horrible groaning as their brains were being battered in, and the ground seethed with their blood. Leiodes implored Ulysses to spare his life, but Ulysses would give him no quarter.

The minstrel Phemius now begged for mercy. He was standing near towards the trap-door, and resolving to embrace Ulysses' knees, he laid his lyre on the ground between the mixing-bowl and the high silver-studded seat. 'Spare me,' he cried, 'you will be sorry for it afterwards if you kill such a bard as I am. I am an original composer, and heaven visits me with every kind of inspiration. Do not be in such a hurry to cut my head off. Telemachus will tell you that I only sang to the suitors because they forced me.'

'Hold,' cried Telemachus to his father, 'do him no hurt, he is guiltless; and we will spare Medon, too, who was always good to me when I was a boy, unless Eumæus or Philœtius has already killed him, or you happened to fall in with him yourself.'

'Here I am, my dear Sir,' said Medon, coming out from under a freshly flayed heifer's hide which had concealed him; 'tell your father, or he will kill me in his rage against the suitors for having wasted his substance and been so disrespectful to yourself.' Ulysses smiled, and told them to go outside into the outer court till the killing should be over. So they went, but they were still very much frightened. Ulysses then went all over the court to see if there were any who had concealed themselves, or were not yet killed, but there was no one; they were all as dead as fish lying in a hot sun upon the beach.

Then he told Telemachus to call Euryclea, who came at once, and found him all covered with blood. When she saw the corpses she was beginning to raise a shout of triumph, but Ulysses checked her: 'Old woman,' said he, 'rejoice in silence; it is an unholy thing to vaunt over dead men. And now tell me which of the women of the house are innocent and which guilty.'

'There are fifty women in the house,' said Euryclea; 'twelve of these have misbehaved, and have been wanting in respect to me and to Penelope. They showed no disrespect to Telemachus, for he has only lately grown up, and his mother never permitted him to give orders to the female servants. And now let me go upstairs and tell your wife.'

'Do not wake her yet,' answered Ulysses, 'but send the guilty women to me.'

Then he called Telemachus, Eumæus and Philœtius. 'Begin,' he said, 'to remove the dead bodies, and make the women help you. Also get sponges and clean water to swill down the tables and the seats. When you have thoroughly cleansed the cloisters take the women outside and run them through with your swords.'

The women came down weeping and wailing bitterly. First they carried the dead bodies out, and propped them against one another in the gate-house of the outer court. Ulysses ordered them about and saw that they lost no time. When they had carried the bodies out they cleaned all the tables and seats with sponges and water, while Telemachus and the two others shovelled up the blood and dirt from the ground and the women carried it all outside. When they had thus thoroughly cleaned the whole court, they took the women out and hemmed them up in the narrow space between the vaulted room and the wall of the outer yard. Here Telemachus determined to hang them, as a more dishonourable death than stabbing. He therefore made a ship's rope fast to a strong bearing-post supporting the roof of the vaulted room, and threw it round, making the women put their heads in the nooses one after another. He then drew the rope high up, so that none of their feet might touch the ground. They kicked convulsively for a while, but not for very long.

As for Melanthius they took him through the cloisters into the outer court. There they cut off his nose and ears; they drew out his vitals and gave them to the dogs, raw; then they cut off his hands and feet. When they had done this they washed their hands and feet, and went back into the house. 'Go,' said Ulysses, to Euryclea, 'and bring me sulphur that I may burn it and purify the cloisters. Go, moreover, and bid Penelope come here with her gentlewomen and the women of the house.'

'Let me first bring you a clean shirt and cloak,' said Euryclea, 'do not keep those rags on any longer, it is not right.'

'Light me a fire,' answered Ulysses, and she obeyed and brought him sulphur, wherewith he thoroughly purified both the inner and outer court as well as the cloisters. Then Euryclea brought the women from their apartment and they pressed round Ulysses, kissing his head and shoulders, and taking hold of his hands. It made him feel as if he should like to weep, for he remembered every one of them.

BOOK TWENTY-THREE

PENELOPE COMES DOWN TO SEE ULYSSES,
AND BEING AT LAST CONVINCED THAT
HE IS HER HUSBAND, RETIRES WITH HIM
TO THEIR OWN OLD ROOM—IN THE MORN-
ING ULYSSES, TELEMACHUS, PHILŒTIUS
AND EUMÆUS GO TO THE HOUSE OF LAERTES

EURYCLEA now went upstairs and told Penelope what had
happened. 'Wake up, my dear child,' said she, 'Ulysses is come
home at last and has killed the suitors who were giving so much
trouble in the house, eating up his estate and ill-treating his son.'

'My good nurse,' answered Penelope, 'you must be mad. The gods
sometimes send very sensible people out of their minds, and make
foolish people sensible. This is what they must have been doing to you.
Moreover, you have waked me from the soundest sleep that I have
enjoyed since my husband left me. Go back into the women's room;
if it had been anyone but you, I should have given her a severe
scolding.'

Euryclea still maintained that what she had said was true, and in
answer to Penelope's further questions told her as much as she knew
about the killing of the suitors. 'When I came down,' she said, 'I found
Ulysses standing over the corpses; you would have enjoyed it, if you
had seen him all bespattered with blood and filth, and looking just like
a lion. But the corpses are now piled up in the gate-house, and he has
sent me to bring you to him.'

Penelope said that it could not be Ulysses, but must be some god
who had resolved to punish the suitors for their great wickedness.
Then Euryclea told her about the scar.

'My dear nurse,' answered Penelope, 'however wise you may be,
you can hardly fathom the counsels of the gods. Still I will go and find
my son that I may see the corpses of the suitors, and the man who has
killed them.'

On this she came down into the cloister and took her seat opposite
Ulysses, in the fire-light, by the wall at right angles to that by which
she had entered, while her husband sat by one of the bearing-posts of
the cloister, looking down and waiting to hear what she would say.

For a long time she sat as one lost in amazement and said nothing, till Telemachus upbraided her for her coldness. 'Your heart,' he said, 'was always hard as a stone.'

'My son,' said his mother, 'I am stupefied; nevertheless if this man is really Ulysses, I shall find it out; for there are tokens which we two alone know of.'

Ulysses smiled at this, and said to Telemachus, 'Let your mother prove me as she will, she will make up her mind about it presently. Meanwhile let us think what we shall do, for we have been killing all the picked youth of Ithaca.'

'We will do,' answered Telemachus, 'whatever you may think best.'

'Then,' said Ulysses, 'wash, and put your shirts on. Bid the maids also go to their own room and dress. Phemius shall strike up a dance tune, so that any who are passing in the street may think there is a wedding in the house, and we can get away into the woods before the death of the suitors is noised abroad. Once there, we will do as heaven shall direct.'

They did as he had said. The house echoed with the sound of men and women dancing, and the people outside said, 'So the queen has been getting married at last. She ought to be ashamed of herself, for not staying to protect her husband's property.'

Eurynome washed and anointed Ulysses; Minerva also beautified him, making the hair grow thick on the top of his head and flow down in hyacinthine curls. He came from the bath looking like an immortal god, and sat down opposite his wife. Finding, however, that he could not move her, he said to Euryclea, 'Nurse, get a bed ready for me. I will sleep alone, for this woman has a heart as hard as iron.'

'My dear,' said Penelope, 'I have no wish to set myself up, nor to depreciate you, but I am not struck by your appearance, for I well remember what kind of a man you were when you left Ithaca. Nevertheless, Euryclea, take his bed out of the room he built for it, and make it ready for him.'

Ulysses knew that the bed could not be moved without cutting down the stem of a growing olive tree on the stump of which he had built it. He was very angry, and desired to know who had ventured on doing this, at the same time describing the bed fully to Penelope.

Then Penelope was convinced that he really was Ulysses, and fairly broke down. She flung her arms about his neck, and said she had only held aloof so long because she had been shuddering at the bare thought of anyone deceiving her. Ulysses in his turn melted and embraced her, and they would have gone on indulging their sorrow till morning came, had not Minerva miraculously prolonged the night.

Ulysses then began to tell her of the voyages which Tiresias had told him he must now undertake, but soon broke off by saying that they had better go to bed. To which Penelope rejoined that as she should certainly have to be told about it sooner or later, she had perhaps better hear it at once.

Thus pressed Ulysses told her. 'In the end,' said he, 'Tiresias told me that death should come to me from the sea. He said my life should ebb away very gently when I was full of years and peace of mind, and that my people should bless me.'

Meanwhile Eurynome and Euryclea made the room ready, and Euryclea went inside the house, leaving Eurynome to light Penelope and Ulysses to their bedroom. Telemachus, Philœtius and Eumæus now left off dancing, and made the women leave off also. Then they laid themselves down to sleep in the cloisters.

When they were in bed together, Penelope told Ulysses how much she had had to bear in seeing the house filled with wicked suitors who had killed so many oxen and sheep on her account, and had drunk so many casks of wine. Ulysses in his turn told her the whole story of his adventures, touching briefly upon every point, and detailing not only his own sufferings but those he had inflicted upon other people. She was delighted to listen, and never went to sleep till he ended his story and dropped off into a profound slumber.

When Minerva thought that Ulysses had slept long enough she permitted Dawn to rise from the waters of Oceanus, and Ulysses got up. 'Wife,' said he to Penelope, 'now that we have at last come together again, take care of the property that is in my house. As for the sheep and goats that the wicked suitors have eaten, I will take many by force from other people, and will compel the men of the place to make good the rest. I will now go out to my father's house in the country. At sunrise it will get noised about that I have been killing the suitors. Go upstairs, therefore, and stay there with your waiting women. See nobody, and ask no questions.'

As he spoke he girded on his armour; he roused the others also and bade them arm. He then undid the gate, and they all sallied forth. It was now daylight, but Minerva enshrouded them in darkness, and led them quickly out of the town.

BOOK TWENTY-FOUR

THE GHOSTS OF THE SUITORS IN HADES —ULYSSES SEES HIS FATHER—IS ATTACKED BY THE FRIENDS OF THE SUITORS—LAERTES KILLS EUPEITHES—PEACE IS MADE BETWEEN HIM AND THE PEOPLE OF ITHACA

THEN Mercury took the fair golden wand with which he seals men's eyes in sleep or wakes them just as he pleases, and led the ghosts of the suitors to the house of Hades whining and gibbering as they followed. As bats fly squealing about the hollow of a great cave when one of them has fallen from the cluster in which they hang — even so did they whine and squeal as Mercury the healer of sorrow led them down into the dark abode of death. When they had passed the waters of Oceanus and the rock Leucas, they came to the gates of the Sun and the land of dreams, whereon they reached the meadow of asphodel where dwell the souls and shadows of men that can labour no more.

Here they came upon the ghosts of Achilles, Patroclus, Antilochus and Ajax, and that of Agamemnon joined them. As these were conversing, Mercury came up with the ghosts of the suitors, and Agamemnon's ghost recognized that of Amphimedon who had been his host when he was in Ithaca; so he asked him what this sudden arrival of fine young men — all of an age too — might mean, and Amphimedon told him the whole story from first to last.

Thus did they converse in the house of Hades deep within the bowels of the earth. Meanwhile Ulysses and the others passed out of the city and soon reached the farm of Laertes, which he had reclaimed with infinite labour. Here was his house with a lean-to running all round it, where the slaves who worked for him ate and slept, while inside the house there was an old Sicel woman, who looked after him in this his country farm.

'Go,' said Ulysses to the others, 'to the house, and kill the best pig you have for dinner; I wish to make trial of my father and see whether he will know me.'

So saying he gave his armour to Eumæus and Philœtius, and turned off into the vineyard, where he found his father alone, hoeing a vine.

He had on a dirty old shirt, patched and very shabby; his legs were bound round with thongs of ox-hide to keep out the brambles, and he wore sleeves of leather against the thorns. He had a goat-skin cap on his head and was looking very woebegone.

When Ulysses saw him so worn, so old and full of sorrow, he stood still under a tall pear tree and began to weep. He doubted whether to embrace him, kiss him and tell him all about his having come home, or whether he should first question him and see what he would say. On the whole he decided that he would be crafty with him, so he went up to his father who was bending down and digging about a plant.

'I see, Sir,' said Ulysses, 'that you are an excellent gardener — what pains you take with it to be sure. There is not a single plant, not a fig-tree, vine, olive, pear nor flowerbed, but bears the traces of your attention. I trust, however, that you will not be offended if I say that you take better care of your garden than of yourself. You are old, unsavoury and very meanly clad. It cannot be because you are idle that your master takes such poor care of you; indeed, your face and figure have nothing of the slave about them, but proclaim you of noble birth. I should have said you were one of those who should wash well, eat well and lie soft at night as old men have a right to do. But tell me, and tell me true, whose bondsman are you, and in whose garden are you working? Tell me also about another matter — is this place that I have come to really Ithaca? I met a man just now who said so, but he was a dull fellow, and had not the patience to hear my story out when I was asking whether an old friend of mine who used to live here was still alive. My friend said he was the son of Laertes son of Arceisius, and I made him large presents on his leaving me.'

Laertes wept and answered that in this case he would never see his presents back again, though he would have been amply requited if Ulysses had been alive. 'But tell me,' he said, 'who and whence are you? Where is your ship? or did you come as passenger on some other man's vessel?'

'I will tell you everything,' answered Ulysses, 'quite truly. I come from Alybas, and am son to King Apheides. My name is Eperitus; heaven drove me off my course as I was leaving Sicania, and I have been carried here against my will. As for my ship, it is lying over yonder off the open country outside the town. It is five years since Ulysses left me — Poor fellow! we had every hope that we should meet again and exchange presents.'

Laertes was overcome with grief, and Ulysses was so much touched that he revealed himself. When his father asked for proof, he showed him the scar on his leg. 'Furthermore,' he added, 'I will point out to you the trees in the vineyard which you gave me, and I asked you all about them as I followed you round the garden. We went over them all, and you told me their names and what they all were. You gave me thirteen pear trees, ten apple trees and forty fig trees, and you also said you would give me fifty rows of vines; there was corn planted between each row, and the vines yield grapes of every kind when the heat of heaven has beaten upon them.' He also told his father that he had killed the suitors.

Laertes was now convinced, but said he feared he should have all the people of Ithaca coming to attack them. Ulysses answered that he need not trouble about this, and that they had better go and get their dinner, which would be ready by the time they got to the house.

When they reached the house the old Sicel woman took Laertes inside, washed him and anointed him. Minerva also gave him a more imposing presence and made him look taller and stronger than before. When he came back, Ulysses said, 'My dear father, some god has been making you much taller and better looking.' To which Laertes answered that if he was as young and hearty as when he took the stronghold Nericum on the foreland, he should have been a great help to him on the preceding day, and would have killed many suitors.

Dolius and his sons, who had been working hard by, now came up, for the old Sicel woman, who was Dolius' wife, had been to fetch them. When they were satisfied that Ulysses was really there, they were overjoyed and embraced him one after the other. 'But tell me,' said Dolius, 'does Penelope know, or shall we send and tell her?' 'Old man,' answered Ulysses, 'she knows already. What business is that of yours?' Then they all took their seats at table.

Meanwhile the news of the slaughter of the suitors had got noised abroad, and the people gathered hooting and groaning before the house of Ulysses. They took their dead, buried every man his own, and put the bodies of those who came from elsewhere on board the fishing vessels, for the fishermen to take them every man to his own place. Then they met in assembly and Eupeithes urged them to pursue Ulysses and the others before they could escape over to the mainland.

Medon, however, and Phemius had now woke up, and came to the assembly. Medon dissuaded the people from doing as Eupeithes

494

advised, inasmuch as he had seen a god going about killing the suitors, and it would be dangerous to oppose the will of heaven. Halitherses also spoke in the same sense, and half the people were persuaded by him. The other half armed themselves and followed Eupeithes in pursuit of Ulysses.

Minerva then consulted Jove as to the course events should take. Jove told her that she had had everything her own way so far, and might continue to do as she pleased. He should, however, advise that both sides should now be reconciled under the continued rule of Ulysses. Minerva approved of this and darted down to Ithaca.

Laertes and his household had now done dinner, and Eupeithes with his band of men were seen to be near at hand. Ulysses and the others put on their armour, and Minerva joined them. 'Telemachus,' said Ulysses, 'now that you are about to fight in a decisive engagement, see that you do no discredit to your ancestors, who were eminent all the world over for their strength and valour.'

'You shall see, my dear father,' replied Telemachus, 'if you choose, that I am in no mind, as you say, to disgrace your family.'

'Good heavens,' exclaimed Laertes, 'what a day I am enjoying. My son and grandson are vying with one another in the matter of valour.' Minerva then came up to him, and bade him pray to her. She infused fresh vigour into him, and when he had prayed to her he aimed his spear at Eupeithes and killed him. Ulysses and his men fell upon the others, routed them, and would have killed one and all of them had not Minerva raised her voice and made every one pause. 'Men of Ithaca,' she cried, 'cease this dreadful war, and settle the matter without further bloodshed.'

On this they turned pale with fear, dropped their armour, and fled every man towards the city. Ulysses was swooping down upon them like an eagle, but Jove sent a thunderbolt of fire that fell just in front of Minerva. Whereon she said, 'Ulysses, stay this strife, or Jove will be angry with you.'

Ulysses obeyed her gladly. Minerva then assumed the voice and form of Mentor, and presently made a covenant of peace between the two contending parties.

EXTRACTS FROM 'THE NOTE-BOOKS'

EDITOR'S PREFACE

BUTLER began keeping a regular note-book in 1874, while he was in Montreal. Thereafter he kept up the habit to the end of his life, periodically revising, transcribing, selecting and indexing his entries, which were in part citations or accounts of things seen or heard, but for the most part his own observations on anything that interested him or about which he was thinking at the time. Many of them were used, commonly in an altered form, in his published works; but many remained unused, and of those which were used the unpublished variants have often an interest of their own. Butler's friend and biographer, Festing Jones, published a selection in *The Note-Books of Samuel Butler* (1912) and made use of a number of others, mostly autobiographical, in his two-volume *Memoir of Samuel Butler* (1919). The autobiographical material, including much not contained in the Memoir, was collected in the volume, *Butleriana*, issued by the Nonesuch Press in 1932. In 1934 A. T. Bartholomew, Butler's literary executor, edited a further selection from the manuscripts, under the title *Further Extracts from the Note-Books of Samuel Butler*. This included some of the material already published in *Butleriana*. In the Introduction to this volume the editor gave his opinion that no further selection should be attempted. In the extracts here printed, I have deliberately limited my choice to very short sayings, sometimes extracted from longer notes, but in most cases taken just as they stood from one or other of the volumes already published. I had only a very limited space; and if I had attempted to give longer extracts the number would have been perforce very small. I am aware that this restriction of the choice to pithy sayings fails to give at all a fair, all-round impression of what the *Note-Books* contain; but it seemed to me that within a few pages it was better to convey an impression of Butler's range of interests than to miss this by citing only a few passages which I happen to like best. Anyone who wants to get the full flavour of Butler's 'commonplace books' must go to the volumes in which the best part of them has been reproduced.

N. = from *The Note-Books of Samuel Butler*
Selections arranged and edited by Henry Festing Jones
FE. = from *Further Extracts from the Note-Books of Samuel Butler*
Chosen and Edited by A. T. Bartholomew

FE. p. 15 These are the sayings of me Samuel Butler and of my friends — the prophesyings which my mother did not teach me at all, nor my father, nor any of my uncles and aunts, but altogether otherwise.

A. GOD

N. p. 26 *God's Laws.* The true laws of God are the laws of our own well-being.

N. p. 28 God does not intend people, and does not like people, to be too good. He likes them neither too good nor too bad, but a little too bad is more venial with him than a little too good.

N. p. 33 To love God is to have good health, good looks, good sense, experience, a kindly nature and a fair balance of cash in hand. 'We know that all things work together for good to them that love God.' To be loved by God is the same as to love Him. We love Him because He first loved us.

N. p. 93 Thought pure and simple is as near to God as we can get; it is through this that we are linked with God. The highest thought is ineffable; it must be felt from one person to another but cannot be articulated. All the most essential and thinking part of thought is done without words or consciousness. It is not till doubt and consciousness enter that words become possible.

N. p. 217 It must be remembered that we have only heard one side of the case. God has written all the books.

N. p. 223 To put one's trust in God is only a longer way of saying that one will chance it.

N. p. 226 *God is Love.* I dare say. But what a mischievous devil Love is!

N. p. 226 God and the Devil are an effort after specialization and division of labour.

N. p. 324 God is the unknown, and hence the nothing *qua* us.

501

He is also the ensemble of all we know, and hence the everything *qua* us. So that the most absolute nothing and the most absolute everything are extremes that meet (like all other extremes) in God.

N. p. 337   *Theist and Atheist.* The fight between them is as to whether God shall be called God or shall have some other name.

FE. p. 26   *An Honest God.* An honest God's the noblest work of man.

N. p. 333   It is the manner of gods and Prophets to begin: 'Thou shalt have none other God or prophet but me.' If I were to start as a god or a prophet, I think I should take the line: 'Thou shalt not believe in me. Thou shalt not have me for a god. Thou shalt worship any damned thing thou likest except me.' This should be my first and great commandment, and my second should be like unto it.

FE. p. 32   The invention of God as a moral ruler was like the invention of him as a material creator — to save trouble to a dominant party; and no doubt for a long time it did save them a good deal of trouble.

FE. p. 32   God as now generally conceived of is only the last witch.

FE. p. 32   Resist God and he will fly from you.

FE. p. 67   *To the Lexicographer.* God is simply the word that comes next to 'go-cart', and nothing more.

N. p. 347   I do not know or care whether the expression 'God' has scientific accuracy or no, nor yet whether it has theological value; I know nothing either of one or the other, beyond looking upon the recognized exponents both of science and theology with equal distrust; but for convenience, I am sure that there is nothing like it — I mean for convenience of getting quickly at the right or wrong of a matter. While you are fumbling away with your political economy or your biblical precepts to know whether you shall let old Mrs. So-and-so have 5s. or no, another, who has just asked himself which would be most well-pleasing in the sight of God, will be told in a moment that he should give her — or not give her — the 5s. As a general rule she had better have the 5s. at once, but sometimes we must give God to understand that, though we should be very glad to do what he would have of us if we reasonably could, yet the present is one of those occasions on which we must decline to do so.

FE. p. 69   As for God, if a thousand years to him are but as yesterday, he is an unaccountable person with whom the less we have to do the better.

FE. p. 95   Epicurus held that there are gods, but they are careless about human affairs. I hold that there is a God, but that human beings should be careless about him.

FE. p. 33   We profess to accept with thankfulness the position of being God's sheep, yet few lambs are allowed to become full grown and it is not intended that any should die a natural death. A sheep's *raison d'être* is to be fleeced as often as possible, and then to have its throat cut.

Uriah the Hittite, if his own life had been spared, would no doubt have sat down to the little ewe lamb which he carried so tenderly in his bosom, and dined off it with much satisfaction; and when, again, we see pictures of our Saviour with sheep behind him, and a lamb in his bosom, we should remember that the matter will not end here. If a shepherd caressing a lamb is a fair statement of the case, a cat playing with a mouse should be hardly less so. We may be asked to bless the grass, the sunshine and our fellow sheep, but can we reasonably be expected to bless the butcher? Is it not time to drop that metaphor?

FE. p. 110   Christ. He is like species. He has descended with modification.

FE. p. 117   Jesus! with all thy faults I love thee still.

FE. p. 133   God is not so black as he has been painted — nor yet so white.

FE. p. 170   A man had better sin against the Holy Ghost than against money. Whether God is a respecter of persons or no, he certainly is a respecter of money; and he seldom goes behind the money. If a man has money this seems to be enough.

FE. p. 181   Our heavenly Father does indeed give us our daily bread, in some sort, but he does not supply us with the regularity of a professional baker.

FE. p. 284   *God.* There is little hope of his improving. He was satisfied with his own work, and that is fatal. Hence the same old 'As it was in the beginning, is now and ever shall be, world without end, amen' from everlasting to everlasting, without a sign of any effort at amendment of life on God's part.

FE. p. 291   *God.* If, as the apostle says, he is no respecter of persons, then he is a greater fool than I take him to be.

FE. p. 48   God is not so punctilious as some people would make him out, and provided he gets his dinner fairly good and fairly punctual and fairly cheap, he will not make a fuss about want of napkins.

B. *RELIGION*

N. p. 35   Heaven is the work of the best and kindest men and women. Hell is the work of prigs, pedants and professional truth-tellers. The world is an attempt to make the best of both.

N. p. 36   *Science and Religion.* These are reconciled in amiable and sensible people but nowhere else.

N. p. 189   What a pity it is that Christian never met Mr. Common-Sense with his daughter, Good-Humour, and her affianced husband, Mr. Hate-Cant; but if he ever saw them in the distance he steered clear of them, probably as feeling that they would be more dangerous than Giant Despair, Vanity Fair and Apollyon all together — for they would have stuck to him if he had let them get in with him.

N. p. 212   Prayers are to men as dolls are to children. They are not without use and comfort, but it is not easy to take them very seriously.

N. p. 334   As an instrument of warfare against vice, or as a tool for making virtue, Christianity is a mere flint implement.

N. p. 334   It is not the church in a village that is the source of the mischief, but the rectory. I would not touch a church from one end of England to the other.

N. p. 336   You can do very little with faith, but you can do nothing without it.

N. p. 336   The just live by faith, but they not infrequently also die by it.

N. p. 339   Admitting for the moment that Christ can be said to have died for me in any sense, it is only pretended that he did so in the same sort of way as the London and North Western Railway was made for me. Granted that I am very glad the railway was made and use it when I find it convenient, I do not suppose that those who projected and made the line allowed me to enter into their thoughts; the debt of my gratitude is divided among so many that the amount due from each one is practically nil.

N. p. 343   If Vesuvius does not frighten those who live under it, is it likely that Hell-fire should frighten any reasonable person?

N. p. 363   Just as the kingdom of heaven cometh not by observation, so neither do one's own ideas, nor the good things one hears other people say; they fasten on us when we least want or expect them. It is enough if the kingdom of heaven be observed when it does come.

FE. p. 19   Christianity has been to the world on a larger and more disastrous scale what Puritanism has been to the English nation. And yet it may be questioned whether Puritanism did not save the English nation at a very critical time.

FE. p. 19   Whatever religion is not natural is unnatural. And yet whatever is is natural.

FE. p. 23   What is faith but a kind of betting or speculation after all? It should be, 'I bet that my Redeemer liveth.'

FE. p. 25   *Sunday.* The great and terrible day of the Lord.

FE. p. 26   *Christ and the Church.* If he were to apply for a divorce on the grounds of cruelty, adultery and desertion, he would probably get one.

FE. p. 27   *A Lawyer's Dream of Heaven.* Every man reclaimed his own property at the resurrection, and each tried to recover it from all his forefathers.

FE. p. 44   *Christ.* He has been so important an organ in the world's body for so long a time that he must surely remain as a rudimentary organ even when no longer actively employed.

FE. p. 46   Faith without capital is like faith without works — dead being alone.

FE. p. 51   *Christ.* He had not been married to the Church a twelve-month before he began to flirt with a most respectable married woman, the wife of a man called Grundy, and he has continued in the most open adultery with her ever since.

FE. p. 65   I should like to add an eighth sacrament to those of the Roman Church — I mean the sacrament of Divorce.

FE. p. 68   The Jews would not have stoned the Prophets if the Prophets had not stoned the Jews first. Just as I am sure the literary and scientific people of today would not dislike me as much as they do if I had not shown my dislike to them pretty openly first. 'We hate him, because he first hated us.' This is what they would say, and they would be quite right.

FE. p. 71   The Bible is like the poor; we have it always with us, but we know very little about it.

FE. pp. 74-5   A new curate was explaining to the village blacksmith the nature of miracles. The blacksmith was docile and accepted the story of Jonah in the whale's belly. As the curate put it, he said he saw no difficulty in it, and was ready to believe it. The curate then went on to Shadrach, Meshach and Abednego in the burning fiery furnace. 'Now the furnace,' said the curate, 'was many times larger and hotter than your forge.' This riled the blacksmith; he was proud of his forge which had been his father's before him, besides he could realize a furnace to himself. 'No,' he said, 'I don't believe it, and I don't believe the bloody fish story either.' And so the matter dropped.

FE. p. 80   *The Church of Rome.* It is not its doctrines, but its intolerance that we object to — the way in which it claims that it must be right and everyone else wrong.

FE. p. 91   Christ was only crucified once and for a few hours. Think of the hundreds of thousands whom Christ has been crucifying in a quiet way ever since.

FE. p. 85   I do not presume to be a judge of Catholic doctrine, but I do presume to be as good a judge as other people of the way in which the cat is jumping. I hold that it is jumping away from Catholicism. If I thought the Catholics were permanently in the long run on the winning side I would join them tomorrow.

FE. p. 107   On the formation of opinion. Take the subject of free trade and see how opinions differ about it; but how does opinion come to be formed on such a matter? Priestcraft arises from men's desire to have their opinions formed for them. This desire is like nature; you may expel it with a fork, but it will always return.

FE. p. 114   There was an inland African tribe in a country too hot for sheep, who had therefore no definite idea about a lamb. The missionary who converted them brought the idea somewhat nearer to their comprehension by calling Christ 'the little woolly pig of God'.

FE. p. 120   People in general are equally horrified at hearing the Christian religion doubted, and at seeing it practised.

FE. p. 120   *The Seven Deadly Sins.* Want of money, bad health, bad temper, chastity, family ties, knowing that you know things and believing in the Christian religion.

FE. p. 133   The devils were probably as thankful to be turned out of Mary Magdalene as she was to be rid of them. At least if I was a devil I would rather have lived in old Mrs. Boss by a good long way.

FE. p. 133   If God wants us to do a thing he should make his wishes sufficiently clear. Sensible people will wait till he has done this before paying much attention to him.

FE. p. 134   'He hath filled the hungry with good things, but the rich he hath sent empty away.' Surely this must be wrong.

FE. p. 134   The cross of Christ is too wide a cross for fertility with myself.

FE. p. 134   *A Bible in an Hotel Parlour.* I like to see this, but it should have a lot of mats and vases or profane ornaments on top of it.

FE. p. 139   *Early Communion.* Why don't they send it round from house to house with the milk, and have telephones from each house to the chancel?

FE. p. 257   The Church of Rome generally knows whom to burn. Its burnees will generally be people of some weight.

FE. p. 139   A man should sack his Church just as he should sack his footman, if it does not give him satisfaction.

FE. p. 163   There will be no comfortable and safe development of our social arrangements — I mean, we shall not get infanticide, and the permission of suicide, nor cheap and easy divorce — till Jesus Christ's Ghost has been laid; and the best way to lay it is to be a Moderate Churchman.

FE. p. 163   Christians say that Christianity has stood so many attacks for so long that it cannot be false. That is just what others say about rationalism.

FE. p. 177   'My Kingdom is not of this world.' Perhaps not; but being in this world no other kingdom is of much use, after all. Christ might just as well have said at once, 'I am a very unpractical person, and my Father has not made the world as He should have done.'

FE. p. 179   The reason why the Church in the Middle Ages hated the Stage was because she smelt a rival from afar. The theatre was a building like the church; it was a place of public assembly; it was run by a special class who were its priests; and there was no knowing what it might not end in.

FE. p. 181   A bona fide argument in favour of Christianity is that it trains us to believe all manner of contradictions in terms.

FE. p. 208   Christianity was only a very strong and singularly well-timed Salvation Army movement that happened to receive help from an unusual and highly dramatic incident. It was a Puritan reaction in an age when, no doubt, a Puritan reaction was much wanted; but like all sudden violent reactions, it soon wanted reacting against.

FE. p. 222   No one supposes that Christ himself, were he now living, would be a Christian; but he would find his mother and sisters and his brethren all of them devout believers.

FE. p. 258   Belief like any other moving body follows the path of least resistance.

FE. p. 271   *Religion.* We must first learn to distinguish between this and vested interests.

FE. p. 291   Clergymen ought to be like barristers, and allowed to plead on a side which they know to be a wrong one without its being expected of them to pretend that they believe it true.

FE. p. 284   If the Son of God ever does come to us again the only thing to do with him will be to disregard him. No human ingenuity can devise any scheme whereby a bold and independent thinker can be allowed to go about un-

LIFE AND DEATH

molested except at the cost of all continuity of development, and hence of all development at all. If the thing were possible it would have been done long ago, but it is like perpetual motion or the philosopher's stone — an impossible and barren dream.

C. LIFE AND DEATH

N. p. 9   When I was a boy at Shrewsbury, old Mrs. Brown used to keep a tray of spoiled tarts which she sold cheaper. They most of them looked pretty right till you handled them. We are all spoiled tarts.

N. p. 9   He is a poor creature who does not believe himself to be better than the whole world else. No matter how ill we may be, or how low we may have fallen, we would not change identity with any other person. Hence our self-conceit sustains and always must sustain us till death takes us and our conceit together so that we need no more sustaining.

N. p. 10   We have got into life by stealth and *petitio principii*, by the free use of that contradiction in terms which we declare to be the most outrageous violation of our reason. We have wriggled into it by holding that everything is both one and many, both infinite in time and space and yet finite, both like and unlike to the same thing, both itself and not itself, both free and yet inexorably fettered, both every adjective in the dictionary and at the same time the flat contradiction of every one of them.

N. p. 10   Life is not so much a riddle to be read as a Gordian knot that will get cut sooner or later.

N. p. 10   Murray (the publisher) said that my *Life of Dr. Butler* was an omnium gatherum. Yes, but life is an omnium gatherum.

N. p. 11   Life is a superstition. But superstitions are not without their value. The snail's shell is a superstition, slugs have no shells and thrive just as well. But a snail without a shell would not be a slug unless it had also the slug's indifference to a shell.

509

N. p. 11   Life is one long process of getting tired.

N. p. 11   Life is the art of drawing sufficient conclusions from insufficient premises.

N. p. 11   A sense of humour keen enough to show a man his own absurdities, as well as those of other people, will keep him from the commission of all sins, or nearly all, save those that are worth committing.

N. p. 11   Life is like music, it must be composed by ear, feeling and instinct, not by rule. Nevertheless one had better know the rules, for they sometimes guide in doubtful cases — though not often.

N. p. 12   The world may not be particularly wise — still, we know of nothing wiser.

N. p. 11   There are two great rules of life, the one general and the other particular. The first is that every one can, in the end, get what he wants if he only tries. This is the general rule. The particular rule is that every individual is, more or less, an exception to the general rule.

N. p. 12   All progress is based upon a universal innate desire on the part of every organism to live beyond its income.

N. p. 12   The world will always be governed by self-interest. We should not try to stop this, we should try to make the self-interest of cads a little more coincident with that of decent people.

N. p. 13   I have squandered my life as a schoolboy squanders a tip. But then half, or more than half the fun a schoolboy gets out of a tip consists in the mere fact of having something to squander. Squandering is in itself delightful, and so I found it with my life in my younger days. I do not squander it now, but I am not sorry that I have squandered a good deal of it. What a heap of rubbish there would have been if I had not! Had I not better set about squandering what is left of it?

N. p. 14   When we grumble about the vanity of all human things, inasmuch as even the noblest works are not eternal but must become sooner or later as though they had never been, we should remember that the world, so far as we can see, was made to enjoy rather than to last. Come-and-go pervades everything of which we have knowledge, and though great things go more slowly, they are built up of small ones and must fare as that which makes them.

N. p. 17   Is life worth living? This is a question for an embryo, not for a man.

N. p. 20   I have gone out sketching and forgotten my water-dipper; among my traps I always find something that will do, for example, the top of my tin case (for holding pencils). This is how organs come to change their uses and hence their forms, or at any rate partly how.

N. p. 23   Death is not more the end of some than it is the beginning of others. So he that loses his soul may find it, and he that finds may lose it.

N. p. 37   Death in anything like luxury is one of the most expensive things a man can indulge himself in. It costs a lot of money to die comfortably, unless one goes off pretty quickly.

N. p. 219   Time is the only true purgatory.

N. p. 77   *The Power to make Mistakes.* This is one of the criteria of life as we commonly think of it. If oxygen could go wrong and mistake some other gas for hydrogen and thus learn not to mistake it any more, we should say oxygen was alive.

N. p. 207   One can bring no greater reproach against a man than to say that he does not set sufficient value upon pleasure, and there is no greater sign of a fool than the thinking that he can tell at once and easily what it is that pleases him.

N. p. 219   The merest spark may set all Europe in a blaze, but though all Europe be set in a blaze twenty times over, the world will wag itself right again.

N. p. 219   *The Vanity of Human Wishes.* There is only one thing vainer and that is the having no wishes.

N. p. 220   People are lucky and unlucky not according to what they get absolutely, but according to the ratio between what they get and what they have been led to expect.

N. p. 228   Behold and see if there be any happiness like unto the happiness of the devils when they found themselves cast out of Mary Magdalene.

N. p. 356   If a man has sent his teeth and his hair and perhaps two or three limbs to the grave before him, the presumption should be that, as he knows nothing further of these when they have once left him, so will he know nothing of the rest of him when it too is dead. The whole may surely be argued from the parts.

N. p. 357   The dead are often just as living to us as the living are, only we cannot get them to believe it. They can come to us, but till we die we cannot go to them. To be dead is to be unable to understand that one is alive.

N. p. 359   The memory of a love that has been cut short by death remains still fragrant though enfeebled, but no recollection of its past can keep sweet a love that has dried up and withered through accidents of time and life.

N. p. 365   The world will, in the end, follow only those who have despised as well as served it.

N. p. 365   The world and all that has ever been in it will one day be as much forgotten as what we ate for dinner forty years ago. Very likely, but the fact that we shall not remember much about a dinner forty years hence does not make it less agreeable now, and after all it is only the accumulation of these forgotten dinners that makes the dinner of forty years hence possible.

FE. p. 21   The young man was leading a starved existence; therefore he was sinning and Nature hated him. His parents were not leading a starved existence, so she did not come down on them. Why should she?

FE. p. 22   It has been said that the love of money is the root of all evil. The want of money is so quite as truly.

FE. p. 23   It is not the interest of honesty or talent or virtue, but that of health and happiness that should take the highest place. Honesty is made for happiness, not happiness for honesty.

FE. p. 25   When I die at any rate I shall do so in the full and certain hope that there will be no resurrection, but that death will give me quittance in full.

FE. p. 81   Nothing could be satisfactory even for a short time if anything could be so for very long.

FE. p. 84   If a little dose of judgment and reason enters into the most instinctive actions, so a little dose of unreason and instinct enters into our most deliberate ones.

FE. p. 89   'Ye suffer fools gladly,' says the Apostle. 'Why no, Paul,' I feel inclined to answer, 'not exactly gladly.'

FE. p. 103   How hardly do they that have riches enter into the kingdom of Heaven. Yes, they take longer in dying than other people.

FE. p. 117   Death is only a greater modification than any after which we have been able to remember ourselves.

FE. p. 145   Eternal Life: we mean eternal at both ends.

     The whole art of life consists in knowing how to draw
     one knows how to draw them in respect of
     e or two things.

     House in Order. If a man should do this when
     die, surely much more should he do it if he
     ve. But if things are in a great mess let him
     tidy up a very little at a time.

     rn. Let this question be solved by finding out
     is, in practice, that you can no longer get on
     y without.

     ath is only a larger kind of going abroad.

     hether we can take anything with us or no, it is
     t we can leave more or less behind us according
as we have done our best or no; and this is tangible, for this lives whether we live or no.

FE. p. 220   *Familiar Misquotation*

     ''Tis not in mortals to deserve success,
       But we'll do more, Sempronius, we'll command it.'

FE. p. 233   To know is to know the things belonging to one's peace.

FE. p. 233   Life is a matter about which we are lost if we reason either too much or too little.

FE. p. 235   Towns, like organisms, descend with modification.

FE. p. 243   The same difficulty that met us when we tried to define a thing meets us again when we try to define an action. Any action is a bundle or body of actions.

FE. p. 262   Money is dead men's bones and dead men's souls. The money that men make lives after them.

FE. p. 269   The social ladder is all very well as long as you can keep on climbing or stick at the top; but it is hard to come down it without tumbling off.

FE. p. 279   I can understand anyone's allowing himself to be bullied by the living, but not, if he can help it, by the dead.

FE. p. 283   To die is but to leave off dying and do the thing once for all.

D. MAN AND SOCIETY

N. p. 9   We are like billiard balls in a game played by unskilful players, continually being nearly sent into a pocket, but hardly ever getting right into one, except by a fluke.

N. p. 9   We are like thistle-down blown about by the wind — up and down, here and there — but not one in a thousand ever getting beyond seed-hood.

N. p. 9   A man is a passing mood coming and going in the mind of his country; he is the twitching of a nerve, a smile, a frown, a thought of shame or honour, as it may happen.

N. p. 10   Man must always be a consuming fire or be consumed. As for hell, we are in a burning fiery furnace all our lives — for what is life but a process of combustion?

N. p. 18   Man is but a perambulating tool-box and workshop, or office, fashioned for itself by a piece of very clever slime, as the result of long experience; and truth is but its own most enlarged, general and enduring sense of the coming togetherness or convenience of the various conventional arrangements which, for some reason or other, it has been led to sanction. Hence we speak of man's body as his 'trunk'.

N. p. 18   The body is but a pair of pincers set over a bellows and a stewpan and the whole fixed upon stilts.

N. p. 78   Man is a substance, he knows not what, feeling, he knows not how, a rest and unrest that he can only in part distinguish. He is a substance feeling equilibrium or want of equilibrium; that is to say, he is a substance in a statical or dynamical condition and feeling the passage from one state into the other.

N. p. 179   All men can do great things, if they know what great things are.

N. p. 217   It does not matter much what a man hates provided he hates something.

N. p. 222   Woe to the specialist who is not a pretty fair generalist, and woe to the generalist who is not also a bit of a specialist.

N. p. 320   Our choice is apparently most free, and we are least obviously driven to determine our choice, in those cases where the future is most obscure, that is, when the balance of advantage appears most doubtful.

FE. p. 19   I once heard two elderly men comparing notes about the way in which they still sometimes dreamed they were being bullied by their schoolmasters, and that their fathers had come to life again.

FE. p. 19   A man's expression is his sacrament; it is the outward and visible sign of his inward and spiritual grace — or want of grace.

FE. p. 25   I have seen thoughts and fancies playing upon people's faces like the wind upon young heather.

FE. p. 31   The one serious conviction that a man should have is that nothing is to be taken too seriously.

FE. p. 46   There was a man who maintained that no man ought to let himself be made a martyr to his convictions. He held this opinion so strongly that, rather than give it up, he allowed himself to be burned alive — thus becoming, after all, a martyr to his convictions.

FE. p. 50   I don't know what nobleness is any more than you do; but I imagine that to be noble a man must be strong in body and position, handsome, amorous and kind; with a contempt for all the vices of meanness — and the meannesses of virtue.

FE. p. 58   If a man is man enough to go to the University he is man enough to begin his profession at once without any University.

FE. p. 58   Someone said of another that he was cultured. 'Yes,' was the rejoinder, 'not to say manured.'

FE. p. 60   A man should be just cultured enough to be able to look with suspicion upon culture, at first, not second hand.

FE. p. 71 Reforms and discoveries are like offences; they must needs come, but woe unto that man through whom they come.

FE. p. 73 *Sudden Accessions of Wealth.* It is upon the evolution principle that these are so often fatal. The jump is too sudden.

FE. p. 102 The three desiderata for a cross are: 1. that it shall not be too wide; 2. that it shall be wide enough; 3. that the thing with which one crosses oneself shall be good of its kind. It is hard to say what is too wide, what is wide enough and what good of its kind. Reason is apt to make mistakes on all these heads, and so is inclination. A mixture of reason and inclination is the safest guide.

FE. p. 112 One's stomach is one's internal environment.

FE. p. 116 Man is God's highest present development. He is the latest thing in God.

FE. p. 123 People are always good company when they are doing what they really enjoy.

FE. p. 139 They say that only about 10 per cent of the heat in coal is not wasted; so with the energies even of the most able and industrious men.

FE. p. 150 Man is a jelly which quivers so much as to run about.

FE. p. 159 Man is only the amœba in another shape, and several of them, and after they have had a superior education.

FE. p. 165 Our sense of identity is in reality an intensified sense of sympathy. It is a sense on the part of a large number of beings that they have something more in common with one another than with anything else.

FE. p. 178 The struggle for existence is the struggle for the existence of our own opinions. In the end it resolves itself into an act of mere mulish obstinacy in sticking to it that we are right, and in insisting that as much of the outside world as we can manage shall see things as we see them ourselves.

FE. p. 200 The poor are compelled to work and use their muscles, and when there are no more poor there will ere long be no more muscles. The poor are a mode whereby the physical energy of the race is conserved.

FE. p. 244   People care more about being thought to have taste than about being thought either good, clever or amiable.

FE. p. 255   They who would win immediate success must not aim, as it were, at the top of a mountain but at the middle of a bull's eye. He who would win lasting fame must aim at both at once as best he can.

FE. p. 262   To do great work a man must be very idle as well as very industrious.

FE. p. 294   A man said to me last night that all good men were socialists. I thought to myself, 'No doubt, but no good man will so dub himself; he will let all that go without saying.'

E. *TRUTH*

N. p. 297   We can neither define what we mean by truth nor be in doubt as to our meaning. And this I suppose must be due to the antiquity of the instinct that, on the whole, directs us towards truth. We cannot self-vivisect ourselves in respect of such a vital function, though we can discharge it normally and easily enough so long as we do not think about it.

N. p. 298   There is no such source of error as the pursuit of absolute truth.

N. p. 298   The firmest line that can be drawn upon the smoothest paper has still jagged edges if seen through a microscope. This does not matter until important deductions are made on the supposition that there are no jagged edges.

N. p. 299   Truth generally is kindness, but where the two diverge or collide, kindness should override truth.

N. p. 299   Truth consists not in never lying but in knowing when to lie and when not to do so. *De minimis non curat veritas.*

Yes, but what is a minimum? Sometimes a maximum is a minimum and sometimes it is the other way.

N. p. 300   Any fool can tell the truth, but it requires a man of some sense to know how to lie well.

N. p. 300   I do not mind lying, but I hate inaccuracy.

FE. p. 35   Truth on any subject is the opinion which either has, or may come to have the whip-hand.

FE. p. 32   No man's opinions can be worth holding unless he knows how to deny them easily and gracefully, upon occasion, in the cause of Charity.

FE. p. 32   *Ultimate Triumph of Good.* When we say we believe in this, we mean that we are cocksure of our own opinions.

FE. p. 36   I do not seek Truth for her sake: let her look to herself. I seek her for my own. It is true, I believe I like her, but I do so mainly because I know I can trust her — better, at any rate, than I can anyone else. If I did not think this I would have nothing to do with her.

FE. p. 71   People should learn to lie as they learn anything else — from very small beginnings.

FE. p. 93   Our highest 'is' is still only a very strong 'may be'.

FE. p. 107   We should not aim at knowledge — this is beyond our grasp. We should aim at that way of looking at things which will give us least trouble, as fitting in most harmoniously with our other ideas.

F. HISTORY

FE. p. 254   It is said the world knows little or nothing of its greatest men; it might be added that its greatest men have known very little of the world. Indeed they never can, for they and the world have nothing, or at any rate very little, in common, and so cannot understand each other.

FE. p. 122   Do not say that luxury was the cause of Greek decline. Greece was too small, and the favourable variation was swamped by unmodified neighbours.

FE. p. 239   When a thing is old, broken and useless, we throw it on the dust-heap, but when it is sufficiently old, sufficiently broken and sufficiently useless, we give money for it, put it into a museum, and read papers over it which people come long distances to hear.

FE. p. 301   All nations have a sneaking kindness for their own devils.

G. NATIONS

N. p. 179 America will have her geniuses, as every other country has, in fact she has already had one in Walt Whitman, but I do not think America is a good place in which to be a genius. A genius can never expect to have a good time anywhere, if he is a genuine article, but America is about the last place in which life will be endurable at all for an inspired writer of any kind.

FE. p. 20 *Canadian Jokes.* When I was there I found their jokes like their roads — very long and not very good, leading to a little tin point of a spire which has been remorselessly obvious for miles without seeming to get any nearer.

FE. p. 64 An American candidate during the war decried his opponent as one who had run away to Canada to avoid the conscription. 'I,' he exclaimed, 'never shirked the ful-filment of a patriotic duty. I stayed at home and braved the terrors of the conscription. My name was drawn. I paid for a substitute, and *his* bones are whitening the plains of Manassas.'

FE. p. 158 America was too big to have been discovered all at one time. It would have been better for the graces if it had been discovered in pieces of about the size of France and Germany at a time.

FE. p. 158 *The Anglo-Saxon Race as Colonists.* They say this race degenerates in the colonies. It does not do so more than, or perhaps so much as, others. All races resume feral characteristics to a certain extent when they find them-selves in a new country. Pressure of civilization is taken off them and they are therefore freer to do exactly what they like.

H. PHILOSOPHY AND SCIENCE

N. p. 217 The best class of scientific mind is the same as the best class of business mind. The great desideratum in either case is to know how much evidence is enough to warrant action.

N. p. 218 *Scientific Terminology.* This is the Scylla's cave which men of science are preparing for themselves to be able to pounce out upon us from it, and into which we cannot penetrate.

N. p. 329   *Science.* If it tends to thicken the crust of ice on which, as it were, we are skating, it is all right. If it tries to find, or professes to have found, the solid ground at the bottom of the water, it is all wrong. Our business is with the thickening of this crust by extending our knowledge downward from above, as ice gets thicker while the frost lasts; we should not try to freeze upwards from the bottom.

N. p. 330   The voices of common sense and of high philosophy sometimes cross; but common sense is the unalterable canto fermo and philosophy is the variable counterpoint.

FE. p. 50   We shall never get people whose time is money to take much interest in atoms.

FE. p. 76   There is no such metaphysics as physics in the hands of a scientist who goes too far for his facts.

N. p. 327   As a general rule philosophy is like stirring mud or not letting a sleeping dog lie. It is an attempt to deny, circumvent or otherwise escape from the consequences of the interlacing of the roots of things with one another. It professes to appease our ultimate 'Why?' though in truth it is generally the solution of a *simplex ignotum* by a *complex ignotius*. This, at least, is my experience of everything that has been presented to me as philosophy. I have often had my 'Why' answered with so much mystifying matter that I have left off pressing it through fatigue. But this is not having my ultimate 'Why?' appeased. It is being knocked out of time.

N. p. 339   Science is being daily more and more personified and anthropomorphized into a god. By and by they will say that science took our nature upon him, and sent down his only begotten son, Charles Darwin, or Huxley, into the world so that those who believe in him, etc.; and they will burn people for saying that science, after all, is only an expression for our ignorance of our own ignorance.

FE. p. 84   There is the mystification of absolute ignorance, and the mystification of fogged science.

FE. p. 112   *'Life and Habit.'* One aim of this book was to place the distrust of science on a scientific basis.

FE. p. 108   There is no drawing the line between physics and metaphysics. If you examine everyday facts at all closely you are a physicist; but if you press your physics at all home you become a metaphysician; if you press your metaphysics at all home you are in a fog.

For example we say such and such a thing is so and so. But what is 'a thing'? Strictly speaking there is only one thing – the universe; all other things are called so through arbitrary classifications like species, and tend to vanish as 'things' if examined with any closeness.

FE. p. 135   The charlatans of science will never accept a new truth from the hands of an outsider till the outsiders make them do it, and then they will say they found it out themselves.

FE. p. 136   'Scientific' to men like Herbert Spencer means little else than the power to say in hard words and involved sentences what could be better said in easy ones.

FE. p. 137   A man may say what he likes about Christ, but he must be very careful how he attacks Mr. Darwin or indeed any of the scientific or literary bigwigs.

FE. p. 151   Whether there is a limit to the divisibility of matter or no, there is certainly a limit, though ill defined, to our power of perceiving differences. There is a limit to the divisibility of our consciousness. By means, however, of certain appliances we can extend these limits.

FE. p. 164   *Sir John Lubbock*. He is trying about this time (May 1884) to teach dogs to converse. If I was his dog and he taught me, the first thing I should tell him would be that he is a damned fool.

FE. p. 167   Bequests for scientific and educational purposes are taking the place of those for charitable purposes. They will be as mischievous or more so, and will no less surely have one day to be restricted if not forbidden.

I. *THOUGHT AND LANGUAGE*

N. p. 9   How loosely our thoughts must hang together when the whiff of a smell, a band playing in the street, a face seen in the fire, or on the gnarled stem of a tree, will lead them into such vagaries at a moment's warning.

N. p. 27   Intellectual over-indulgence is the most gratuitous and disgraceful form which excess can take, nor is there any the consequences of which are more disastrous.

N. p. 106   Every new idea has something of the pain and peril of childbirth about it; ideas are just as mortal and just as immortal as organized beings are.

N. p. 164   Many, if not most, good ideas die young — mainly from neglect on the part of the parents, but sometimes from over-fondness. Once well started, an opinion had better be left to shift for itself.

N. p. 180   *Covery.* This is as important and interesting as Dis-covery. Surely the glory of finally getting rid of and burying a long and troublesome matter should be as great as that of making an important discovery. The trouble is that the coverer is like Samson who perished in the wreck of what he had destroyed; if he gets rid of a thing effectually he gets rid of himself too.

N. p. 216   An idea must not be condemned for being a little shy and incoherent; all new ideas are shy when introduced first among our old ones. We should have patience and see whether the incoherency is likely to wear off or to wear on, in which latter case the sooner we get rid of them the better.

N. p. 221   A definition is the enclosing a wilderness of idea within a wall of words.

N. p. 261   The public buys its opinions as it buys its meat, or takes in its milk, on the principle that it is cheaper to do this than to keep a cow. So it is, but the milk is more likely to be watered.

N. p. 300   Cursed is he that does not know when to shut his mind. An open mind is all very well in its way, but it ought not to be so open that there is no keeping anything in or out of it. It should be capable of shutting its doors sometimes, or it may be found a little draughty.

N. p. 310   Imagination depends mainly upon memory, but there is a small percentage of creation of something out of nothing with it. We can invent a trifle more than can be got at by mere combination of remembered things.

N. p. 303   The arrangement of our ideas is as much a matter of convenience as the packing of goods in a druggist's or draper's store and leads to exactly the same kind of difficulties in the matter of classifying them. We all admit the arbitrariness of classifications in a languid way, but we do not think of it more than we can help — I suppose because it is so inconvenient to do so. The great advantage of classification is to conceal the fact that subdivisions are as arbitrary as they are.

N. p. 315   Contradiction in terms is not only to be excused but there can be no proposition which does not more or less involve one.

FE. p. 28   Argument goes for very little with most people — assertion carries more weight generally.

FE. p. 31   Not only is nothing good or ill but thinking makes it so, but nothing is at all, except in so far as thinking has made it so.

FE. p. 57   The Seasons are like species — there is only an artificial arbitrary division between them. When two things present so many differences to us that we can easily take note of them, we call them different names, but strictly there is only one thing, one place and one time.

FE. p. 72   *Words and Ideas.* These two things act and react upon one another like demand and supply, desire and power, faith and experience; but it is impossible to say which came first if the signification of words be extended so as to embrace every expression of an idea.

FE. p. 80   *Reason.* If you follow it far enough, it always leads to conclusions that are contrary to reason.

FE. p. 81   *Formers of Opinion.* Who are the men who do this? Not the experts, but the public who, though they do not know enough to be experts, yet know enough to decide between them.

FE. p. 83   When we think consciously we do so in words; it is for this reason that we do not realize to ourselves the way in which the lower animals think. Before we could speak we used to think as the lower animals think, but we have forgotten that.

FE. p. 90   Speech is a kind of mean proportional between thought and action.

FE. p. 138   *A little knowledge is a dangerous thing.* Certainly, but a little want of knowledge is also a dangerous thing.

FE. p. 103   The accumulation of matter shows itself in a growing, visible heap; the accumulation of thought shows itself in changed habits and appearances. Thought cannot be hoarded otherwise. There was not so much thought in the world 200,000 years ago as there is now, but all the makings of the thought were there.

FE. p. 120   Reason is founded on faith and faith on reason; there is no 'I know', but there is an 'I think', which is found to answer all practical purposes.

FE. p. 136   There is always some statics in dynamics, and *vice versa*; so in the fullest content there is a little discontent and *vice versa*. But the more discontented we are the more we are conscious, and the more we approach a dynamical state; and the more content we are the more unconscious we are, and the more statical.

FE. p. 137   Words only convey ideas to us because we have arbitrarily associated them with certain things, so that presence of the word recalls the thing.

FE. p. 178   There is nothing so unthinkable as thought, unless it be the entire absence of thought.

FE. p. 142   As food must be prepared for us by animals and plants before we can assimilate it, so we can digest thoughts more easily that have already been digested by many minds.

FE. p. 202   Words are to thought much what a nervous system is to sentience.

FE. p. 236   *Our Ideas.* So long as we grasp them firmly, all is well. They are our slaves, and if we would be well served we must rule them with a strong judgment. If we drive them too hard, or try to vivisect them, they will either rise in rebellion and dethrone our reason, or, which is much the same thing, will perish together.

FE. p. 263   All analogies are false, yet all our reasoning is founded on analogies.

FE. p. 275   The latest authority is generally, though not always, the one that is going to be next exploded. It is never safe to neglect the older authorities, on the assumption that later ones will tell you all about them.

FE. p. 280   Logic and consistency are luxuries for the gods and the lower animals.

FE. p. 279   Logic is like religion; it has only two enemies, the too much and the too little, and the too much is the more dangerous.

FE. p. 282   The test of a good critic is whether he knows when and how to believe on insufficient evidence.

FE. p. 294   Communication from mind to mind is only possible by the help of conventions which both the minds have accepted as inseparably connected with the representation of certain things.

K. NATURE

N. p. 12   Nature is essentially mean, mediocre. You can have schemes for raising the level of this mean, but not for making everyone two inches taller than his neighbour, and this is what people really care about.

FE. p. 29   *The Nature of Things in Themselves.* A thing 'is' whatever it gives us least trouble to think it is. There is no other 'is' than this.

FE. p. 30   We often hear it said that the world owes more to its illusions than to its realities. But are not its realities based on, and do not they grow out of its illusions? If so, a reality is only an illusion so strong and so universal that no one can resist it.

FE. p. 69   I take it that all plants feel, but some make more fuss about their feelings than others.

FE. p. 77   There is no such change as changelessness under changed surroundings.

FE. p. 84   Same is as same does.

FE. p. 95   When I see food in a shop window I see latent or potential action.

FE. p. 97   Providence itself could not be more absolutely improvident.

FE. p. 112   *The Elements.* If they get into one kind of company they become one thing; if into another, another.

FE. p. 113   *The Simplicity of Nature.* This is due to her not being so clever and prescient as people try to make out. Unless an idea is pretty obvious it will seldom occur to any, either animal or plant.

FE. p. 135   Because we do not make a noise, and are unconscious when we are asleep if we are moved about a little, we say that everything which does not make a noise when it is pushed about a little is unconscious.

FE. p. 145   Adaptation and purpose resolves itself into 'removal of a want'. When an organ causes a want to disappear quickly and completely we say that it is well adapted to its purpose.

FE. p. 150   Animal and vegetable organism does not change by large and few convulsions, but by small ones and many of them. So for the most part do states and men's opinions.

FE. p. 156   *Design in Nature.* I can no more believe that a burglar's jemmy is fortuitous, or that the artificial flowers in a woman's bonnet get there accidentally, or that a police-man puts on plain clothes without any idea of escaping observation, than I can that the chicken's horny tip, and mimicry on the part of animals, have not an intentional reference to the needs of the creature which develops them.

FE. p. 157   Protoplasm is sticky and so are ideas.

FE. p. 195   The question of individualism goes right down to the atom, and is just as troublesome here as it is everywhere else.

FE. p. 196   Everything knows something and has had some experiences; and everything is a record of its own experiences; knowledge and condition are as convertible as force and heat.

FE. p. 237   Time and space only exist on being marked; where not marked they do not exist; they exist to those who are marking them but not to those who do not.

FE. p. 244   *The Underlying Substance.* It is nonsense to say that this does not change, if its conditions change. These conditions are the only things we can cognize, and stand to us for the underlying substance. That which is uncognizable is, as far as we are concerned, non-existent. A thing is to us that by which we cognize it.

L. MORALS

N. p. 24   *The Foundations of Morality*. These are like all other foundations; if you dig too much about them the superstructure will come tumbling down.

N. p. 24   To attempt to get at the foundations is to try to recover consciousness about things that have passed into the unconscious stage; it is pretty sure to disturb and derange those who try it on too much.

N. p. 24   It is all very well for mischievous writers to maintain that we cannot serve God and Mammon. Granted that it is not easy, but nothing that is worth doing ever is easy. Easy or difficult, possible or impossible, not only has the thing got to be done, but it is exactly in doing it that the whole duty of man consists. And when the righteous man turneth away from his righteousness that he hath committed and doeth that which is neither quite lawful nor quite right, he will generally be found to have gained in amiability what he has lost in holiness.

N. p. 27   Virtue is something which it would be impossible to over-rate if it had not been over-rated.

FE. p. 24   Justice is my being allowed to do whatever I like. Injustice is whatever prevents my doing so.

N. p. 25   Truly he visiteth the virtues of the fathers upon the children unto the third and fourth generation. The most that can be said for virtue is that there is a considerable balance in its favour, and that it is a good deal better to be for it than against it; but it lets people in very badly sometimes.

N. p. 28   The extremes of vice and virtue are alike detestable; absolute virtue is as sure to kill a man as absolute vice is, let alone the dullnesses of it and the pomposities of it.

N. p. 28   If virtue had everything her own way she would be as insufferable as dominant factions generally are. It is the function of vice to keep virtue within reasonable bounds.

FE. p. 20   *Say of some very respectable work on morality — the Bible for example*. 'We shall have these crude and subversionary books from time to time, until it is recognized as an axiom of morality that luck is the only fit object of human veneration. How, and how far, a man has a right to be lucky, and hence venerable, at the expense of other people, is a point that has always been settled and always must be settled by a kind of higgling and haggling of the market.'

FE. p. 30   The greatest happiness of the greatest number will be best promoted by increasing the prosperity of those who are now best and comeliest.

FE. p. 34   Unless morality brings a man peace at the last, it is an imposture. Peace at the last is the *raison d'être* of morality. I have known very moral old men living with wives whom they have long ceased to love (if indeed they ever loved them), fathers of sons whom they hate for having either distanced or disgraced them, and of ugly, disagreeable daughters whom they loathe in secret, but from whom there is no escape.

Is it moral for a man to have brought this upon himself? Is it moral for a man to have an old wife and ugly daughters at all? If this is moral, what is immorality? Someone should do for morals what Bacon is supposed to have done for science.

FE. p. 35   *My Uncle Philip's Conscience.* He became a partner in Whitbread's brewery, but on conscientious grounds refused a partnership in a distillery. He drew the line at gin. What odd lines conscience does sometimes draw, to be sure!

FE. p. 51   The English strive after a fixed immutable code of morality, as classifiers strive after irrefragable definitions of species or foreign nations after a written and unquestionable constitution.

FE. p. 54   Vouchsafe, O Lord, to keep us this day without being found out!

FE. p. 54   *The Country of the People who are above Suspicion.* Once upon a time there was a youth whose fairy godmother had given him a sword; on the blade, near the hilt, was damascened the word Fairplay, and this was the name of the weapon. She told him to keep it bright and use it well and it would never fail him. Being a simple, straightforward boy he believed her, put all his faith in his sword, and learnt how to sharpen it, to polish it and to use it. When the time came for him to leave his father's roof, he girded it on and went forth to seek his fortune in the world. And it was as his fairy godmother had predicted. He slew all the dragons, entered all the enchanted castles and restored all the bewitched princesses to their parents. He swam the great river that turns the mill that grinds the winds of the world, and did it as easily as an ordinary man jumps over a ditch. He had no idea that there was anything unusual about him. He succeeded in all he attempted and his progress was as the march of an ever-victorious army until he came to The Country of the People who are Above Suspicion. And the ruler of that land is King Logomachy the $(n + 1)$th, and the name of his queen is Aringa Rossa. No sooner had the youth crossed the frontier than he became powerless; for it is a property of the climate of that country to corrode the metal of which his sword was made, so that he could not draw it from its scabbard.

FE. p. 60   Things can never be either very right or very wrong for long together.

FE. p. 76   When I was a small boy I used to be made to recite a poem about conscience. I forget it, but it came to this — that if one did not take very great care, one's conscience would leave off talking. I think one's conscience had better not speak at all than be always jabbering, as some men's do.

FE. p. 92   'Cleanse Thou me from My Secret Sins.' I heard a man moralizing on this, and shocked him by saying demurely that I did not mind these so much, if I could get rid of those that were obvious to other people.

FE. p. 96   We have all sinned and come short of making ourselves as comfortable as we easily might have done, or rather as it now seems to us that we easily might have done.

FE. p. 113   'They're a rum lot,' as the Devil said of the Ten Commandments.

FE. p. 134   He had, indeed, all the vices, but in such unbridled moderation that the ascetic was a libertine in comparison with him.

FE. p. 125   The desideratum is for some way in which men may reap the reward of their labour more certainly after the flesh. The future state dodge was tried, but it did not do;

the want however is a genuine one, and will one day probably be supplied.

FE. p. 138   If you feel strongly you must persecute, and if you don't feel strongly you will never get on.

FE. p. 138   *Virtue.* There should be a subdivision of this as well as of any other labour.

FE. p. 139   He excels most who hits the golden mean most exactly in the middle.

FE. p. 158   Let us settle about the facts first and fight about the moral tendencies afterwards.

FE. p. 165   The first duty of a conscientious person is to have his or her conscience absolutely under his or her own control.

FE. p. 182   I do not greatly care whether I have been right or wrong on any point, but I care a good deal about knowing which of the two I have been.

FE. p. 190   One man's gnat is another man's camel.

FE. p. 257   I really do not see much use in exalting the humble and meek; they do not remain humble and meek long when they are exalted.

FE. p. 277   There was a young prince whom the fairies at his birth endowed with fabulous wealth, etc. etc., but an uninvited fairy came in and marred all by endowing the baby with a spirit of compassion.

FE. p. 313   Freely you have received — then freely take as much more as you can get.

M. THE FAMILY

N. p. 31   *The Family.* I believe that more unhappiness comes from this source than from any other — I mean from the attempt to prolong family connection unduly and to make people hang together artificially who would never naturally do so. The mischief among the lower classes is not so great, but among the middle and upper classes it is killing a large number daily. And the old people do not really like it much better than the young.

N. p. 33   *Melchisedec.* He was a really happy man. He was without father without mother and without descent. He was an incarnate bachelor. He was a born orphan.

FE. p. 19   I could stand my relations well enough if they would only let me alone. It is my relations with my relations that I sometimes find embarrassing.

FE. p. 90   I am sorry to have to admit it, but I do not observe that even gross cruelty and selfishness on the part of parents towards their children is followed by any very bad effects upon the parents. Parents may make their children very unhappy without having to suffer anything that makes them unhappy in return.

FE. p. 90   Those who have never had a father can at any rate never know the sweets of losing one. To most men the death of his father is a new lease of life.

FE. p. 91   The Ancients attached such special horror to the murder of near relations because the temptation was felt on all hands to be so great that nothing short of this could stop people from laying violent hands upon them. The fable of the Erinyes was probably invented by fathers and mothers and uncles and aunts.

FE. p. 133   It is not nice to be wedded to anything — not even to a theory.

FE. p. 134   'Henceforth,' said she sadly, 'let us be to one another as brother and sister.' 'No,' said I, as I thought of my own sisters, 'not so bad as that.'

FE. p. 295   'Home, Sweet Home' must surely have been written by a bachelor.

FE. p. 209   The tenth plague was no good at all. The Egyptians would have been strangely unlike any papas and mammas that I have ever known if they had emancipated their slaves merely because one of their children died. What made them let the Jews go was an eleventh plague in conquence of which their papas and mammas were endowed with immortality. On this they let the Jews go immediately.

N.   MIND AND MATTER

N. p. 67   *The Universal Substance.* We shall never get straight till we leave off trying to separate mind and matter. Mind is not a thing or, if it be, we know nothing about it; it is a function of matter. Matter is not a thing or, if it be, we know nothing about it; it is a function of mind.

N. p. 81   All eating is a kind of proselytizing — a kind of dogmatizing — a maintaining that the eater's way of looking at things is better than the eatee's. We convert the food, or try to do so, to our own way of thinking, and, when it sticks to its own opinion and refuses to be converted, we say it disagrees with us. An animal that refuses to let another eat it has the courage of its convictions and, if it gets eaten, dies a martyr to them.

FE. p. 44   When consciousness has been reawakened about any matter, unconsciousness can as a general rule only be regained by beginning again at a very early stage, and repeating, in an abbreviated form, the earlier stages of experiment and failure. Man has resumed consciousness about some things in respect of which the lower animals are still unconsciously satisfied, as that self-interest is the mainspring of ordinary action. Hence self-interest is less paramount with him than with them.

FE. p. 91   We have, or at any rate think we have, a fairly definite idea before us when we talk of matter, but I don't think we ever think we have any definite idea about our own meaning when we talk of mind.

FE. p. 93   The two most important things man has are his body and his mind. The unanimous verdict of those best qualified to form an opinion is, that the less ninety-nine hundredths of us know about either one or the other, the better. The more important a thing is the more important it is that we should know nothing about it.

FE. p. 94   The things we do with most unconsciousness are those which we die quickest if we do not do.

FE. p. 94   Every habit seems to come from some other habit, as much as 'omne ovum' comes 'ex ovo'; and every habit seems to have a reproductive system, for the mere fact of our having done a thing once inclines us to do it again, provided it has not positively hurt us.

FE. p. 111   The amœba has more mind in proportion to its body than man has in proportion to his.

FE. p. 117   All organisms are self-made people.

FE. p. 155   *Mind and Matter.* When we try to think of them as one, we find so many analogies that we get along quite nicely till they fly asunder and get as distinct as ever again just as we are on the point of finally uniting them.

FE. p. 207   Curious, that the part they call most living should be so singularly devoid of organ as to resemble the inorganic rather than the organic world. Nothing can be more inorganic than protoplasm.

FE. p. 257   *Thought and Thing.* So a thought of sage and onions *is* sage and onions.

FE. p. 331   When I see a number of people at a dinner table, I see their mouths as the ends of the roots of a lot of plants sucking up their sustenance out of the earth.

O.   *LOVE AND FRIENDSHIP*

N. p. 226   The sexes are the first — or are among the first great experiments in the social subdivision of labour.

N. p. 227   The question of marriage or non-marriage is only the question of whether it is better to be spoiled one way or another.

FE. p. 30   A man is shorn of his strength if he belongs to one set or to one woman.

FE. p. 229   *All Things to All Men.* I suppose this was all right, but there can be no doubt about being all things to all women.

FE. p. 315   I heard a man say that brigands demand your money *or* your life, whereas women require both.

N. p. 228   I can generally bear the separation, but I don't like the leave-taking.

FE. p. 135   The best of friends must meet.

FE. p. 184   The pleasure of love is that it is the one place where you may let yourself go and feel as strongly as you like.

P.   *THE ARTS*

N. p. 14   If, however, any work is to have long life it is not enough that it should be good of its kind. Many ephemeral things are perfect in their way. It must be of a durable kind as well.

N. p. 123   If Bach wriggles, Wagner writhes.

N. p. 137   Art has no end in view save the emphasizing and recording in the most effective way some strongly felt interest or affection. Where there is neither interest nor desire to record with good effect, there is but sham art, or none at all: where both these are fully present, no matter how rudely and inarticulately, there is great art. Art is at best a dress, important, yet still nothing in comparison with the wearer, and, as a general rule, the less it attracts attention the better.

N. p. 138   Painting is only possible by reason of association's not sticking to the letter of its bond, so that we jump to conclusions.

N. p. 209   I should like to like Schumann's music better than I do; I dare say I could make myself like it better if I tried; but I do not like having to try to make myself like things; I like things that make me like them at once and no trying at all.

N. p. 209   To know whether you are enjoying a piece of music or not you must see whether you find yourself looking at the advertisements of Pear's soap at the end of the programme.

FE. p. 38   When we go to pictures, we go for the most part to be taken both into common life and out of it.

FE. p. 62   All that is not pertinent in art is impertinent.

FE. p. 85   'Insist again on doing the first thing that comes. No matter how small a thing you see, if you see anything, attend to that.' This is all wrong. It should rather be, 'Never do anything till you are sure that it is the most important thing as yet left undone.'

FE. p. 115   *Looking Ahead*. We cannot do this much either in writing or painting. We must do something roughly as near as we can, and then cut it about and rearrange it.

FE. p. 156   *The Literary Instinct*. A man will show this by writing at all odd times as people show the artistic instinct by sketching in season and out of season.

FE. p. 159   *Hurrying*. In art this is one of the hardest things to unlearn, but until one has unlearned it one can learn nothing more.

FE. p. 164   *Art Note*. Men who get misled by schools and academies begin by wanting to do and not knowing how, and end by knowing how and not wanting.

FE. p. 175   Any fool can paint a picture but it takes a wise man to be able to sell it.

FE. p. 232   *Genius*. I should say it was best defined as hereditary aptitude — the inheritance, without conscious trouble, of a faculty acquired by an ancestor. It is instinctive, and like other instincts is hard to repress.

FE. p. 257   *The Art of Heaven*. I should fear it will be a good deal tainted with Barocco, if not with Rococo, if not with First Empire.

N. p. 107   A man's style in any art should be like his dress — it should attract as little attention as possible.

Q. *LITERATURE*

N. p. 186   I never knew a writer yet who took the smallest pains with his style and was at the same time readable. Plato's having had seventy shies at one sentence is quite enough to explain to me why I dislike him.

N. p. 196   Homeric commentators have been blind so long that nothing will do for them but Homer must be blind too. They have transferred their own blindness to the poet.

N. p. 197   If you wish to preserve the spirit of a dead author, you must not skin him, stuff him and set him up in a case. You must eat him, digest him and let him live in you, with such life as you have, for better or worse. The difference between the Andrew Lang manner of translating the *Odyssey* and mine is that between making a mummy and a baby. He tries to preserve a corpse (for the *Odyssey* is a corpse to all who need Lang's translation), whereas I try to originate a new life and one that is instinct (as far as I can effect this) with the spirit though not the form of the original.

N. p. 229   '*The Ancient Mariner*.' This poem would not have taken so well if it had been called 'The Old Sailor', so that Wardour Street has its uses.

N. p. 235   *Two Writers*. One left little or nothing about himself and the world complained that it was puzzled. Another, mindful of this, left copious details about himself, whereon the world said that it was even more puzzled about him than about the man who had left nothing, till presently it found out that it was also bored, and troubled itself no more about either.

N. p. 237   The true writer will stop everywhere and anywhere to put down his notes, as the true painter will stop everywhere and anywhere to sketch.

FE. p. 144   Words on many subjects are like trying to paint a miniature with a mop.

FE. p. 267   *Chaucer.* When he wrote was his English at all Wardour Street?

FE. p. 282   *Tennyson.* I don't know about there being any moaning of the bar when he died, but there was fuss made enough.

FE. p. 293   The oldest books are still only just out to those who have not read them.

R.   MISCELLANEOUS

N. p. 220   The great pleasure of a dog is that you may make a fool of yourself with him and not only will he not scold you, but he will make a fool of himself too.

N. p. 222   *Oxford and Cambridge.* The dons are too busy educating the young men to be able to teach them anything.

N. p. 222   There is a higher average of good cooking at Oxford and Cambridge than elsewhere. The cooking is better than the curriculum. But there is no Chair of Cookery, it is taught by apprenticeship in the kitchens.

N. p. 224   *Solomon in all his Glory.* But, in the first place, the lilies do toil and spin after their own fashion, and, in the next, it was not desirable that Solomon should be dressed like a lily of the valley.

N. p. 243   A little boy and a little girl were looking at a picture of Adam and Eve.

'Which is Adam and which is Eve?' said one.

'I do not know,' said the other, 'but I could tell if they had their clothes on.'

N. p. 244   A woman once stopped me at the entrance to Doctors' Commons and said:

'If you please, sir, can you tell me — is this the place that I came to before?'

Not knowing where she had been before I could not tell her.

N. p. 250   *At Abbey Wood.* I heard a man say to another: 'I went to live there just about the time that beer came down from 5d. to 4d. a pot. That will give you an idea when it was.'

N. p. 255   *The Channel Passage.* How holy people look when they are sea-sick! There was a patient Parsee near me who seemed purified once and for ever from all taint of the flesh.

N. p. 280   When the water of a place is bad, it is safest to drink none that has not been filtered through either the berry of a grape, or else a tub of malt. These are the most reliable filters yet invented.

N. p. 321   Where we have an opinion that assures us promptly which way the balance of advantage will incline – whether it be an instinctive, hereditarily acquired opinion or one rapidly and decisively formed as the result of post-natal experience – then our action is determined at once by that opinion, and freedom of choice practically vanishes.

FE. p. 51   *Silence.* There is none so impressive as that of a hushed multitude.

FE. p. 55   *Greatest Benefactor?* The man who invented the steam engine, or he who invented melted butter?

FE. p. 59   From all them that travel by land or water, from all women labouring with child, from all young children and sick persons, Good Lord deliver us.

FE. p. 62   *Dentists and Solicitors.* These are the people to whom we always show our best side.

FE. p. 65   Another working-man said to me about the giraffe that it must get up at six in the morning if it wants to have its breakfast in its stomach by nine.

FE. p. 87   She went up the Nile as far as the first crocodile.

FE. p. 67   *Auberon Herbert.* He and his wife resolved that they and the servants should henceforth dine together at one time and one table; they would thus diffuse sweetness and light over their whole household. This might have answered very well if the servants after a few days had not given warning *en masse*.

FE. p. 79   *Ballooning.* There was an article in *The Times* (1882) which convinces me that the navigation of the air must be near at hand. When *The Times* dismisses a subject so contemptuously as this, it is generally on the point of succeeding.

FE. p. 95   Miss Potter who works a good deal among the poor in Seven Dials asked me at a conversazione, rather abruptly, if I liked poor people. I said I did not, and there the conversation ended.

FE. p. 105   *Advertisement.* The following has appeared lately: 'Mrs. Smith having cast off clothing of every description invites inspection.'

FE. p. 105   'Oh, what do you think Madame told me this afternoon? She says she has a friend — let me see if I can remember her words — "Une amie qui va épouser en secondes noces un officier de la Sale-Vache Armée." '

FE. p. 123   Why does the fresh fallen August snow lie so long on the top of that high peak when it is so thin and the weather is so hot? I suppose because it is not thin, and because the weather up there is not hot, and because it does not lie long.

FE. p. 133   *Ted Jones.* He was very shy. Once a visitor called and tried to make himself agreeable, but after a while Ted began to cry and said, 'Mamma — he's talking to me.'

FE. p. 134   Bread cast upon the waters is not likely to be found for many days, if then, and will be good for very little when it *is* found.

FE. p. 134   *The Lions would not eat Daniel.* They could eat most things, but they drew the line at prophets.

FE. p. 138   *Matthew Arnold and the Majority.* He says in his New York address that the majority are always wrong. People are generally wrong so long as a subject is new to them; but by far the greater number of things about which we are conversant are not new, and about these the majority is much the safest guide we can follow.

FE. p. 287   In old times people used to try and square the circle; now they try and devise schemes for satisfying the Irish nation.

FE. p. 187   It is a mistake to think you are giving letters most faithfully by printing them as they were written, without the smallest alteration; for you do not give the letters unless you reproduce their environment, and this cannot be done. He who undertakes to edit letters undertakes to translate them from one set of surroundings to other very different ones.

FE. p. 281   He was the first to conceive the happy thought of scraping the lichen off the rocks near the St. Gothard Pass, painting them chocolate, and advertising Mother Seigel's Syrup upon them.

FE. p. 298   In 1824 Lord Orford was invited to become president of the Norwich Bible Society. His reply was as follows:

> Sir — I am surprised and annoyed by the contents of your letter — surprised, because my well-known character should have exempted me from such an application; and annoyed, because it compels me to have even this communication with you.
>
> I have long been addicted to the gaming table; I have lately taken to the turf; I fear I frequently blaspheme; but I have never distributed religious tracts. All this was known to you and your society, notwithstanding which you think me a fit person to be your president. God forgive your hypocrisy.
>
> I would rather live in the land of sinners than with such saints.

S. PERSONALIA

N. p. 14   And yet I do not know — I could not keep myself going at all if I did not believe that I was likely to inherit a good average three-score years and ten of immortality. There are very few workers who are not sustained by this belief, or at least hope, but it may well be doubted whether this is not a sign that they are not going to be immortal — and I am content (or try to be) to fare as my neighbours.

N. p. 15   When I am inclined to complain about having worked so many years and taken nothing but debt, though I feel the want of money so continually (much more, doubtless, than I ought to feel it), let me remember that I come in free, gratis, to the work of hundreds and thousands of better men than myself who often were much worse paid than I have been. If a man's true self is his karma — the life which his work lives but which he knows very little about and by which he takes nothing — let him remember at least that he can enjoy the karma of others, and this about squares the account — or rather far more than squares it.

N. p. 157 If I die prematurely, at any rate I shall be saved from being bored by my own success.

N. p. 163 Or the public ear is like a common; there is not much to be got off it, but that little is for the most part grazed down by geese and donkeys.

N. p. 184 I am not one of those who can repeat the General Confession unreservedly. I should say rather:

'I have left unsaid much that I am sorry I did not say, but I have said little that I am sorry for having said, and I am pretty well on the whole, thank you.'

N. p. 366 I have often told my son that he must begin by finding me a wife to become his mother who shall satisfy both himself and me. But this is only one of the many rocks on which we have hitherto split. We should never have got on together. I should have had to cut him off with a shilling either for laughing at Homer, or for refusing to laugh at him, or both, or neither, but still cut him off. So I settled the matter long ago by turning a deaf ear to his importunities and sticking to it that I would not get him at all. Yet his thin ghost visits me at times and, though he knows that it is no use pestering me further, he looks at me so wistfully and reproachfully that I am half-inclined to turn tail, take my chance about his mother and ask him to let me get him after all. But I should show a clean pair of heels if he said 'Yes'.

Besides, he would probably be a girl.

FE. p. 57 I don't like Plato, but I suppose I prefer him to Carlyle.

FE. p. 50 Above all things, let no unwary reader do me the injustice of believing in *me*. In that I write at all I am among the damned. If he must believe in anything, let him believe in the music of Handel, the painting of Giovanni

Bellini, and in the thirteenth chapter of St. Paul's First
Epistle to the Corinthians.

FE. p. 56   One great complaint against me is that I am not a
professional scientist. It is not shown that what I say is
unsound, but it is contended that I cannot know the
particular matter on which I am writing because I have
given no public proof that I know all manner of other
things which have no connection with it.

FE. p. 63   Some complain of me that they never know whether I
am not laughing, and others that they are never sure but
what I am in earnest.

FE. p. 66   *My Books.* When anything in them is rather strange and
outré, it is probably drawn straight from nature as close as
I could draw it; when it is very plausible, there is probably
no particular and especial foundation for it.

FE. p. 83   It may conceivably matter to someone else whether he
has read my books or no, but it does not matter to me.

FE. p. 91   I see myself cribbed from continually, but never named;
and my books, I am told, can hardly be mentioned in
scientific circles without making people lose their temper.
I know I ought to be ashamed of myself for caring what
such people do, or for paying any attention to what may
or may not be said about me, but I am afraid I do care,
and do pay attention.

FE. p. 102   Posterity will not have imagination enough to tell it
what a fool I am, and, if I dangle enough works before it,
it may be caught by some of them. Why I should wish to
trouble posterity — what harm it has done me for which I
would punish it; what good for which I would reward it
— I know not; all I know is that I mean catching posterity
if I can.

FE. p. 105   I have written so much about myself because I am the
subject on which I am the best informed.

FE. p. 140   '*The Way of All Flesh.*' Mr. Heatherley said I had taken all
the tenderest feelings of our nature and, having spread
them carefully over the floor, stamped upon them till I
had reduced them to an indistinguishable mass of filth,
and then handed them round for inspection. I do not take
this view of the matter myself.

FE. p. 140   Last week (Oct. 27th, 1883) I went to Basingstoke and met Mrs. Thiselton Dyer. She is a daughter of Sir Joseph Hooker and is very advanced. I said I should go to church in the evening. I said this, partly because I knew she would not like it, and partly to please Miss Burd, who I knew would. Mrs. Dyer did her best to dissuade me. 'Didn't it bore me? And, holding my opinions, ought I not to let people see what I thought?' etc. I said that, having given up Christianity, I was not going to be hampered by its principles. It was the substance of Christianity, and not its accessories of external worship, that I so objected to; and I would be unprincipled whenever and in whatever way I thought convenient. So I went to church out of pure cussedness. She could not make it out at all. But I won't go again, not just yet awhile if I can help it, for it *did* bore me. I had not been for more than seven years.

FE. p. 183   I said somewhere about myself, but I forgot where: 'I attacked the foundations of morality in *Erewhon*, and nobody cared two straws. I tore open the wounds of my Redeemer as he hung upon the Cross in *The Fair Haven*, and people rather liked it. But when I attacked Mr. Darwin they were up in arms in a moment.'

FE. p. 173   At dinner at Seebohm's I met Skertchley, who told me about a rat-trap invented by Dunkett, Mr. Tylor's coachman.

Dunkett found all his traps fail one after another, and was in such despair at the way the corn got eaten that he resolved to invent a rat-trap. He began by putting himself as nearly as possible in the rat's place.

'Is there anything,' he asked himself, 'in which, if I were a rat, I should have such complete confidence that I could not suspect it without suspecting everything in the world and being unable henceforth to move fearlessly in any direction?'

He pondered for a while and had no answer, till one night the room seemed to become full of light, and he heard a voice from Heaven saying, 'Drain-pipes'.

Then he saw his way. To suspect a common drain-pipe would be to cease to be a rat. Here Skertchley enlarged a little, explaining that a spring was to be concealed inside, but that the pipe was to be open at both ends; if the pipe were closed at one end, a rat would naturally not like going into it, for he would not feel sure of being able to get out again; on which I interrupted and said: 'Ah, it was just this which stopped me from going into the Church.'

FE. p. 228   I am anxious to have it generally known that I am well off, because if I were poor my history would be too depressing; because a cheerful figure is more attractive than a wronged and unhappy one; because, in fact, it leaves the laugh on my side.

FE. p. 186   I must have a cat whom I find homeless, wandering about the court, and to whom, therefore, I am under no obligation. There is a Clifford's Inn euphemism about cats which the laundresses use quite gravely: they say people come to this place 'to lose their cats'. They mean that, when they have a cat they don't want to kill, and don't know how to get rid of, they bring it here, drop it inside the railings of our grass-plot, and go away under the impression that they have been 'losing' their cat. This happens very frequently and I have already selected a dirty little drunken wretch of a kitten to be successor to my poor old cat. I don't suppose it drinks anything stronger than milk and water but so much milk and water must be bad for a kitten that age — at any rate it looks as if it drank; but it gives me the impression of being affectionate, intelligent and fond of mice, and I believe, if it had a home, it would become more respectable; at any rate I will see how it works.

FE. p. 260   It is not by what I have done nor yet by what I have left undone that I praise or blame a day now. It is by what I have undone, reversed and got rid of that I call it well or ill. I do not want to leave a lumber room behind me.

FE. p. 292   I do not want to shake the dust of Cambridge off my feet or any of that rubbish, but I have been at some pains to get it out of my eyes, and I think that I have got rid of most of it.

N. p. 377   Nevertheless these three books [*The Way of All Flesh*, Butler's translations of the *Iliad* and the *Odyssey*] also were

a kind of picking up of sovereigns, for the novel contains
records of things I saw happening rather than imaginary
incidents, and the principles on which the translations are
made were obvious to anyone willing to take and use
them.

FE. p. 344

I FALL ASLEEP
IN THE FULL AND CERTAIN HOPE
THAT MY SLUMBER SHALL NOT BE BROKEN
AND THAT
THOUGH I BE ALL-FORGETTING
YET SHALL I NOT BE ALL-FORGOTTEN
BUT CONTINUE THAT LIFE
IN THE THOUGHTS AND DEEDS OF THOSE I LOVED
INTO WHICH
WHILE THE POWER TO STRIVE WAS YET VOUCHSAFED ME
I FONDLY STROVE TO ENTER

FIRST PUBLISHED 1950

B50-00064

Dewey Classification
823.89

PRINTED IN GREAT BRITAIN IN THE CITY OF OXFORD
AT THE ALDEN PRESS
BOUND BY A. W. BAIN & CO. LTD., LONDON

THE ESSENTIAL
SAMUEL BUTLER

Selected with an Introduction by

G. D. H. COLE

JONATHAN CAPE
THIRTY BEDFORD SQUARE
LONDON

SAMUEL BUTLER
Reproduced from a self-
portrait dated April 1878.

The originals of both

pictures are at St. John's

College, Cambridge

FAMILY PRAYERS

'I did this in 1864 and if I had gone on doing things out of my own head
instead of making studies, I should have been all right.'   S. B.

Books by Samuel Butler

ALPS AND SANCTUARIES

THE AUTHORESS OF THE ODYSSEY

EREWHON

EREWHON REVISITED

EVOLUTION, OLD AND NEW

EX VOTO

THE FAIR HAVEN

A FIRST YEAR IN CANTERBURY SETTLEMENT

FURTHER EXTRACTS FROM THE NOTE-BOOKS

GOD THE KNOWN AND GOD THE UNKNOWN

THE HUMOUR OF HOMER

THE ILIAD OF HOMER

LIFE AND HABIT

LUCK OR CUNNING

THE NOTE-BOOKS OF SAMUEL BUTLER

THE ODYSSEY

SHAKESPEARE'S SONNETS RECONSIDERED

UNCONSCIOUS MEMORY

THE WAY OF ALL FLESH

★

LETTERS BETWEEN SAMUEL BUTLER AND

MISS E. M. A. SAVAGE

THE ESSENTIAL SAMUEL BUTLER

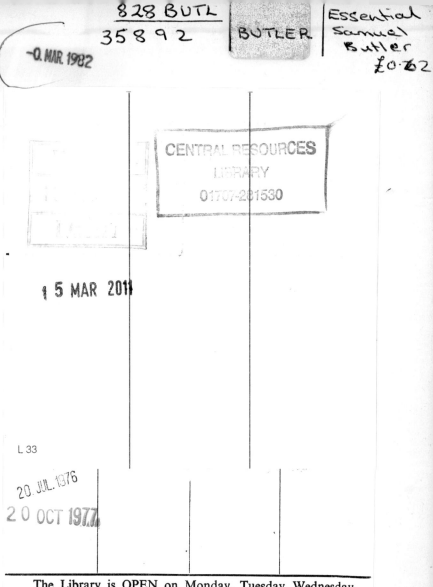

The Library is OPEN on Monday, Tuesday, Wednesday and Friday from 9.30 a.m. to 7 p.m. Thursday 9.30 a.m. to 1 p.m. Saturday 9.30 a.m. to 6 p.m.

Books must be protected against wet weather, leaves should not be turned down, and writing on the pages is an offence. Fines will be levied on borrowers returning books in a damaged condition.